FOUNDATIONS OF NUTRITION

MARY SWARTZ ROSE, 1874–1941

Mary Swartz Rose, a pioneer in nutrition, was author of the first three editions of this text, 1927, 1933, and 1938. The above portrait, painted by Ivan Olinsky, was presented to Teachers College, Columbia University, by her students in appreciation of a great and beloved teacher. It now hangs in the Grace Dodge Room at Teachers College.

SIXTH EDITION

FOUNDATIONS OF NUTRITION

CLARA MAE TAYLOR, Ph.D.
Professor Emeritus of Nutrition
Teachers College, Columbia University

and

ORREA FLORENCE PYE, Ph.D.
Professor of Nutrition
Teachers College, Columbia University

THE MACMILLAN COMPANY, New York
COLLIER-MACMILLAN LIMITED, London

Second Printing, 1967

Earlier editions, entitled *Foundations of Nutrition*,
© copyright 1927, 1933, 1938, 1956 by The Macmillan
Company. Fourth edition, entitled *Rose's Foundations of
Nutrition*, copyright 1944 by The Macmillan Company.

Library of Congress catalog card number: 66–16098

THE MACMILLAN COMPANY, NEW YORK
COLLIER-MACMILLAN CANADA, LTD., TORONTO, ONTARIO

Printed in the United States of America

Preface to the Sixth Edition

In this, a classic text, it is fitting to include the rich contributions of the great nutrition scientists of yesterday and their bearing on our present concepts of nutrition. A review of the successive advances of the science should help the reader better to understand and interpret the complexities of our new knowledge of nutrition.

In preparing the first three editions of this text, Professor Rose had in mind those who desired to "live more intelligently," and her aim was "to present within a small space some of the fundamental principles of human nutrition in terms which call for no highly specialized training in those natural sciences upon which the science of nutrition rests." In the fourth edition by MacLeod and Taylor and the fifth edition by Taylor and MacLeod the objective was the same.

In this, the sixth edition, although the authors have a similar objective, they recognize that students entering college in this highly technological age have a stronger background in science and a keener interest in scientific developments. With this in mind, they have included more citations to the literature and comprehensive reference lists at the end of each chapter. These references include supplementary reading adapted to students of varying scientific background.

It is our desire that the text will be interesting and understandable to the student and at the same time be stimulating and arouse the intellectual curiosity in the intricacies of the functioning of the human body and its nutritional requirements.

In lieu of a glossary, less familiar terms have been described or defined within the text. For other terms unfamiliar to them, students are referred to standard handbooks and medical, chemical, and other dictionaries. It is desirable for students to develop the habit of using reference books to expand their knowledge of nutrition and its closely related sciences.

As would be anticipated, the vast expansion of the science of nutrition has necessitated the reorganizing and rewriting of a major portion of the

v

fifth edition. New chapters dealing with fats and carbohydrates in metabolism, nutrition and dental health, food in relation to weight control, international nutrition, and nutrition education programs have been included. Many new, meaningful illustrations have been carefully selected to help in the interpretation of the text.

Attention has been directed throughout the text to international problems and programs in nutrition because of the special interest manifested in international affairs by today's young men and women.

The table of food values in weights is reproduced from the United States Department of Agriculture Home and Garden Bulletin No. 72. The table of food values expressed in shares is also based on Bulletin No. 72, and provides a timesaving, practical, and graphic means of checking diets.

The 1963–64 Recommended Dietary Allowances suggested by the Food and Nutrition Board of the National Research Council will be found in the Appendix along with a number of new tables which have been included to assist the student in dealing with practical problems and their interpretation. Growth curves for children of all ages, height-weight tables, and family food plans will be found.

We wish to acknowledge our indebtedness and express deep appreciation to the following members of the staff of the Institute of Nutrition Sciences of the School of Public Health and Administrative Medicine, Columbia University, for reviewing chapters related to their particular interests: W. Henry Sebrell, Jr., M.D., Director; Charles Glen King, Ph.D., Associate Director; Elmer L. Severinghaus, M.D., Associate Director; Oswald A. Roels, Ph.D., Associate Professor; and Mary E. R. Bal, Ph.D., Assistant Professor.

Our sincere gratitude is given to Florence MacLeod, Ph.D., Professor Emeritus of Nutrition, University of Tennessee, for her interest in the new edition and her careful review of a few of the chapters.

We thank Edna R. Sostman, Ed.D., Associate Professor of Home Economics, Douglass College of Rutgers University, the State University of New Jersey, for reading some of the chapters and making helpful suggestions.

We wish to thank Eleanor Williams, Ph.D., Associate Professor of Nutrition, Teachers College, Columbia University, for her assistance in reading proof.

Also, our sincere thanks are given to Ella McCollum Vahlteich, Ph.D., for her invaluable assistance in the compilation and calculation of tabular material, a service she has continued to render with each edition.

To many students who have made helpful suggestions and to individuals and organizations who have generously contributed illustrations for this edition, we express our appreciation.

C. M. T.
O. F. P.

New York City

Contents

Appendix

Tables

Figures

FOUNDATIONS OF NUTRITION

1

Historical Introduction

Does the food we eat make a difference? This is a question which the wise men and philosophers of ancient times asked themselves and were unable to answer because of the lack of scientific facts. As one progresses through the pages of this text the intricacies of the development of this science of nutrition will be revealed. The unfolding of the many inter-related facts involved in the understanding of the significance of each nutrient in relation to health is a story in itself. The answer to our question "Does the food we eat make a difference?" is not a simple one, as the student of nutrition will appreciate. The acceleration of research in this the twentieth century has added much to our knowledge. Many questions have been answered only to open up new ones to excite the curiosity of our present-day scientist with his modern technologically improved tools.

Historical Epochs in the Development of the Science of Nutrition

DIETARY EXPERIENCE FROM PRESCIENTIFIC ERA

Man's curiosity concerning the possible relationship between diet and his well-being is evident in the documents of antiquity. In a chronicle dated 607 B.C., it is recorded that "Nebuchadnezzar, king of Babylon, came to Jerusalem and besieged it." After conquering it, he commanded that "youths without blemish, handsome and skillful in all wisdom" be selected for training as courtiers. "The King assigned them a daily portion of the rich food which the king ate, and of the wine which he drank. They were to be educated for three years, and at the end of that time they were to stand before the king." One of these youths, Daniel, objected to the dietary part of the program and "resolved that he would not defile him-self with the king's rich food or with the wine which he drank," but the prince of the eunuchs, who had him in charge, protested, saying, "I fear lest my lord the king, who appointed your food and your drink, should see that you were in poorer condition than the youths who are of your own age." Then Daniel answered, "Test your servants for ten days, let us be given vegetables to eat and water to drink. Then let our appearance and the appearance of the youths who eat the king's rich food be observed." This seemed a fair bargain and so the nutrition experiment was undertaken, with the result that "at the end of ten days it was seen that they were better in appearance and fatter in flesh than all the youths who ate the king's rich food. So the steward took away their rich food and the wine they were to drink and gave them vegetables." At the end of the probationary period when the king examined them he found that "in every matter of wisdom and understanding" they were "ten times better than all the magicians and enchanters that were in all of his kingdom."[1] Although this is one of the earliest references to the influence of diet on record, and the vegetables undoubtedly included a mixture of pulses, it is still difficult to interpret in the light of present knowledge.

WHAT BECOMES OF FOOD EATEN?

For many centuries man gave much thought to the question of what becomes of food eaten and what it does to the one who eats it but the answers to these questions were philosophical rather than scientific. Hippocrates (460–370 B.C.), a Greek physician in the time of Socrates and Plato, and the greatest philosopher among the ancients with regard to food, was credited with the separation of medicine from superstition, thus giving it a scientific basis. Through his wisdom and skill he earned the title of Father of Medicine. The historian Strabo says that he was trained in dietetics, and some of his aphorisms have a modern sound, for example: "Growing bodies have the most heat; they therefore require the most food. . . . In old persons the heat is feeble and therefore they require little fuel. . . ." (Aphorism 14.)[2] But Hippocrates and his successors for two thousand years accounted for the disappearance of food as "insensible perspiration" and "heat" without any real understanding of what either term meant.

In A.D. 1614 a university professor with a practical turn of mind devised a chair connected with a steelyard to weigh himself before and after meals, so that he might find out the amount of this "insensible perspiration," for he said: "He only who knows how much and when the body does more or less insensibly perspire will be able to discern when or what is to be added or taken away, either for the recovery or the preservation of health." (Aphorism 3.)[3] Even Sanctorius' painstaking efforts did not

[1] Daniel 1:1–20. The Holy Bible, Revised Standard Version.
[2] Adams, F. *Genuine Works of Hippocrates*, p. 197. New York: William Wood and Co. (1891).
[3] Lusk, G. *The Elements of the Science of Nutrition*, 4th edition, p. 18. Philadelphia: W. B. Saunders Co. (1928).

solve the mystery because in his day there was no science of chemistry.
(See Figure 1–1.)

AIR IS ESSENTIAL FOR LIFE

Our earliest record of air as essential to life will be found in Genesis 2:7:
". . . then the Lord God formed man of dust from the ground, and
breathed into his nostrils the breath of life; and man became a living
being."[4] It was not until early in the seventeenth century, however, that
investigations of the properties of air were carried out.

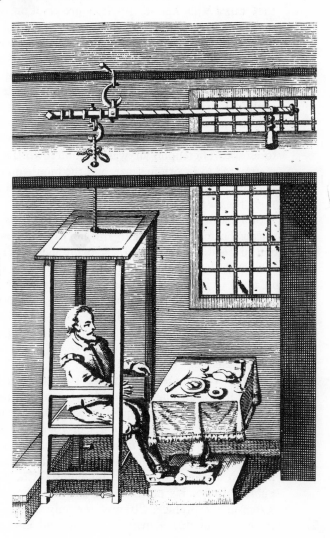

FIGURE 1–1. SANCTORIUS ON
THE STEELYARD HE DEVISED
TO WEIGH HIMSELF BE-
FORE AND AFTER MEALS.

[4] The Holy Bible, Revised Standard Version.

In 1627 the Honorable Robert Boyle was born, seventh son of "the great Earl of Corke," destined to receive the best education of his day in England and on the continent and to become known to every student of chemistry or physics as a result of his studies on the relationship between pressure and volume of gas. In the course of his extensive investigations of the properties of the air, he put into the receiver of his "pneumatical engine" all sorts of small animals—"a kitling newly kittened," "a duckling that was yet callow," "a large and lusty frog"—to find out "whether there reside in the heart of animals such a fine and kindled, but mild substance, as they call a Vital Flame, to whose preservation, as to that of other flames, the Air (especially as is taken in and expelled again by respiration) is necessary." And Boyle found that it was necessary[5] by placing a young mouse in a cylinder that was covered tightly with a thin bladder and putting this into a larger glass vessel out of which he could pump the air and observe the effect of this upon the animal. As the air was gradually withdrawn from the outer vessel, the bladder on the inner vessel expanded. The mouse showed the effect of the resulting rarefaction of the air in the inner vessel by becoming very restless and leaping about as though trying to escape. Thereupon air was readmitted to the outer vessel, the bladder contracted to its original size, and the mouse quieted down. So this ardent chemist demonstrated to his full satisfaction the dependence of animals upon the air they breathe for life.

Still more significant respiration experiments were made by a young chemist named John Mayow, who came under the influence of Boyle and in 1668, at the age of 28, published a "Treatise on Respiration" in which he showed that if a burning candle and an animal be put together in a bell jar both will expire sooner than either one alone. Mayow seems to have been the first to recognize that breathing brings the air into contact with the blood. Mayow's death at the age of 34 delayed the development of true conceptions of respiration for nearly a hundred years.

THE GASES OF RESPIRATION

In 1754 a young Scottish medical student at the University of Edinburgh, named Joseph Black, published his dissertation for his M.D. degree on the subject of magnesia and quicklime, substances in which he was specially interested because the medicines in vogue for the cure of gallstones all seemed to derive their efficacy from quicklime. He had discovered that a cubic inch of marble yielded about half its weight of pure lime and "as much air as would fill a vessel holding six wine gallons." His lectures were published after his death from his manuscript notes, and his biographer wrote in the preface: "It was not only a most unexpected and curious thing to find that a matter so solid and impenetrable as marble could

[5] *Works of Robert Boyle,* Vol. 3, p. 128. New York: A. Millar (1744).

appear in the form of air, and this air be again put into our hands in the form of marble; but . . . this air can be poured from one jar into another like as much water; and when it is poured out on a candle, or even on a fire in sufficient quantity, they are extinguished in an instant, as if water had been poured on them. . . . It has also been discovered that this air, so destructive and salutary, is forming in vast quantities every moment around us."[6] Black called it "fixed air," a little later to be identified as carbon dioxide. He also found that limewater was made cloudy by breathing into it through a tube, as well as by shaking it in a jar in which a candle had just gone out, and concluded that the breathing of animals changes "common air" into "fixed air."

While Black was winning renown as a professor in the University of Edinburgh and a devoted following as a practicing physician in the city, a dissenting clergyman in England, by the name of Joseph Priestley,[7] was earning his living by acting as librarian for a rich patron, but devoting all his spare time to chemical experimentation.

Priestley took a living plant (a sprig of mint) and put it into a closed receptacle in which a candle had already burned out (see Figure 1–2). After several days another candle was introduced into the same jar, and this time it did not go out but burned brightly. Soon after this, he took a jar, filled it with mercury, and carefully inverted it in a vessel containing mercury, so that no air entered the jar. He then introduced through the opening, under the mercury, some red oxide of mercury, which rose and floated on top of the mercury inside the mouth of the jar. Upon this he converged the heat of the sun by means of a powerful burning glass, and this is how he described the result: "I presently found by means of this lens air was expelled from it (the mercuric oxide) very rapidly. Having got about three or four times the bulk of my materials, I admitted water and found that it was not imbibed by it. But what surprised me more than I can well express was that a candle burned in this air with a remarkable brilliant flame."[8] Priestley had discovered a new gas, given off by the growing plant and by the heated mercuric oxide, which the candle flame fed upon so readily.

At almost the same time a similar experiment had been performed by a Swedish apothecary named Scheele, who called the gas which he had discovered "fire air." Scheele next took two bees, put them in a chamber

[6] Lectures on the Elements of Chemistry, delivered in the University of Edinburgh by the late Joseph Black, M.D., professor of chemistry in that university. Published from his manuscripts by John Robinson (1807).

[7] He was born in Yorkshire, in 1733, and came to the United States on June 4, 1794, following his persecution in contempt for his sympathy with the arms of the French Revolution. He lived in Northumberland, Pennsylvania, until his death on February 6, 1814. His burning glass is preserved in the museum of Dickinson College, Carlisle, Pennsylvania.

[8] Priestley, J. Experiments and Observations on Different Kinds of Air, Vol. 2, p. 107. Birmingham, England: Thomas Pearson (1790).

FIGURE 1–2. APPARATUS USED BY PRIESTLEY. Plate 1 from *Experiments and Observations on Different Kinds of Air* (1790). (*Courtesy of the New York Public Library.*)

with a little honey, connected the chamber with a glass cylinder filled with the "fire air," and immersed its lower end in limewater (see Figure 1–3). Day by day the limewater rose in the tube and the volume of gas diminished, until at the close of a week the limewater nearly filled the cylinder and the bees were dead. The "fire air" had been used up by the bees, and the carbon dioxide given off by them was absorbed by the limewater that filled the space originally occupied by the "fire air."

FIGURE 1–3. SCHEELE'S APPARATUS SHOWING BEES IN THE UPPER CHAMBER OF A GLASS APPARATUS FILLED WITH OXYGEN.

RESPIRATION A MEASURE OF FOOD BURNING IN THE BODY

Priestley and Scheele were both in communication with a brilliant young French nobleman, Antoine Laurent Lavoisier, a member of the French Academy of Science. At their urgent request, he repeated their experiments, making use of his exceptionally fine equipment (see Figure 1–4), and confirmed the discovery that "fixed air" was carbon dioxide; he gave to "fire air" the name of oxygen. Lavoisier then proceeded on his own account to demonstrate how living animals affect the air. He took a sparrow, shut it up in a small chamber, and concluded from his observations that oxygen disappeared from the air, and that after the animal had died, the carbon dioxide which it produced could all be absorbed from the chamber by limewater. Then Lavoisier and the great physicist Laplace together took another step forward. They put a guinea pig into a chamber and measured for ten hours the carbon dioxide formed by its respiration. This was found to equal that produced by burning in a closed vessel 3.33 gm of carbon. Next the guinea pig was confined for ten hours in a chamber containing a known weight of ice, and the quantity of ice melted by the animal's body was determined. This required for its melting almost exactly the same amount of heat as was evolved in burning the 3.33 gm of carbon. The obvious conclusion was that the carbon dioxide formed by the guinea pig came from burning in its body the equivalent of 3.33 gm of carbon.[9]

[9] A slight discrepancy was accounted for in the reduction of the guinea pig's body temperature by the cold.

FIGURE 1–4. LAVOISIER'S BURNING GLASS (1774). (*Courtesy of Science Museum, London.*)

Similar observations were subsequently extended to human subjects, and drawings made by Mme Lavoisier from memory after her husband's death in 1794 show Lavoisier's associate, Seguin, sitting in a chair breathing through a mask into a series of globes by means of which the oxygen consumed and the carbon dioxide given off were measured (see Figure 1–5). Lavoisier came to the conclusion that "respiration is only a slow combustion of carbon and hydrogen, which is similar in all respects to that which takes place in a lamp or lighted candle; and from this point of view the animals which respire are truly combustible bodies which burn and consume themselves."[10] Because of his grasp of the significance of the respiratory process in relation to food, Lavoisier is accounted the father of the science of nutrition.

Methods and Apparatus Developed for the Measurement of Energy Transformation

WATER CALORIMETERS

Lavoisier was the first investigator who applied the balance and the thermometer to the study of vital phenomena. His work with Laplace on the measurement of the heat production of a guinea pig has already been mentioned. After Lavoisier's death the French Academy offered a prize for further investigation, and two young men, Dulong and Depretz,

[10] Cited by Mathews, A. P. *Physiological Chemistry*, 5th ed., p. 287. New York: William Wood and Co. (1930).

Figure 1–5. Lavoisier in His Laboratory Making the First Measurements of Energy Expenditure by a Human Being. (*From a drawing by Mme Lavoisier.*)

entered the lists. They improved upon Lavoisier's methods, putting small animals into a chamber surrounded by water to absorb the heat and weighing the carbon dioxide and the water given off from the animals' bodies. Dulong won the prize (1823), although Depretz's work appears now to have been somewhat superior (see Figure 1–6).

THE MEASUREMENT OF RESPIRATION

In 1849, Regnault, professor of physics at the University of Paris, with his assistant, Reiset, constructed an apparatus which enabled him to keep small animals respiring normally in an enclosed space. The animal was placed in a glass case containing a known quantity of oxygen, which was replenished as it was consumed, and the air in the apparatus was continually pumped through a solution which took out the carbon dioxide exhaled. By means of this device, Regnault was able to show that eating different kinds of food made a difference in the amount of oxygen used and in the amount of carbon dioxide excreted. He also noticed that the small animals absorbed more oxygen and produced more heat and more carbon dioxide in proportion to their size than did the larger ones—sparrows, ten times as much as chickens; that cold-blooded animals (fish and reptiles) consumed less oxygen per unit of body weight than warm-blooded animals; and that insects consumed much more than reptiles (see Figure 1–7). Regnault and Reiset hoped to study man in the same way, but the apparatus proved too expensive for them to construct.

THE NATURE OF BODY FUEL

Liebig (1803–73), a German chemist and recognized as the father of organic analysis, was among the first to establish a chemical teaching laboratory which soon became a center for the training of many of the leading nineteenth-century chemists. He was the first to understand clearly that the three substances oxidized for fuel in the body are organic (carbon-containing) compounds of three types, protein, fat, and carbo-

FIGURE 1–6. A WATER CALORIMETER OF 1823. The inner chamber containing the animal was submerged in a larger receptacle filled with water. Air entered at A, circulated through a coil under the inner chamber, and connected at C with the exit pipe, B. Thermometers extending into the water recorded the rise in temperature caused by the animal.

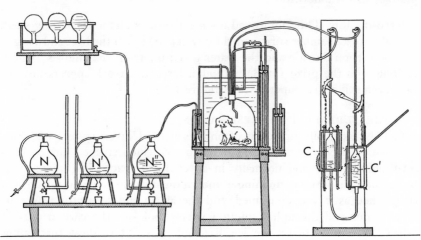

FIGURE 1–7. RESPIRATION APPARATUS OF REGNAULT AND REISET. Oxygen was supplied to the animal from a large flask, *N"*. (*N* and *N'* are other flasks in reserve.) Water pressure from the flasks above at the left drove the oxygen into the apparatus. An exit tube from the chamber containing the animal was connected with bulbs for absorbing carbon dioxide, *C* and *C'*. (From *Annales de Chimie et de Physique*, Series 3, Vol. 26, Plate III, 1849.)

hydrate. He showed that 1 gm of fat requires for complete combustion 2,050 cc of oxygen, and 1 gm of starch 832 cc—values nearly those in use today.

THE REGULARITY OF HEAT PRODUCTION

Bidder and Schmidt, two Germans working at the University of Dorpat (then under Russia), at about the same time (1850), concluded that for every species of animal there is a regular minimum of necessary metabolism, which is apparent in experiments when no food is given. "The extent of respiration, like every other component of the metabolism process, is to be regarded as a function of one variable, the food taken, and one constant, a distinctly typical metabolism, which varies with the age and sex of the individual. This factor characterizes every animal of given race, size, age, and sex."[11]

THE FIRST RESPIRATION CHAMBER

Ten years later, Voit, then professor of physiology at the University of Munich, suggested to the physicist Pettenkofer, head of the hygienic laboratory of the city of Munich, that he devise a respiration apparatus which would accommodate a fairly large dog. Pettenkofer aspired to work with men, however; so he constructed (1862) an airtight chamber

[11] Lusk, G. "History of Metabolism." Barker's *Endocrinology and Metabolism,* Vol. 3, p. 63. New York: D. Appleton and Co. (1922).

as large as the stateroom of a steamer, in which a man could live with comfort. It was ventilated by means of pumps which drew air from the outside through the chamber, and at the point of exit samples were measured, after having been passed through suitable solutions for the removal of carbon dioxide and water.

Voit and Pettenkofer, working together with this apparatus, established many points hitherto uninvestigated or obscure. Rubner, later one of the masters of the science of nutrition, found, while working as a pupil in Voit's laboratory, that the energy values to the body of starch and fat were equal to the heat produced by burning them in a special apparatus for heat determinations, called a calorimeter; but that the energy value of protein was different, since it could not be burned as completely in the body as in the calorimeter.

THE LAW OF CONSERVATION OF ENERGY IN THE ANIMAL WORLD

Rubner became professor of physiology at Marburg, and in 1892 in his own laboratory he evolved a calorimeter large enough for a dog, which very accurately measured the heat production of the animal. This was connected with a Pettenkofer-Voit respiration apparatus, and the heat measured by the calorimeter exactly corresponded (within 1 per cent) to the heat calculated from the measurement of the oxygen intake, carbon dioxide output, and losses of energy-bearing material in urine and feces. Thus, one hundred years after its initial conception by Lavoisier, Rubner established by animal experimentation the fundamental law that energy is neither created nor destroyed in the animal body.

THE RESPIRATION CALORIMETER IN THE UNITED STATES

While Rubner was engaged in these researches in Germany, Atwater, also at one time a pupil of Voit and later professor of chemistry at Wesleyan University, Middletown, Connecticut, began to work on a respiration calorimeter with the expert assistance of the physicist Rosa. This calorimeter enabled him to carry out on man such experiments as Rubner was conducting on dogs. The respiration part embodied the principles of the Regnault-Reiset apparatus; the heat-measuring part depended on removing the body heat as fast as produced by means of a current of cold water, thus maintaining a comparatively constant temperature in the chamber. Improvements were soon instituted by Benedict, and the Atwater-Rosa-Benedict respiration calorimeter was developed (see Figure 1–8).

Briefly, this apparatus consisted of an airtight copper chamber surrounded by zinc and wooden walls with air spaces between. By means of thermoelectric junctions between the copper and zinc walls connected with a delicate galvanometer, the temperature of each wall was measured

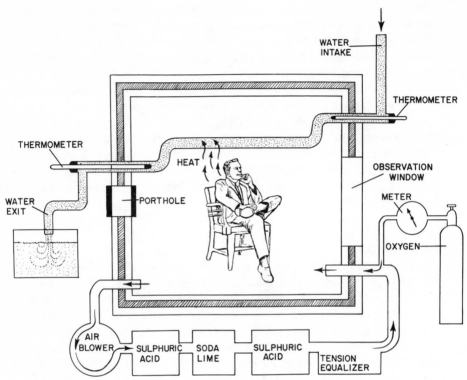

FIGURE 1–8. DIAGRAM OF THE ATWATER-ROSA-BENEDICT RESPIRATION CALORIMETER. The heat produced by the subject is absorbed by the circulating water and the rise in temperature noted from the thermometers, one at the intake and one at the outlet. Food may be introduced and excreta removed by way of the porthole. Air is recirculated through the chamber after passing over absorbents to remove moisture and carbon dioxide. Oxygen is added to the system as the air enters the calorimeter. (*Courtesy of Sigmund Grollman,* The Human Body, Its Structure and Physiology. *New York: Macmillan* [1964].)

at frequent intervals during an experiment to preclude any possibility of the results being influenced by the passage of heat through the walls of the chamber. The ventilation was so regulated as to keep the temperature of the incoming and outgoing air the same. The heat evolved by the subject was absorbed by a current of cold water passing through a pipe coiled near the ceiling of the chamber, except for a small amount which escaped as latent heat of water vapor. The amount of heat removed from the chamber was computed from the rise in the temperature of the water flowing through the pipe.

The perfecting of the respiration calorimeter for human experiments opened a new era in nutrition in this country. Calorimeters were built in

Washington by the United States Department of Agriculture; at the Pennsylvania State College by Armsby; in New York by Lusk for Cornell University Medical College and the Russell Sage Institute of Pathology; in Boston by Benedict for the Carnegie Institution of Washington. These men and their associates made signal contributions to our knowledge of energy requirements, many of which will be referred to later.

PORTABLE RESPIRATION APPARATUS

The conclusive demonstration, by means of the respiration calorimeter, that energy calculated from the amounts of carbon dioxide excreted and oxygen absorbed by a man lying quietly in the apparatus exactly equals the heat given off by his body in the same period made it possible to dispense with the actual measurement of body heat (direct calorimetry) in a great many experiments, and to rely on studies of the respiration (indirect calorimetry).

The principle upon which Regnault and Reiset built their apparatus in 1850 was that upon which modern respiration apparatus were constructed. Zuntz, long chief of the Agricultural College in Berlin, made a portable respiration apparatus to measure the energy expenditure of a man walking at sea level or on the snow fields of Monte Rosa. This apparatus was subsequently used with great success by one of his pupils, Magnus-Levy, for the study of respiration in disease. This type of apparatus was further developed in 1918 when F. G. Benedict, then director of the Nutrition Laboratory of the Carnegie Institution of Washington in Boston, produced his portable respiration apparatus, which was easy to operate and enabled students with relatively little training in physics and chemistry to have firsthand experience in determining energy expenditure from oxygen consumption.

The Benedict portable respiration apparatus depends upon the principle that the oxygen breathed in by a subject is used in response to a need of the body and is not stored. Consequently, the oxygen consumed is a measure of the amount of combustion going on in the body. The ratio of the amount of the carbon dioxide produced in combustion to the amount of oxygen consumed is called the respiratory quotient. When a normal person in good health has fasted 12 or 15 hours, this ratio is practically constant, giving a respiratory quotient of 0.82. Under these standard conditions 1 liter of oxygen consumed represents 4.825 calories.

One type of respiration apparatus, designed by Dr. Benedict for the use of students, is shown in diagram in Figure 1–9. A rubber cap covering the metal can containing soda lime serves as a spirometer. This is inflated with oxygen from a cylinder of the compressed gas, until a small button attached to the cap exactly touches a disc on the metal rod above it. As

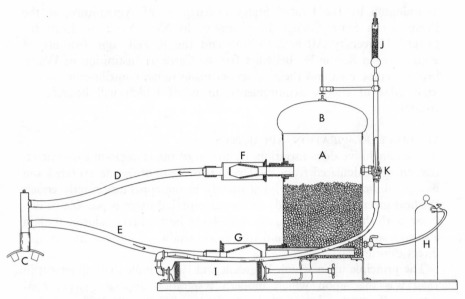

FIGURE 1–9. DIAGRAM OF BENEDICT'S STUDENT RESPIRATION APPARATUS.
A. Metal can containing soda lime to absorb carbon dioxide.
B. Cap inflated so that button almost touches marker above it.
C. Rubber mouthpiece.
D and E. Rubber tubes connecting can and mouthpiece.
F and G. Valves controlling direction of air current.
H. Oxygen tank from which a supply of pure oxygen for starting an experi-
   ment is introduced into the can.
I. Pump by means of which additional air is supplied to can; it is drawn in
   through a moist sponge in tube J to saturate the air with water vapor.
K. Valve through which air from pump is admitted to can.

the oxygen is consumed by the subject, the button soon fails to touch
the mark, and the oxygen is replaced by pumping in room air, using a
small pump of known volume. The air pumped in will measure exactly
the oxygen removed, since gases at the same temperature and pressure have
the same volume. If the capacity of the pump and the number of strokes
required to inflate the cap to the disc are known, the amount of oxygen
consumed in a given time can be calculated. For example, a man of average
weight, sitting attached to the apparatus for ten minutes, will consume
about 2.5 liters of oxygen and the calories corresponding will be 12
(2.5 × 4.825 calories per liter) or 72 calories per hour. A description of
an apparatus of this type made and used by high school students will be
found in the dissertation by Bingham noted in the references at the end
of the chapter.

Apparatus currently in use in energy metabolism investigations will be
described in Chapters 2, 3, and 4.

Early Investigations into Other Phases of the Developing Science of Nutrition

Thus far our discussion has centered around the early developments in the area of energy metabolism. Let us not overlook, however, the fact that simultaneously the science of nutrition was branching out from the time of Lavoisier in many other directions parallel with other rapidly advancing sciences.

The effect of starvation and exercise on the fat in a normal individual concerned the physiologist in the eighteenth century and today continues to present many unsolved problems. During the nineteenth century the first descriptions of the separation of fatty acids from fats were reported. In 1814, Chevreul gave the names of stearin and elain to two oily bodies (fats) found in hog's lard. As the century advanced, many types of fats were recognized and their properties studied and reported.

Investigations of carbohydrates were also being conducted during the eighteenth and nineteenth centuries and were concerned for the most part with the study of the sources, properties, and classification of starches and sugars.

The earliest quantitative distinction between proteins was made by Berthollet in 1811. His work was soon followed by the discoveries of Braconnot, who distinguished himself by making the first preparation of an amino acid (glycine), and in the same year, 1820, a second amino acid (leucine) was prepared by him from the proteins in muscle tissue and wool.

The historical development of the study of the mineral elements will be found in Chapters 9, 10, and 11 and that of the vitamins in Chapters 12 through 18.

This brief introduction to the historical development of the science of nutrition would not be complete without special mention of the contributions of Wilbur Olin Atwater (1844–1907), who has been referred to as the father of American nutrition and to whom we can give credit for three nutrition firsts: (1) He designed with his research partners, Rosa and Benedict, the first calorimeter to be used for human-nutrition research, which has been described in this chapter, (2) in 1869, he published the first analysis of an American food—corn, and (3) in 1896, he and his associates published the first edition of the United States Department of Agriculture bulletin containing tables showing the composition of familiar foods, which for years was a bible for nutritionists throughout the world. In 1889 he organized the Office of Experiment Stations and became its first director.

Much of the nutrition research today stems from the blueprint established by Atwater at the turn of the century. His main goals were: "Find out what the body needs in its food; what nutrients, and how much of them, different foods contain; and how the body uses these nutrients. Then find out what foods people are accustomed to eat. Learn what foods, and what methods of preparing them, will furnish the most economical and healthful diet. All this," said Atwater, "leads up to the fundamental question: How can national food production be made to yield best returns in economic progress and social welfare?"[12]

For those students who are interested in further details dealing with the fascinating early developments of the many phases of the science of nutrition, the authors direct attention to McCollum's *A History of Nutrition* and other references given at the end of this chapter.

REFERENCES

Atwater, W. O., and Benedict, F. G. *A Respiration Calorimeter with Appliances for Direct Determination of Oxygen.* Washington, D.C.: Carnegie Institution of Washington. Publication No. 42 (1905).

Bingham, N. E. *Teaching Nutrition in Biology Classes,* pp. 56–58. New York: Bureau of Publications, Teachers College, Columbia University (1939).

Bourne, G. H. *World Review of Nutrition and Dietetics.* New York: Hafner, Vol. I (1959). McCollum, E. V. Chapter on "History of Nutrition," p. 5.

Editorial. "The Chemical Revolutionist (Lavoisier)." *J. Amer. Med. A.,* 180:778 (1962).

———. "The Reverend Joseph Priestley—Natural Philosopher." *J. Amer. Med. A.,* 181:437 (1962).

———. "Robert Boyle—Natural Philosopher." *J. Amer. Med. A.,* 180:968 (1962).

Goldblith, S. A., and Joslyn, M. *Milestones in Nutrition.* Westport, Conn.: The AVI Publishing Co. (1964).

Holt, A. *A Life of Joseph Priestley.* New York: Oxford U. P. (1931).

Jaffe, B. *Crucibles,* rev. ed., Chaps. 4 and 6. New York: Simon and Schuster (1948).

Kendall, E. C. "Henry Clapp Sherman." *J. Chem. Educ.,* 32:510 (1955).

Lusk, G. *Clio Medica,* a Series of Primers on the History of Medicine, X, "Nutrition." New York: Hoeber (1933).

———. *The Elements of the Science of Nutrition,* 4th ed., Chaps. 1 and 3. Philadelphia: Saunders (1928).

Martin, E. A. "Lydia Jane Roberts—June 30, 1879–May 28, 1965." *J. Amer. Dietet. A.,* 47:127 (1965).

Maynard, L. A. "Early Days of Nutrition Research in the United States of America." *Nutr. Abstr. & Rev.,* 32:345 (1962).

[12] *USDA,* April 1, 1944, Vol. 111, No. 7.

————. "Wilbur O. Atwater—A Biographical Sketch (1844–1907)." *J. Nutr.*, **78**:3 (1962).

McCollum, E. V. *A History of Nutrition*. Boston: Houghton (1956).

————. *From Kansas Farm Boy to Scientist: An Autobiography*. Lawrence: U. of Kansas (1964).

McKie, D. *Antoine Lavoisier*. Philadelphia: Lippincott (1935).

Mendel, L. B. *Nutrition: The Chemistry of Life*, Chap. I. New Haven, Conn.: Yale (1923).

Rosenberg, H. R. "The Fiftieth Anniversary of Casimir Funk's 'Vitamines.'" *Nutr. Rev.*, **20**:353 (1962).

Taylor, C. M. "Mary Davies Swartz Rose." *Notable American Women, 1607–1950*. A Biographical Dictionary. Cambridge, Mass.: Radcliffe College (1965).

Todhunter, E. N. "Development of Knowledge in Nutrition. I. Animal Experiments"; "II. Human Experiments." *J. Amer. Dietet. A.*, **41**:328, 335 (1962).

————. "Grace MacLeod—August 6, 1878–November 16, 1962." Biographical Notes from the History of Nutrition. *J. Amer. Dietet. A.*, **44**:495 (1964).

————. "Some Classics of Nutrition and Dietetics." *J. Amer. Dietet. A.*, **44**:100 (1964).

————. "The Evolution of Nutrition Concepts." *J. Amer. Dietet. A.*, **46**:120 (1965).

❧ 2 ❧

The Basal Metabolism and Factors Affecting It

It is clear from the foregoing chapter that by the beginning of the twentieth century nutrition as a pure science was well established and many fruitful areas of research in nutrition had been identified. However, not only because of its historical interest is it fitting to begin our study of nutrition with the energy exchange, but also because, quantitatively speaking, the greatest demand we make upon food is that it must supply us with calories. There are other food factors equally important qualitatively to be discussed in their turn, but in ordinary daily life few of these can be secured independently of the energy supply, while all of them may and most of them must be obtained incidentally to it.

Our first task is to learn how many calories we need and then to see how, by intelligent choice of foods that yield them, we may make them the carriers of every other dietary essential. This will eventually involve much study of individual foods. Atwater, in 1895, described food as material, which when taken into the body, serves to form tissues, keep them in repair, yield energy, and create strength for the work of the body.[1]

In approaching the study of the energy requirement we must bear in mind the fact that energy expenditure varies greatly with conditions of existence: it rises rapidly, for instance, when a man who has been sitting in a railroad station and has fallen asleep while waiting for his train wakens to find it pulling out, and bolts through the doorway on a dead run to catch it; it falls when an athlete who has been doing a hundred-yard dash crosses the line and sinks down to rest after his sprint.

[1] U.S. Department of Agriculture, Office of Experiment Stations, Bulletin No. 21, Washington, D.C., (1895).

The Basal Metabolism

The term "metabolism" is used broadly for all the chemical changes that take place within the living cells in the body. Some of these changes are concerned with the construction of body substance, some with the maintenance of essentially stable tissues in an organism in which flux is the law of life, and some with the use by the body of energy-yielding materials for its internal and external activities. It is with the last of these that we are now concerned, and the general term "energy metabolism" is employed to designate those chemical processes which have to do with the combustion of fuel to run the human machine.

If we determine the energy expenditure of an adult each morning after he awakens, but before he rises from his bed and begins to take food or to dress, we shall find in the course of a week a striking similarity in the daily measurement, and we may be surprised at the amount of "internal work" that is going on. There is an irreducible minimum of energy expenditure, without which life is impossible. The absolute minimum for many persons is reached not in the waking but in the sleeping state; it is, however, more practical to take as the line of reference the energy output of the subject awake, lying quietly, comfortably warm, and relaxed, 12 to 15 hours after the last meal. These are recognized as the standard conditions to be observed in the measurement of the basal metabolism.

The energy expenditure of an individual under these basal conditions is reduced to a practical minimum comprising the "internal work" of the body, namely, the work involved in respiration, in circulation, and in the maintenance of muscle tone. This is called the basal metabolism.

The expression basal metabolism was according to Lusk introduced as a translation of the German word *Grundumsatz*, employed by Magnus-Levy, a German scientist who came to the United States where he held a professorship at Yale University until retirement.

The Determination of the Basal Metabolism

Among the various types of apparatus used to determine the basal metabolism, the Benedict-Roth portable respiration apparatus has been commonly used (see Figure 2–1). The subject must observe the standard conditions for the measurement of the basal metabolism as have been described in the preceding section if an accurate basal metabolism level is to be obtained.

When the Benedict portable respiration apparatus is used, the subject is connected with it by means of a soft rubber mouthpiece so devised as to prevent escape of air through the lips, while the circulation of air through the nose is prevented by a spring or a screw clip. The person breathes

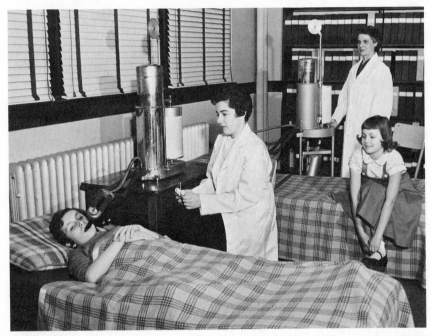

FIGURE 2–1. PREPARATION FOR THE MEASUREMENT OF BASAL METABOLISM USING THE BENEDICT-ROTH PORTABLE RESPIRATION APPARATUS IN THE NUTRITION LABORATORY, TEACHERS COLLEGE, COLUMBIA UNIVERSITY. Note that observer is about to place clip on subject's nose.

from a current of oxygen-enriched air, which is kept in circulation by a set of valves that allows the current to go in only one direction. The air is constantly purified by the removal of carbon dioxide as it passes through a container of soda lime. It is kept supplied with oxygen by means of a spirometer into which, before the experimental period, oxygen is run from a storage cylinder. As the oxygen is used up by the subject, the spirometer falls. In the Benedict portable respiration apparatus shown in Figure 2–2, measurement of the oxygen consumed is made by means of a pen attached to the spirometer which writes on a moving drum covered with paper. The drum is driven by a clock mechanism and revolves at a constant rate. The paper is ruled vertically so that the time required for the pen to move from one vertical line to the next is one minute. Horizontal lines correspond to the change in position of the spirometer as the oxygen is consumed, the space between two lines indicating the withdrawal of a definite amount of oxygen. As the spirometer rises and falls, the pen records also the rate and depth of respirations. A line drawn along the points which mark the end of each expiration will give the difference between the first and last readings, as shown in Figure 2–3. The actual volume of oxygen consumed per minute can thus be calculated. To get the true value of oxygen, corrections must be made

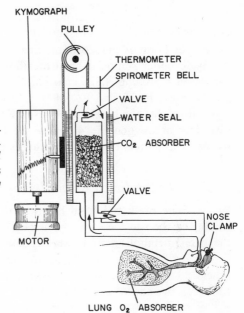

FIGURE 2–2. DIAGRAM OF THE BENE-
DICT PORTABLE RESPIRATION APPA-
RATUS. (*Courtesy of Sigmund
Grollman*. The Human Body, Its
Structure and Physiology. *New
York: Macmillan [1964].*)

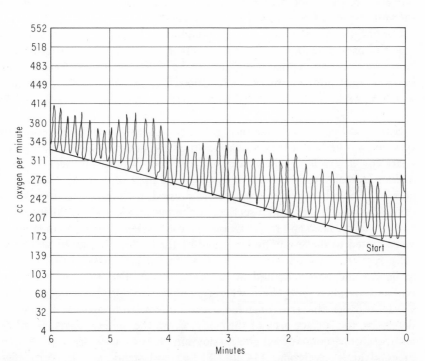

FIGURE 2–3. RESPIRATION RECORD IN A BASAL METABOLISM TEST. The tracings
mark the rise and fall of the spirometer with each inhalation and exhalation.
The difference between the start and the finish gives the volume of oxygen
consumed per minute.

for the temperature, the atmospheric pressure, and the moisture in the spirometer. After these corrections are made, the liters of oxygen consumed per hour or per 24 hours can be calculated. When measurements are made under standard basal metabolism conditions, 1 liter of oxygen consumed represents 4.825 calories. The total number of liters of oxygen per 24 hours multiplied by 4.825 calories per liter will give the energy expenditure for the basal metabolism. For example, if a subject consumed 280 liters of oxygen in 24 hours, the basal metabolism for this subject would be 280 liters times 4.825 calories per liter, or 1,351 calories.

The Predicted Basal Metabolism

The predicted basal metabolism can be calculated from weight, height, or the surface area of an individual. It is convenient to think of the basal metabolism in terms of body weight. If Mr. Jones and Mr. Brown are both the same age, but one weighs 150 lb (68 kg) and the other 180 lb (82 kg), the total basal metabolism of the one will be about 1,632 calories and of the other about 1,968 calories. These figures do not tell us that the basal metabolic rate of these men is actually the same; however, if we divide total calories by body weight, in each case we get the same figure, 24 calories per kilogram per day.

For the young adult of average weight for height it has been found that the basal metabolism lies very close to 1 calorie per kilogram per hour. At this rate, a man weighing 70 kg (154 lb) would have for 24 hours a basal metabolism of 1,680 calories ($1 \times 70 \times 24$). A woman weighing 58 kg (128 lb) would have a basal metabolism of 1,392 calories ($1 \times 58 \times 24$).

Scientifically, a more accurate prediction of the basal metabolism can be made on the basis of the surface area of the body. DuBois developed a chart for determining the body surface from height and weight after making actual measurements of the surface area of a large number of persons. The subject to be studied was dressed in close-fitting underwear, thin socks and gloves, and a section of the leg of a knitted garment made a covering for head and neck. Upon this foundation strips of manila paper were pasted to make a complete mold of the body. This mold was carefully removed in sections, then these were cut into pieces small enough to lie flat and photographed on weighed paper. The imprints were cut out and weighed, and their weight compared with that of the whole sheet of paper the area of which was known, thus making it easy to determine the surface area of the body. From the DuBois chart, Boothby and Sandiford constructed the nomogram shown in Figure 2–4. A man in good health weighing 154 lb (70 kg) and standing 5 ft, 9 in. high (175 cm) will have, according to the nomogram, a body surface of 1.86 sq m, and if he is 25 years of age, his predicted basal metabolism, accord-

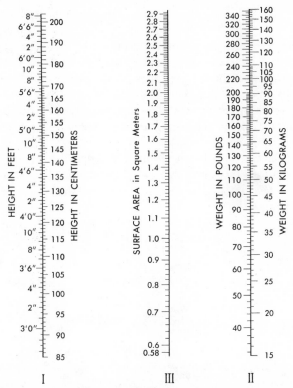

FIGURE 2–4. NOMOGRAM FOR DETERMINING SURFACE AREA FROM HEIGHT AND WEIGHT PREPARED BY BOOTHBY AND SANDIFORD OF THE MAYO CLINIC FROM THE DUBOIS SURFACE AREA CHART. To determine the surface area locate height on line I and weight on line II, draw a line connecting these two points, and read surface area where this line intersects line III.

ing to Table 2–3 on page 25, will be 38.4 calories per square meter per hour. His predicted basal metabolism for 24 hours will then amount to 1,714 calories (38.4 × 1.86 × 24). A healthy woman 25 years of age weighing 128 lb (58 kg) and 5 ft, 4 in. tall (163 cm) will have a body surface of 1.63 sq m and a basal metabolism of 35.1 calories per square

TABLE 2–1. AVERAGE BASAL METABOLISM
OF A MAN AND A WOMAN TWENTY-FIVE YEARS OF AGE*

	Weight, kg	Surface Area, sq m	Calories per sq m per hr	Calories per 24 hr
Man	70	1.86	38.4	1,714
Woman	58	1.63	35.1	1,373

*For other ages see page 25.

meter per hour, and a predicted basal metabolism of 1,373 calories per day (35.1 × 1.63 × 24). These figures are summarized in Table 2–1.

Comparing the basal metabolism predicted in this way with the result of the actual determination of the basal metabolism observing standard conditions will show agreement in the majority of cases within plus or minus 10 to 15 per cent. Reasons for divergence from the predicted rate are discussed in the following sections. The basal metabolism is fairly constant for an individual as long as a state of health, weight, and height is maintained.

Foods providing the calories required for the basal metabolism for a man and woman are listed in Table 2–2. The additional calories needed by the man to meet his basal metabolism are furnished by extra slices of bread and butter.

TABLE 2–2
FOODS YIELDING CALORIES APPROXIMATELY EQUAL TO THE BASAL METABOLISM FOR ONE DAY

Foods	Man		Woman	
	Measure	*Calories*	*Measure*	*Calories*
Bread	5 slices	300	3½ slices	210
Butter	4 tbsp	400	1½ tbsp	150
Lamb chop	1 med. lean and fat	400	1 med. lean and fat	400
Milk	1 pt	320	1 pt	320
Orange	1 med.	75	1 med.	75
Potato, boiled	1 med.	105	1 med.	105
Shredded wheat (1 oz)	1 biscuit	100	1 biscuit	100
		1,700		1,360

A number of formulas have been used in predicting the basal metabolism of normal persons, namely, Aub and DuBois; Harris and Benedict; Dreyer; Boothby, Berkson, and Dunn; Robertson and Reid; and Fleisch. With a deviation in the actual basal metabolism of normal individuals of 10 to 15 per cent being recognized, any one of these predictions could be used. Table 2–3 is based on the data from three sets of prediction standards.

Factors Affecting the Basal Metabolism

INFLUENCE OF SIZE AND SHAPE

For practical purposes we tend to minimize the degree of fatness or thinness in adults if we estimate basal metabolism on the basis of body surface instead of body weight. We cannot apply the average of ap-

TABLE 2-3
BASAL METABOLISM OF ADULTS AT DIFFERENT AGES*

Age, years	Calories Predicted per sq m per hour		Calories Predicted per sq m per 24 hr	
	Males	Females	Males	Females
18–20	40.1	35.4	962	850
21–23	39.2	35.2	941	845
24–26	38.4	35.1	922	842
27–29	37.8	35.0	907	840
30–32	37.4	35.0	898	840
33–35	37.0	34.9	888	838
36–39	36.7	34.6	881	830
40	36.5	34.3	876	823
45	36.3	33.9	871	814
50	36.0	33.4	864	802
55	35.4	32.9	850	790
60	34.8	32.4	836	778
65	34.0	31.8	816	763
70	33.1	31.3	794	751
75 (and over)	31.8	31.1	763	746

*Values are based on three of the largest and most authoritative sets of original data: (1) the Mayo Foundation Standards of Boothby, Berkson, and Dunn; (2) the British studies of Robertson and Reid; and (3) the data of Harris and Benedict. For original table see Albritten, *Standard Values in Nutrition and Metabolism*, p. 241. Philadelphia: Saunders (1952).

proximately 1 calorie per kilogram per hour without some error if the individual is taller, shorter, thinner, or fatter than the average. Basal metabolism being more closely correlated with surface than with weight, we must consider what effect changes in size have on the relationship between it and weight. A small body has a greater surface in proportion to mass than a large one.

If we take two men of about the same age and the same body weight but one much taller than the other and estimate the basal metabolism of each for 24 hours, we can see in Table 2–4 how metabolism is related to body weight and surface. On the basis of body surface the metabolism is practically the same, but when we calculate this according to calories per kilogram of body weight, the taller figure shows a metabolism higher by 8 per cent.

INFLUENCE OF BODY COMPOSITION

Two individuals of exactly the same weight and height and consequently of the same surface area may differ in their basal metabolic rate. The explanation lies in the nature of the body composition.

Metabolically, the most elementary analysis of the body mass begins with the differentiation between part of the body that is relatively active in

**TABLE 2–4. BASAL METABOLISM OF TWO MEN OF
THE SAME WEIGHT BUT DIFFERENT HEIGHT**

| | | | Body | Surface | Basal Metabolism for 24 hr | | |
Subject	Age yr	Height cm	Weight kg	Area sq m	Cal Total	Cal per sq m	Cal per kg
Mr. B.	40	183	83.1	2.06	1,805	876	21.7
Mr. C.	36	169	83.0	1.89	1,665	881	20.1

energy metabolism and the relatively non-active part. In the latter category are the body fat, the extra cellular fluids, the mineral portion of the bony skeleton, and a negligible mass in the horny epidermis, the nails and the hair. The body fat tends to be the most variable compartment, though the extra-cellular fluid mass may increase considerably in cases of edema. If, from the total mass of the body, the relative non-active masses of fat, extra-cellular fluid and bone mineral are subtracted, the remainder may be termed the "active tissue mass" or "cell residue." This mass, primarily cells, may represent anything from perhaps 30 to 65 per cent of the total body weight but it accounts for substantially all of the energy consumption.[2]

Thus, the large fat person not only has a size and shape favorable to an economical energy expenditure per unit of weight, but also has less active body mass in proportion to bulk. Athletes, having by vigorous exercise rid themselves of surplus fat and built up firm muscle tissue, show a basal metabolism of about 6 per cent higher than nonathletic individuals carefully paired with them as to size and shape. Women, with a higher proportion of body fat, have on the basis of body surface an average metabolism about 8 per cent lower than that of normal men.

INFLUENCE OF UNDERNUTRITION

The most comprehensive study of the effects of chronic caloric undernutrition is that of Keys and his co-workers at the University of Minnesota, which was conducted during World War II. Thirty-two conscientious objectors served as subjects. They lived in the Laboratory of Physiological Hygiene for a year. During the first three months the subjects lived on a controlled adequate diet. Then followed six months of semistarvation and next, three months on the adequate diet of the prestarvation period. During the prestarvation, or control, period the subjects maintained their average body weight on an average daily intake of 3,492 calories. Their activities consisted of a regular schedule of laboratory and housekeeping duties, 20 miles of walking each week, and

[2] Wohl, M. G., and Goodhart, R. S. *Modern Nutrition in Health and Disease,* 3rd ed., Chap. 1 by Keys, A., and Grande, F., p. 23. Philadelphia: Lea (1964).

participation in an educational program. During the semistarvation period that followed immediately after the control period their energy intake averaged 1,570 calories daily (slightly less than half the control value). Their diet consisted of cereals, potatoes, cabbage, and turnips—foods commonly used in cases of famine in Northern Europe. At the end of six months on this diet the subjects had lost 24 per cent of their body weight and showed symptoms characteristic of famine victims such as weakness, depression, anemia, edema, polyuria, and marked slowing of the heart (bradycardia). They suffered a marked loss of strength and endurance as the period progressed and said they felt as if they were rapidly growing old. They felt weak, tired easily, moved cautiously, and reduced unnecessary movements to a minimum. Also, they developed marked personality changes, apathy, depression, and irritability.

At the end of the 24-week period the basal oxygen consumption was reduced by 39 per cent and the body weight by 24 per cent. Per square meter of body surface, the average drop in the oxygen consumption was 28 per cent, while per kilogram of body weight, the reduction was only 15 per cent. These differences are explained by the change in proportional composition of the body, decreases in the fat content resulting in relative increases in bone and water content. Allowing for the increase in water, these investigators found that the basal values were only about 10 per cent below those of the prestarvation period, a small but significant drop in the basal metabolic rate per unit of weight of the active tissue of the body (lean body mass).

When the men were returned to living on the prestarvation (control) diet, the basal metabolic rate rose in parallel with the food intake and the gain in body weight, but before body weight was fully restored and for some time thereafter the basal rate exceeded that of the prestarvation period. When body weight had been restored after 20 weeks of refeeding, the basal metabolism per unit of body weight averaged 13 per cent above the average of the prestarvation period.

A full report of this investigation will be found in *The Biology of Human Starvation* by Keys, Brozek, Henschel, Michelsen, and Taylor, published by the University of Minnesota Press, 1950.

INFLUENCE OF MUSCLE TENSION

In making a determination of basal metabolism on any person, every effort is made to have as complete muscular relaxation as is possible. This is one reason why the basal metabolism is determined early in the morning; even under quiet conditions, tension becomes higher as the day progresses. If the person has risen from bed, dressed, perhaps traveled to the laboratory, he is required to lie quietly for a time to let the effect of exercise upon the tone of the muscles wear off. It is also important that he be in a calm frame of mind, as emotion will raise

the muscle tension. If proper precautions are observed in making laboratory tests, most of the determinations on normal individuals will fall
within 10 to 15 per cent of the predicted basal metabolism.

INFLUENCE OF MENTAL STATES

Do we increase our energy expenditure when we think? The classic
demonstration that mental activity does not materially change the
metabolic rate was made by Benedict and Carpenter with the respiration
calorimeter. In it 22 young college men took three-hour examinations
and later sat the same length of time copying printed material which
required no mental effort. The metabolism increased only slightly in the
first case.

Interesting measurements of the effect of mental exertion were made
by Dr. Benedict and his wife. The mental effort consisted in solving,
without writing or talking aloud, certain mathematical problems, a
typical one being to multiply 73 by 47. The problems were given
orally. It was found that the mental effort of multiplying "in the head"
increased the metabolism 3 or 4 per cent. Commenting on this work, they
said: "The professor absorbed in intense mental effort for one hour
has an extra demand for food or for calories during the entire hour not
greater than the extra needs of the maid who dusts off his desk for five
minutes. The cloistered scholar at his books may be surprised to learn that
the extra calories needed for one hour of intense mental effort would be
completely met by the eating of one oyster cracker or one-half of a
salted peanut."[3]

Tashiro, a Japanese investigator working at the University of Chicago,
demonstrated by an exceedingly delicate apparatus for measuring carbon
dioxide excretion that when an impulse is transmitted along a nerve, the
carbon dioxide production may be increased to two and one-half times
that of the resting nerve. If we should assume all the nervous tissue in
the body to be as active as this, the total carbon dioxide output would
not equal that produced by lifting one's hand to one's face. As the nervous
tissue is only about 2 per cent of the total body weight, when its
metabolism is increased with thinking, the total will be small. Students
sometimes ask, "Why do we get hungry when we study?" forgetting
that we would get hungry anyway. They are generally more active in
their periods of relaxation and actually need more food on holidays
than on study days.

Aside from the question of the basal metabolism of the nervous system itself, mental states are, however, not without influence upon the
muscles. As Stiles said, "An emotional experience is much more than
a cerebral phenomenon." It is a form of exercise. Increased heart action,.

[3] Benedict, F. G., and Benedict, C. G. "The Energy Requirement of Intense Mental
Effort." *Science*, **71**:567 (1930).

more rapid respiration, tenser muscles are characteristic of more than one emotional state, and seem to be the direct result of the changed emotional condition.

INFLUENCE OF INTERNAL SECRETIONS

One of the very fascinating fields of modern physiology is that embracing the endocrine glands, which deliver to the blood internal secretions containing hormones (sometimes called chemical messengers) which are quite as important as the nervous system in keeping all parts of the body working harmoniously together. Many of these hormones have been isolated, their chemical structures have been investigated, and they have been found to be protein or related to protein. They are chemically very powerful, so that minute quantities introduced into the circulation produce remarkable effects. For example, absence in childhood of thyroxine and triiodothyronine, the hormones of the thyroid gland, results in failure to grow physically or mentally; a superabundance of one of the several hormones of the pituitary gland brings about abnormal growth, and a giant may develop; or again, failure of the pancreas to function normally to produce insulin results in impairment of the body's power to use its fuel foods in the normal way, and a disease marked by undernutrition, called diabetes mellitus, ensues.

Of all the glands of internal secretion, the thyroid has the closest connection with the energy change. In health it may be regarded as responsible in large measure for the constancy of the normal basal metabolism. In diseases of the thyroid characterized by overproduction of the thyroid hormones, the chemical processes of the body are speeded up, and the basal metabolism in very severe instances may increase as much as 75 per cent. Moderately severe cases will show increases of from 40 to 50 per cent, while in mild cases the rise may be from 15 to 30 per cent. On the other hand, a subnormal production of thyroxine causes a lowering of the basal metabolism, in severe cases amounting to a fall of as much as 30 per cent. So characteristic of thyroid disturbance is a change in the basal metabolism that the determination of it has been one of the routine measures in the clinical diagnosis of thyroid disease. Deviations of 10 to 15 per cent from the normal average are not by themselves significant, such variation occurring in normal persons, as has been pointed out. The amount and nature of the change must be studied in connection with all other factors in the situation. Other diagnostic measures currently used include the determination of protein-bound iodine (PBI) and uptake of radioactive iodine by the thyroid gland.

In addition to a high basal metabolism, the patient suffering from hyperthyroidism is in a state of almost incessant movement. Consequently his total food requirement may be so high that only when resting in bed can he eat enough food to compensate for his high energy output.

If he attempts any muscular work, this is done with difficulty and at a cost that may amount to twice the calories required for the same work by a normal man. Hyperthyroidism tends to bring the person very quickly to a state of undernutrition, and the only remedy is reduction of the production of thyroid hormones by suitable treatment in which rest is always a prominent feature.

Epinephrine (also called Adrenalin), a secretion of the adrenal glands, has an effect much less powerful than that of thyroxine. A single injection of 1 mg of epinephrine will cause an increase in the energy metabolism of only 50 calories which reaches its height in an hour, whereas the effect of the same dosage of thyroxine may be spread over a period of several weeks and cause an extra energy production of 1,000 calories. Cannon of Harvard University showed that under stress of emotional states, such as fear, rage, or pain, the adrenals are stimulated to an increased output of epinephrine, the heart action becomes more vigorous, blood is shifted to the organs immediately necessary for muscular action, and these are put under greater tension, so that the body has power to carry out any of the actions that may take place under the force of these emotions. All this means a temporary increase in the basal metabolism. Muscular action alone causes some increase in epinephrine production, but the most profound effect is from emotion and vigorous muscle action together. Cold also stimulates adrenal activity, which in turn causes increased heat production, as discussed under influence of temperature.

The basal metabolic rate of human beings has been found to be somewhat low in many cases of subnormal functioning of the pituitary gland, or hypophysis. The discovery of a specific hormone (the thyrotropic) in the secretion of the anterior lobe has made it evident that the influence of the pituitary gland on metabolism is exerted chiefly through the stimulation of thyroid activity by this hormone. Another hormone of the anterior lobe (the adrenalotropic) influences the adrenal gland and may also be a factor in changes in the basal metabolic rate in pituitary disturbance.

INFLUENCE OF AGE

The influence of age during childhood will be considered in Chapter 4. This discussion is confined to adults. Harris and Benedict concluded from a statistical study of adult men and women that for each year of age after 20 a man's decrease in basal heat production amounted to 7.15 calories per day. For a woman, the decrease was estimated to be only 2.3 calories per day for each year of age. While this annual fall seems slight, in 40 years it would result in an appreciable lowering of the basal energy expenditure of 286 calories for men (40 × 7.15) and 92 calories for women (40 × 2.3). A summary of the basal metabolisms of 243 healthy women subjects from 20 to 60 years of age determined in the Nutrition

Laboratory of Teachers College, Columbia University, by Pye, Taylor, and Bal[4] reveals a slight decrease in the average basal metabolism for each decade. The total difference in average calories per day between the 20- to 30-year-old women (1,270 calories) and the 50- to 60-year-old women (1,201 calories) was found to be 69 calories. This difference is less than that predicted by Harris and Benedict, Boothby (1952), Robertson and Reid, and others.

A study of 23 aged women was made by Benedict and Meyer[5] in a home for elderly women in Boston. All but two of the subjects were at least 70 years old and ten ranged from 78 to 86 years. They found a range of 800 to 1,500 calories in 24 hours for these older women. McKay and Patton, in a study of women in the seventh decade, found a mean basal metabolism of 1,128 calories.

Roberts, Kerr, and Ohlson[6] studied the basal heat production of eight women 52 to 74 years of age and observed a wide range in values between individuals. They state that "the basal heat output was well correlated with the physical and physiological pattern and suggests that the prolongation of adult basal heat output into the latter decades may be one measure of continued adult vitality."

THE INFLUENCE OF SLEEP

People differ in their ability to relax when awake or asleep. One investigator so completely mastered the art of assuming at will a state of complete muscular relaxation that no difference was found between his basal and his sleeping metabolism. It is possible, however, that another person, who has achieved the greatest voluntary muscular relaxation of which he is capable, may exhibit a basal metabolism somewhat above the sleeping level because such influences as light and sound can act reflexively to increase the tonus of the muscles. This is well illustrated by Benedict's observations on Levanzin, the man who fasted in his laboratory 31 days. The metabolism of the subject while in the bed calorimeter during the night was compared with his metabolism immediately afterward when he was connected with the respiration apparatus in the morning, and it was always higher after waking, the increases varying from 4.5 to 27 per cent.

Everyone realizes that sleep is not equally profound at all times, and that during sleep there may be muscular movements which would be suppressed were one awake and having his basal metabolism determined. This tendency to slight muscular movements may well account for

[4] Unpublished data.
[5] Benedict, F. G., and Meyer, M. H. "The Basal Heat Production of Elderly Women." *Proc. Amer. Philosoph. Soc.,* **71**:143 (1932).
[6] Roberts, P. H., Kerr, C. H., Herman, C., and Ohlson, M. A. "Nutritional Status of Older Women." *J. Amer. Dietet. A.,* **24**:292 (1948).

some of the variations in sleeping periods, even with the same subject. Furthermore, what one has been doing previous to falling asleep may have some influence. In many of the experiments of Benedict and Carpenter with the respiration calorimeter at Wesleyan University the night periods were preceded by day periods in which the muscular activity varied greatly, and there was a tendency for the heat output to be greater on nights following work upon the bicycle ergometer than on nights following days of rest. Thus two subjects after moderate exercise showed a sleeping metabolism 7 to 8 per cent higher than their sleeping metabolism after rest, and one after severe exercise showed a metabolism 20 per cent higher.

Buskirk and his associates, who have conducted recent studies on men sleeping under various conditions, summarize the influence of sleep on the energy expenditure as follows: "In general, average energy expenditure for the night hours by many people approximately equals basal metabolic rate; it is oversimplification, however, to state this as categorical truth for all people, or for all nights for the same person. The energy expenditure associated with sleep is not constant; it varies hour by hour during the night and may vary considerably between nights in the same individual. This variation is associated with changes in the depth of sleep, body movements during sleep, the amount and kind of food eaten before retiring, and environment in which sleep is attempted."[7]

INFLUENCE OF TEMPERATURE

A frog's body temperature changes as the thermometer rises or falls. On a cold day the animal is cold; on a warm day it is warm. When its body is cold, metabolism is reduced; when its body is warm, metabolism is increased. The difference between 39° F. (winter) and 86° F. (summer) may cause an increase of 400 per cent in the amount of carbon dioxide produced. A man's body temperature, on the other hand, is practically constant (close to 98.6° F.), regardless of the external temperature. Changes in the normal person's body temperature in the course of a day scarcely exceed 1° F., while in a single hour the temperature of the environment may rise or fall many degrees. In Texas, a drop of 40° F. in one hour is not uncommon; in New York in August one may step from the hot summer street into an air-conditioned theater. How do these changes in temperature affect the basal metabolism?

To get to the root of the matter, we must first rule out the influence of housing and clothing, which may greatly modify the situation. About 80 per cent of the heat usually produced in the body is lost through the skin.

[7] Buskirk, E. R. "Problems Related to the Caloric Cost of Living." *Bull. New York Acad. Med.*, 2nd ser., **36**:371 (1960).

The path of heat elimination varies with the environment. There is little evaporation of water when the temperature is low, and since there is no opportunity for loss of heat by radiation and conduction when the surrounding atmosphere has a temperature as high as, or higher than, the body, water evaporation must remove all the heat.

EFFECT OF HIGH TEMPERATURE INCLUDING FEVER. If the person is free to perspire and the humidity of the atmosphere does not interfere with the evaporation of the moisture on the skin, there will be no change in body temperature or in the rate of heat production since as the evaporation of water cools the skin, the blood beneath it will be cooled. If we put a man into a bath at body temperature, there will be no way of getting rid of body heat—no chance for radiation, conduction, or evaporation; but the body will continue to produce heat and consequently the body temperature will rise. A bath at 42° C. (107.6° F.) has been shown to cause an increase in the oxygen consumption amounting to 15 per cent. Studying the basal metabolism under a variety of conditions in which body temperature was above normal (fevers), DuBois calculated that the increase in energy expenditure in fever amounts to 7.2 per cent for every degree Fahrenheit. What this means is readily seen from the estimates given in Table 2–5 on a man whose basal metabolism is 1,700 calories.

TABLE 2–5. INCREASES IN ENERGY EXPENDITURE WITH RISE IN BODY TEMPERATURE

Rise in Temperature, degrees Fahrenheit	Increase in Energy Expenditure, per cent	Extra Calories Due to Elevation of Temperature
1	7.2	122
2	14.4	245
3	21.6	367
4	28.8	490

With only a moderately high fever the food requirement may easily reach more than 2,500 calories per day. If the energy requirement can be covered by food, the patient will be less weakened by his disease. This is most strikingly shown in the case of typhoid fever. Years ago, it was thought necessary to give very little food in fevers; for example, in typhoid, a disease causing a long wasting illness, the patient became so weak and emaciated that convalescence was almost as dangerous as the febrile state. But in 1909 Shaffer and Coleman, using the calorimeter of the Russell Sage Institute of Pathology at the Bellevue Hospital in New York City, demonstrated that it was possible to feed typhoid patients a diet high enough in calories and protein to prevent all loss of body substance. The treatment of typhoid was thus revolutionized and patients fed according to Shaffer and Coleman's plan actually gained weight during the progress of the disease.

The metabolism in malarial fever is influenced by the chills as well as by the fever. The changes are well illustrated by one of the cases studied by Barr and DuBois (Table 2–6).

TABLE 2–6
ENERGY CHANGES IN A CASE OF MALARIAL FEVER

	Per Cent above Normal Basal Metabolism
One hour before severe chill, no fever	+14
Rising temperature before chill	+21
Violent chill (40 min)	+216
Rising temperature after chill	+80
High constant temperature after chill (41.2° C.)	+71

EFFECT OF TEMPERATURES BELOW THAT OF THE BODY.   How greatly the sudden stimulation of cold may affect the metabolism can easily be demonstrated by a cold shower. It was found that taking a shower for three and a half to five minutes in water at 15° C. (59° F.) more than doubled the oxygen consumption and that it took an hour and a half for the metabolism to return to normal. This increase in response to the stimulus of cold is called "chemical regulation" of temperature, in contrast to those changes in heat loss which involve no change in metabolism and are grouped under the term "physical regulation."

How the chemical regulation is accomplished was shown by Cannon and his associates. When cold water or crushed ice is introduced into the stomach quickly, heat-producing factors must be set at work to restore body temperature. In other words, a "heat debt" is incurred which must be paid. Such a debt may be met by doing extra work, i.e., by shivering, but it may also be met, if not too great, by increased secretion of epinephrine, which causes a higher metabolic rate in response to the body's need for heat. When shivering occurs, the rise in heat production is sudden and much more marked and it may nearly double the energy output. When conditions are such as to induce shivering, they are also such as to induce a faster rate of adrenal secretion.

Population groups living under different climatic conditions adapt differently to their environment. In Korea, the ama, women divers, who harvest plant and animal life from the coastal waters from the age of 12 and dive daily throughout the year in light clothing, show a marked seasonal variation in basal metabolic rate. A rise of 35 per cent has been reported in the winter at a water temperature of 10° C. In contrast, the

Australian aborigines who sometimes sleep on the ground without clothing when the air temperature is between 0° and 5° C., their only protection being a brush windbreak and small fires, show no elevation in basal metabolic rate in response to a night's cold exposure. Caucasian control subjects sleeping under similar conditions showed a basal metabolism about 50 per cent above that of the aborigines. These examples of adaptations to climatic conditions, along with many others, were discussed at a symposium sponsored by the National Research Council and the Federation of American Societies for Experimental Biology.[8]

In studies by Suzuki[9] of the basal metabolism of the Japanese, he emphasizes the importance of skinfold thickness in tolerance to cold. Figure 2–5 shows two Japanese women divers whose basal metabolism, like that of the Korean ama, has a seasonal rise but who have marked tolerance to cold.

EFFECT OF BODY FAT ON REGULATION OF BODY TEMPERATURE

At low temperatures, a layer of subcutaneous fat is effective in preventing rapid loss of body heat and saving the body from burning fuel merely to keep warm. With rising temperatures, fat hinders heat loss, and a fat man's body temperature is more likely to rise than a thin man's, because the former cannot easily dispose of heat by radiation and conduction. Therefore, the fat person is more liable to heat prostration than the thin individual and needs to be cautious about exercise which will produce heat when getting rid of it is difficult. Humidity facilitates heat loss when associated with low temperature and wind, but hinders it when associated with high temperature, especially if the atmosphere is quiet. The fat person suffers most from high temperatures with high humidity, as what little cooling power the perspiration may have does not act as effectively through a covering of fat. In such a person, rise in body temperature easily occurs, with a resultant rise in the basal metabolism, adding further to the heat to be dissipated. Such a person works with difficulty in hot, humid weather, as each movement adds its quota of heat to the general discomfort.

See Chapter 3 for further discussion of the effect of temperature and climate on the total energy metabolism.

INFLUENCE OF SEX

The sex glands have secretions which account for certain sex characteristics, but no clearly defined differences in basal metabolism due to

---

[8] "Proceedings of the International Symposium on Temperature Acclimation." *Federation Proceedings*, **22**:No. 3, Part I (1963).

[9] Suzuki, S. "Basal Metabolism in the Japanese Population." *World Rev. Nutr. & Dietet.* Vol. 1, p. 107. Bourne, G. H. (ed.). New York: Hafner (1959).

FIGURE 2–5. TWO WOMEN DIVERS OF JAPAN. Their job is to dive into the cold sea to collect marine plants and shellfish. Their thick subcutaneous fat helps to conserve body heat. (*Courtesy of Dr. Shinjiro Suzuki. From "Basal Metabolism in the Japanese Population." In Bourne, G. (ed.).* World Review of Nutrition and Dietetics. *New York: Hafner [1959].*)

sex hormones have been produced experimentally. Women, as has already been stated, have a basal metabolism about 8 per cent lower than that of men of corresponding age. Menstruation has little influence, changes which occur ranging from 2 to 5 per cent. Castrated males tend to have the higher body fat which characterizes women as a class, but there is no evidence that a total absence or diminished activity of the sex glands regularly causes a decrease in the metabolic rate.

INFLUENCE OF PREGNANCY

A woman's gain in body weight during pregnancy may range somewhere between 20 and 27 lb. During the early months weight tends to remain stationary, while in the last three months the gain increases rapidly. A large proportion of the gain is due to general increase in body tissue on the part of the woman herself. (See Figure 24–1 in Chapter 24.)

A detailed study of a pregnant woman made by her husband[10] showed that after the fourth month the basal metabolism rose slowly, until a few days before delivery it was about 23 per cent above what it was in the fourth month.

MacLeod, Taylor, and others[11] studied the basal metabolism of four primipara at frequent intervals during pregnancy and following delivery. Two of the subjects were followed through their second pregnancy. The increase in calories per square meter per hour ranged from 15.6 to 23.4 per cent, with increases in body weight ranging from 9.1 to 25.4 per cent.

Murlin, at the University of Rochester, found that the energy metabolism of a mother and child together a few days after parturition just about equaled that of the mother before confinement. He found a striking instance of this relationship between parent and offspring in two experiments with a dog that bore at one time a litter of one pup and at another a litter of five; the extra calories attributable to the lone pup were 46 (164 per kilogram) and to the five pups, 258.5 (165 per kilogram).[12]

REFERENCES

Benedict, F. G. *Vital Energetics: A Study in Comparative Basal Metabolism.* Washington, D.C.: Carnegie Institution of Washington, Publication No. 503 (1938).

Bogert, L. J. *Nutrition and Physical Fitness,* 7th ed., Chap. 3. Philadelphia: Saunders (1960).

Buskirk, E. R., Thompson, R. H., Moore, R., and Whedon, G. D. "Human Energy Expenditure Studies in the National Institute of Arthritis and Metabolic Diseases Metabolic Chamber. I. Interaction of Cold Environment and Specific Dynamic Action. II. Sleep." *Amer. J. Clin. Nutr.,* 8:602 (1960).

DuBois, E. F. *Basal Metabolism in Health and Disease,* 3rd ed., Chaps. 13, 14, 15, and 18. Philadelphia: Lea (1936).

———. "Energy Metabolism." *Ann. Rev. Physiol.,* 16:125 (1954).

———. *Fever and the Regulation of Body Temperature.* Springfield, Ill.: Thomas (1948).

Miller, C. D., Wenkam, N. S., Kimura, A. M. "Basal Metabolism in the Elderly. A Study of Japanese Men and Women in Hawaii." *J. Amer. Dietet. A.* 33:1259 (1957).

[10] Root, H. F., and Root, H. K. "The Basal Metabolism During Pregnancy and the Puerperium." *Arch. Inter. Med.,* 32:411 (1923).

[11] MacLeod, G., Taylor, C. M., Robb, E., Baker, D., O'Donahoe, M., and McCrery, P. "The Basal Metabolism in Pregnancy." *J. Nutr.,* 17:20 (1939).

[12] Murlin, J. R. "Normal Processes of Energy Metabolism." Barker's *Endocrinology and Metabolism,* Vol. 3, p. 622. New York: Appleton (1922).

Sherman, H. C. *Chemistry of Food and Nutrition,* 8th ed., Chap. 9. New York: Macmillan (1952).

Swift, R. W., and French, C. E. *Energy Metabolism and Nutrition.* Washington, D.C.: The Scarecrow Press (1954).

Thomson, A. M., and Hytten, F. E. "Calorie Requirements in Human Pregnancy." *Proc. Nutr. Soc.,* **20**:76 (1961).

Young, C. M., McCarthy, M., Fryer, J. H., and Tensuan, R. S. "Basal Oxygen Consumption as a Predictor of Lean Body Mass in Young Women." *J. Amer. Dietet. A.,* **43**:125 (1963).

ૐ **3** ૐ

The Energy Requirement of Adults

Although the basal metabolism constitutes an important and strikingly constant quota of the energy expenditure, it is not the sole determinant of the total energy requirement. The taking of food itself increases the metabolism above the basal level, and the total energy metabolism will vary widely depending on the form and severity of the muscular activity.

The Allowance for the Influence of Food

Lavoisier was the first to note that eating food increased the amount of oxygen absorbed by a human being. Sixty years later, Bidder and Schmidt gave a starving cat all the meat it would eat and found that oxygen absorption and carbon dioxide output were doubled in consequence. Ten years after this (1862), Pettenkofer and Voit fed a dog different quantities of meat and found that the larger the meat meal, the greater the combustion within the organism. They then tried fat and starch and found that the increase with fat was smaller than with starch, and neither had any such marked effect as meat. Rubner carried this investigation much further and learned that bones, water, and meat extracts had no effect. He called the stimulating effect of food, which he found to be of a different order of magnitude for protein, fat, and carbohydrate, "specific dynamic action."

Rubner conducted similar studies on man and found that giving sugar alone raised the energy expenditure 2.2 per cent in 24 hours, while the same number of calories from meat alone raised it more than 25 per cent, or more than ten times as much. If the food fed is practically all carbohydrate, the rise of metabolism following its ingestion will be about 6 per cent of the total; i.e., for every 100 calories an extra 6 must be allowed for the whipping up of cell activity as this food is absorbed from the intestinal tract and begins to circulate in the blood stream. The effect of fat is about the same, 6 to 14 per cent, but that of protein is very marked, amounting to at least 30 per cent.

We are most interested in the effect of a mixed diet, because we do not usually eat a single kind of fuel food by itself. DuBois summarized all the work of investigations made in the Nutrition Laboratory of the Carnegie Institution of Washington and in the Russell Sage Institute of Pathology. A very small breakfast (222 calories for men weighing 65 and 74 kg, respectively) increased the heat production 5.4 calories, or a little over 2 per cent of the total calories. A heavy breakfast (over 2,142 calories) increased it 111 calories (5.2 per cent), while a very heavy breakfast (3,936 calories) gave an increase of 290 calories (7.4 per cent).

The effect of a beefsteak by itself is strikingly shown in an experiment by Benedict and Carpenter, where approximately 9 oz (418 calories) were eaten, with the result that the heat production was raised 139 calories, or one third of the total energy value of the steak. These calories were lost as heat and were not available for any useful work in the body. DuBois aptly remarked: "In this manner some of the excess food is burned and wasted just as a surtax diminishes a large income."

Using modern instrumentation (see Figure 3–1) Buskirk[1] and co-workers made a continuous record of oxygen consumption for two subjects after meals, throughout the day. The peak oxygen-consumption values varied for the two individuals. In one subject peak values occurred within 30 minutes after eating and then declined steadily until the next meal was consumed. There is some evidence that an individual may be able to adapt to a high-protein diet and not have as high a specific dynamic effect after eating.

In summarizing studies of the influence of food (specific dynamic action) increases varying from 6 to 17 per cent have been found on a mixed diet. These increases are in any case a very small part of the total energy metabolism, and it is concluded by most investigators that 10 per cent is probably a safe allowance on average mixed diets.

Allowances for the Influence of Muscular Activity

When a person sits absolutely quietly in a chair, the metabolism will average about 8 per cent higher than when he is lying down. However, no one can sit perfectly still for long. If one watches his neighbors "sitting still" for a short time, listening to a sermon in church or to a lecture in the classroom, he will find few who do not make a good many minor motions.

As soon as one begins to move about, as in walking even at a very slow pace, the expenditure becomes double that of "sitting at rest," and if one

---

[1] Buskirk, E. R. "Problems Related to the Caloric Cost of Living." *Bull. New York Acad. Med.*, 2nd ser., **36**:365 (1960).

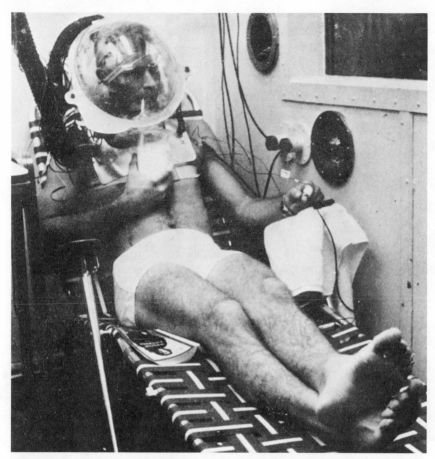

FIGURE 3–1. A VIEW OF THE SUBJECT AND THE EQUIPMENT USED IN A TYPICAL EXPERIMENT ON SPECIFIC DYNAMIC EFFECT IN THE METABOLIC CHAMBER AT THE NATIONAL INSTITUTES OF HEALTH. The subject is consuming a liquid meal through a straw and the glass is inside a front sleeve designed to prevent escape of expired air while eating. (*Courtesy of R. H. Thompson, E. R. Buskirk, and G. D. Whedon, NIAMD, National Institutes of Health.*)

walks rapidly it may rise to four, five, or six times the sitting value. The treadmill is a specialized type of equipment used to regulate specific speeds of walking on the level or on graded elevations. See Figure 3–2 showing a subject walking on a treadmill in the metabolic chamber at the National Institutes of Health.

Benedict and Parmenter, using a very simple type of respiration apparatus, found the energy expended by 12 young women in stair climbing to be about 15 times that required for walking the same distance on the level at the rate of about 2 or 2½ miles per hour. These college women climbed a stairway of 522 steps up the side of Mount Holyoke at a rate of about 80 steps a minute.

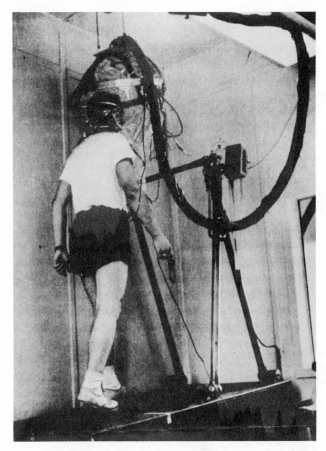

FIGURE 3–2. THE SUBJECT IS WALKING ON A TREADMILL IN THE METABOLIC CHAMBER OF THE NATIONAL INSTITUTES OF HEALTH. A plastic hood with attached hose, supported from the ceiling, collects expired air. (*Courtesy of R. H. Thompson, E. R. Buskirk, and G. D. Whedon, NIAMD, National Institutes of Health.*)

Atwater, in his experiments with the respiration calorimeter, used a stationary bicycle (ergometer) which could be adjusted to work against different degrees of electrical resistance. This made it possible to compute the mechanical work actually done by his subjects as well as their heat production. See Figure 3–3 showing an ergometer designed for use with children in the studies of the energy expenditure and mechanical efficiency in cycling.

In one study by Atwater[2] to determine the influence of work, a subject remained in the respiration calorimeter for a period of four days with a minimum amount of activity. For this rest period the average energy expenditure for the four days was found to be 2,310 calories per day. This was followed by a four-day work experiment involving active muscular

[2] Atwater, W. O., and Rosa, B. B. *Description of a New Respiration Calorimeter and Experiments on the Conservation of Energy in the Human Body*, p. 76. Washington, D.C.: Office of Experiment Stations, Bulletin No. 63, U.S. Department of Agriculture (1899).

FIGURE 3–3. THE BICYCLE ERGOMETER FORMERLY USED IN THE NUTRITION LABORATORY, TEACHERS COLLEGE, COLUMBIA UNIVERSITY. A bicycle frame mounted on a baseboard with the rear wheel replaced by a motorcycle hub fitted to a copper disk and connected to an electromagnet. To increase the work done, the magnetic drag on the disk was increased. The revolutions of the pedals were counted by means of a mechanical counter.

labor such as cycling using the ergometer. The average energy expenditure for this work period amounted to 3,830 calories per day, thus showing the additional calories representing the work to be 1,520 per day.

With a bicycle ergometer, Benedict and Carpenter studied the work done by a professional cyclist. In a "ride" of four hours and 22 minutes he accomplished a "century run" (over 100 miles), expending on the average 9.75 calories per minute (585 per hour), which was two and one-half times as much as when simply sitting on the bicycle and revolving the freely moving wheel. Another sustained effort even greater than this was recorded by Robinson, manager of the Pike's Peak Hotel and long accustomed to mountain climbing, who in two hours and 31 minutes ascended Pike's Peak from Manitou, 8.9 miles, the difference in altitude being 7,485 ft. His estimated energy expenditure was about 12.8 calories per minute (768 per hour). Recent reports of assaults on Mount Everest indicate an oxygen consumption of about 3 liters per minute or an energy expenditure of approximately 14½ calories per minute. The use of apparatus to provide oxygen has enabled the climber to better endure the stress of ascending great heights. At 28,000 ft a given volume of air is known to contain only a third as much oxygen as at sea level.

For short periods, still more amazing feats of energy transformation have been accomplished by the human engine. By severe muscular work the energy output may be increased ten times in two minutes. A study of the maximum physical power of highly trained athletes was made by Henderson and Haggard on the Yale University boat crew which won the Olympic championship at Paris. No exertion calls into play so large a proportion of the muscular tissue as rowing. The energy expenditure of the oarsmen in action was 13 to 20 times the basal metabolism.

The foregoing are but a few striking examples of experiments to determine the energy expenditure during muscular work, in which nutrition literature abounds. Figure 3–4 shows how even changes of posture and light muscular effort quite definitely increase the energy output.

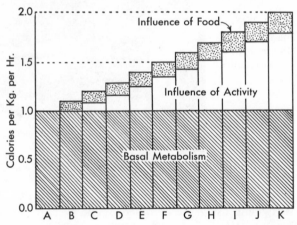

FIGURE 3–4. CHANGES IN ENERGY OUTPUT DUE TO INCREASING MUSCULAR ACTIVITY.

State of Activity	*Calories per Kg per Hr**
A. Lying absolutely still, no food taken (basal metabolism)	1.0
B. Lying absolutely still, food taken	1.1
C. Sitting in bed, absolutely still	1.2
D. Sitting quietly in bed, reading	1.3
E. Sitting at ease	1.4
F. Standing relaxed	1.5
G. Standing "at attention"	1.6
H. Dressing	1.7
I. Singing	1.8
J. Driving car	1.9
K. Walking very slowly (about 1 mph)	2.0

*These figures include the basal metabolism.

The possible changes in the energy cost of muscular activity with age have not been fully explored. Taylor and Pye[3] studied the energy expenditure of women in two age groups, 20 to 30 years and 50 to 60 years, engaged in two activities: (1) sitting writing and (2) walking at a moderate speed. The younger women had an energy expenditure on the average of 1.20 calories per kilogram per hour and the older women 1.16 calories per kilogram per hour for sitting writing. The energy expenditure for walking at a moderate speed was found to be 3.88 calories per kilogram per hour for the younger women and 4.10 calories per kilogram per hour for the older women. Although these differences were not statistically significant, it is interesting to note the change in direction of the difference. In sitting writing where the activity was less strenuous the energy expenditure was slightly lower for the older women, while in the more strenuous activity of walking, it was slightly higher. This is in line with studies reported by Durnin[4] in Britain of the energy expenditure of two groups of men, 20 to 30 years of age and 55 to 65 years of age, engaged in four types of graded exercise, two concerned with arm movements and two with speeds of walking. Although there was little difference between the two groups doing the arm exercises there was a significant difference between the two groups when walking, the older men expending more energy when walking especially at the faster speed.

Estimating the Total Energy Requirement

Data are available from which we can estimate the energy requirement of a given individual. For example, let us take Miss A., a college student, weighing 123 lb, or 56 kg. Her daily schedule will not include much muscular activity, as much of her time will be spent sitting in classes or reading in the library or perhaps writing. By keeping a diary of her activities through the day, a table can be made giving the total time for each activity. Thus, dressing in the morning will take perhaps half an hour; changing for an afternoon tea, 20 minutes; and undressing and an unhurried bath at night, 55 minutes. All the time spent in dressing and undressing, therefore, amounts to one and three-fourths hours. Time for other activities is estimated in the same way.

By using such factors as are shown in Table 3–1 for each kind of activity, the cost of all the activities of the day can be calculated. By adding to this cost the calories of the basal metabolism and then 10 per cent of this total for the influence of food, we shall arrive at a satisfactory estimation of the total calorie requirement for the day. It is thus clear that

[3] Contract Project with Agricultural Research Service, U.S. Department of Agriculture, Washington, D.C. (unpublished).
[4] Durnin, J. V. G. A. "Energy Expenditure in the Elderly." *Proc. Nutr. Soc.*, **15**:89 (1956).

TABLE 3–1. THE ENERGY COST OF ACTIVITIES
(EXCLUSIVE OF BASAL METABOLISM AND
INFLUENCE OF FOODS)*

Activity	Cal. per kg per hr	Activity	Cal. per kg per hr
Bedmaking	3.0	Playing ping pong	4.4
Bicycling (century run)	7.6	Piano playing (Mendelssohn's	
Bicycling (moderate speed)	2.5	Song Without Words)	0.8
Boxing	11.4	Piano playing (Beethoven's	
Carpentry (heavy)	2.3	Appassionata)	1.4
Cello playing	1.3	Piano playing (Liszt's Tarantella)	2.0
Cleaning windows	2.6	Reading aloud	0.4
Crocheting	0.4	Rowing	9.8
Dancing, moderately active	3.8	Rowing in race	16.0
Dancing rhumba	5.0	Running	7.0
Dancing, waltz	3.0	Sawing wood	5.7
Dishwashing	1.0	Sewing, hand	0.4
Dressing and undressing	0.7	Sewing, foot-driven machine	0.6
Driving car	0.9	Sewing, electric machine	0.4
Eating	0.4	Singing in loud voice	0.8
Exercise		Sitting quietly	0.4
Very light	0.9	Skating	3.5
Light	1.4	Skiing (moderate speed)	10.3
Moderate	3.1	Standing at attention	0.6
Severe	5.4	Standing relaxed	0.5
Very severe	7.6	Sweeping with broom, bare floor	1.4
Fencing	7.3	Sweeping with carpet sweeper	1.6
Football	6.8	Sweeping with vacuum sweeper	2.7
Gardening, weeding	3.9	Swimming (2 mi per hr)	7.9
Golf	1.5	Tailoring	0.9
Horseback riding, walk	1.4	Tennis	5.0
Horseback riding, trot	4.3	Typing, rapidly	1.0
Horseback riding, gallop	6.7	Typing, electric typewriter	0.5
Ironing (5 lb iron)	1.0	Violin playing	0.6
Knitting sweater	0.7	Walking (3 mi per hr)	2.0
Laboratory work	2.1	Walking rapidly (4 mi per hr)	3.4
Laundry, light	1.3	Walking at high speed	
Lying still, awake	0.1	(5.3 mi per hr)	8.3
Office work, standing	0.6	Walking down stairs	†
Organ playing ($\frac{1}{3}$ handwork)	1.5	Walking up stairs	‡
Painting furniture	1.5	Washing floors	1.2
Paring potatoes	0.6	Writing	0.4
Playing cards	0.5		

*To obtain total energy expenditure, add 1.1 calorie per kg per hr for each activity.
† Allow 0.012 calorie per kilogram for an ordinary staircase with 15 steps, without regard to time.
‡ Allow 0.036 calorie per kilogram for an ordinary staircase with 15 steps, without regard to time.

the total energy requirement of the adult is made up of three quotas: (1) the calories for the basal metabolism, (2) the calories for activities, and (3) the calories for the influence of food. An example of such an estimation of the total energy requirement for one day, using the factors listed, is given in Table 3–2.

ESTIMATION OF THE TOTAL ENERGY REQUIREMENT BY A SHORT METHOD

To estimate the energy cost of activities by a short method, attention is called to Table 3–3 in which activities for various types of days are described and the corresponding calories per kilogram per hour and per pound per hour are given. The first step is to select the type of day's activity which most closely corresponds to that of your most typical days.[5]

TABLE 3–2. THE ENERGY REQUIREMENT OF ADULTS (ESTIMATE OF CALORIES FOR ACTIVITIES FOR ONE DAY)

| I | II | III | IV |
| | | Factor | |
Activity	Time	cal. per kg per hr	Cal. per kg II × III
Lying still, awake	0.50	0.1	0.05
Sitting	1.25	0.4	0.50
Standing relaxed	0.75	0.5	0.38
Sitting, writing, or eating	8.00	0.4	3.20
Standing at attention	0.25	0.6	0.15
Dressing and undressing	1.75	0.7	1.23
Light exercise	1.00	1.4	1.40
Walking (3 mi per hr)	1.00	2.0	2.00
Dancing	1.00	3.8	3.80
Skating	1.00	3.5	3.50
Walking up stairs (4 flights)		0.036	0.14
Walking down stairs (4 flights)		0.012	0.05
	16.50		16.40

Body weight, 56 kg
Total calories for activities per kg (sum of column IV), 16.40 cal.
Total cost of activities (56 × 16.40 cal.), 918 cal.

TOTAL FOR DAY

	Calories
Basal metabolism for 24 hours	1,335*
Cost of day's activities	918
Total cost of metabolism	2,253
Influence of food (10 per cent)	225
Day's requirement	2,478

* To calculate basal metabolism:
Wt., 56 kg (123 lb); ht., 157 cm (62 in.); surface area, 1.57 sq m
850 cal per sq m per day (see Table 2–3) × 1.57 sq m = 1,335 cal

[5] In selecting the type of day, if your day does not seem to be like any one of those described, estimate a factor between two of those given.

TABLE 3–3. ESTIMATION OF CALORIES FOR ACTIVITIES FOR VARIOUS TYPES OF DAYS (SHORT METHOD)

Type of Day's Activity	Calories* per kg per hr	Calories* per lb per hr
A. At rest most of day (sitting, reading, etc., very little walking and standing)	0.5	0.23
B. Very light exercise (sitting most of the day studying, with about two hours of walking and standing)	0.6	0.27
C. Light exercise (sitting, typing, standing, laboratory work, walking, etc.)	0.8	0.36
D. Moderate exercise (standing, walking, housework, gardening, carpentry, etc., little sitting)	1.1	0.50
E. Severe exercise (standing, walking, skating, outdoor games, dancing, etc., little sitting)	1.7	0.77
F. Very severe exercise (sports such as tennis, swimming, basketball, football, running, heavy work, etc., little sitting)	2.4	1.09

* Exclusive of basal metabolism and the influence of food.

For example, suppose you select type C with an allowance of 0.8 calorie per kilogram per hour. If you weigh 56 kg, multiply 0.8 by 56 and then by the number of active hours in the day, which is obtained by subtracting sleeping time from 24 hours. If you sleep 7.5 hours, your active hours would be $24 - 7.5$, or 16.5. The energy cost for the day's activities would then be $0.8 \times 56 \times 16.5$, or 739 calories.

To estimate the total calories for the day you then add together the following:

1. Calories for basal metabolism	1,335
2. Calories for activities	739
3. Calories for influence of food (10 per cent of the sum of the calories for basal metabolism and activities)	207
Estimated total calories for 24 hours	2,281

TOTAL ENERGY REQUIREMENT ACCORDING TO OCCUPATION

The total daily energy requirement shows a wide variation between one occupation and another depending on the severity of the muscular work involved. Studies made by hundreds of women students at Teachers College, Columbia University, of their energy expenditure for a typical college day enable one to predict that the students with lowest activity need a total of about 33 calories per kilogram per day, while even the most active, being unable as students to escape a number of hours in the classroom, will seldom require more than 42 to 45 calories per kilogram. A man engaged for an eight-hour working day in such vigorous activity as lumbering will expend at least twice as much per kilogram per day as a quiet student. Extensive studies of the food consumption of various people indicate that those performing like amounts of work will have about the same average energy requirement. Women at sedentary occupations need about as much per day as quiet students, i.e., generally from 1,800 to 2,200 calories per day. The energy requirement for farming will vary according to the type of farming equipment available and the length of the work day from about 3,500 to 6,000 calories per day. Studies of United States soldiers in hard training showed a requirement of about 4,500 calories and of British cadets in training about 3,400 calories per day.

Lehman, Müller, and Spitzer of the Max Planck Institute, Germany, using the Kofranyi–Michaelis (see Figure 3–5) apparatus, have made determinations of the energy expenditure of a large number of subjects at work on industrial jobs. Some of their results are as follows: men in printing-plant jobs, 2,500 to 2,880 calories per day; men doing shoe repairing and shoemaking by hand, 2,970 to 3,140; locomotive engineers, 3,130 to 3,530; locomotive firemen, 3,450 to 4,670; railroad bed repairmen, 4,800 to 4,850; coal miners, 3,060 to 3,750; men in steel mill operations, 2,620 to 4,210; iron workers, 3,100 to 4,680. For three industrial jobs performed by women they reported 2,460 to 2,730 for steel grinding, 2,720 for placing bricks on carts, and 2,940 for carrying tile.

FIGURE 3–5. THE KO-FRANYI-MICHAELIS RESPIRATION APPARATUS. This is a lightweight apparatus consisting of a gas meter which measures the volume of the expired air. This air can be collected in rubber bladders and later analyzed for oxygen and carbon dioxide content. The energy expenditure can be calculated from these measurements. (*Courtesy of Drs. E. A. Müller and H. Franz, Max Planck Institut für Arbeitsphysiologie, Dortmund, Germany.*)

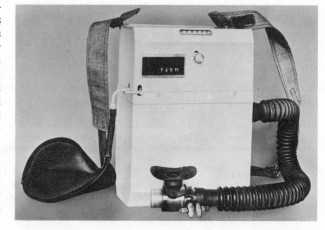

Droese, Kofranyi, Kraut, and Wildemann, also of the Max Planck Institute, using the Kofranyi-Michaelis apparatus, have reported determinations of the energy expended by three housewives, each of whom did all her own housework. The study began with observations of the women doing their work in their own homes, without the modern push-button equipment, each activity of the day being accurately timed with a stop watch from the time of arising in the morning until they went to bed at night. The next step was the determination of the energy expenditure for each kind of activity listed. Multiplying the number of minutes spent during the day on each activity by the energy required per minute and adding these products gave the total energy expenditure for the work of the day. These totals for the three women were 3,070, 2,987, and 3,088 calories, respectively. These results are higher than those usually reported for housework. The difference, as suggested by the authors, may be at least in part due to the fact that the average body weight of the women was 76 kg and their working day 15 to 16 hours long, figures rather different from those for which results are usually given in the literature. In connection with work-simplification studies, McCracken and Richardson, at the U.S. Department of Agriculture, measured the energy expenditure at different working heights using the Kofranyi-Michaelis Respiration Apparatus and different types of kitchen equipment (see Figure 3–6).

Passmore and his associates[6] at the University of Edinburgh used the Kofranyi-Michaelis apparatus to measure the energy expenditure in various activities of five students, 19 to 25 years of age. They obtained an average of approximately 2,900 calories per day when the boys were engaged in sedentary activities and approximately 4,700 calories per day when they were engaged in hard physical work. Garry and his associates[7] have used this apparatus to determine the energy expenditure of 19 underground miners and ten clerks in a colliery in Fife, Scotland. The energy expenditure of these men for all their other activities of the 24-hour day was also determined in order to obtain the total daily energy expenditure. For the miners, this total averaged 3,660 calories; for the clerks, 2,800 calories.

Recent studies emphasize the need for more data on energy expended in various tasks under field conditions. An investigation by Humphreys, Lind, and Sweetland[8] in 1962 of the energy expended by coal miners hew-

---

[6] Passmore, R., Thomson, J. G., and Warnock, G. M. "A Balance Sheet of the Estimation of Energy Intake and Energy Expenditure as Measured by Indirect Calorimetry, Using the Kofranyi-Michaelis Calorimeter." *Brit. J. Nutr.*, **6**:253 (1952).

[7] Garry, R. C., Passmore, R., Warnock, G. M., and Durnin, J. V. G. A. *Studies on Expenditure of Energy and Consumption of Food by Miners and Clerks, Fife, Scotland, 1952.* Medical Research Council, Special Report Series No. 289. London: Her Majesty's Stationery Office (1955).

[8] Review. "The Energy Expenditure of Coal Miners at Work." *Nutr. Rev.*, **21**:198 (1963).

FIGURE 3–6. MEASURING THE ENERGY EXPENDED IN WORKING AT DIFFERENT OVEN HEIGHTS. Waist-high ovens were found to require less energy and were more convenient than "eye-level" ovens with racks higher than 44 in. (*Courtesy of U.S. Department of Agriculture.*)

ing and shoveling coal in various postures and at various angles in a colliery showed appreciable differences in calorie expenditure. Weight of clothing worn and equipment carried by the miner also probably affected the results.

A correlation between calorie intake and work output was observed in a German steelworks during World War II. In 1939 the workers received 1,900 calories daily and the monthly production of steel was more than 120 tons per man. But when food rations were reduced the work output fell, and by 1944 when calories had been reduced to 1,150, the production of steel was less than 80 tons monthly (see Figure 3–7).

The oxygen consumption of underwater divers and frogmen was measured by Donald and Davidson in 1954. At rest under water, oxygen uptake was little above the basal level. When working strenuously under water, booted divers used as much as 2 liters of oxygen per minute (about 10 calories per minute). Finned underwater swimmers, moving about freely, used from 1.6 to 3.6 liters of oxygen per minute (about 8 to 17 calories per minute).

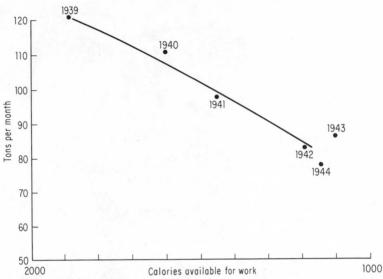

FIGURE 3–7. RELATIONS BETWEEN CALORIE INTAKE AND WORK OUTPUT IN A STEEL-WORKS. (*Courtesy of FAO. Basic Study No. 5,* Nutrition and Working Efficiency [*1962*].)

For the man or the woman of average height and weight the total energy requirement for 24 hours will vary according to the type of occupation, as indicated in Table 3–4.

TABLE 3–4. DAILY ENERGY REQUIREMENT ACCORDING TO OCCUPATION

	Total Calories per Day	
Type of Occupation	Men	Women
At rest but sitting most of day	2,000–2,200	1,600–1,800
Work chiefly done sitting	2,200–2,700	1,800–2,200
Work chiefly done standing or walking	2,800–3,000	2,300–2,500
Work developing muscular strength	3,100–3,500	2,600–3,000
Work requiring very strong muscles	4,000–6,000	—

TOTAL ENERGY REQUIREMENT ACCORDING TO THE NATIONAL RESEARCH COUNCIL

In Table A–1 in the Appendix will be found daily calorie allowances for the "reference man," 25 years old and weighing 70 kg, and the "reference woman", 25 years old and weighing 58 kg. It is presumed that these individuals live in an environment with a mean temperature of 20° C.; they are moderately active physically with occupations which are neither sedentary nor strenuous. It is recognized that the typical American man and woman of today may be less active than in the past and hence need slightly lower calorie allowances. Allowances are recommended for men and women between 18 and 35 years of age, 35 and 55 years of age, and 55 and 75 years of age. Adjustments are recommended for individuals differing from the reference man and woman in body size and activity. Recommended calorie allowances for pregnancy and lactation will also be found in Table A–1.

INFLUENCE OF CLIMATIC CONDITIONS ON TOTAL ENERGY REQUIREMENT

Studies of the adequacy of army rations as to both quantity and quality demand careful attention when the men of our armed forces live and fight in parts of the world ranging from tropical to arctic regions. Johnson and Kark in 1947 reported results on North American (United States and Canadian) troops in surveys carried out for the United States Army in arctic and subarctic, temperate, desert, jungle, and mountain regions in North America, Europe, and Asia. The average day's food chosen by groups of 50 to 200 healthy, physically fit ground troops from the ample rations was carefully determined. The daily energy value of the food thus voluntarily consumed ranged from 3,100 calories in the desert (92° F.) to 4,900 calories in the arctic (−30° F.). The average caloric intakes reported for the different climates were as follows: tropics, 3,200 and 3,400; temperate zone, 3,800; temperate mountain region (9,000 ft), 3,900; arctic and subarctic regions, 4,400. Differences in energy expenditure reported from studies in different climates frequently seem contradictory owing to types of clothing worn, degree of physical activity, housing conditions, and degree of acclimatization.

An interesting report is that of Swain, Toth, and associates, who studied the voluntary food consumption of garrison troops in the subarctic at Fort Churchill, in Canada, during ten-day periods at different seasons. The average daily consumption, including purchases between meals at the canteen, approximated 5,600 calories, results somewhat higher than the 4,400 calories reported by Johnson and Kark for arctic and subarctic regions.

Still another report on requirements in cold climates was that of Rodahl, who made surveys for weekly periods during the four seasons of the years 1950 and 1952 on a group of infantry soldiers and one of airmen on garrison duty at Ladd Air Force Base in Alaska and also of Eskimos in four different locations in Alaska. Members of the infantry and air force groups had lived in Alaska approximately a year at the time the study began. An average daily calorie consumption per man of 2,950 was found for the air force group and 3,200 for the infantry men. Calorie expenditure was estimated from time-activity observations of the men and found to average 2,800 calories. Rodahl concluded that the average man engaged in similar activities in similar climatic regions would require approximately 3,000 to 3,500 calories per day at any season of the year. The studies of adult male Eskimos indicated that an average daily consumption of approximately 3,100 calories sufficed to maintain body weight. The estimated average daily expenditure was approximately 2,700 calories.

Consolazio[9] and co-workers, of the U.S. Army Medical Research and Nutrition Laboratory, conducted a study in the extreme hot desert heat at Yuma, Arizona with eight healthy young conscientious objectors as subjects. The energy expenditures of different activities were measured using the Müller-Franz metabolimeter. They concluded from this and other studies that there is an increase in the energy requirement and the food consumption when men live and work hard in extreme heat. Under these conditions there is an elevation of body temperature associated with a rise in metabolic rate.

The Food and Nutrition Board of the National Research Council summarizes the adjustment for climate in developed countries as follows:

A mean environmental temperature of 20° C. probably applies to most persons in the United States. Most are protected against the effects of cold by warm clothes, central heating, and heated means of transportation. Many also live and work in air-conditioned atmospheres so that the effects of high temperatures are somewhat reduced. When there is exposure to cold or heat, calorie allowances need adjustment.[10]

The Board states that no increase in calorie allowances is needed for activity in the cold except to compensate for the small 2 to 5 per cent increase in energy expenditure when very heavy, hampering cold-weather clothing is worn. When the body is inadequately clothed, calorie needs will increase because of the effect of shivering and other involuntary movement. Activity may be increased in the cold and tends to be decreased in the heat.

Man's triumph over every climate is due to his ingenuity in extending the realm of physical regulation through his dwelling and his clothing. Even a rude hut protects from wind, wet, and heat, while a modern, air-conditioned house may maintain the same temperature when the thermometer outside stands at zero as when it stands at "95 in the shade." Wherever there is cold, the home of civilized man is equipped with some kind of heating device, which greatly limits the work his muscles are called upon to do in order to keep him warm, while in the hot season

[9] Consolazio, C. F. "The Energy Requirements of Men Living Under Extreme Environmental Conditions." Chap. 4, *World Review of Nutrition and Dietetics*, Vol. 4. New York: Hafner (1963).

[10] Food and Nutrition Board. *Recommended Dietary Allowances*. Washington, D.C.: National Research Council Publication 1146, p. 6 (1964).

the electric fan or air conditioning keeps the temperature of the modern house below that of the outer air.

The variety of ways in which clothing is related to a life almost devoid of shivering or sweltering is too numerous to record here. Silk, cotton, wool, fur, and synthetic fibers such as Nylon, Dacron, and others and thick or thin cloth all have a part to play. It is wonderful to think that an arctic explorer can lie down and sleep to awaken warm and even perspiring after an arctic night with the thermometer 60° below zero (F.) and the wind blowing a gale, provided there is not the tiniest hole in his garment. The smallest opening would be fatal as it would cause a heat loss that no chemical regulation could ever offset. Thus today man with relatively lightweight clothing is able to conserve his body heat even more effectively than when bundled in the heavy, awkward clothing of the past. In today's world not only do military personnel, mountain climbers, and others need specially designed clothing, but clothes for the "space" age present an even greater challenge in adapting to environmental conditions.

REFERENCES

Buskirk, E. R. "Problems Related to the Caloric Cost of Living." *Bull. New York Acad. Med.*, 2nd ser., No. 36, p. 365 (1960).

Buskirk, E. R., Thompson, R. H., Moore, R., and Whedon, G. D. "Human Energy Expenditure Studies in the National Institute of Arthritis and Metabolic Diseases Metabolic Chamber. I. Interaction of Cold Environment and Specific Dynamic Effect." *Amer. J. Clin. Nutr.*, 8:602 (1960).

Consolazio, C. F., Johnson, R. E., and Pecora, L. J. *Physiological Measurements of Metabolic Functions in Man.* New York: McGraw- (1963).

DuBois, E. F. *Basal Metabolism in Health and Disease*, 3rd ed., Chaps. 6, 7, and 8. Philadelphia: Lea (1936).

Food and Agriculture Organization. *Calorie Requirements.* Rome: FAO Nutritional Studies No. 15 (1957).

———. *Nutrition and Working Efficiency.* Rome: Basic Study No. 5 (1962).

Keys, A. "Energy Requirements of Adults." *Handbook of Nutrition*, 2nd ed., Chap. 13. New York: American Medical Association (1951).

McCracken, E. C., and Richardson, M. "Human Energy Expenditures as Criteria for the Design of Household-Storage Facilities." *J. Home Econ.*, 51:198 (1959).

Mitchell, H. H., and Edman, M. *Nutrition and Climatic Stress.* Springfield, Ill.: Thomas (1951).

Passmore, R., and Durnin, J. V. G. A. "Human Energy Expenditure." *Physiol. Rev.*, 35:801 (1955).

Richardson, M., and McCracken, E. C. *Energy Expenditures of Women Performing Selected Activities.* Washington, D.C.: Home Economics Report No. 11, U. S. Department of Agriculture (1960).

Sherman, H. C. *Chemistry of Food and Nutrition*, 8th ed., Chaps. 9 and 10. New York: Macmillan (1952).

Spector, W. S. *Handbook of Biological Data*. Philadelphia: Saunders (1956).

Taylor, C. M. *Food Values in Shares and Weights*, 2nd ed., pp. 10–14. New York: Macmillan Co. (1959).

Taylor, C. M., and MacLeod, G. *Rose's Laboratory Handbook for Dietetics*, 5th ed., pp. 5–20. New York: Macmillan (1949).

U.S. Army Medical Research and Nutrition Laboratory. *Energy Requirements of Men Exposed to Solar Radiation and Heat,* Report 240 (1959).

Whedon, G. D. "New Research in Human Energy Metabolism." *J. Amer. Dietet. A.,* **35**:682 (1959).

Widdowson, E. M., Edholm, O. G., and McCance, R. A. "The Food Intake and Energy Expenditure of Cadets in Training." *Brit. J. Nutr.,* **8**:147 (1954).

Wilson, E. D., Fisher, K. H., and Fuqua, M. E. *Principles of Nutrition,* 2nd ed., Chap. 8. New York: Wiley (1965).

Wohl, M. G., and Goodhart, R. S. *Modern Nutrition in Health and Disease,* Chap. 39 by Shils, M. E. "Food and Nutrition Relating to Work and Environmental Stress." Philadelphia: Lea (1964).

≰ **4** ≰

The Energy Requirement of Children

Some Early Studies of Children's Energy Metabolism

The aphorism of Hippocrates, "Growing bodies have the most heat; they therefore require the most food," was based on accurate observation, but any quantitative measurements of the differences between the young and the adult were not forthcoming for 23 centuries. Fifty years after the death of Lavoisier, two other French investigators, Andral and Gavarret, following in his footsteps, conducted the first respiration experiments on 12 children between the ages of 8 and 16 years. About 30 years later (1877) the first observations on a baby's metabolism were made by Forster of Munich, using a Pettenkofer-Voit respiration chamber just large enough to hold a child's cot. He studied a number of children varying in age from 14 days to 13 years. In 1894, the first study of heat production during the initial week of life was made by Mensi in Italy. He placed the baby under a large glass bell in which the oxygen was replenished and measured as the infant used it up.

At almost the same time, in Stockholm, Sondén and Tigerstedt, who had constructed a very large respiration chamber to study the problem of ventilation of school buildings, took various groups of children between 8 and 15 years of age, who were induced by reading or eating to sit quietly for periods of four and a half hours, so that their carbon dioxide excretion might be determined. This was the first extensive study covering different ages of both sexes. A little later (1899) the first comprehensive study of the changes in the metabolism throughout the whole life cycle of the individual from childhood to old age was undertaken in Germany by Magnus-Levy and Falk. Twenty boys and girls ranging in age from 2½ to 14 years were studied. Although carried out 66 years ago, this study was made with such skill that it is comparable with our best modern work.

In these and other experiments little attention was paid to keeping the subject in absolute repose or to controlling the influence of food; nevertheless, it was clearly established that the energy metabolism of the growing child is not only greater, weight for weight, than that of the adult, but that it varies markedly with the age of the child.

The Basal Metabolism

THE BASAL METABOLISM OF INFANTS

Any study of the basal metabolism of the human infant must be made during sleep and not more than three or four hours after a meal, because there is no way of keeping a baby perfectly quiet when awake or hungry. It is therefore impossible to make studies of the basal metabolism of infants on exactly the same basis as those of older children and adults. The food raises the metabolism about 8 per cent; the sleep may lower it about 15 per cent. Probably the actual figures obtained are somewhat higher than true basal values.

Among the outstanding studies on infants are those of Benedict and Talbot, who established a respiration laboratory at the Massachusetts General Hospital and investigated, all told, 105 newborn infants, varying in age from 43 minutes to eight days.[1] They measured the basal metabolism using a respiration chamber containing a wire crib supported at one end upon a spiral spring and at the other upon a knife edge, so that every movement of the child could be detected and recorded. In order to study children of various ages, they subsequently transferred their respiration apparatus to the New England Home for Little Wanderers, and in 1921 published a survey of the basal metabolism which included 108 boys and 70 girls from birth to 15 years.[2]

During the first week of life the baby's basal metabolism, estimated on the basis of calories per square meter of body surface, is at least one third lower than that of the adult and very much lower than that of older infants and children, averaging 20 to 24 calories per square meter per hour. This low heat production is attributable to the low muscle tonus of the newborn infant. A similar condition exists in the premature infant, whose heat production is still lower.

The average infant at birth has about one seventh the surface area of the adult man, but only one twentieth his weight. Comparison of an actual study of an infant six months old, weighing 6.1 kg and having a surface area of 0.34 sq m, with an average adult having a surface area of 1.81 sq m will show the difference in results when the daily energy output is calculated both to surface and to weight (see Table 4–1).

[1] Benedict, F. G., and Talbot, F. B. *The Gaseous Metabolism of Infants with Special Reference to Its Relation to Pulse-Rate and Muscular Activity*. Washington, D.C.: Carnegie Institution of Washington, Publication No. 201 (1914). Also Benedict, F. G., and Talbot, F. B. *The Physiology of the New-born Infant; Character and Amount of the Katabolism*. Washington, D.C.: Carnegie Institution of Washington, Publication No. 233 (1915).

[2] Benedict, F. G., and Talbot, F. B. *Metabolism and Growth from Birth to Puberty*. Washington, D.C.: Carnegie Institution of Washington, Publication No. 302 (1921).

TABLE 4–1. AN INFANT'S BASAL METABOLISM
COMPARED WITH AN ADULT'S

	Infant Calories	Adult Calories
Total basal metabolism for 24 hours	312	1,700
Calories per square meter per hour	38.2	39.5
Calories per kilogram per hour	2.1	1.0

Here it appears, as already stated, that on the basis of surface this young child's metabolism is very close to that of the adult, but on the basis of body weight it is more than twice as great. As the child grows larger, the metabolism in terms of body weight as well as in terms of body surface gradually falls.

By the end of the first two weeks the sleeping metabolism of the baby will have risen to approximately adult level, but it does not stop there; instead it keeps on rising rapidly until the end of the first year or early part of the second, when it reaches the highest point in the life of the individual. Thereafter, it declines, the rate varying with age and size until the adult level is reached, as shown in Table 4–2.

THE BASAL METABOLISM OF CHILDREN

At the University of Chicago, Blunt, in 1918, conducted studies on children from the University Elementary School, one of the most important being on 96 normal children who came in the latter part of the morning after a light breakfast, with no meat, eggs, or coffee to cause any special stimulation of metabolism. Preliminary experiments had shown that the effect of this small breakfast would be negligible after an interval of four hours.

In 1924, G. MacLeod[3] reported tests on 43 girls from 11 to 14 years of age from the Horace Mann School of Teachers College, Columbia University. The girls came without breakfast and after their test they had a "breakfast party." Fifteen of these subjects were followed through two or three years. From this time on for a period of 20 years, Dr. MacLeod continued her active interest in the energy metabolism work with children, and under her leadership a number of studies of the basal metabolism and energy expenditure of children were carried out.

A study of the basal metabolism of the nursery school child by means of the Benedict respiration apparatus was reported in 1934 by Robb.[4] Twenty-nine children (12 boys and 17 girls) three to four years of age were included. The children played with the mouthpiece and noseclip in

---

[3] MacLeod, G. "Studies of the Normal Basal Energy Requirement." Dissertation, Columbia University (1924).

[4] Robb, E. "The Energy Requirement of Normal Three- and Four-Year-Old Children." Dissertation, Columbia University (1934).

TABLE 4-2. BASAL ENERGY METABOLISM
OF CHILDREN FROM BIRTH TO EIGHTEEN YEARS

Age	Calories per sq m per hr		Calories per kg per hr	
	Boys	Girls	Boys	Girls
Premature infants	25	25		
Birth to 2 weeks	26–29	26–29		
3 months	39	36	2.21	2.21
6 months	43	41	2.25	2.25
9 months	47	46	2.29	2.29
12 months	48	46	2.33	2.33
2 years	48–54	45–53	2.29	2.29
3 years	47–53	43–51	2.13	2.00
4 years	46–52	41–50	1.96	1.83
5 years	45–51	42–49	1.88	1.75
6 years	44–53	41–50	1.79	1.67
7 years	43–53	40–52	1.71	1.63
8 years	42–52	40–47	1.67	1.58
9 years	42–50	40–46	1.58	1.54
10 years	41–48	37–46	1.54	1.50
11 years	39–48	38–45	1.46	1.42
12 years	39–51	38–44	1.42	1.33
13 years	39–49	37–43	1.67	1.29
14 years	38–46	37–43	1.71	1.54
15 years	41–46	31–43	1.50	1.33
16 years	41–45	31–40	1.38	1.25
17 years	41–44	31–40	1.25	1.17
18 years	41–43	32–38	1.25	1.08

the laboratory to become familiar with them. "A child was judged ready for a basal metabolism test when, during a preliminary play period, he would lie still with mouthpiece and noseclip adjusted, listening to a story for at least five minutes." During the test one adult sat by the child, telling him a story, while a second operated the apparatus.

In cooperation with the Human Nutrition Research Branch, Agricultural Research Service, U.S. Department of Agriculture, an extensive study over a 12-year period was made of the energy expenditure of children 9 to 11 years of age in the Nutrition Laboratory, Teachers College, Columbia University, under the direction of Taylor and Pye. Basal metabolism determinations were made on 116 children (57 boys and 59 girls), repeated determinations having been made on a number of these children during a two- to three-year period. These data have been included in the compilation published by the U.S. Department of Agriculture.[5]

Studies of the basal metabolism of normal healthy children have also been conducted in a number of other laboratories in the United States. Boothby, Berkson, and Dunn (1936), working at the Mayo Foundation; Lewis, Duval, and Iliff (1943), at the School of Medicine, University of Colorado; Lamb (1945) and Lamb and Michie (1954), at the Texas Technological College; Macy and her associates, at the Research Laboratory, Children's Fund of Michigan; and others have published results of their studies of the basal metabolism of children varying in age from two years on through the period of growth up to 15 to 20 years.

The interest in the basal metabolism of children has also extended to laboratories in other parts of the world. Nakagawa, working in Tokyo (1934), reported findings on 31 Japanese children three years and ten months to six years and six months of age, and later, in 1937, he reported studies on high school children. Robertson and Reid (1952) studied English boys and girls 3 to 20 years old. In 1932, Wang and Hawks reported studies of the basal metabolism of 21 Chinese children reared or born and reared in the United States and ranging in age from 5 to 11 years.

Space does not permit the reporting of the detailed findings of all this research. Although there are variations in the basal metabolism of children living in different locations, the final averages do not differ as much as one might anticipate. The reader is referred to Table 4–2, compiled by the authors, which will serve as an indication of typical changes in the basal metabolism occurring from birth throughout the period of growth. It is commonly considered that a basal metabolism within plus or minus 10 to 15 per cent of the average figure for each age is normal unless other diagnostic findings indicate a pathological disturbance.

It will be observed that the basal metabolism increases rapidly during the first year, reaching a maximum between one and two years, thereafter falling rather rapidly for two or three years and then more gradually, until the onset of puberty. At this time there is a slight rise for a period of two or three years and then a gradual decrease to the adult level. The summary of the U.S. Department of Agriculture previously cited suggests that possibly the traditional method of relating heat production per unit of body surface to age does not entirely correct for differences in physical growth and indicates that chronological age may not be the most satisfactory reference base.

DuBois in 1916 determined the basal metabolism of eight Boy Scouts 12 to 14 years of age and found it to be 25 per cent above the adult level on the basis of surface area. Three of the boys showed no sign of ap-

[5] *An Evaluation of Basal Metabolic Data for Children and Youth in the United States.* Washington, D.C.: Home Economics Research Report No. 14, U.S. Department of Agriculture (1961).

proaching puberty; five gave more or less definite signs. Two years later (1918), when puberty was established in every case, the boys had an average increase in weight of 46 per cent and in height of 10 per cent, but the basal metabolism had dropped rather sharply and was, on the basis of surface area, 13 per cent less than before, but still about 11 per cent higher than the adult level.

In a group of six boys 10 to 16 years of age studied by Taylor and MacLeod[6] over a period of six years, the basal metabolism of each boy being determined at intervals of six months, there seemed to be in each case two rather abrupt increases in the basal metabolism, one occurring at about 12 years, with a sharp drop thereafter, and the second at about 14½ years. On the other hand, Webster and his co-workers[7] reported that they obtained no evidence of an increase in the basal metabolism at the time of puberty in a group of 13 boys and eight girls between the ages of 10 and 16 years on whom basal metabolism determinations were made at intervals of four months over a period of five years.

In the study of 43 girls between 11 and 14 years of age made by MacLeod there was evidence of an increase in the basal metabolism at puberty corresponding to that found in boys by DuBois and by Taylor and MacLeod. In the study reported by Shock[8] (1943) of 50 normal girls on whom tests were made at intervals of six months beginning at 11½ years of age and continuing for six years, the observations did not begin early enough to show a distinct premenstrual rise, but in each case a rapid fall in the basal metabolism occurred throughout the three years following the onset of menstruation. The basal oxygen consumption of those girls between 12 and 14 years of age who had already passed the menarche was about 10 per cent lower than that of those who had not yet menstruated. When the results were averaged according to chronological age, these changes were obscured owing to the wide range of chronological ages at which individual girls mature.

The Energy Requirement for Activity

In the child, as in the adult, muscular activity increases energy expenditure in proportion to its severity. It is difficult, however, to standardize the activities of infants and children. Attention has already been called in this chapter to the studies of Benedict and Talbot on infants. They observed instances in which a baby's metabolism was raised

[6] Taylor, C. M., and MacLeod, G. "The Influence of Age on the Basal Metabolism of Boys throughout Six Consecutive Years." *J. Home Econ.*, 32:561 (1940).

[7] Webster, B., Harrington, H., and Wright, L. M. "The Standard Metabolism of Adolescence." *J. Pediat.*, 19:347 (1941).

[8] Shock, N. W. "The Effect of Menarche on Basal Physiological Functions in Girls." *Amer. J. Physiol.*, 139:233 (1943).

as much as 200 per cent above the basal level by vigorous crying. However, few babies can cry as hard as that, and an average baby is not likely to exceed his basal output by more than 65 per cent and that for only a short time. Murlin has also studied infants and found the extra expenditure in crying proportional to the time spent and estimated that an allowance of 30 per cent would be sufficient for an average normal infant and 40 per cent for an infant crying "most of the time." Benedict and Talbot suggested an allowance of 25 per cent above the basal for young infants, and for older infants, not confined to the crib, an allowance of 30 to 40 per cent.

In 1922, Bedale, in a private school in England, measured the energy cost of 25 separate activities, 45 boys and 55 girls, 8 to 18 years of age, serving as subjects. The increases over the basal metabolism of some of the activities are reported in Table 4–3.

TABLE 4–3. INCREASE OVER BASAL METABOLISM IN DIFFERENT ACTIVITIES*

Activities	Per Cent over Basal
Piano practice	56
Standing	80
Dressing	170
Cricket	259
Gymnastics	298
Gardening	305
Cold bath	503
Dancing	547
Swimming	669
Football	762

* Bedale, E. M. "Energy Expenditure and Food Requirements of Children at School." *Proc. Roy Soc. B*, London, 94:368 (1923).

For studies of energy expenditure under a variety of conditions, a respiration chamber is accurate and convenient. With such a chamber, MacLeod and her associates made a number of studies of the cost of activity in children. In the investigation with Robb (1934), already referred to, the first study of the energy output of nursery school children at quiet play was made by means of a respiration chamber. Three children were taken into the chamber at a time by an adult who remained with them, sitting quietly at one side, during a half-hour test period while the children played with blocks, trains, balls, tinker toys, etc. The energy expenditure of the adult was measured separately and deducted from the total.

In 1933, Potgieter[9] reported a study on girls, nine and ten years old, during quiet play and when climbing up and down steps in the respiration chamber.

In 1937, the first studies of 9- to 11-year-old boys using a bicycle ergometer in a respiration chamber (Figure 4–1) were reported by Taylor.[10] The energy expenditure of quiet play and cycling was measured. The children went into the chamber in pairs, one sitting at quiet play while the other pedaled the bicycle ergometer. Red and green lights helped the cycler to maintain a constant speed. These studies were followed by similar studies on girls of the same age range by Thompson[11] (1940). Robertson[12] (1942) studied boys and girls (six to eight years of age) performing similar activities, and Lamb[13] (1942) reported studies on boys 12 to 15 years of age.

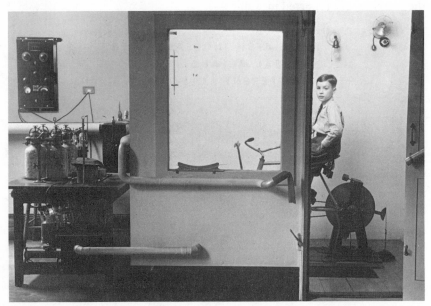

FIGURE 4–1. THE RESPIRATION CHAMBER AND BICYCLE ERGOMETER, NUTRITION LABORATORY, TEACHERS COLLEGE, COLUMBIA UNIVERSITY.

[9] Potgieter, M. "The Energy Cost of Physical Activity of Nine-Year-Old Girls." Dissertation, Columbia University (1933).

[10] Taylor, C. M. "The Energy Metabolism and Mechanical Efficiency of Young Boys." Dissertation, Columbia University (1937).

[11] Thompson, E. M. "A Study of the Energy Expenditure and Mechanical Efficiency of Young Girls and Adult Women." Dissertation, Columbia University (1940).

[12] Robertson, M. E. "A Study of the Energy Metabolism and Mechanical Efficiency of Children Six to Eight Years of Age." Dissertation, Columbia University (1942).

[13] Lamb, M. M. W. "A Comparison of the Energy Expenditure and Mechanical Efficiency of Boys and Young Men and Some Observations upon the Influence of Age and Work Done on the Mechanical Efficiency of Boys." Dissertation, Columbia University (1942).

The most extensive of the studies of energy expenditure of children of any one age group is that conducted by Taylor, Pye, and associates (1944–56) in the Nutrition Laboratory of Teachers College in cooperation with the Human Nutrition Research Branch, Agricultural Research Service, U.S. Department of Agriculture. The energy expenditure of boys and girls between 9 and 11 years of age was measured for more than 40 different activities. Many types of apparatus were used including the respiration chamber (Figure 4–2), Benedict's knapsack apparatus

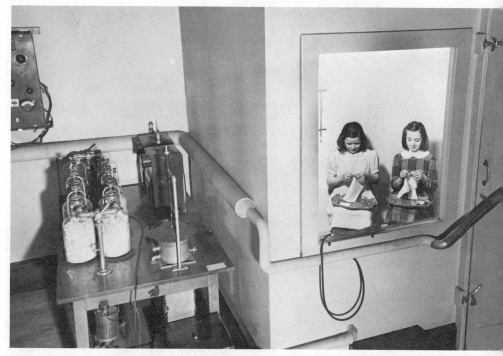

FIGURE 4–2. USING THE RESPIRATION CHAMBER TO MEASURE THE ENERGY EXPENDITURE OF SEWING IN THE NUTRITION LABORATORY, TEACHERS COLLEGE, COLUMBIA UNIVERSITY.

(Figure 4–3), and his field respiration apparatus (Figure 4–4), and the Douglas bag, the apparatus selected being that best suited for the study of the particular activity. Preliminary surveys of the activities of children of this age group living in different situations (cities, suburbs, rural areas, at home, and in institutions) were made. These surveys gave a good idea of how many different types of activities the 9- to 11-year-olds engaged in and which activities needed to be studied in order to obtain a better idea of the total energy expenditure of children of this age range. Other studies have been carried out in the Nutrition Laboratory at Teachers College using different types of apparatus with older boys and girls.

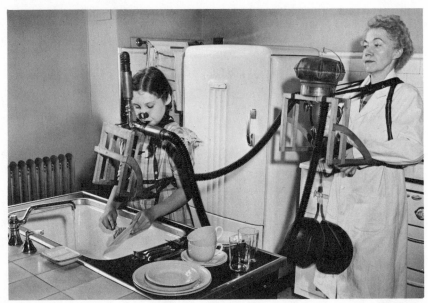

FIGURE 4–3. DETERMINING THE ENERGY EXPENDITURE FOR WASHING DISHES WITH THE BENEDICT KNAPSACK APPARATUS IN THE NUTRITION LABORATORY, TEACHERS COLLEGE, COLUMBIA UNIVERSITY.

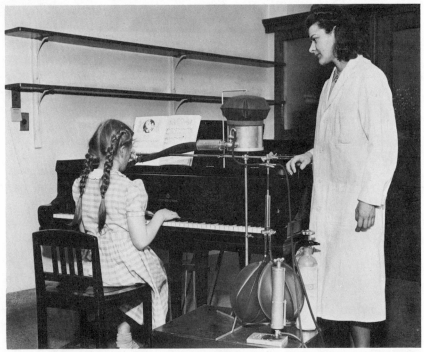

FIGURE 4–4. USING THE BENEDICT FIELD RESPIRATION APPARATUS TO MEASURE THE ENERGY EXPENDED IN PIANO PLAYING IN THE NUTRITION LABORATORY, TEACHERS COLLEGE, COLUMBIA UNIVERSITY.

Becker,[14] using the Kofranyi-Michaelis apparatus (see Figure 4–5) for her studies on girls 12 to 14 years of age, found their average energy expenditure for walking at moderate speed to be 3.95 calories per kilogram per hour and for bedmaking 3.24 calories per kilogram per hour. The results of studies of a number of activities for two age groups are listed in Table 4–4.

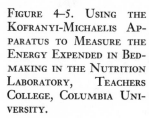

FIGURE 4–5. USING THE KOFRANYI-MICHAELIS APPARATUS TO MEASURE THE ENERGY EXPENDED IN BED-MAKING IN THE NUTRITION LABORATORY, TEACHERS COLLEGE, COLUMBIA UNIVERSITY.

A comparison of the cost of energy expenditure of the same activity for boys and girls in different age groups is shown in Table 4–5. These studies indicate quite clearly that the younger the child, the greater is the energy expenditure per unit of weight in any given type of activity. Thus, sitting quietly playing games in the case of a nursery school boy resulted in an output of 1.62 calories per kilogram per hour above the basal metabolism; for the six- to eight-year-old boy, 1.05 calories; for the 9-to 11-year-old boy, 0.96 calorie; and for the 12- to 15-year-old boy, 0.67 calorie per kilogram per hour. In all cases the boys have a higher energy expenditure than the girls per unit of body weight, and both boys and girls usually have a higher energy expenditure than adults performing similar activities (see Figure 4–6 for comparisons).

[14] Becker, Mary Misko. "The Energy Expenditure of Girls 12 to 14 years of Age Engaged in Activities Using the Respiration Chamber and the Kofranyi-Michaelis Apparatus." Dissertation. Columbia University (1957).

TABLE 4-4. THE TOTAL ENERGY EXPENDITURE FOR DIFFERENT ACTIVITIES FOR BOYS AND GIRLS*

Activity	Total Calories per kg per hr Boys	Girls	Activity	Total Calories per kg per hr Boys	Girls
Age 9–11 years			*Age 9–11 years*		
Carpentry (light)	3.58	—	Playing with		
Cycling	5.12	4.93	puzzles	2.42	2.19
Descending stairs	4.41	3.94	Roller skating	6.24	5.09
Drawing (sitting)	2.26	2.11	Sewing	—	1.84
Drawing (standing)	3.19	2.60	Singing		
Dressing	4.25	4.13	Standing	2.35	2.13
Dusting	—	4.00	Sitting	2.23	2.06
Eating	2.27	2.06	Sweeping	5.01	4.54
Hopscotch	—	4.48	Typing	2.12	1.76
Listening (radio)	2.07	1.80	Violin playing	2.18	—
Mopping	5.01	4.54	Walking		
Piano playing	2.12	1.97	2 miles per hour	3.86	3.53
Picking up toys	4.37	—	3 miles per hour	5.64	5.17
Playing			Walking with		
Chinese checkers	2.42	2.19	schoolbag	—	3.86
Jacks	—	3.03	Washing and		
Marbles	3.94	—	wiping dishes	2.92	2.64
Paper dolls	—	2.10			
Age 12–14 years			*Age 12–14 years*		
Bedmaking	—	3.24	Playing games		
Cycling	4.47	3.74	(sitting)	1.98	1.85
Dressing	—	3.17	Sewing	—	1.79
Piano playing	—	1.83	Walking		
			3 miles per hour	—	4.38

STRENUOUS ACTIVITIES

Activity	Total Calories per kg per min Boys	Girls	Activity	Total Calories per kg per min Boys	Girls
Age 9–11 years			*Age 9–11 years*		
Climbing stairs	0.212	0.193	Running	0.313	0.300
Climbing wall ladder	0.184	—	Walking		
Dancing (Irish jig)	—	0.138	4 miles per hour	0.156	0.152
Jumping rope	—	0.198	Wrestling	0.173	—

*Results of studies carried out in the Nutrition Laboratory, Teachers College, Columbia University, under the direction of Taylor and Pye.

TABLE 4–5. COMPARISON OF COST OF ENERGY EXPENDITURE FOR SIMILAR ACTIVITIES FOR DIFFERENT AGE GROUPS*

Activity	Age Group	Basal Metabolism† cal. per kg per hr		Cost of Activity Above Basal Metabolism cal. per kg per hr	
		Boys	Girls	Boys	Girls
Sitting quietly	3–4	2.36	2.19	1.62	1.43
playing games	6–8	1.91	1.81	1.05	0.99
	9–11	1.51	1.47	0.96	0.94
	12–14	1.31	1.21	0.67	0.64
Cycling (same speed)	6–8	1.91	1.81	4.47	4.38
	9–11	1.51	1.47	3.61	3.46
	12–14	1.31	1.21	3.19	2.10
Dressing and undressing	9–11	1.51	1.47	2.74	2.66
	12–14	1.31	1.21	—	1.96
Playing piano	9–11	1.51	1.47	0.61	0.50
	12–14	1.31	1.21	—	0.62
Sewing	9–11	1.51	1.47	—	0.36
	12–14	1.31	1.21	—	0.41
Walking	9–11	1.51	1.47	4.13	3.70
(3 miles per hour)	12–14	1.31	1.21	—	3.17

* Results of studies carried out in the Nutrition Laboratory, Teachers College, Columbia University.
† Average basal metabolism of all subjects within the designated age range.

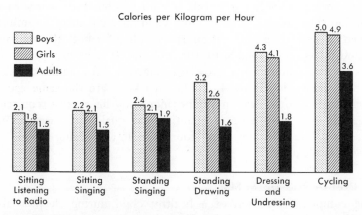

FIGURE 4–6. A COMPARISON OF THE ENERGY EXPENDITURE FOR DIFFERENT ACTIVITIES OF 9-TO-11-YEAR-OLD BOYS AND GIRLS WITH THAT OF ADULTS (Including the Basal Metabolism). (Nutrition Laboratory, Teachers College, Columbia University.)

Other Factors Influencing the Energy Requirement of Children

THE INFLUENCE OF FOOD

We have seen, in studying the energy requirements of adults, that an allowance must be made for the influence of food (specific dynamic action). This varies with the nature of the diet, but is not likely in ordinary life to exceed 10 per cent of the calories for basal metabolism plus activity.

THE INFLUENCE OF GROWTH

The proportion of the total calories ingested which will be used for growth will vary directly with the rates of growth. The charts in Chapter 26, showing the average annual gain from birth to the age of 17 years for both boys and girls, will serve to make clear that the periods of greatest storage in growth occur in the first year of life and again between the ages of 12 and 16. The fourteenth year in boys and the twelfth year in girls on the average are the times when the rapid growth of adolescence generally reaches its maximum. In any one of these years from 10 to 15 lb may be added to the body weight.

Just how many calories are needed for growth at any given time will always be difficult to say, since the rate of growth varies considerably with the individual; at the present time we have no standard figures for the growth quota, but with the exception of the periods of most rapid growth, 10 to 15 per cent of the basal metabolism probably represents the growth requirement fairly well. It must be constantly borne in mind that storage in growth is possible only when the basal energy requirement has been met, and the additional calories supplied for both the influence of food and the energy expenditure for activities. If there are no calories in excess of these requirements, growth is retarded. An example of retarded growth is shown in Figure 4–7. The two boys are the same age. The shorter of the two worked in a mine, increasing his energy requirements and eating food inadequate in quantity and quality to meet his needs for growth. The taller boy spent four years in a boarding school where the diet was adequate.

THE INFLUENCE OF SLEEP

The complete relaxation of a healthy child during sleep is always impressive, and appears to differ from that of many adults. Benedict in 1922 studied two newborn babies in the respiration chamber and found their sleeping metabolism 6 and 15 per cent lower, respectively, than

FIGURE 4–7. TWO BOYS OF
THE SAME AGE DEMON-
STRATE THE EFFECTS OF A
GOOD AND A POOR DIET ON
GROWTH. (*Courtesy of
FAO*)

their basal metabolism. A few years later Wang and Kern studied five boys and seven girls between the ages of four and seven years in the same type of chamber at the Michael Reese Hospital in Chicago. The average saving in sleep was 16 per cent. In the same year Wilson, Levine, and Rivkin studied five children, seven to nine years of age, and found a saving in sleep of 11 to 27 per cent. In 1934 Williams[15] determined the sleeping metabolism of four nursery school children, taking their midday nap in the respiration chamber at Teachers College, Columbia University, and then their energy output with the Benedict student apparatus immediately upon waking. The differences between the two ranged from 12 to 23 per cent, showing the great relaxation in the first hour of sleep after a morning of active exercise in the nursery school. It seems safe to assume that the energy saved in sleep by children may be in the neighborhood of 17 per cent.

[15] Williams, D. E. "The Influence of Sleep on the Energy Metabolism of Three- and Four-Year-Old Children." Dissertation, Columbia University (1934).

The Total Energy Requirement of Children

We have now considered separately the four quotas which together constitute the total energy requirements of children, viz.,

1. Basal metabolism.
2. Metabolism due to influence of activity.
3. Metabolism due to influence of food.
4. Storage of energy-yielding material in growth.

Since basal metabolism and activity are relatively greater than in the adult and there is an additional requirement for growth, it is clear that children's total food needs will be considerably higher than those of adults in proportion to body weight.

Much of our information as to the total energy requirement of children has come from studies of the actual food consumption of healthy children.

When account is taken of (1) the basal metabolism of children through the years of rapid growth, (2) their almost ceaseless activity when awake, involving the expenditure of more calories per unit of weight than similar activities in adults, and (3) the necessity of energy-yielding materials to be stored in the process of growth, it is easy to see why children of all ages need a liberal energy supply.

EARLY RECORDS OF FOOD CONSUMPTION

Changes in the feeding of boys are illustrated by the history of Christ's Hospital, the famous English school established by Edward VI in 1553. Records of the diet and the physical development of the boys were made available by the chief medical officer of the school.[16] An existing diet sheet for the week ending August 12, 1704, shows that the boys, 9 to 18 years old, received only 1,170 calories in solid food (mostly bread, with cheese and a little butter) and an estimated 730 calories in crude, home-brewed beer. Charles Lamb, who attended the school from 1782 to 1789, bears touching testimony in his *Essays of Elia* to the miserable quality as well as quantitative inadequacy of the dietary regime of that period when, as Drummond aptly stated, "Food restriction in both quantity and quality was widely regarded as one of the disciplines to which the child was subjected for the good of its soul."[17]

Following World War I there was steady improvement, the calories being increased from 2,830 in 1922 to 3,014 in 1933. The most marked

---

[16] Friend, G. E. *The Schoolboy. A Study of His Nutrition, Physical Development and Health.* Cambridge, England: W. Heffer and Sons (1935).

[17] Drummond, J. C. *Lane Medical Lectures: Biochemical Studies of Nutrition Problems,* p. 17. Stanford, Calif.: Stanford U. P. (1934).

changes in the dietary were an increase in fat and an increase in milk from half a pint in 1922 to nearly a full pint in 1933. By 1928–29 the boys' weight had increased an average of 10 lb and their height more than an inch. This trend is similar to that of children in English schools reported by Boyne, Aitken, and Leitch.[18] They reviewed all available records of height and weight of English boys and girls from 1883 to 1954. Forty-two-year records (1911–53) showed a consistent increase in both height and weight. For example, the 15-year-old boys showed an increase in height of 4 to 5 in. and over 31 lb in weight. Records of heights and weights of college freshmen, selected service records, life insurance statistics, and other data show a similar trend in the United States and Canada.

Miss Lucy Gillett, director of nutrition for the Association for Improving the Condition of the Poor (now known as the Community Service Society), reported on 563 studies including all the available data relating to food requirement of children, covering the period from 1878 to 1917. From this report were formulated the first American standards for total energy requirements of children. Satisfactory growth has been used as an indication that the calories eaten must have been sufficient to compensate for the energy expenditure and permit storage of energy-yielding materials in growth. Roberts and her students applied this principle in a study of 35 boys doing farm work in comparison with 34 boys engaged in the ordinary activities of school life, and also in one of 52 girls from 10 to 16 years of age, most of them living in well-managed institutions.[19]

An extended study of the food consumption of girls 6 to 13 years old was conducted by Koehne and Morell[20] at University Hospital, Ann Arbor. Quantitative records were kept for 28 girls, 11 of whom were under observation for from 91 to 192 days and only three for less than 40 days. The portions eaten by each child were weighed. The children were weighed once a week and measured once a month, and the nutritive value of each diet was calculated from average analyses. During the course of these investigations, 35 balance studies for periods of one week each furnished evidence that the estimations of food intake were reasonably accurate.

Wang and her associates[21] worked with girls 12 to 15 years of age at the University of Cincinnati living for two weeks in a metabolism ward, going out to school and returning for meals and the night's rest. Their

[18] Boyne, A. W., Aitken, F. C., and Leitch, I. "Secular Change in Height and Weight of British Children." *Nutr. Abstr. & Rev.*, 27:1 (1957).

[19] Wait, B., and Roberts, L. J. "Studies in the Food Requirement of Adolescent Girls. I. The Intake of Well Nourished Girls." *J. Amer. Dietet. A.*, 8:209 (1932).

[20] Koehne, M., and Morell, E. "Food Requirement of Girls from Six to Thirteen Years of Age." *Amer. J. Dis. Child.*, 47:548 (1934).

[21] Wang, C. C., Kaucher, M., and Wing, M. "Metabolism of Adolescent Girls." *Amer. J. Dis. Child.*, 51:801 (1936).

food was weighed and samples were analyzed. It was found that their basal metabolism accounted for fully half the total calories represented in their food. Such an allowance, while sufficient for children whose activities may be classed as light, would not be sufficient for those who are more active.

LONGITUDINAL STUDIES OF FOOD INTAKE

Beal[22] reported 604 dietary histories on 46 children (18 boys and 28 girls) of Northern European extraction. Dietary histories at monthly intervals were recorded for the mothers during pregnancy. For the first five years beginning with the newborn infant, histories were recorded at monthly intervals for the first six months and thereafter at three-month intervals. The median calorie intake was found to be close to the Recommended Allowance of the National Research Council. Individual children revealed a variety of patterns of intake, "reflecting the capricious eating habits of the preschool child."

Burke and co-workers[23] reported on a longitudinal study of the calorie and protein intakes of children from 1 to 18 years of age, representing a 17-year period for each of 125 individual children (64 boys and 61 girls). The 2,707 dietary histories collected represent an average of 15½ years out of 17 for each child. A wide variation in intake of calories and protein was found at each age and in each sex. Differences in eating patterns occurred, with consistently high, medium, and low groups. The individual child showed short-term fluctuations in intake and might change from one pattern to another at different ages.

Recommended Calorie Allowances for Infants, Children, and Adolescents

The Food and Nutrition Board of the National Research Council (1963) has made recommendations as follows for infants, children, and adolescents.

> Allowances for infants during the first year have been set at levels reflecting the general pattern of intake of thriving infants. During the first year of life calorie allowances are reduced in suitable steps from a level of 130 calories/kg at birth to 100 calories/kg by the end of the year. There are wide individual variations in physical activity in infants and children. Inactive children may become obese even when the calorie intake is well below the recommended allowance, while extremely active children must have larger allowances.

[22] Beal, V. A. "Nutritional Intake of Children. I. Calories, Carbohydrate, Fat, and Protein." *J. Nutr.,* **50**:223 (1953).

[23] Burke, B. S., Reed, R. B., van den Berg, A. S., and Stuart, H. C. "Calorie and Protein Intakes of Children Between 1 and 18 Years of Age." *Pediat.,* **24**:922 (1959).

The allowances represented in Figures 4–8 and 4–9 pertain to children of average activity in the United States.

Healthy children and adolescents exhibit marked variations in energy intake; for this reason, individual values for calorie allowances must be interpreted with caution. Because of major differences in growth rates between boys and girls after age nine, the present recommended allowances separate boys and girls after this age. The calorie allowances cited

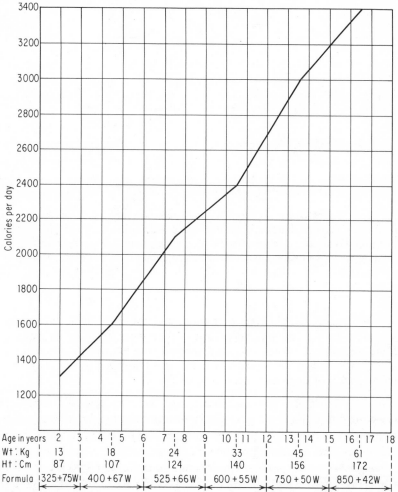

FIGURE 4–8. FOR ESTIMATING THE DAILY RECOMMENDED CALORIE ALLOWANCE FOR BOYS. The solid line indicates average calorie allowance for boys according to age. To adjust for an individual boy whose weight and height differ from the average, the calorie allowance can be calculated by using the appropriate formula. (*From* Recommended Dietary Allowances, *p. 6. Washington, D.C.: National Research Council [1964].*)

Foundations of Nutrition

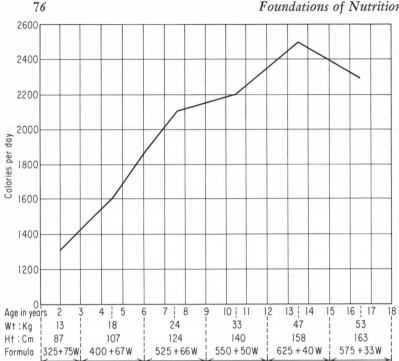

FIGURE 4–9. FOR ESTIMATING THE DAILY RECOMMENDED CALORIE ALLOWANCE
FOR GIRLS. The solid line indicates average calorie allowance for girls according to age. To adjust for an individual girl whose weight and height differ from
the average, the calorie allowance can be calculated by using the appropriate
formula. (*From* Recommended Dietary Allowances, *p. 7. Washington, D.C.:
National Research Council [1964].*)

here for infants and children, even more importantly than for adults, are
proposed as average and approximate allowances for feeding groups.
More appropriate allowances for individual children may be derived by
observation of growth, appetite, activity, and body fatness as determined
by the extent of deposits of subcutaneous fat.

To use Figure 4–8 for estimating the daily calorie allowances for
boys who differ from the average in weight and height, the calorie allowance can be calculated by using the appropriate formula. For example,
to calculate the calorie allowance for John, who is five years of age
and weighs 45 lb, the appropriate formula to use is $400 + 67W$. W in the
formulas refers to weight in kilograms. To convert to pounds, divide the
factor by 2.2. Therefore $67 \div 2.2$ equals the factor 30.5. Thus multiplying
30.5 by 45 lb equals 1,373. To this add 400, giving a total of 1,773 calories.
Comparing John's calorie allowance with that of the average boy of
five years in Figure 4–8, it will be noted that John, weighing more than
the average, has a higher calorie requirement.

To use Figure 4–9 for estimating the daily calorie allowances for girls who differ from the average in weight and height, the calorie allowance can be calculated by using the appropriate formula. For example, to calculate the calorie allowance for Mary, who is ten years of age and weighs 74 lb, the appropriate formula to use is $550 + 50W$. W in the formulas refers to weight in kilograms. To convert to pounds divide the factor by 2.2. Therefore, $50 \div 2.2$ equals the factor 22.7. Thus multiplying 22.7×74 pounds equals 1,680. To this add 550, giving a total of 2,230 calories. Comparing Mary's calorie allowance with that of the average girl of ten years in Figure 4–9, it will be noted that Mary, weighing more than the average, has a higher calorie requirement.

REFERENCES

DuBois, E. F. *Basal Metabolism in Health and Disease*, 3rd ed., Chap. 8. Philadelphia: Lea (1936).

Eppright, E. S., Roderuck, C., Sidwell, V. D., and Swanson, P. P. "Nutritive Value of the Diets of Iowa School Children." *J. Nutr.*, **54**:371 (1954).

Food and Nutrition Board. *Recommended Dietary Allowances*. Washington, D.C.: Publication No. 1146, National Research Council (1964).

Gillett, L. H. *Food Allowances for Healthy Children*. New York: New York Association for Improving the Condition of the Poor (1917).

Martin, E. A. *Roberts' Nutrition Work with Children*, 3rd ed. Chicago: U. Chicago (1954).

Morgan, A. F. *Nutritional Status, U.S.A.* Berkeley, California: California Agricultural Experiment Station Bulletin 769 (1959).

Review. "The Energy Expenditure of Children." *Nutr. Rev.*, **9**:312 (1951).

Sherman, H. C. *Chemistry of Food and Nutrition*, 8th ed., pp. 163–65, 167–68, 189–91. New York: Macmillan (1952).

U.S. Department of Agriculture. *An Evaluation of Basal Metabolic Data for Infants in the United States*. Home Economics Research Report No. 18 (1962); *An Evaluation of Basal Metabolic Data for Children and Youth in the United States*. Home Economics Report No. 14 (1961).

Weinberg, B. G., Boedeker, M. T., and Schuck, C. "Nutritive Value of Diets of Indian Boarding Schools in the Dakotas." *J. Amer. Dietet. A.*, **46**:96 (1965).

White House Conference on Child Health and Protection. *Growth and Development of the Child*, Part III, "Nutrition." New York: The Century Co. (1932).

❧ 5 ❧

Food as the Source of Energy for the Body

The Body as a Working Machine

In an attempt to get an exact balance between the carbon dioxide given off by a guinea pig and the ice melted by the guinea pig's body heat, Lavoisier inquired whether or not the body used more oxygen when it was cold than when it was warm; also, whether or not more heat was generated when the animal was quiet than when it was moving about. He extended these inquiries to work on man and found, as has been stated in the preceding chapters, that oxidation was increased by food, by exercise, and by exposure to the influence of cold. "This kind of observation," he wrote, "suggests a comparison of forces concerning which no other report exists. One can learn, for example, how many pounds of weight-lifting correspond to the effort of one who reads aloud, or of a musician who plays a musical instrument. . . . What fatality ordains that a poor man, who works with his arms and who is forced to employ for his subsistence all the power given to him by nature, consumes more of himself than does an idler, while the latter has less need of repair?"[1]

Scientific investigations spanning more than 170 years repeatedly emphasize that in regard to its combustion the body must be thought of as a working machine. Just as in the engine every revolution of the wheel means so much fuel consumed, so in the body the lifting of the hand, the turning of the head, the bending of the knee, or the "tightening" of all the muscles under excitement means an increase in the combustion going on. But the analogy between the body and the engine breaks down when they come to a standstill. The engine then ceases to work; but the body does not, however hard one may try not to move a muscle. The chest and the diaphragm continue to rise and fall with every breath;

[1] Lusk, Graham. "History of Metabolism." Barker's *Endocrinology and Metabolism*, Vol. 3, p. 27. New York: Appleton (1922).

the heart pumps away—70 powerful contractions per minute; the muscles, though at rest, are not by any means fully relaxed; in other words, a great deal of internal work is going on even when one is in a state of apparent repose. The important thing to remember is that *life means work*. We burn fuel to support the work our bodies are doing. It varies in amount with circumstances, as we have seen, but it never ceases.

Food as the Source of Energy

When work is to be done, fuel is demanded. This fuel must be supplied as food which is burned chiefly in the muscles. The chemical union, in muscle cells, of the oxygen breathed in with the carbon (and hydrogen) of the food is not unlike the combustion of gasoline in the automobile engine. The chemical change liberates energy which moves the machine. But in the machine, the oxidation of fuel occurs at elevated temperatures, above that of the body temperature (98.6° F.) and proceeds with explosive force. Oxidation of fuel in the body is often referred to as "braked"; thus the potential free energy to be made available by combustion is not produced in one explosive burst but in many individual and successive steps monitored by enzyme action.

Whether the fuel material being burned in the body is carbohydrate, fat, or protein, the free energy released with each oxidative step is then used, as a rule, to manufacture a specific phosphate storage compound with so-called "high-energy phosphate bonds," whose potential stored energy in turn becomes available for various processes in the body. Thus combustion or oxidation of fuel material proceeds smoothly at body temperature, and the energy transfer essential for work to be done is accomplished swiftly.

Muscular work is done preferably and most economically at the expense of carbohydrate food. Mixtures of fat and carbohydrate in which carbohydrate predominates are burned with practically the same ease as pure carbohydrate. Fat alone is utilized with less ease than a mixture of the two and with a loss of from 8 to 12 per cent of its energy value. Protein can be economically used when a small proportion is mixed with the carbohydrate or carbohydrate and fat, but when taken as the sole source of energy, it is burned at a rate that is wasteful, the loss amounting to about 30 per cent. As long as carbohydrate and fat are available, muscular work is not done at the expense of the protein supply.

In the absence of other sources of fuel it is possible for muscular work to be done exclusively at the expense of protein. However, the protein so used is first deprived of its nitrogen and thus put on a par, so to speak, with the other fuel foods, carbohydrate and fat. It is as if one should undertake to make a fire with boards full of nails. The boards would burn like any others, but the nails would add nothing to the fire.

Atwater showed clearly the influence of work on nitrogen excretion. Several persons were studied in the respiration calorimeter for many days, first at rest and then at work. In the rest experiments they metabolized 1.51 gm of protein per kilogram; when they worked hard enough to double their energy expenditure, they did not raise their nitrogen output at all, as it averaged 1.49 gm per kilogram. Thus it is clear that in severe muscular exercise, the foodstuff needed to prevent exhaustion is not protein but carbohydrate.

When protein is used as fuel, the nitrogen which it contains is not an asset but a liability, which must be gotten rid of as speedily as possible. The protein is transformed within the body into simpler compounds and the nitrogen is excreted by the urine, chiefly in the form of urea, together with a relatively small amount of ammonia. Then the simpler compounds, free of nitrogen, are burned to carbon dioxide and water.

The physicist defines energy as ability to do work. Energy exists as a force whose sum total cannot be changed. This is known as the law of the conservation of energy. Energy may be manifested in different forms, such as light, heat, or mechanical and electrical energy. One form of energy can be transformed into another. Thus heat energy may be transformed into motion, into electric current, or, in living organisms, into growth and reproduction.

THE SUN AS A SOURCE OF ENERGY

The process by which green plants utilize the energy of sunlight to manufacture carbohydrates from carbon dioxide and water in the presence of chlorophyll (green pigment) is known as photosynthesis. Water is taken up by the roots and transported to the leaves. Carbon dioxide from the air enters the leaves and is diffused to the cells containing chlorophyll. This green pigment is uniquely capable of converting the active energy of light into a potential form of stored energy—the carbohydrate, glucose. Several enzymes (catalysts) reacting with the coenzymes (cocatalysts) are involved in the intermediary reactions in the formation of glucose. Recent studies using radioactive carbon molecules indicate that fats and proteins are also direct products of photosynthesis. Indeed, the entire animal world depends on the process of photosynthesis for the continuation of life, for the food we eat and the oxygen in the air we breathe.

Fats, carbohydrates, and proteins burn because they all contain a considerable amount of carbon and some hydrogen, both of which are capable of uniting with oxygen. Chemically, starch is closely related to sugar, which is also available as fuel in the body. These both belong to a group of chemical substances called carbohydrates. Carbohydrates and fats are alike in that they each yield only three chemical elements: carbon (C), hydrogen (H), and oxygen (O). The proteins yield these three, and in addition nitrogen (N) and usually one or more of the following sulfur

(S), phosphorus (P), iron (Fe). These last four have nothing directly to do with the use of protein as fuel. All the food fuels burn because of their carbon and hydrogen and all yield carbon dioxide and water when oxidized. We may think of the situation thus:

$$\begin{matrix} \text{Energy of} \\ \text{sun's rays} \end{matrix} + \begin{matrix} \text{chlorophyll} \\ \text{of plants} \end{matrix} + \begin{matrix} \text{carbon dioxide} \\ \text{of air} \end{matrix} + \begin{matrix} \text{water from} \\ \text{soil} \end{matrix} =$$

$$\text{Energy-yielding materials} \begin{cases} \text{carbohydrates} \\ \text{fats} \\ \text{proteins} \end{cases} + \text{oxygen} = \begin{cases} \text{Carbon dioxide} \\ \text{Water} \\ \text{Energy} \end{cases}$$

Just as the plant stores up the energy derived from the sun in the form of carbohydrates, fats, and proteins—in roots, as in the beet; in thickened stems (tubers), as in the potato; in fruits, as in the orange—so animals, eating these fuel foods in excess of their immediate needs, may store the surplus energy in their own bodies against a time of future need.

The Measurement of Energy in Food Materials

We have recalled the fact that energy is a force that manifests itself in various forms: as work, lifting a weight or pulling a load; as heat, liberated from burning coals in the furnace; as light, from the burning tallow of the candle; as electricity, from the stored force of the river raging over the precipice. This force can be measured in various ways: the light, in terms of candle power; the heat, in calories; the electricity, in kilowatts; the work, as foot-pounds or kilogram-meters. In the laboratory, it is easy to convert all the potential energy of a food into heat, and to use a heat unit for the measurement of the potential energy in food. This unit is called the calorie and it has long been in use in physical laboratories for all sorts of energy measurements.[2]

THE BOMB CALORIMETER

We cannot see a calorie any more than we see the feet of gas which the meter registers or the kilowatts for which we pay when the monthly electricity bill comes in. We are bound to depend on the meters for those measurements and, similarly, we must depend on a special device in determining the energy values of foods. The apparatus commonly used is called a bomb calorimeter (see Figure 5-1). It consists of an inner chamber or "bomb" made of steel and lined with gold or platinum so as to be noncorrosive, into which the material to be tested is put. This

[2] The large calorie (the kilogram calorie) is taken as the standard in the science of nutrition. It is defined as the amount of heat required to raise the temperature of 1 kg of water 1° C., i.e., from 15° to 16° C. This is very nearly the same as the heat required to raise 4 lb of water 1° F. It should not be confused with the small calorie (the gram calorie), which is the amount of heat required to raise the temperature of 1 gm of water 1° C.

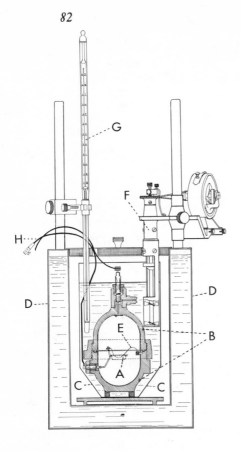

FIGURE 5–1. DIAGRAM OF BOMB
CALORIMETER WITH BOMB IN
POSITION.
A. Platinum dish holding food
sample.
B. Bomb filled with pure oxy-
gen enclosing food sample.
C. Can holding water, in which
bomb is submerged.
D. Outer double-walled insu-
lating jacket.
E. Fuse, which is ignited by an
electric current.
F. Motor-driven water stirrer.
G. Thermometer.
H. Electric wires to send cur-
rent through fuse.
(*Courtesy of the Emerson
Apparatus Co., Boston, Massa-
chusetts.*)

chamber is filled with pure oxygen, so that combustion may be quick
and complete when a tiny "fuse" of iron wire is ignited by an electric
spark. The bomb is immersed in a known weight of water, and the heat
generated by the burning of the food is measured by observing the
change in temperature of the water.

This apparatus is used to determine the energy values of fuels, such as
coal and oil, as well as of foods. While simple in principle, it requires
skill to operate, because the chances of losing heat and not getting a correct
measure are great.

THE OXYCALORIMETER

Another apparatus devised to use especially for foods is the Benedict
oxycalorimeter. The food under consideration is burned in a current of
nearly pure oxygen, and the volume of oxygen consumed in its complete
combustion is measured in much the same way as in the Benedict respiration apparatus, as described in Chapter 2. Oxygen is introduced into a
closed circuit, changes in volume are indicated by a spirometer, circulation is maintained by a blower, and carbon dioxide is absorbed by soda
lime. The various parts are indicated in Figure 5–2. Standard factors for

converting liters of oxygen into calories have been obtained by use of the bomb calorimeter. For example, in burning pure sugar, if the oxygen consumption amounts to 1,000 cc, this will represent energy equivalent to 5 calories. For each kind of food the number of calories represented by an oxygen consumption of 1,000 cc has been determined and can be applied to any quantity of the food which the apparatus can take care of.[3]

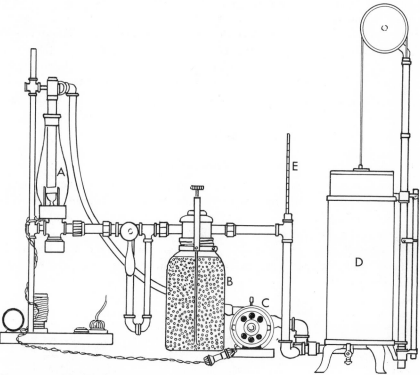

Figure 5–2. The Benedict Oxycalorimeter.
A. Combustion chamber.
B. Vessel containing soda lime to absorb carbon dioxide.
C. Blower to circulate air current.
D. Spirometer to measure by contraction the volume of oxygen used.
E. Thermometer.
   (*Courtesy of Dr. F. G. Benedict*)

Calculation of Energy Value of Food

Foods contain sometimes one kind of fuel only, such as sugar; sometimes two, such as beef; sometimes all three, such as milk; and these will be in different combinations and different proportions, according to the

[3] For such factors as have been determined, see Benedict, F. G., and Fox, E. L. "The Oxycalorimeter." *Indust. & Engin. Chem.*, **17**:912 (1925).

food under consideration. Using tables of chemical composition we can calculate the calories. The physical laboratory gives us the following average values:

> 1 gm of pure carbohydrate, 4.1 calories
> 1 gm of pure fat, 9.45 calories
> 1 gm of pure protein, 5.65 calories

The physiological laboratory tells us that we must make certain deductions from these values because protein is never quite completely burned in the body, and in the case of all three foodstuffs slight losses occur owing to incomplete absorption from the alimentary tract. The average discounts proposed for an ordinary mixed diet by Atwater and Bryant after much careful study of the situation were: for carbohydrate, 2 per cent; for fat, 5 per cent; for protein, 29.2 per cent. Thus we get as final average figures to use in our estimates of the fuel values of food to the body:

> 1 gm of pure carbohydrate, 4 calories
> 1 gm of pure fat, 9 calories
> 1 gm of pure protein, 4 calories

If we take cane sugar as an example, our problem will be very simple, since cane sugar is 100 per cent carbohydrate, and each gram will yield 4 calories; if we take olive oil, which is pure fat, each gram will yield 9 calories; and if we take dry gelatin, which is pure protein, each gram will yield 4 calories. But if we undertake to determine in this way the fuel value of milk we shall find the situation a little more complicated, for milk contains all three:

CALCULATION OF ENERGY VALUE OF 1 GM OF MILK

	Amount in Gm	Factor	Calories
Protein	0.035	4	0.140
Fat	0.035	9	0.315
Carbohydrate	0.049	4	0.196
			0.651

The average factors 4, 9, 4 are known as the Atwater or Atwater and Bryant factors and are, for practical purposes, satisfactory for calculating the energy values of typical American mixed diets; but since World War II it has been felt that more specific physiological factors are needed for use in situations in which it may be necessary to deal with food supplies differing in proportions from those of the ordinary American diet. A committee of the Food and Agriculture Organization of the United Nations in 1947 took this question under consideration and recommended that for international use more specific factors should be agreed upon and used in calculating calorie values of foods. In 1949 the

FAO published *Food Composition Tables for International Use*, prepared by Charlotte Chatfield, in which the energy values were calculated from specific factors. The U.S. Department of Agriculture published Agriculture Handbook No. 8 entitled *Composition of Foods—Raw Processed, Prepared*, using the specific factors. Table 6, page 160 (1963) in Handbook No. 8, gives the data used for calculating specific energy values of foods or food groups by the Atwater system. The calorie values in Tables A–4 and A–8 in the Appendix of this book are based on those of Agriculture Handbook No. 8. A list of the specific physiological factors and an example of how to use them will be found in *Rose's Laboratory Handbook for Dietetics* by Taylor and MacLeod. For a further discussion of the "Energy Value of Foods . . . Basis and and Derivation" see Agriculture Handbook No. 74.

Estimating Energy Values of Foods for Practical Purposes

It is worthwhile to spend the time necessary to learn the energy values of ordinary food materials, and one may begin with various common units in the diet, as shown in Table 5–1.[4]

TABLE 5–1. ENERGY VALUES OF COMMON FOOD UNITS

Food Material	Energy Value in Calories
1 almond	8
1 apple, medium	70
1 banana	85
1 date	20
1 egg, large	80
1 orange, medium	75
1 oyster cracker	4
1 potato, boiled	105
1 shredded-wheat biscuit	100
1 tomato, $2\frac{1}{2}''$ diam.	35

One may profitably extend such tables to include one's own customary portions of all sorts of dishes, but as individuals differ in regard to their habits of eating, it is often necessary to make adjustments in the portions found in food tables.[5] For useful equivalents of some common

[4] Calorie values of other foods will be found in Tables A–4 and A–8 in the Appendix and in Taylor's *Food Values in Shares and Weights*, 2nd ed. New York: Macmillan (1959).

[5] Taylor's *Food Values in Shares and Weights*. New York: Macmillan (1959); Watt and Merrill, *Composition of Foods—Raw, Processed, Prepared*. Washington, D.C.: Agriculture Handbook No. 8, U.S. Department of Agriculture (1963).

weights and measures, see Table A–3 in the Appendix (page 465).

It is obvious that the calorie values of portions of cooked food materials depend on the recipes used. The values of cooked foods and combinations are usually based on standard recipes. The ingredients are often indicated in footnotes. With suitable tables of food values, however, it is possible to estimate the energy yield of a day's ration with a degree of accuracy sufficient for all practical purposes. See references for food composition tables available for use in calculating the calorie and other nutritive values of diets in different parts of the world.

REFERENCES

Aykroyd, W. R., Patwardhan, V. N., and Ranganathan, S. *The Nutritive Value of Indian Foods and Planning of Satisfactory Diets.* New Delhi: Indian Research Council, revised (1963).

Chatfield, C. *Food Composition Tables for International Use.* Rome: Food and Agriculture Organization of the United Nations, Nutritional Studies No. 3 (1949) and No. 11 (1954).

Food Composition Table Recommended for Use in the Philippines. Manila: Food and Nutrition Research Center, National Institute of Science and Technology, Manila. Handbook No. 1, 3rd revision (1964).

Food Composition Tables for Use in the Middle East. Beirut, Lebanon: Division of Food Technology and Nutrition, Faculty of Agricultural Sciences, American University of Beirut. Publication No. 20 (1963).

Food Composition Table for Use in Latin America. Washington, D.C.: Institute of Nutrition of Central America and Panama, and Interdepartmental Committee on Nutrition for National Defense (1961). Available in both English and Spanish.

An Appraisal of the Health and Nutritional Status of the Eskimo. Food Composition Tables of Alaskan Foods, pp. 75–88. Washington, D.C.: Interdepartmental Committee on Nutrition for National Defense (1959).

Leung, W. T., Pecot, R. K., and Watt, B. K. *Composition of Foods Used in Far Eastern Countries.* Washington, D.C.: U.S. Department of Agriculture, Handbook No. 34 (1952).

McCance, R. A., and Widdowson, E. M. *The Chemical Composition of Foods.* London: Special Report Series, British Medical Research Council, No. 297, 3rd revision (1960).

McMasters, V. "History of Food Composition Tables of the World." *J. Amer. Dietet. A.,* **43**:442 (1963).

Merrill, A. L., and Watt, B. K. *Energy Value of Foods . . . Basis and Derivation.* Washington, D.C.: U.S. Department of Agriculture, Agriculture Handbook No. 74 (1955).

Miller, C. D., and Branthoover, B. *Nutritive Values of Some Hawaii Foods in Household Units and Common Measures.* Honolulu: Hawaii Agricultural Experiment Station Circular No. 52 (1957).

Platt, B. S. *Tables of Representative Values of Foods Commonly Used in Tropical Countries.* London: British Medical Research Council Special Report Series No. 302 (1962).

Robinson, M., and Scoular, F. I. "Caloric Value of Food Served in a Woman's Residence Hall. Determination with a Bomb Calorimeter." *J. Amer. Dietet. A.*, **33**:1270 (1957).

Sherman, H. C. *Chemistry of Food and Nutrition*, 8th ed., Chap. 8 and Appendix A. New York: Macmillan (1952).

Taylor, C. M. *Food Values in Shares and Weights*, 2nd ed. New York: Macmillan (1959).

Taylor, C. M., and MacLeod, G. *Rose's Laboratory Handbook for Dietetics*, 5th ed., pp. 1–6; 206–8. New York: Macmillan (1949).

Watt, B. K. "Concepts in Developing Food Composition Tables." *J. Amer. Dietet. A.*, **40**:297 (1962).

Watt, B. K., and Merrill, A. L. *Composition of Foods—Raw, Processed, Prepared.* Washington, D. C.: U.S. Department of Agriculture, Agriculture Handbook No. 8 (1963).

❧ 6 ❧

Fats and Carbohydrates in Metabolism

Fats and carbohydrates are the principal sources of energy, as discussed in Chapter 5. In terms of national food consumption data for 1962, fats supplied 41 per cent, and carbohydrates 47 per cent, of the calories available in American diets.[1] In food preparation and practice, studies indicate that more of the fat is wasted than the carbohydrate. Even though fats and carbohydrates are interchangeable sources of calories, both are needed to make a satisfactory diet for human beings. Dietary carbohydrates can be converted into depot fat when excess calories are consumed, as every individual with a weight-control problem recognizes. Fats are composed of fatty acids and glycerol. Fatty acids do not contribute significantly to carbohydrate synthesis, and glycerol contributes only to a small degree.

Fats

Man has consumed fatty substances in foods since his earliest beginnings, as a hunter of animals, a fisherman, and a gatherer of seeds and other vegetable foods. The ancient Egyptians prepared oils from nuts, seeds, olives, and cinnamon leaves. In the Bible we find records of "feasts of fats" and the prized "fatted calf." At present, according to the Third World Survey of the Food and Agriculture Organization (1963),[2] the annual per capita consumption of fat is 16 to 21 kg in the more developed countries, or two to seven times the levels used in less developed regions.

Fat is the most concentrated form of body fuel. It takes only ½ oz (1 tbsp) of fat to yield 100 calories, and a person could get a whole day's fuel from ¾ lb of fat if he were able to eat it. On the other hand, people

[1] *Consumption of Food in the United States.* Washington, D.C.: U.S. Department of Agriculture (Supplement for 1962).
[2] FAO Basic Study No. 11. *Third World Food Survey.* Rome: Food and Agriculture Organization of the United Nations (1963).

of the Orient, who because of poverty live largely upon rice, have to eat a great quantity of food to secure sufficient fuel for their daily activities. It would take 5 lb of cooked rice to give the same number of calories as ¾ lb of fat or oil. The latter would not fill a pint measure; the former would measure about 3½ qt.

Fat gives the diet "staying" qualities. Other things being equal, one feels hungry sooner after a meal with little fat than after one in which it is liberally supplied. This is because fat leaves the stomach more slowly than proteins or carbohydrates and tends to retard the digestion of either of these when used in combination with them. A mixture of fat and protein digests more slowly than one of fat and carbohydrate.

Used with proper discretion, all our common food fats, both animal and vegetable, digest easily and almost completely. As sources of energy the different food fats are practically interchangeable. Some people prefer olive oil; some, pork fat; others revel in seal oil. The ancient Romans prized vegetable oil for food and butter for cosmetics. Table 6–1 shows some changes in sources of food fats in the United States food supply during this century. Changes are still continuing.

TABLE 6–1. CHANGES IN SOURCES OF FAT IN THE UNITED STATES FOOD SUPPLY*

Sources of Fat	1909–13 per cent of total	1935 per cent of total	1956–58 per cent of total
Milk, cream, cheese, ice cream	15	16	17
Butter	14	14	6
Eggs	4	4	4
Meat, poultry, fish	24	19	24
Bacon and salt pork	13	9	11
Lard	12	10	8
Subtotal	82	72	70
Margarine	1	2	6
Shortening	8	12	9
Salad oils and salad dressings	2	6	9
All other foods	7	8	6
Subtotal	18	28	30
Total from all foods	100	100	100

* U.S. Department of Agriculture.

KINDS OF FATS AND FATTY ACIDS

Only recently has interest been aroused in the kind of fat (or lipid) eaten and its possible relation to health. Biochemists use the term "lipid" to cover related fatty substances found in foods such as triglycerides, phospholipids, and sterols. The term "oil" is often applied to liquid triglycerides. Triglyceride is the form in which fats principally occur in both foods and fat depots of animals. Triglycerides are esters, formed from fatty acids and glycerol. The triglycerides make up about 98 to 99 per cent of most separated natural fats of which 92 to 95 per cent is fatty acid and the remainder glycerol.

Fatty acids found in nature are of three types: (1) saturated, (2) monounsaturated, and (3) polyunsaturated. The degree of saturation refers to whether or not the fatty acid has all the hydrogen it can carry, that is, to the presence or absence of double bonds. The degree of saturation of fat determines whether it is solid or liquid at room temperature. Liquid fat, which may be mono- or polyunsaturated, can be hydrogenated to a semisolid or fully solid state. Thus liquid vegetable oils such as corn or cottonseed oils may be made into table spreads or margarines by various processes. The type of processing determines how much or how little polyunsaturated fat may remain.

In general, fatty acids in vegetable oils are less saturated than those in animal fats. Olive oil and peanut oil have more monounsaturated fatty acids and less polyunsaturated fatty acids. On the other hand, corn oil and cottonseed oil have more polyunsaturated fatty acids than mono-unsaturated ones. Fatty acids differ in chain length (number of carbon atoms in the molecule) in addition to the degree of saturation.

Most fish are relatively low in total fat and consequently may have little effect on the total fatty acids of human diets. The fatty acids in fish oils contain long-chain polyunsaturates; however, some fish oils contain appreciable amounts of saturated and monounsaturated fatty acids.[3] See Table A–4 in the Appendix for fatty-acid values in foods.

The late Dr. Hansen initiated a study of the essential fatty acid (EFA) requirement in infants. See Figure 6–1 illustrating essential fatty-acid deficiency in an infant. Holman and associates,[4] continuing this work, indicate that the minimal requirement of linoleate (ester of linoleic acid) is approximately 1.4 per cent of the calorie intake for young infants. The Food and Nutrition Board of the National Research Council (1963) states that the linolenic acid group of polyunsaturated fatty acids is less effective in promoting growth and does not prevent dermatitis in infants. The Council suggests that the polyunsaturated linoleic acid in the range of 1 to 3 per cent of the total calories appears to meet not only the infant requirements but adult needs, which are probably less than those of infants. Human milk contains normally about three times as much linoleate as cow's milk.

[3] Review. "Fatty Acid Composition of Fish Oils." *Nutr. Rev.*, **23**:51 (1965).
[4] Holman, R. T., Caster, W. O., and Weise, H. F. "The Essential Fatty Acid Requirement of Infants and the Assessment of Their Dietary Intake of Linoleate by Serum Fatty Acid Analysis." *Amer. J. Clin. Nutr.*, **14**:70 (1964).

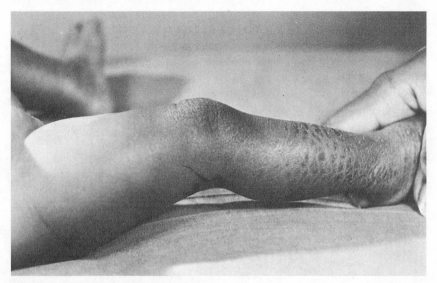

FIGURE 6–1. LINOLEIC ACID DEFICIENCY IN AN INFANT. Appearance of skin in a three-month-old infant fed a milk mixture deficient in linoleic acid (< 0.1 per cent of the calories). (*Courtesy of Dr. Hilda F. Wiese, Bruce Lyon Memorial Research Laboratory. From* Pediatrics, **31** [*Supplement 1, 1963*].)

There are a number of compound fats, where glycerides are combined with other chemical structures, such as the phospholipids. Although they have no obvious structural relationship to fatty acids, there are many biologically important substances classed as lipids because they exhibit similar solubility properties. Such a group of lipids are the steroids, which show marked diversity of physiological activity. The bile acids, important in the digestion of fats, are members of this group. Many important hormones secreted by the adrenal (cortex) and sex glands are steroids, such as cortisone and estrogens.

Closely related chemically to the steroids are the sterols, of which cholesterol is a well-known member. Cholesterol, a waxy, white solid, occurs in almost all animal lipid, especially large amounts in that of nervous tissue, as well as in blood and bile. Ergosterol is a similar sterol found in plants. Both an oxidized form of cholesterol and of ergosterol give rise upon irradiation to products with vitamin D activity. Most of the cholesterol found in the body is synthesized there; that is, it is of endogeneous origin. Obviously, since cholesterol is found in animal lipids, foods of animal origin such as meat and eggs, contain cholesterol. Whole milk contains cholesterol, but since it is found in the fat (cream and butter), the skimmed milk contains almost none. See Table 6–2.

TABLE 6-2. CHOLESTEROL CONTENT OF FOODS* (MILLIGRAMS PER 100 GM)

Meats		Butter	250
Beef	70	Margarine	
Lamb	70	(vegetable fat)	0
Pork	70	Lard and other	
Veal	90	animal fat	95
Organ meats		Milk	
Liver	300	Whole	11
Sweetbread	250	Skim	3
Brains	2,000	Cheese	
Kidney	375	Spread	65
Poultry, chicken	60	Cheddar	100
Fish		Cream	120
Roe	300	Cottage	15
Steak fillet	70	Eggs	
Shellfish		Whole	550
Crab	125	White	0
Shrimp	125	Yolk	1,500
Oysters	200		
Lobster	200		

*Composition of Foods. Washington, D.C.: U.S. Department of Agriculture. Agriculture Handbook No. 8, Compiled from Table 4, page 146 (1964).

FAT-CONTROLLED DIETS AND HEART DISEASE

Evidence has been gathered over the last 15 or 20 years that indicates a possible relationship between the quantity and quality of fats consumed and some types of heart disease. Comparative studies of diets of population groups (epidemiological studies) in various parts of the world reveal that certain dietary differences seem to be associated with differences in blood lipids and the incidence of heart disease. Knowledge of what causes diseases of the heart and blood vessels (cardiovascular) is still far from complete. In most people as they grow older, fatty substances deposit inside the walls of the blood vessels. This fatty plaque is extensive in some persons and may restrict blood flow in the vessels, a condition called atherosclerosis. If this fatty plaque collects in the coronary arteries serving the heart, it is called coronary atherosclerosis, a condition frequently associated with coronary thrombosis (clotting) and damage to the heart muscle (myocardial infarction). This type of heart disease is often called ischemic.

Population groups in various areas of the world show marked differences in blood cholesterol levels as well as differences in the incidence of atherosclerosis and ischemic heart disease. In general, these studies have indicated that lower levels of blood cholesterol are associated with lower

intakes of fat, especially unsaturated kinds, and less heart disease. However, there are many contradictions in the evidence. Data from recent
literature on 26 diverse groups with little ischemic heart disease were
reviewed by Lowenstein.[5] American Indians, Benedictine and Trappist
monks, Central and South American groups, Asian Indians and other
Asian groups, and African groups were among those included. Some of
the pastoral tribes with little ischemic heart disease had an extremely high
intake of calories and saturated fat. Lowenstein points out that there are
great gaps in our knowledge of the influence of such factors as infections
and infestations on atherosclerotic and heart changes. It is clear that this
is a "multifactor" problem; that is, there are many different factors involved as well as diet, including heredity, endocrine gland function,
obesity, physical activity, and stress factors of various kinds including
emotional disturbances. A study by Trulson and associates[6] on 174 pairs
of brothers, one of whom lived in Boston, the other in Ireland, illustrates
clearly the multifactors involved. The death rate from coronary heart
disease is higher in the United States than in Ireland for men 45 to 65
years of age. The Irish brothers were found to be much more physically
active, had a higher calorie intake with a higher proportion of fat from
animal sources, were thinner, smoked fewer cigarettes per day, and had
lower average values for blood pressure and serum cholesterol.

If the blood lipids of persons with atherosclerosis are analyzed, certain
abnormalities may be found. Often the blood cholesterol is higher than
average and the blood triglycerides may also be high. It is known that a
fat-controlled diet, such as the one suggested by physicians of the American Heart Association, will lower blood cholesterol in most people. This
diet also affects the character of body fat. In the fat-controlled diet the
total fat content is lowered somewhat and modified to include foods
higher in polyunsaturated fat and to decrease foods higher in saturated
fats. This changes the polyunsaturated to saturated fatty-acid ratio
(P/S ratio). This is an experimental, therapeutic diet which must be
prescribed for the individual patient under medical supervision. Meats
must be limited because even though the visible fat may be removed, a
considerable amount of the fat in beef, pork, and lamb is invisible. Eggs
are also limited, but fish and chicken are used more frequently. Skim
milk must be substituted for whole milk. A relatively small quantity of
special vegetable oils and margarines is added to the diet. It is most important that adequate supplies of fat-soluble vitamins be included.

It is not established that this diet affects fatty plaques or influences

[5] Lowenstein, F. W. "Epidemiologic Investigations in Relation to Diet in Groups
Who Show Little Atherosclerosis and Are Almost Free of Coronary Ischemic Heart
Disease." *Amer. J. Clin. Nutr.*, **15**:175 (1964).
[6] Trulson, M. F., Clancy, R. E., Jessop, W. J. E., Childers, R. W., and Stare, F. J.
"Comparisons of Siblings in Boston and Ireland." *J. Amer. Dietet. A.*, **45**:225 (1964).

coronary heart disease, although an anticoronary research study conducted by Dr. Christakis and his associates in New York City indicated a favorable effect in their patients on a similar diet. Because coronary heart disease is a serious medical problem in the United States especially among relatively young men, research is exceedingly active in this field. The National Heart Institute Diet-Heart Study, being conducted on a nationwide scale with male volunteers given special experimental diets, should make a real contribution to our knowledge. Meat packers, canners, baking companies, and other food processors have produced the special foods for diets with different quantities of fat and cholesterol and different fat patterns. Hundreds of other studies of the relationship of diet and atherosclerotic heart disease are being conducted in the United States, and indeed all over the world. Studies reviewed in 1965[7] again point out that there is no simple solution to the multifactor problem of the effect of dietary cholesterol and other dietary fats on blood lipids. Investigations often differ in small but significant ways from one another when conducted at different times and under slightly varying conditions.

FATS AS SOURCES OF FAT-SOLUBLE VITAMINS

Fats are important sources of the fat-soluble vitamins, A, D, E, and K. Whole milk, liver, and eggs are basic food sources of vitamin A. When these foods are omitted from the diet, attention must be given to other sources of vitamin A such as dark-green and deep-yellow vegetables. These sources must be used liberally if whole milk and other animal sources are limited. Vegetable oils, whether fluid or hardened by hydrogenation, are lacking in vitamin A, and most animal fats have relatively little. Margarines have vitamin A added in the process of manufacture in amounts which make them the equivalent of average butter. Fish liver oils and their concentrates supply liberal amounts of vitamins A and D.

REQUIREMENT

In reference to fat consumption, the Food and Nutrition Board (1963) states that "there is insufficient evidence to make decisions as to desirable amounts of fat and patterns of fatty acid for the general population."[8]

Carbohydrates

KINDS OF CARBOHYDRATES

Simple carbohydrates such as starches and sugars are readily digested and absorbed by the body. More complex carbohydrates, however, such as the celluloses are mostly indigestible.

[7] Review. "Fat and Cholesterol in the Diet." *Nutr. Rev.*, **23**:3 (1965).
[8] *Recommended Dietary Allowances*. Washington, D.C.: National Research Council, Publication 1146 (1964).

The common food sugars are cane sugar or sucrose, milk sugar or lactose, malt sugar or maltose, glucose or dextrose, and fructose or levulose. Cane sugar (sucrose) of commerce is derived from the sugar cane and sugar beet. Milk sugar differs chemically from cane sugar, being less sweet, less easily dissolved in water, and less easily fermented. Malt sugar is formed by the partial digestion of starch. Glucose occurs widely in nature but is obtained commercially by chemical treatment of starch. It does not appear in the food market as pure glucose but as "commercial glucose" or "corn syrup," which contains dextrin, glucose, and maltose. It is not very sweet, and table syrups made from it are flavored with the sweeter refiner's syrup from the manufacture of cane sugar. Fructose occurs in many fruits, but honey is the only common food containing a high percentage. Honey contains nearly equal proportions of fructose and glucose plus a little dextrin and sucrose. Its flavor comes from substances found in minute quantities in the nectar of the flowers from which it is made.

Maple syrup and maple sugar consist of the concentrated sap of the sugar maple and contain very small amounts of mineral matter. They are lacking in all vitamins. Molasses in the mother liquor remaining after the removal of part of the cane sugar from the boiled-down juice of the sugar cane. In addition to the sugar (sucrose) it contains, it has some calcium and iron. Mixed syrups of various kinds are on the market and their ingredients may be ascertained from their labels.

Cane sugar resembles fat in being a concentrated form of body fuel, but differs from it in its effect on appetite and digestion. Two tablespoons of granulated sugar will yield 100 calories and can be eaten in a meal without adding perceptibly to the volume of food consumed. As body fuel, any kind of sugar is practically interchangeable with starch, calorie for calorie. In the process of digestion, starch is converted to sugar, and much cornstarch is processed into glucose (corn syrup) before it is eaten. Sugar and starch are both delivered to the blood stream from the alimentary tract as simple sugars, glucose, fructose, etc.

CONSUMPTION OF SUGAR AND ITS RELATION TO HEALTH

Many peoples value sugar for its sweetness. "Sweeter than honey in the honeycomb" is a time-honored phrase of high appreciation. The bakery, the candy shop, and the soda fountain bear abundant testimony to our love of sweets. For a number of years the people of the United States have consumed an average of approximately 103 lb per person of sugars and syrups per year, or over ¼ lb daily. About two thirds of this is used in commercial products and the rest in households and institutions.[9]

[9] Scholl, J. C., and Hurt, L. C. "Sugar and Other Sweeteners." *The Yearbook of Agriculture,* p. 177. Washington, D.C.: U.S. Department of Agriculture (1964).

If too much sugar is allowed to displace other foods, the diet will be deficient in the building and regulating materials which sugar lacks. Sugar creates an appetite, not for other foods, but for itself. Children who are allowed to eat candy whenever they feel like it may become undernourished because the candy spoils their appetite for the foods they need for growth. Also, such overindulgence in sugar may have a deleterious effect on their teeth, as discussed in Chapter 19.

Sugar taken alone on an empty stomach may be irritating to the mucous lining, from which it abstracts water just as a piece of candy held in the cheek causes it to "pucker." Hence the most suitable place for sweet food is at the end of a meal, when it will be mixed with food already consumed, and will not come directly into contact with the stomach wall.

In 1964 Yudkin, of the University of London,[10] noted that the world production of sugar is increasing more rapidly than that of most other food commodities. The average consumption including that of poorer regions has increased nearly threefold in this century. Sugar consumption in the United States, although quite high, is not now increasing. In the wealthier countries sugar contributes almost 20 per cent of the calories. There is also concern over increases in sugar consumption in developing countries where intake of protective foods is low. The etiological relationship between excess sugar consumption and the development of diabetes mellitus in susceptible individuals has been established. Yudkin believes there is accumulating evidence that there may also be a causal relationship between excess sugar intake and certain types of heart disease such as coronary artery disease or ischemic heart disease.

Macdonald,[11] of Guy's Hospital, London, has reviewed (1964) the relationship of dietary carbohydrates to lipid metabolism. He points out that until recently the kind of carbohydrate consumed was thought to be of minor importance. Early reports stated that starch and sucrose had different effects on water retention by the organism. Experiments with animals revealed that ingestion of sucrose instead of starch makes a difference in the amount of lipid deposited in the blood and liver. The possible relation of the type of dietary carbohydrate to ischemic heart disease is currently being investigated. Sucrose may not be as favorable as starch in terms of the lipid changes in this condition. Serum lipid and fat depot studies were conducted by Macdonald and Braithwaite (1964), with healthy, male volunteers for 25 days. When sucrose in place of starch was added to a low-fat, adequate-protein diet, differences were observed in the fatty-acid pattern of the serum, changes were noted in

[10] Yudkin, J. "Patterns and Trends in Carbohydrate Consumption and Their Relation to Disease." *Proc. Nutr. Soc.*, 23 (No. 2):149 (1964).

[11] Macdonald, I. "Dietary Carbohydrates and Lipid Metabolism." *Nutr. Rev.*, 22:257 (1964).

depot fat, and there were alterations in certain serum enzymes. Substitution of starch for sugar caused serum cholesterol and phospholipids to fall.

DEFECTS IN CARBOHYDRATE METABOLISM

In recent years many inborn errors of metabolism have been identified. Some of these involve carbohydrate metabolism such as diabetes mellitus, fructose and other sugar intolerances, and galactosemia. In the last-named condition mental and growth retardation occur as well as other symptoms. Manifestations of this relatively rare disease occur early in life and may be controlled by removal of galactose from the diet. Early medical diagnosis and treatment are important.

REQUIREMENT

Although too much sugar is undesirable, as the Food and Nutrition Board (1963) states, "the body has a specific need for carbohydrate as a source of energy for the brain and for certain other specialized purposes." This need for glucose cannot be entirely supplied from the glycerol portion of triglycerides. "A precise minimal requirement for carbohydrate is difficult to assess; but the normal adult requires approximately 500 carbohydrate calories daily; this must be provided in the diet or derived from protein and fat." Diets maintaining individuals in health contain widely varying proportions of carbohydrates.[12]

REFERENCES

American Heart Association. *What We Know About Diet and Heart Disease.* Booklet (1958); *Planning Fat Controlled Meals for Unrestricted Calories; and Planning Fat Controlled Diets for 1200 and 1800 Calories* (1962).

Antar, M. A., Ohlson, M. A., and Hodges, R. E. "Changes in Retail Market Food Supplies in the United States in the Last Seventy Years in Relation to the Incidence of Coronary Heart Disease with Special Reference to Dietary Carbohydrates and Essential Fatty Acids." *Amer. J. Clin. Nutr.,* 14:169 (1964).

Council on Foods and Nutrition. "Regulation of Dietary Fat." *J. Amer. Med. A.,* 181:139 (1962).

Dayton, S., Pearce, M. L., and Hiscock, E. "Can Changes in the American Diet Prevent Coronary Heart Disease?" *J. Amer. Dietet. A.,* 46:20 (1965).

Grollman, S. *The Human Body: Its Structure and Physiology,* Chap. 12. New York: Macmillan (1964).

Jellinck, P. H. *An Introduction to Biochemistry.* New York: Holt (1963).

McHenry, E. W. *Basic Nutrition.* Philadelphia: Lippincott (1963).

[12] Food and Nutrition Board. *Recommended Dietary Allowances.* Washington, D.C.: National Research Council, Publication 1146 (1964).

National Research Council. *The Role of Dietary Fat in Human Health.* A Report of the Food and Nutrition Board (1958).

Public Health Service. *The Food You Eat and Heart Disease.* Health Information Series, No. 89 (1963).

———. *A Handbook of Heart Terms.* Washington, D. C.: U.S. Department of Health, Education and Welfare (1964).

Review. "Fat and Cholesterol in the Diet." *Nutr. Rev.,* 23:3 (1965).

———. "Linoleic Acid in Infant Nutrition." *Nutr. Rev.,* 22:45 (1964).

Sherman, H. C. *Food Products,* 4th ed., Chaps. 12 and 13. New York: Macmillan (1948).

Soskin, S., and Levene, R. "The Role of Carbohydrates in the Diet." Chap. 7, Wohl, M. G., and Goodhart, R. S. *Modern Nutrition in Health and Disease.* Philadelphia: Lea (1964).

U.S. Department of Agriculture. Coons, C. M. "Fats and Fatty Acids," p. 74; Harper, A. E. "Carbohydrates," p. 88. *Food—The Yearbook of Agriculture* (1959)

West, E. S., and Todd, W. R. *Textbook of Biochemistry,* 3rd ed. New York: Macmillan (1961).

Zukel, M. C. "Fat-Controlled Diets." *Amer. J. Clin. Nutr.,* 16:270 (1965).

❧ **7** ❧

Water

Water Essential for Life

Next to oxygen, water is of prime importance in survival. Life cannot exist without water, and in a matter of hours, a water deficit can cause clinically important deterioration and death within a few days. In contrast, one can survive without food for days before the ill effects become intolerable and may survive for five weeks or more.

The earth's surface is 70 per cent water to a depth of over 4 km and yet man has been faced with the problem of having enough water since earliest times. It has been said that his "sense of belonging to a community was bound up with sharing a source of water."

The vital importance of water in the human economy is graphically illustrated in many lands around the world where the sun burns down with searing heat and rainfall is inadequate; vast tracts of desert present one of the most serious problems in the fight against famine and malnutrition. Irrigation has made only a fraction of land arable in these arid tracts such as we find in the Middle East, and this fraction of productive soil is often overpopulated and overworked. This need for water initiated the development of primitive devices for the irrigation of crops (see Figure 7–1), many of which are still used in remote rural areas today. And so—the endless struggle for water continues. This is true even in arid parts of America today. Mickelsen[1] describes the symptoms of lack of water as follows:

Weakness, lassitude, thirst, and dryness of the mouth are the first signs of dehydration. Loss of weight and mental confusion set in later. The individual becomes uncooperative and sullen. The cheeks become pale, and the lips are dry and bluish. The skin loses its elasticity. The eyeballs have a sunken appearance. The volume of urine decreases, and its specific gravity rises. At the end, the respiration ceases, even though the pulse and general circulation may be well maintained.

[1] *Food—The Yearbook of Agriculture,* 1959. Mickelsen, O. "Water," p. 168. Washington, D.C.: U.S. Department of Agriculture.

99

FIGURE 7–1. AN EARLY CHINESE WOODCUT SHOWS IRRIGATION BY FOOTPOWER. Water is still moved by this method in some areas. (*Courtesy of The Bettmann Archive, Inc.*)

Water as Body-Building Material

When a rubber water bottle is full of water, one is quite well aware that the water is there, even though the stopper holds every drop inside and the outside is perfectly dry; but how many realize that a potato skin, neatly encasing the useful tuber in a dry covering, also holds water like the rubber bottle? We do not realize that there is water in the potato because it is held in the cells; but when we break the cell walls, as in grating a raw potato, we can squeeze out a surprising amount of water (see Figure 7–2). It is the same with the body of a man. Muscles, liver, and kidney hold as much water in proportion to their weight as does the potato; brain tissue holds more; and even bone, proverbially dry, is more than one-third water. All together, about 55 to 65 per cent by weight of the adult human body is water, while that of the newborn infant is 75 per cent water.

Water is essential to the constitution of protoplasm. No cell functions when it is absolutely dry, and most cells must be constantly bathed with fluid, in order to do their work. Furthermore, the cells depend on having

FIGURE 7–2. A HALF-
POUND POTATO CONTAINS
NEARLY A TUMBLERFUL OF
WATER.

their food transported to them by the water route (the blood), a demand which alone requires about 10 lb of water constantly in circulation. The cells also depend on having their waste products flushed away; so there must be waste-bearing water (urine) while there is life. The surface of the lungs must be kept moist or there can be no intake of oxygen or riddance of carbon dioxide.

Water is so commonly taken in response to the feeling of thirst that we ordinarily think little about our water supply, save to be sure that it is sanitary and refreshing. But we also get more or less water in food, as even the driest cracker is not absolutely water-free. The amounts in some common foods are indicated in Figures 7–3 and 7–4.[2]

A certain amount of water is produced within the body by the combustion of the fuel foods. The oxidation of 100 gm of fat results in the production of 107 gm of water; the oxidation of 100 gm of carbohydrate, 55 gm; and the oxidation of 100 gm of protein, 41 gm. Benedict calculated that Levanzin, the subject of a 31-day fast, produced on the twenty-first day by combustion of his own body substance 341 gm of water. This metabolic water is useful for the distribution of nutrients, making changes in concentration within the cell which facilitate movement of substances into the cell.

Many varieties of insects have nearly all their water needs met by this metabolic water, subsisting on food containing less than 10 per cent of water and never taking a drink. For animals in hibernation, it is sufficient for several months. Dogs do not have as high water loss as man because they do not perspire through the skin. Another interesting instance of meeting the body need for water by internal production is furnished by the camel, which, according to Babcock,[3] can go for long periods without

[2] For amounts in other foods, see Table 1, Agriculture Handbook No. 8, *Composition of Foods—Raw, Processed, Prepared.* Washington, D.C.: U.S. Department of Agriculture (1963).

[3] Babcock, S. M. *Metabolic Water.* Madison: Wisconsin Agricultural Experiment Station, Research Bulletin No. 22 (1912).

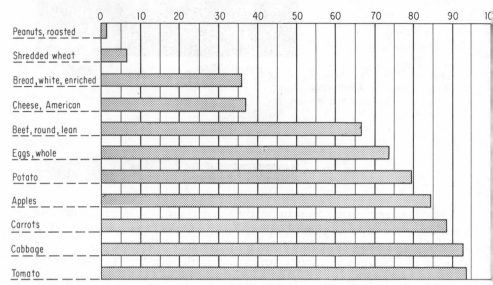

FIGURE 7–3. A COMPARISON OF THE WATER IN SOME COMMON FOODS IN PERCENTAGE.

drinking, more because of the fat of its hump and its carbohydrate food than because of the water in its stomach, the water formed in the process of food combustion being unusually well conserved by the coat of fine hair which reduces evaporation from the skin.

DuBois found the loss of water from lungs and skin in the normal resting man to be 700 to 1,000 gm per day, at a temperature of 23° C. (73.4° F.) and medium humidity. Benedict and Milner accounted for the water intake and output of a man for a day as follows:

Intake		*Output*	
Drink	1,950.00 gm	Feces	191.30 gm
Food	2,972.43 gm	Urine	1,089.20 gm
		Respiration and perspiration	3,929.73 gm
	4,922.43 gm		5,210.23 gm

The water content of the body is subject to considerable fluctuation. Benedict and Joslin reported a marathon runner who lost 8.5 lb in three hours and a football player who lost 14 lb in one hour and ten minutes, of which 13.75 lb was calculated to be water. Hard physical work in a hot environment may bring about a loss of 5 to 12 liters per day. Under these conditions the frequent replacement of salt and water is essential. Also, certain changes in diet affect the water content of the body; for example, when the body changes from a strictly carbohydrate diet to one of fat or protein exclusively, there is a considerable loss of water which will be regained upon resumption of the carbohydrate diet.

A   B

C

FIGURE 7–4*A*, *B*, *C*. COMPARISONS OF FRESH AND DEHYDRATED FOODS.

Food	Fresh		Dehydrated		Water	
	MEASURE	GM	MEASURE	GM	MEASURE	GM
Milk, whole	1 cup	244	⅓ cup	32	⅞ cup	212
Eggs	2 medium	108 A.P.*	¼ cup	28	⅜ cup	80
Apple	1 medium	150 A.P.	½ cup	24	⅝ cup	126

* As purchased.

There are three important sources of body water:

1. Water taken as a beverage or in other liquids.
2. Water contained in solid foods, especially fruits and vegetables.
3. Water formed in the tissues in combustion of the fuel foods.

The normal avenues for water loss are (1) the skin, so-called, insensible perspiration, (2) the skin, visible sweating, (3) the respiratory passages, (4) the alimentary tract, and (5) the kidneys. Any considerable loss or storage of water usually results in a change in body weight. But in under-nutrition water may be stored in the tissues in place of fat, and, conversely, in obesity fat may replace water. Hence an underweight person may increase his food intake with real advantage even though there is no visible gain in weight at first; and an obese person may be disappointed that reduction in food intake does not bring about an immediate loss of weight, owing to the replacement by water of body fat burned. This failure to

103

lose weight will be discussed in greater detail in Chapter 23 (see Figure 23–2).

In health the water balance is easily maintained by a liberal water intake, but in disease the disturbance of the water (along with the electrolyte) balance may be serious and call for special measures to bring about normal equilibrium.

Water as a Regulator of Body Processes

The regulating substances in the body include mineral elements, vitamins, amino acids, and water. Any considerable decrease in the normal amount of water in the body interferes with the manifold physical and chemical processes essential to life and health. Rubner estimated that a man could lose practically all his stores of glycogen and fat and even half his protein without serious danger to life, but a loss of 10 per cent of body water is a serious matter and a loss of 20 per cent usually results in death.

The serious conditions brought about by severe and protracted vomiting or diarrhea, or by fever, are partly due to dehydration. Infants with nutritional disorders may lose water from the body to such an extent that the flow of digestive secretions is reduced and the condition of the intestinal tract altered, with the result that food cannot be digested and absorbed, and feeding does no good until some means are found to restore the lost water to the tissues. Since water-soluble substances, such as minerals, may be lost simultaneously, they need to be replaced along with the water.

Man, and most other large animals which excrete the nitrogenous products of their protein metabolism as urea, require a liberal supply of drinking water in addition to whatever they may acquire by metabolism or in food, to keep the urea content of blood and urine at a low concentration favorable to its excretion. If we do not drink enough to make good the water loss, the body soon ceases to function properly. Hawk stated that in his laboratory normal young men put on a very low water ration soon gave evidence of abnormal function as shown by headaches, nervousness, loss of appetite, digestive disturbances, and inability to concentrate on their work, symptoms which were promptly relieved by increased water intake.

Similar symptoms were found among the troops stationed in the arctic regions during World War II where, because of the extreme cold and the amount of fuel needed to melt ice or snow, it was difficult to obtain enough water to maintain a positive water balance. Chronic thirst, sullenness, and a change in disposition which affected the discipline were also noted.

Hawk[4] made an extensive investigation of the effect of water on the digestive process in normal persons and found that water stimulated the

---

[4] Hawk, P. B. "Water as a Dietary Constituent." Barker's *Endocrinology and Metabolism*, Vol. 3, p. 294. New York: Appleton (1922).

gastric glands to greater activity and improved digestion, while the dilution of the contents of the intestine by a liberal water intake facilitated the absorption of the digested food.

Of purely regulatory functions attributable to water the most conspicuous is related to the control of body temperature. The pathway for heat loss varies with the temperature of the environment; at low temperature there is little evaporation of water, but when the temperature of the air approximates or exceeds body temperature, water evaporation must remove all the excess heat. In the normal resting man, at a temperature of 23° C. (73.4° F.) and medium humidity, about one fourth of the calories of the basal metabolism are dissipated through the evaporation of water as insensible perspiration and moisture from the lungs. Sweating promotes heat loss through evaporation if environmental conditions permit, and also favors conduction and radiation by increasing the moisture of the skin and perhaps of clothing. In a hot, dry atmosphere, the amount of water lost as perspiration is enormous. On the other hand, at a low temperature, sweating not only ceases but there is an actual mobilization of water from the blood into the tissues, so that less of it is brought to the surface to suffer cooling; thus the body heat is conserved.

Water Balance and Electrolytes

The many mechanisms maintaining the water balance of the body are still not entirely understood. There are fluid "compartments" in the body differing in composition, mainly the extracellular fluid outside the cells and the intracellular fluid within the cells. The composition of the fluid bathing the cells is regulated with a precision so delicate that it defies even modern methods of analysis.

One of the controlling mechanisms involves the presence in solution in body fluids of negatively and positively charged mineral particles such as positively charged sodium, potassium, and magnesium ions and negatively charged chlorine, phosphate, and sulfate ions. These we term "electrolytes" as their presence enables a solution to carry an electric current. The various body fluids (plasma, interstitial, and intracellular) tend to maintain osmotic equilibrium in spite of the occurrence of variations in electrolyte distribution.

Water balance is brought about through the control of intake by the stimulus of thirst and the hormone vasopressin, which controls renal excretion. The thirst center located in the hypothalamus, an area of the brain near the pituitary, is thought to induce the sensation of thirst.

Another group of hormones, produced in the adrenal cortex, affect the water content of the body by their action on sodium and potassium metabolism. Clinical evidence calls attention to the association of thirst to salt depletion and the fact that sweating in hot climates cannot be assuaged by drinking water alone but is relieved by salt tablets.

Space Nutrition

Flights into space present a tremendous challenge in terms of water requirement as well as food needs. Short flights, of course, do not pose the problems of the proposed space flights of months to years in duration. For brief orbits, a variety of liquid and semisolid foods can be packaged in collapsible "squeeze" tubes, and bite-size solids. Intensive research still remains to be accomplished to solve the nutritional and mechanical problems of adequate feeding over prolonged flights. To provide for water needs, reutilization of wastes must be considered using a regenerative, recycling system. Currently a research, manned orbiting space station is being intensively investigated, which could periodically resupply spacecraft.[5]

Johnson[6] emphasizes that not only must ample water supplies be provided on long space flights, but the astronauts need to be reminded of the importance of regular consumption of water. During the May 1963 Mercury flights astronaut Cooper lost 3 kg in weight in one day and appeared dehydrated. Astronaut Schirra showed similar symptoms. Consideration of the water needs of astronauts is an integral part of the extensive investigations necessitated in space flights.

Requirement

In the 1963 recommendations of the Food and Nutrition Board of the National Research Council the minimum water requirement under the most favorable conditions is approximately 1 liter per day, and a rational standard for calculating water allowances is 1 ml per calorie of food. Infants have a relatively higher water requirement under ordinary conditions than adults, and mixtures providing 1.5 ml per calorie will be adequate. Care must be taken to prevent dehydration in infants.

Water taken freely is desirable for optimum health of both adults and children, and thirst can usually be depended upon as a guide. However, for infants, sick people, and those subjected to extreme heat and excessive sweating, thirst may not keep up with the actual water requirements. Walker and associates[7] studied the water intake of 797 normal children in four dissimilar geographical locations in the United States. The mothers

[5] Finklestein, B., and Symons, J. J. "Feeding Concepts for Manned Space Stations." *J. Amer. Dietet. A.*, **44**:353 (1964).

[6] Johnson, R. E. "Human Nutritional Requirements for Water in Long Space Flights," p. 159, from *Proceedings of Conference on Nutrition in Space and Related Waste Problems.* Univ. of Southern Florida, Tampa, April 1964. NASA-SP-70. Washington, D.C.: National Aeronautics and Space Administration.

[7] Walker, J. S., Margolis, F. J., Teate, H. L., Weil, M., and Wilson, H. L., "Water Intake of Normal Children." *Science,* **140**:890 (1963).

who cooperated in keeping records were considered very reliable. It was found that children rarely took more than 500 ml of tap water per day, although milk and the water used for mixing fruit juice, soup concentrates, and dried milk brought the total fluid intake to around 900 ml for children under five years and close to 1,300 ml daily for ten-year-old boys and girls. Dehydration was not found to be a problem in the United States. Studies reported previously by Galagan and his associates showed that the environmental temperature was directly related to the fluid intake other than milk.

Johnson[8] recently reported on his study of water and osmotic economy on survival rations. He concluded that an "all-purpose, all-environment survival ration" was both possible and desirable for all environments. Their ration consisted of 2,000 calories per man per day and a water allowance of no less than 910 ml per day for ordinary circumstances and 3 liters a day for hot weather. They found a great individual variability in water economy, and the progressive increase in water deficit was not necessarily accompanied by an appropriate thirst response. An eight-hour recovery period was required when severe deficits were imposed. Also, when bouts of exposure to physical work and water deficits were studied, it was found that one could not be trained to get along with decreasing amounts of water.

Lack of appreciation of the large water requirement of men at high altitudes may have contributed to the failure of early expeditions attempting to scale Mount Everest. Even the Swiss party of 1952 probably failed because they had less than 1 pt of water daily per man for the final days of their ascent. In the British expedition of 1953, knowledge of the necessity for an allowance of at least 5 to 6 pt of fluid per man per day in addition to that in food undoubtedly helped Sir Edmund Hillary in his conquest of Mount Everest. The British expedition provided special stoves and fuel to melt the snow in their assault on Everest, thus providing a supply of water.[9]

Lassitude and weakness may build up quickly at altitudes over 8,000 ft caused in part by water deficiency. There is a high rate of water loss from the lungs due to the dryness of the air and the increase in rate and depth of breathing. Loss of fluid in perspiration may also be considerable in men climbing on glaciers in the intense heating effect of the sun's radiation at high altitudes.

In the consideration of emergency survival rations for shelters, the Committee on Environmental Nutrition of the Food and Nutrition Board has recommended approximately 2 liters of water daily per person with

[8] Johnson, R. E. "Water and Osmotic Economy on Survival Rations." *J. Amer. Dietet. A.*, **45**:124 (1964).

[9] Hunt, Sir J. *The Conquest of Everest*, pp. 43, 229, and 275. New York: Dutton (1954).

1,500 calories providing 35 gm of protein, not less than 150 gm of carbohydrate, not more than 83 gm of fat, and 3 gm of sodium chloride. The minimal water requirement of 1 liter per day was recommended for the most favorable conditions.

It was also suggested by the Food and Nutrition Board that in the evaluation of diets it should be kept in mind that drinking water in certain areas frequently contains substantial amounts of calcium, magnesium, sodium, and trace elements.

REFERENCES

Bradley, C. C. "Human Water Needs and Water Use in America." *Science*, **138**:489 (1962).

Browe, J. H., "Principles of Emergency Feeding," *Recent Advances in Applied Nutrition*. Halpern, S. L. (ed.). *Med. Clin. North America*, **48**:1271 (1964).

Carlisle, N. "Water, Thirst and Your Health." *Today's Health*, August, p. 26 (1962).

DuBois, E. F. *Basal Metabolism in Health and Disease*, 3rd ed., Chap. 19. Philadelphia: Lea (1936).

Ebbs, J. C. "New Horizons for Food." *J. Amer. Dietet. A.*, **39**:101 (1961).

Falk, G. L. "The Physiological Basis of Thirst." *Nutr. Rev.*, **18**:289 (1960).

Finklestein, B. "Space Travel: Current Research in Nutrition and Food Technology." *J. Home Econ.*, **54**:755 (1962).

Food and Nutrition Board. *Recommended Dietary Allowances*, Publication 1146, p. 31. Washington, D. C.: National Research Council (1964).

Food—The Yearbook of Agriculture, 1959. Mickelsen, O. "Water." Washington, D.C.: U.S. Department of Agriculture.

Johnson, R. E. "Water and Osmotic Economy on Survival Rations." *J. Amer. Dietet. A.*, **45**:124 (1964).

Malde, H. E. "Environment and Man in Arid America." *Science*, **145**:123 (1964).

Review. "Water." *World Health*. July-August (1964).

———. "Water Intake of Children." *Nutr. Rev.*, **22**:5 (1964).

Stieglitz, E. J. *Handbook of Nutrition*, 2nd ed., pp. 338–40. Chicago: American Medical Association (1951).

Thomas, M. H., and Calloway, D. H. "Nutritional Value of Dehydrated Foods." *J. Amer. Dietet. A.*, **39**:105 (1961).

Van Reen, R., Minard, D., Dasler, A. R., Raica, N., Jr., and Nelson, R. A. "Nutrition of Recruits During a Summer Habitability Study." *J. Amer. Dietet. A.*, **45**:117 (1964).

Wohl, M. G., and Goodhart, R. S. *Modern Nutrition in Health and Disease*, Chap. 12, Alper, C. "Fluid and Electrolyte Balance." Philadelphia: Lea (1964).

❧ 8 ❧

Proteins and Amino Acids

The beginning of a human being is an egg (cell) too tiny to be studied with the naked eye. Initiated by the union of sperm and ovum, a complicated system of chemical processes which we call life at once enables the minute organism to take up materials from its environment for its own growth. During its prenatal life the human fetus increases its weight more than 5 million times. By the fourth month of intrauterine life it may have attained a weight of 36 gm; at birth it will have increased this latter weight one hundred times. Even after birth the increase in substance is great. A newborn baby weighs on the average about 7.5 lb; the adult into which he grows may weigh 20 to 30 times as much. The newborn infant accumulates about 450 gm of protein, largely during the second and third trimesters of prenatal life.

The Cell

In studying the complicated organization of the living body, the cell is a good starting point since it is the unit structure of plant and animal life. The use of the electron microscope has given us great insight into the intricacies of the cell not previously recognized. Cells vary markedly in size, function, and shape, but have fundamental characteristics in common. Most cells are so microscopic in size that the highest magnification possible is necessary to see them. Other cells are macroscopic in size, for example, the yolk of a hen's egg.

All cells contain protoplasm, the basic material of living matter, which consists of two distinct areas, the cytoplasm and the nucleus. The cytoplasm is the material between the nucleus and the cell wall which contains numerous smaller structures, including the mitochondria, endoplasmic reticulum, lysosomes, and ribosomes. See Figure 8–1 for a diagram of the cell and its various components. The nucleus is primarily concerned with the transmission of hereditary traits from generation to generation. The

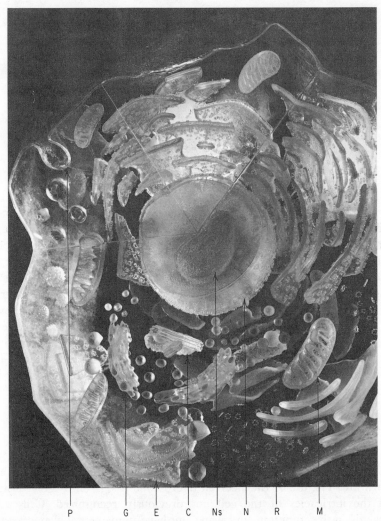

FIGURE 8–1. DIAGRAM OF THE CELL. From a three-dimensional model of a cell in an exhibit on the "Origin and Structure of Life" at the American Museum of Natural History, New York City, made available to the Museum by Eli Lilly and Company. Cell structures as seen in electron micrographs are mitochondria (M); ribosomes, both free (R) and those part of the endoplasmic reticulum (E); double-walled nucleus (N); nucleolus (Ns); centriole (C); Golgi body (G); an invagination of the cell surface which may depict entrance of either solid or fluid material into the cell's interior (P). (*Photograph by Ezra Stoller Associates, Rye, New York. Courtesy of Eli Lilly and Company.*)

cell is a highly organized unit each component part of which has a definite biochemical role. The enzymes within the cell are arranged in specialized structures. The enzymes, protein in nature, serve as catalysts of chemical reactions within the living cell. They are effective in minute amounts and are usually unchanged by the reaction they promote. Almost every reaction within the cell is speeded up by a specific enzyme.

At the time of cell division the chromosomes which carry the genes (hereditary units) can be clearly seen. The chromosomes are composed principally of chromatin, which includes a protein combined with deoxyribonucleic acid (DNA), the genetic material of the cell, found in the nucleus which forms the genes. It is thought that the function of DNA is to act as a carrier of coded genetic information and to control the formation of a "special messenger" ribonucleic acid (RNA). In turn, messenger RNA moves to the site of protein synthesis in the ribosomes of the cytoplasm.

The Synthesis of Protein

Proteins are long polymers of amino acids joined by peptide bonds. The first stage of protein synthesis involves the activation of the amino acids. Each amino acid requires a unique activating enzyme. Each protein contains a definite sequence of amino acids formed by linking together various numbers of amino acids listed in Table 8–1. See Figure 8–2. The order in which the amino acids are arranged is controlled by the

TABLE 8–1. AMINO ACIDS THAT TAKE PART IN PROTEIN SYNTHESIS AND THEIR ABBREVIATIONS

Amino Acid	Abbreviation	Amino Acid	Abbreviation
Alanine	ALA	Leucine	LEU
Arginine	ARG	Lysine	LYS
Asparagine	AN	Methionine	MET
Aspartic acid	ASP	Phenylalanine	PHE
Cysteine	CYS	Proline	PRO
Glutamic acid	GLU	Serine	SER
Glutamine	GN	Threonine	THR
Glycine	GLY	Tryptophan	TRY
Histidine	HIS	Tyrosine	TYR
Isoleucine	ILEU	Valine	VAL

sequence of four basic substances (adenine, cytosine, guanine, and thymine) in the molecules of DNA. The difference between a human being and any other organism, such as an animal, bacterium, or plant, is due to the number and sequence of these four bases in DNA which carry the genetic code. Hereditary defects may be caused by a single amino acid change in a protein molecule. For example, in sickle-cell anemia, an inherited disease, valine is substituted for a glutamic acid group in the sixth link of the beta amino acid chain in the hemoglobin molecule. The hemoglobin molecule consists of two polypeptide chains, each containing

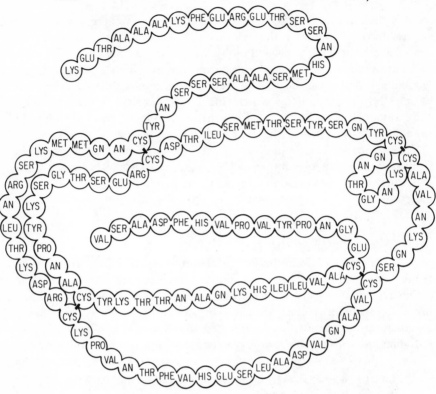

FIGURE 8–2. THE AMINO ACID SEQUENCE OF AN ENZYME, A RIBONUCLEASE FROM THE PANCREAS OF THE OX. The amino acids are linked by peptide bonds, and each enzyme has a precise folded structure. (Adapted from David M. Bonner and Stanley E. Mills, *Heredity*, 2nd ed., 1964. Reprinted by permission of Prentice-Hall, Inc.)

about 146 amino acids. This single amino acid change results in a fatal anemia. Other changes resulting in a defect or deficiency of an enzyme may cause other conditions referred to as inborn errors of metabolism. A deficiency of a liver enzyme causes such an inborn error known as phenylketonuria (PKU). This disease, which leads to severe brain damage, can be controlled by diet if detected in time. Other genetic errors include essential xanthomatoses, essential hyperlipemia, diabetes mellitus, cystinuria, and many others. At present about 70 inborn errors of metabolism have been recognized.

Proteins as Sources of Amino Acids

Mulder, in 1838, was the first to recognize a nitrogenous material as a fundamental constituent of tissue substance. He named this material "protein," a term derived from the Greek verb meaning "to take first place." Proteins are made up of the simpler nitrogen-containing sub-stances, the amino acids. More than 20 of these amino acids have been found in food and body proteins, all having certain characteristics in com-mon, but each one exhibiting properties which mark it as a distinct chemi-cal entity. Proteins, as previously noted, differ in the actual number of amino acids present, but most proteins contain between 15 and 20 occur-ring in many different proportions, combinations, and structural arrange-ments.

It was not until about 1900 that a real interest was developed in the amino acids making up these compounds. Prior to this no quantitative data existed concerning the distribution of amino acids in proteins from different sources, and actually only 12 of those now recognized as con-stituents of proteins had been discovered. From this meager beginning, the vast amount of research on protein and amino acids is now overwhelm-ing.

Recognizing the special value of casein, the chief protein of milk, Dr. W. C. Rose of the University of Illinois studied the amino acid make-up of this paragon of proteins. One by one, amino acids were isolated and identified and various combinations of them tried out on young animals in an attempt to attain the natural mixture in pure casein which would support growth. However, the animals failed to grow on these mixtures, showing that some essential amino acid was still missing. It was not until 1936 that the amino acid now known as threonine (Figure 8–3) was dis-

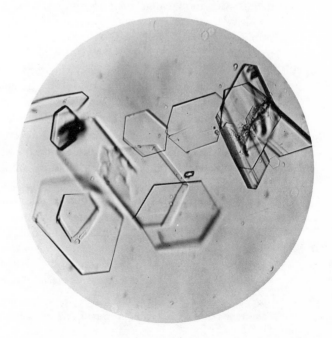

FIGURE 8–3. CRYSTALS OF THE AMINO ACID THREO-NINE. (*Courtesy of Dr. William C. Rose and the* Journal of Biological Chemistry.)

covered and the mystery solved. By 1937, the particular combination of amino acids from casein which provided excellent growth in young animals was identified. Interestingly enough, only 10 of the 20 amino acids in casein were found to be necessary in the diet as such, and these were designated as the essential amino acids. The actual amounts of each of these ten essential amino acids required for growth of the weanling rat were determined.

W. C. Rose defined an essential or indispensable amino acid as "one which cannot be synthesized by the animal organism out of material ordinarily available, at a speed commensurate with the demands for normal growth." The ten amino acids known to be essential for growth in the weanling rat are listed below:

Arginine[1]	Methionine
Histidine[1]	Phenylalanine
Isoleucine	Threonine
Leucine	Tryptophan
Lysine	Valine

In 1942 experiments with human subjects were started by W. C. Rose.[2] Using the standard method for determining protein requirement and synthetic amino acids, he omitted one amino acid at a time in the otherwise adequate diet of graduate-student volunteers. In the standard method nitrogen balance or equilibrium is determined. The food consumed and the excreta (urine and feces) are analyzed for nitrogen. If there is more nitrogen in the food eaten than in the excreta, the balance is said to be "positive," indicating storage of nitrogen in the body. If more nitrogen is found in the feces and urine than in the food eaten, the balance is said to be "negative," indicating a loss of nitrogen from the body. When the nitrogen intake in the food is approximately equal to the nitrogen output in the excreta, the body is said to be in nitrogen equilibrium or balance, indicating that the food is adequate in protein and amino acids.

Within a period of ten years the evidence was sufficient to show conclusively that only eight of the ten amino acids were essential for the maintenance of nitrogen equilibrium in the human adult. Arginine, although essential for the growth of young animals but not for the maintenance of nitrogen equilibrium in adult animals, was found to be dispensable for the maintenance of nitrogen equilibrium in normal human adults. Histidine was also found to be unessential for the maintenance of nitrogen equilibrium in the human adult, but, according to Holt,[3] is essential for

[1] Not essential for maintenance of nitrogen equilibrium or balance in the human adult.

[2] Rose, W. C., "The Amino Acid Requirements of Adult Man." *Nutr. Abstr. & Rev.,* **27**:631 (1957).

[3] Holt, L. E., Jr., György, P., Pratt, E. L., Snyderman, S. E., and Wallace, W. M. *Protein and Amino Acid Requirements in Early Life.* New York: New York U. P. (1960).

growth in infants. When any one of the eight essential amino acids was omitted from the experimental diets of the adults, a negative nitrogen balance resulted, the output of nitrogen exceeding the intake. This was accompanied by a failure of the appetite, nervous irritability, and a feeling of extreme fatigue. These symptoms disappeared when the missing amino acid was again included in the diet.

Table 8–2 summarizes the studies which have been made to determine the precise quantitative amino acid requirements of men and women. The values for male subjects were determined by Rose, as described above. Rose recommended that these requirements be doubled for safety. The values for women were determined by Leverton and other investigators in cooperative studies. These are compared with the United States per capita food supply, which shows that the amino acids are abundantly supplied.

TABLE 8–2. DAILY REQUIREMENTS OF ESSENTIAL AMINO ACIDS COMPARED WITH THE U.S. PER CAPITA FOOD SUPPLY

Essential Amino Acids	Minimal Requirement gm per day		Safe Allowance* gm per day	U.S. per Capita Food Supply 1953‡ gm per day
	Young Men*	Young Women†		
Tryptophan	0.25	0.16	0.50	1.2
Threonine	0.50	0.31	1.00	3.9
Isoleucine	0.70	0.45	1.40	5.2
Leucine	1.10	0.62	2.20	8.0
Lysine	0.80	0.50	1.60	6.1
Methionine	1.10		2.20	2.0
Total sulfur-containing	(1.10)	0.55	(2.20)	3.4
Phenylalanine	1.10	0.22	2.20	4.6
Tyrosine		0.90		
Valine	0.80	0.65	1.60	5.5

* Rose, W. C. "The Amino Acid Requirements of Adult Man." *Nutr. Abstr. & Rev.*, 27: 631 (1957).

† Leverton, R., p. 477. Albanese, A. A. (ed.). *Protein and Amino Acid Nutrition.* New York: Academic (1959).

‡ Computed by Household Economics Research Division, ARS, USDA, based on estimates of per capita consumption supplied by AMS, USDA.

That older men, aged 50 to 70 years, may differ from young ones in the requirement for essential amino acids is suggested by the studies of Tuttle and co-workers.[4] From their results thus far it would appear that

[4] Tuttle, S. G., Bassett, S. H., Griffith, W. H., Mulcare, D. B., and Swendseid, M. E. "Further Observations on the Amino Acid Requirements of Older Men. I. Effects of Nonessential Nitrogen Supplements Fed with Different Amounts of Essential Amino Acids," p. 225; "II. Methionine and Lysine," p. 229; *Amer. J. Clin. Nutr.*, 16 (1965).

the amounts of methionine and lysine needed to maintain nitrogen balance may be greater for older men.

Holt and others[5] are continuing studies of the amino acid requirements of infants using synthetic diets.

There tend to be differences in determinations of minimal needs depending on the source of dietary nitrogen, the amino acid being studied, the mineral, and the vitamin intake. Some of these variations may be responsible for the apparent differences in amino acid requirement between men and women. Although it is useful to have these data on individual amino acid requirements, there are a number of practical considerations to be kept in mind. A much higher caloric intake is necessary for nitrogen balance in diets containing free amino acid mixtures than in a ration of natural foods. Rose noted this in comparing whole casein with mixtures of amino acids. It has been pointed out that the amino acid requirements are in the main dependent on the composition and pattern of the amino acids in the tissues being formed during growth in children or maintenance in adults. For synthesis or maintenance of tissue proteins all the amino acids needed must be available simultaneously for proper utilization; in other words, it is an "all or none" process.

In the United States, where the protein supply is liberal and comes from a variety of foods, we do not need to worry about the proportions of different amino acids. In parts of the world where the protein supply is inadequate and the protein source is limited principally to a single food, the proportions as well as the amounts of the amino acids may be significant. Judging from animal experiments, a surplus of one amino acid might bring about either an imbalance or an antagonism affecting amino acid requirement. It is possible that if a large amount of corn, which has an excess of leucine, is consumed an increase in isoleucine requirement may result as these related amino acids may be "antagonistic." In Table 8–4 it can be observed that in the corn protein, zein, the proportion of leucine to isoleucine is excessive.

A number of reference patterns have been suggested to assist in estimating the quality of protein in a given food. The FAO reference pattern was derived from the minimal daily requirements for the essential amino acids for infants and adults. Other reference patterns have been based on the amino acids present in egg, human milk, and cow's milk. Table 8–3 shows the essential amino acids in the proteins of egg, human milk, and cow's milk compared with the FAO pattern. In each case it will be noted that the amino acids present in the food either satisfy or exceed the amino acid values in the FAO pattern with the exception of the methionine in cow's milk. Although the FAO pattern is not perfect, the proposal has stimulated helpful discussion and research.

[5] Snyderman, S. E., Boyer, A., Norton, P. M., Roitman, E., and Holt, L. E., Jr. "The Essential Amino Acid Requirements of Infants. IX. Isoleucine," p. 313; "X. Methionine," p. 322. *Amer. J. Clin. Nutr.,* **15** (1964).

TABLE 8–3. COMPARISON OF THE FAO PATTERN WITH THE PROTEINS OF EGG, HUMAN MILK, AND COW'S MILK*

Essential Amino Acids	FAO Pattern	Egg	Human Milk	Cow's Milk
Lysine	4.2	6.4	6.6	7.9
Leucine	4.8	8.8	9.1	10.0
Isoleucine	4.2	6.6	5.5	6.5
Methionine (plus cystine)	4.2	5.4	4.3	3.4
Phenylalanine (plus tyrosine)	5.6	10.8	9.9	10.0
Threonine	2.8	5.0	4.5	4.7
Tryptophan	1.4	1.7	1.6	1.4
Valine	4.2	7.4	6.3	7.0

*Adapted from Table 2, p. 4, *Evaluation of Protein Quality*. Washington, D.C., National Research Council, Publication 1100 (1963).

Early Studies on Individual Proteins

At this point in our discussion it will be of interest to compare the percentages of essential amino acids in two kinds of protein: (1) casein from milk and (2) zein from common Indian corn (maize). These amounts expressed in per cent (grams per 100 gm), are listed in Table 8–4.

TABLE 8–4. ESSENTIAL AMINO ACIDS IN TWO KINDS OF PROTEIN*

Amino Acid	Casein per cent	Zein per cent
Isoleucine	6.6	5.1
Leucine	10.0	19.9
Lysine	8.0	0.0
Methionine	3.1	1.8
Phenylalanine	5.4	10.4
Threonine	4.3	3.1
Tryptophan	1.3	0.1
Valine	7.4	4.1

*Orr, M. L., and Watt, B. K. *The Amino Acid Content of Foods.* Home Economics Research Report No. 4. Washington, D.C.: U.S. Department of Agriculture (1957).

All the essential amino acids needed for the human adult are found in the casein of milk, but in the zein of corn it will be observed that there is no lysine and only an insignificant amount of tryptophan.

That zein was deficient in these two amino acids was demonstrated in 1915 in the classic studies by Mendel of Yale University. He reported on the effect on the growth of young animals of feeding each of a number of different proteins. When zein, for example, was fed as the only protein, the young rats not only failed to grow, but lost weight rapidly. When he added tryptophan, the loss of weight stopped but there was no growth. When lysine was also added, growth started at once.

Osborne, working with Mendel on these now classic studies, demonstrated that gliadin, one of the proteins of wheat, was deficient in lysine. The poor growth record of an animal maintained on a diet with gliadin as the sole protein is shown in Figure 8–4. When milk, rich in lysine, was

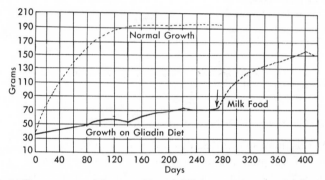

FIGURE 8–4. GLIADIN AND NORMAL DIETS. The growth record of a young rat placed at weaning time on a diet containing gliadin as the sole protein and kept on this diet for 276 days. At this time milk food replaced the gliadin food, and the animal was able to grow at a good rate, although of an age at which normal rats have usually ceased to grow. (*Courtesy of Drs. T. B. Osborne and L. B. Mendel.*)

added to the diet, growth was promptly resumed. When pure lysine was added in place of milk, growth also occurred. These studies of Osborne and Mendel marked the beginning of a vast amount of research on the quality of proteins.

The effect of feeding a lysine-deficient diet to weanling rats, when the diet consisted of zein plus adequate amounts of all other essential amino acids, mineral elements, and vitamins, is shown in Figure 8–5.

Animals on a diet in which gliadin, low in lysine, is the only source of amino acids will remain in seemingly good health over a period of time, although stationary in weight, which indicates some essential difference between the requirements for maintenance and growth. Animals on a diet in which casein is the sole source of amino acids will grow normally if the amount is sufficient but not if it is too small. When the casein is limited to 6 per cent, there will be very little growth, but the animals remain in apparently good condition over long periods because all the essential amino acids are present, though some are in amounts too small to permit

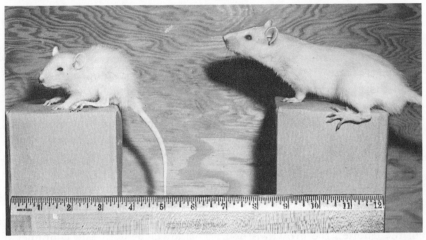

FIGURE 8–5. EFFECT OF LYSINE DEFICIENCY ON THE GROWTH OF THE RAT. The animals are the same age and had been on the diets six weeks. The diet of the animal on the right contained zein plus all the amino acids known to be needed by the rat; that of the animal on the left was the same except that lysine was omitted. All essential mineral elements and vitamins were included in the basal diet. (*Nutrition Laboratory, Teachers College, Columbia University.*)

growth. On the gliadin diet, no increase in the amount of gliadin will make good the deficiency, since the essential lysine is too low. On the casein diet, it is only necessary to increase the amount of casein to the 18 per cent level to secure excellent growth.

The Functions of Proteins and Amino Acids

GROWTH AND MAINTENANCE

Every living cell is continually demanding amino acids for upkeep, working them over into living tissue, or using them for the construction of hormones, enzymes, antibodies, and other body regulators, and ultimately eliminating them in part in the form of simpler compounds (chiefly urea, uric acid from all kinds of active cells, and creatinine from muscle cells), which are excreted in the urine. There is thus a maintenance requirement for protein, which continues throughout life.

Promotion of growth is one of the most important functions of protein. Studies with experimental animals, already reported in this chapter, show that both the quality and the quantity of the protein must be considered if the best growth is to be attained.

When the diet furnishes optimum levels of protein such as are found in mother's milk, the growth of the young infant proceeds at such a rate that the newborn child doubles its weight in six months and triples it in a year, and we find that as much as one third of the protein intake may be stored as body protein. To get the best storage, the protein of the food must in itself be efficient in promoting growth, and the supply of carbohydrate and fat must be liberal enough to protect the protein from being burned as body fuel. Milk is distinctly richer in tryptophan and lysine than the common run of foods, and the amino acids it furnishes least liberally are those which can be derived from other foods.

Nicholls[6] pointed out that infants born of mothers with different racial backgrounds do not differ greatly in size, and if the mother is well-nourished, growth proceeds at about the same rate for the first few months. But when the high-quality protein of mother's milk is supplemented by other foods, differences in the growth patterns are noted. For example, if manioc (cassava, a root vegetable), which is so commonly used in many parts of the world, especially in the tropics, furnishes most of the calories, the growth is poor. This lower growth rate continues if the diet continues to be poor, and at maturity the differences in weight and height attained may be striking.

Proteins are essential constituents of both the nucleus and the cytoplasm of the cells and are the chief organic constituents of the muscle and glandular tissues of the body. They exist in many forms. More recent investigations using radioactive compounds have shown that protein exists in a dynamic state and that the old idea of a more or less static state of body protein and protein synthesis in the adult as being restricted to "wear and tear" of metabolism is no longer tenable.

The role of amino acids as contributors to the metabolic pool of "building blocks" is basic in the synthesis of various tissue proteins. Some labile tissue proteins (referred to sometimes as "protein reserves") are in a dynamic state, continually being broken down and resynthesized and thus contributing to the metabolic pool. (See Figure 8–6.) In the liver, for example, it has been found that more than half of the protein may be broken down and resynthesized within ten days.

In youth, the process of growth requires additional protein for the building of new body substance. This growth requirement makes the total protein requirement of childhood higher in proportion to size than that of the adult. Only under certain circumstances do we have in adult life a growth requirement superimposed on the maintenance requirement. These are chiefly:

1. In athletic training, when muscles increase in size.
2. After a wasting disease, when muscles are regaining substance lost.
3. In pregnancy, owing to the growth of the unborn child and to some development of the maternal organism.

[6] Nicholls, L. *Tropical Nutrition and Dietetics*. Revised by Sinclair, H. M., and Jelliffe, D. B., 4th ed. London: Baillière (1961).

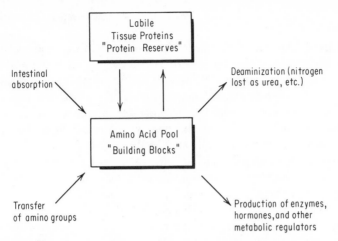

FIGURE 8–6. THE DYNAMIC STATE OF PROTEIN METABOLISM.

SIGNIFICANCE IN METABOLIC PROCESSES

Proteins are intimately involved in all phases of chemical and physical activity that constitute the life of the cell. They serve as enzymes, hormones, oxygen carriers (such as hemoglobin), and antibodies. Still others participate in muscular contraction and as carriers of the genetic code. Indeed, proteins participate in practically every physiological function.

The many functions of proteins are actually well illustrated in protein deficiency. For example, the effects of protein deficiency may be manifested in the deficiency of muscle development which, according to Jeans, may account for the poor posture of some four-year-old children, or low plasma protein with a decline in serum albumin and globulin which leads to hypoproteinemia. The low hemoglobin levels that accompany this condition will respond to an increase of the protein in the diet. Resistance to infections is lowered as well as the level of phagocytes (white cells) and antibodies in the blood. Cannon demonstrated that adult animals maintained on a low-protein diet over a prolonged period lose their ability to form antibodies and resist infection.

Scrimshaw emphasizes the interplay of infection and protein malnutrition in underdeveloped countries. Although not a serious threat to well-nourished children, measles, whooping cough, and diarrheal disease often cause the death of malnourished children. On the other hand, infection may interfere with nutrition and precipitate a child in marginal health into severe protein malnutrition. Many reports show a relationship between prolonged low-protein intakes and tuberculosis, rheumatic fever, and respiratory and intestinal infections. The desirability of high-quality protein for convalescence from surgery, in the healing of wounds, and for superior rate of recovery from disease has been stressed by a number of investigators.

In relation to the rapidity with which many chemical changes occur in living tissue at body temperature, the enzymes play an extremely significant role, as previously noted. In protein deficiency there is a lowering of enzyme activity throughout the body, particularly in the liver.

Numerous enzymes require the presence of cofactors or coenzymes in order to function. Many of these coenzymes contain vitamins in their structure as well as mineral elements. The functions of a number of amino acids are known to be interrelated with those of a number of vitamins; for example, tryptophan serves as a precursor of niacin in the prevention of pellagra. The relation of methionine to vitamin B_{12} and choline, and of tyrosine to ascorbic acid, has been recognized, but it seems desirable to discuss these interrelationships in the respective chapters on minerals and vitamins.

EFFECTS OF PROLONGED PROTEIN MALNUTRITION

A form of malnutrition known as protein malnutrition and occurring in young children in many parts of the world has been recognized only within recent years. In some parts of Africa almost every child suffers from it, and the mortality rate has been as high as 50 per cent among cases admitted to the hospitals. In other areas the mortality rate is between 30 and 40 per cent. The condition is more common in children under five years and is more likely to occur during the weaning and postweaning period. The term "kwashiorkor" was first used by Cicely Williams in 1933 for a syndrome in weanling children which she observed on Africa's Gold Coast (now Ghana). It is said that the literal translation of this native term for the condition refers to the child deposed from the breast when the mother again becomes pregnant. In other parts of the world the FAO reports indicate that this condition is recognized by as many as 50 names, including such terms as "red boy," "infantile pellagra," "sugar baby," "fatty liver disease," and "nutritional edema syndrome." The condition has been found to be common in the Far East, India, the West Indies, Central America, and many parts of South America as well as Africa.

In classic kwashiorkor, the calorie intakes may be adequate or nearly so but the protein is inadequate, creating a protein-calorie imbalance. However, in many parts of the world children do not have enough calories. In this case it may lead to the condition called marasmus. Hansen[7] defines marasmus as "a term applied to infants who are grossly underweight and have atrophy of both muscles and subcutaneous fat. There is a shrunken,

[7] Brock, J. F. *Recent Advances in Human Nutrition*. Chap. 23 by J. D. L. Hansen, p. 269. Boston: Little (1961).

wizened appearance of the face in contrast to the fat, rounded cheeks of kwashiorkor. There are usually no hair or skin changes and oedema is unusual and always minimal. As in kwashiorkor, diarrhoea is common."

The term "protein-calorie malnutrition" was introduced by Jelliffe to cover the many intermediate clinical states between marasmus and kwashiorkor. When calorie needs are not met, as has been pointed out in a previous discussion, some protein will be wasted in the production of energy, thus making less protein available for tissue building.

In kwashiorkor typical diets are usually found to be high in calories from starchy foods but low in protein. This brings about an imbalance of amino acids and a deficiency of factors found in foods in association with animal proteins. Brock and Autret[8] have characterized the syndrome as follows: (1) retarded growth, (2) alterations in skin and hair pigmentation, (3) edema, (4) fatty infiltration, cellular necrosis, or fibrosis of the liver, (5) nutritional dermatosis, (6) gastrointestinal disorders, (7) peevishness and mental apathy. See Figure 8–7 for typical symptoms of kwashiorkor. The hair of children with kwashiorkor often changes in color to red and finally to grey or white. See flag sign, Figure 8–8. Also, the hair is sometimes very thin and can be pulled out with little effort.

Reports from Mexico, Guatemala, and Africa indicate that the serum free amino acids of the blood serum of children acutely ill with kwashiorkor show imbalances in respect to the lowered concentration of the essential to nonessential amino acids.[9]

Studies of Latin American children with protein-calorie malnutrition reveal that psychomotor development is retarded, that there is muscular atrophy and in general underdevelopment of the neuromotor system. It is interesting to note recent studies with rats fed low-protein diets representing the composition of the human diets of the rural area of Gambia, in Africa. The second generation of these rats showed retarded growth and development and poorer intelligence test scores compared with control rats.[10]

An effective treatment for kwashiorkor is the introduction of skim-milk powder. Where this has been successfully accomplished, the mortality rate has fallen rapidly, in some areas almost to the vanishing point. In most cases dietary treatment will restore the health of children in a critical condition within a matter of weeks. In many countries children have no milk except mother's milk, and as they are weaned they are put on cereal, tubers (manioc or cassava), or plantain gruels, which are likely to be high in carbohydrates and poor in protein, and thus protein malnutrition

[8] Brock, J. F., and Autret, M. *Kwashiorkor in Africa*. Geneva: World Health Organization (1952).

[9] Whitehead, R. G., and Dean, R. F. A. "Serum Amino Acids in Kwashiorkor. I. Relationship to Clinical Condition." *Amer. J. Clin. Nutr.*, 14:313 (1964).

[10] Review. "Diet, Development and Intelligence." *Nutr. Rev.*, 22:244 (1964).

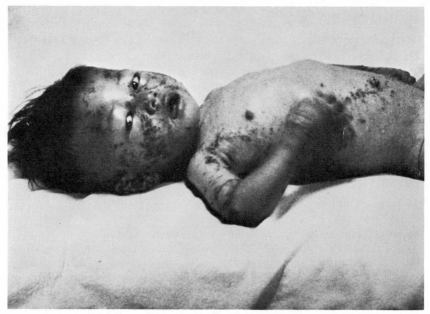

A

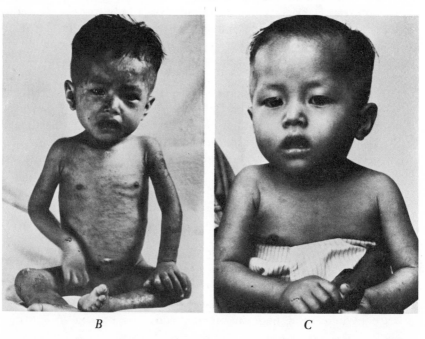

B   C

Figure 8–7. Kwashiorkor in a Child Before and After Treatment. *A* shows
the typical symptoms of protein-calorie malnutrition; *B* shows the progress
after four days of treatment, and C, after a month. (*Courtesy of World Health.
From* World Health Organization Magazine, *pp. 16–17* [*March, 1963*].)

FIGURE 8–8. FLAG SIGN IN THE HAIR OF A CHILD WITH KWASHIORKOR. Depigmentation of the hair indicates the period at which the child's diet was inadequate in protein. (*INCAP Photo. Courtesy of N. S. Scrimshaw, and M. Behar. From "Protein Malnutrition in Young Children."* Science, **133:** *2039 [1961].*)

develops. Since in many places enough milk for children cannot be produced at present and that which is available is too expensive, or may be unsafe, other protein-rich foods must be substituted. The eye disease xerophthalmia may be a complication of kwashiorkor in some areas where vitamin A intake, as well as protein intake, is deficient. Sources of vitamin A consequently should be given attention. See illustration in Chapter 12 (Fig. 12–7) on vitamin A.

Brock and Autret report finding along the roadside in Northern Nigeria a small group of young children who had the typical reddish hair. The area was known to have been affected seriously by famine. When the parents were asked if the color of the hair was natural, they replied without hesitation that it would return to normal when their food improved.

Attention has been called to the high incidence of adult liver cirrhosis in those areas in the world where kwashiorkor is endemic. Although in the United States protein malnutrition is not a public health problem, its frequency and significance elsewhere have stimulated research in liver metabolism.

See Figure 8–9 for the effect in the rat of a diet similar to that which produces kwashiorkor in the human being.

SUPPLEMENTARY FOOD SOURCES OF ESSENTIAL AMINO ACIDS

Early concepts of nutrition divided proteins into those of first and those of second class, the former being of animal and the latter of vegetable origin. With increasing knowledge it became evident that the differences between foods as protein sources were reflecting differences in amino acid

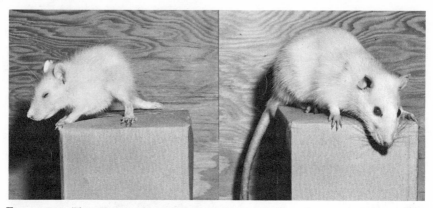

FIGURE 8–9. THE EFFECT OF A CASSAVA DIET IN A RAT COMPARED WITH THAT OF THE SAME DIET PLUS SKIM-MILK POWDER. The animals are the same age and had been on the diets 82 days. The only difference between the two diets was that one contained 86 gm of cassava (tapioca), while in the other 16 gm of the cassava was replaced by skim-milk powder. The other ingredients of the diets were dried beans, banana flakes, meat residue, dried coconut, sugar, and palm oil. Note the symptoms suggestive of kwashiorkor—the dermatosis of the paws, nose, and ears, the edema of the abdomen, and the difference in texture of fur of one rat (*left*) in contrast to that of the other (*right*) having skim milk. (*Courtesy of Nutrition Laboratory, Teachers College, Columbia University.*)

composition and also that the superiority of "first class" was often partly due to accompanying vitamins or minerals. We now know that distinction between animal or vegetable protein is neither rigid nor always justified.[11]

The nutritive value or quality of a dietary protein depends on the pattern and quantity of essential amino acids available to the body after digestion. Formerly proteins were classified as complete, incomplete, or partly complete, depending on their ability to maintain life and support growth in experimental animals. For example, the casein of milk was shown to be a complete protein, while zein was incomplete. Several methods have been devised for determining differences in the nutritive value of proteins. Probably the best known is the determination of the percentage of absorbed nitrogen retained in the body, which is called the biological value of the protein. A method widely used for the estimation of protein quality is the comparison of the amino acid analyses of the protein source with a reference pattern which was discussed earlier in this chapter. For a discussion of other methods for the evaluation of protein quality, see National Research Council Publication No. 1100 (1963).

Proteins of various kinds are associated in many foods. Some foods have very little in proportion to their weight, such as most fruits and

[11] Henry, K. M., and Kon, S. K. "The Nutritive Value of Proteins; General Considerations." *Proc. Nutr. Soc.*, **17**:78 (1958).

vegetables. Others are rich in protein, such as eggs, cheese, nuts, and lean meats of all sorts, "fish, flesh, or fowl." Cereals are not very rich in protein but, because of the relatively large amounts eaten by the human race, they are a source of considerable importance. Among other vegetable foods, the legumes, especially peas and beans, and nuts, are comparatively high in their yield of protein. In animal food, such as milk, cheese, eggs, meat, fish, and poultry, the various proteins present are complete, but in vegetable foods very commonly an incomplete protein is associated with a complete one; and occasionally, the total protein content is of poor quality. The supplementing value of one protein for another must, however, be kept in mind. The supplementing value of milk is exceedingly high.

The nutritive value of the protein mixture of a food can be predicted only as the amino acid content is known. See "Amino Acid Content of Foods" in the Home Economics Research Report No. 4, U.S. Department of Agriculture. Corn is known to be deficient in two amino acids, tryptophan and lysine. Whole wheat, oats, rice, barley, rye, and millet have all been found to be deficient in lysine. It has been pointed out that if the lysine value of wheat were approximately doubled, a given amount of wheat protein would be twice as efficient in the building of tissue in the growing animal. Legumes (peas and beans) are deficient in tryptophan and methionine, but they are relatively high in lysine. Soybeans have a good mixture of amino acids with the exception of the deficiency of methionine. In the developing countries where animal protein is scarce, the use of pulses and other legumes to supplement cereals is important. In India, the gains in height and weight of young children one to five years of age on a test diet of rice with well-selected pulses for 240 days compared favorably with gains of children on the control diet of rice and skim milk.

Even root products, such as potatoes, have been found to be important sources of protein in some areas. The white potato, for example, has a good assortment of amino acids except for a shortage of methionine. In New Guinea, schoolchildren accustomed to sweet-potato diets, including the leaves of the sweet potato, which formed 90 to 95 per cent of the staple food, were studied. Rice, beans, and fish made up the remaining 5 to 10 per cent of the diet. The sweet-potato leaves were found to contribute considerably to the total protein value of the diet. Extracted proteins from plant leaves are being studied as a cheap and effective means of supplementing diets in developing countries.

Since a large proportion of the calories are furnished by vegetable foods in many parts of the world, the amino acids most likely to be deficient in human diets may be summed up as follows: lysine, methionine, threonine, and tryptophan. Diets containing assortments of grains, legumes, and the various root vegetables will provide a better combination of amino acids because these foods when combined supplement one another and provide the essential amino acids needed.

Bressani and Scrimshaw[12] state that "It is now widely accepted that an important and practical approach to supplying the needed dietary protein in areas where milk and other products of animal origin are costly or in short supply is the development of suitable combinations of vegetable protein sources to supply both essential and nonessential amino acids in the proportions required." In Central America Scrimshaw and his associates studied combinations and proportions of local vegetable foods which would supplement each other and provide a protein value superior to that of any one vegetable food. After a study of several different combinations, a mixture now known as Incaparina was devised. Mixture 9B consisted of 29 per cent uncooked corn, 29 per cent uncooked sorghum, 38 per cent cottonseed flour, 3 per cent torula yeast, 1 per cent calcium carbonate with 4,500 I.U. of vitamin A. In field trials mixture 9B was accepted readily when in the form of a thin cereal gruel known as an "atole." The dry mixture, packed in 75-gm plastic bags, was enough for one day when prepared with 3 glasses of water. The effectiveness of this mixture in the treatment of kwashiorkor in children has been repeatedly demonstrated.

Dean successfully used a biscuit mixture in the treatment of children with kwashiorkor in Kampala, Uganda. The mixture consisted of peanuts (ground nuts), corn meal, sugar, cottonseed oil, and dried skim milk.

Fish flour has been used more successfully in some countries than others because of acceptability and keeping qualities. In many lands population groups have for generations used food sources of protein which are not commonly used in the American diet, such as pumpkin seed (pepitorja), the quinia bean, fermented soybean products, and millets such as the Ethiopian teff.

Food Sources of Protein in the United States and in Other Fortunate Lands

There is a striking contrast between the dearth of good-quality protein foods available in the developing countries and the abundant supply in all markets from coast to coast in the United States. The kinds and quantities of foods in the civilian food supply in the United States in 1962 provided about 95 gm of protein per capita per day along with 3,180 calories. Over the last half-century there has been a gradual in-

---

[12] *Progress in Meeting Protein Needs of Infants and Pre-school Children.* Publication 843, p. 35. Washington, D.C.: National Research Council, National Academy of Sciences (1961).

crease in the percentage of protein from animal sources from about 50 per cent in 1909–13 to approximately 67 per cent in 1962.

It is easy to follow the food rules of the U.S. Department of Agriculture when unlimited choices of good-quality protein foods can be made in most food markets. Food known to provide all the essential amino acids, such as milk, eggs, meat, fish, and poultry, ensure generous allowances of essential amino acids. For young children and adolescents probably two thirds to three fourths of the total protein may come from milk and foods containing good-quality proteins in order to provide adequately for growth. During pregnancy and lactation a half to two thirds of the protein should come from foods carrying good-quality proteins, with the greatest emphasis placed on milk.

Leverton, in her studies with young college women on two levels of protein, demonstrated the importance of having high-quality protein in each meal if the nitrogen is to be well utilized. On the lower protein intake, animal protein in the form of milk showed a distinct advantage in reducing the loss of nitrogen in the urine.

Cannon, working with protein-depleted rats, showed clearly that unless all the ten essential amino acids were fed at approximately the same time, the rats failed to make steady gains in weight. When the basal ration contained five amino acids in one portion and five in a second portion and the portions were fed alternately, poor weight recovery resulted. He concluded that for effective tissue synthesis all essential amino acids must be available simultaneously.

"While it cannot be denied that individual cases require consideration and that knowledge in many areas is inadequate, it must be concluded upon the evidence available to date that malnutrition due to protein deficiency is not a general health problem in the United States."[13]

Protein Requirement

When foods are eaten the complex protein molecules are broken down into amino acids in the process of digestion. From what we have learned of the great diversity in amino acid content of different proteins, we shall not be surprised to find that when the final assortment from a meal has entered the blood stream and the cells of the tissues have begun to take up the particular kinds of amino acids which are required for their individual needs, there may be an oversupply of some and a scarcity of others.

When amino acids are burned for fuel they are broken down into simpler compounds, the nitrogen being converted into urea and a small

[13] *Evaluation of Protein Nutrition.* Publication 711, p. 51. Washington, D.C.: National Research Council, National Academy of Sciences (1959).

amount of ammonia, which are withdrawn from the blood by the kidneys and excreted in the urine, the remainder being reduced to compounds containing only carbon, hydrogen, and oxygen, which burn like sugar and fat. Fifty-eight per cent of the weight of the protein may thus turn to sugar (glucose) and be burned along with other carbohydrates and fat for fuel. We have but relatively little power to store protein against future need as we can store fat. However, the labile protein reserves have been reported to represent 2 kg of available protein. Nevertheless, the more protein we eat, the more we burn, and urea excretion becomes a rough measure of the amount of protein used as fuel.

In studying protein requirement, it is simpler to consider first the nitrogen requirement of the healthy adult, uncomplicated by the phenomena of growth. Critical examination by Sherman in 1920 of over 100 nitrogen balance experiments in 25 independent investigations, including work in several countries and with both sexes, gave an average of 44 gm of protein per 70 kg of body weight per day as the minimum requirement. Stare and his co-workers in 1946 reported on experiments with 26 healthy adults on a basal low-protein diet and found the protein requirement to be between 30 and 40 gm for a 70-kg adult. These studies and others indicate that the average minimum requirement is close to 0.5 gm of protein per kilogram of body weight.

The FAO Committee on Protein Requirements and the Food and Nutrition Board of the National Research Council have estimated the minimal need for adults to be between 0.3 and 0.35 gm per kilogram per day when the diet contains proteins of maximal nutritive quality. The minimum requirement may vary from 0.65 to 0.80 gm per kilogram per day when the diet consists of proteins of low biological value.

Since protein in excess of requirement is readily burned as fuel, there is no particular reason for trying to keep the amount in the daily diet down to the minimum. It is actually difficult to do so in the United States because of the richness in protein of many of the foods commonly used. Moreover, considering the somewhat uncertain amino acid assortment of a diversified diet, and the likelihood of fluctuations in completeness of digestion, it would not be wise to adopt a minimum standard for practical living. According to Publication 1100 of the National Research Council (1963), "Stress can alter the adequacy of a given supply of dietary protein." The effects of individual stressors such as infection, injury, undernutrition, climatic extremes, severe exertion, and emotional factors are not always entirely predictable. The level of protein, excessive supplies of certain amino acids, and other dietary factors may have an influence on the response to stress.

The real question, then, is not how little protein do we need, but how much is it desirable to indulge in? The body shows considerable ability to adjust to different levels of protein intake. When the intake and excretion of the body are in nitrogen equilibrium and the intake of protein is suddenly increased, a new higher level of nitrogen equilibrium is reached after a few days. On the other hand, if the intake is decreased, within a few days nitrogen equilibrium is reached at a lower level.

Wide differences of protein intake exist in peoples throughout the world, and within limits, individuals seem to be able to make the adjustment and maintain nitrogen equilibrium. Over the years there has been considerable controversy in regard to the most desirable level of protein intake, and this is still an unsettled question.

Protein does not exert any marked stimulating effect on heat production when it constitutes a relatively small proportion of the total calories, i.e., not over 10 to 15 per cent. Assuming the average daily energy expenditure of a sedentary man (weight, 70 kg) to be 2,500 calories, 10 per cent, or 250 calories, in the form of protein would be equivalent to 62.5 gm of protein, equal to 0.9 gm of protein per kilogram, while actual requirement is, as we have seen, about 0.5 gm per kilogram. Hence, an allowance of 10 per cent of the total calories in this case means 80 per cent more than required. Sherman (1952), reviewing the experimental work on the effects of different levels of protein intake on animals throughout the life cycle, concluded that the results confirmed and strengthened the generally accepted dietetic custom of allowing from 10 to 15 per cent of the total food calories from protein under ordinary conditions.

The Recommended Allowances for Protein

The recommended allowance of 1 gm of protein per kilogram per day has been used for adults since the original allowance was established in 1943. According to the 1963 Recommended Allowance, 1 gm of protein per kilogram per day does not appear excessive. Although the food consumption may fall with increasing age and the calorie requirements are less, in the absence of clear evidence, a protein allowance of 1 gm per kilogram is recommended for adults of all ages. This protein allowance is generous because it has been established that the "protein" requirement can be fulfilled by the minimal requirement for essential amino acids plus "unessential" nitrogen, which may come from nonprotein sources such as urea or ammonium salts.

The protein allowance during pregnancy is increased from 58 gm of protein per day, or about 10 per cent of the calories for the nonpregnant woman, to 78 gm per day, or about 14 per cent of the calories needed for pregnancy, the increase starting in the latter half of pregnancy when the growth of the fetus is most rapid. During lactation the daily allowance is increased still further to 100 gm of protein per day. Since the total calories are also increased, the per cent of the calories coming from protein is about 13 per cent.

In human milk about 7 per cent of the calories are in the form of protein, a relatively low level, but it is generally accepted that the breast-fed infant is adequately nourished with regard to protein.

The recommendations for children vary according to age; these are shown in Table 8–5. They are reported to be approximately double the estimated minimal protein requirement for rapidly growing children.

It will be noted that the protein recommended for children furnishes approximately 10 per cent of the total calories.

In Table 8–6 are listed a selection of common foods furnishing protein equivalent to that in one egg.

TABLE 8–5*. RECOMMENDED ALLOWANCES FOR CHILDREN

| | | | | Protein | |
	Age	Weight kg	Calories	Gm Per Day	Gm per Kg of Wt Per Day
Children	1–3	13	1,300	32	2.4
	3–6	18	1,600	40	2.2
	6–9	24	2,100	52	2.2
Boys	9–12	33	2,400	60	1.8
	12–15	45	3,000	75	1.7
	15–18	61	3,400	85	1.4
Girls	9–12	33	2,200	55	1.7
	12–15	47	2,500	62	1.3
	15–18	53	2,300	58	1.1

Recommended Dietary Allowances, p. 13. Washington, D.C.: National Research Council (1964).

TABLE 8–6. GRAMS OF FOOD YIELDING PROTEIN APPROXIMATELY EQUIVALENT TO THAT IN ONE EGG*

Food	Grams	Food	Grams
Beef, lean	30	Liver, beef	30
Bread, white, enriched	69	Milk, nonfat, dried	17
Cheese, cottage	35	Milk, whole	171
Chicken, canned, boned	28	Peanuts	23
Egg, cooked	50	Peas, fresh	95
Fish, cod, raw	34	Potatoes, A.P.†	342
Garbanzos (chickpeas)	29	Soybeans, dried	18
Lima beans, dried	29		

* 6 gm of protein (calculations based on values in Agriculture Handbook No. 8).
† As purchased.

REFERENCES

Asfour, R. Y., Tannous, R. I., Sabry, Z. I., and Cowan, J. W. "Protein-Rich Food Mixtures for Feeding Infants and Young Children in the Middle East. II. Preliminary Clinical Evaluation with Laubina Mixtures." *Amer. J. Clin. Nutr.*, 17:148 (1965).

Autret, M., and Behar, M. *Sindrome Policarencial Infantil (Kwashiorkor) and Its Prevention in Central America.* FAO Nutrition Studies No. 13. Rome: Food and Agriculture Organization of the United Nations (1954).

Bogert, L. J. *Nutrition and Physical Fitness*, 7th ed., Chap. 6. Philadelphia: Saunders (1960).

Brock, J. F. "Chronic Protein Malnutrition." *Nutr. Rev.*, 13:1 (1955).

Brock, J. F., and Autret, M. *Kwashiorkor in Africa.* Geneva: World Health Organization (1952).

Encouraging the Use of the Protein-Rich Foods. Rome: Food and Agriculture Organization of the United Nations (1962).

Food—The Yearbook of Agriculture, 1959. Leverton, R. M. "Proteins" and "Amino Acids", pp. 57 and 64. Washington, D.C.: U.S. Department of Agriculture.

Jukes, T. H. "Present Status of the Amino Acid Code." *J. Amer. Dietet. A.*, 45:517 (1964).

Lewis, H. B. "Proteins in Nutrition." *Handbook of Nutrition*, 2nd ed., Chap. I. Chicago: American Medical Association (1950).

Mendel, L. B. *Nutrition: The Chemistry of Life*, Chaps. 1 and 4. New Haven, Conn.: Yale (1923).

Orr, M. L., and Watt, B. K. *Amino Acid Content of Foods.* Home Economics Research Report No. 4. Washington, D.C.: U.S. Department of Agriculture (1957).

Patwardhan, V. N. "Pulses and Beans in Human Nutrition." *Amer. J. Clin. Nutr.*, 11:12 (1962).

Protein Malnutrition. Proceedings of a Conference in Jamaica, 1953. FAO, WHO, and J. Macy, Jr. Foundation. Cambridge, England: University Press (1955).

Protein Requirements. FAO Nutritional Study No. 16. Rome: Food and Agriculture Organization of the United Nations (1957).

Recommended Dietary Allowances, 6th rev. ed. Washington, D.C.: National Research Council, National Academy of Sciences, Publication 1146 (1964).

Sherman, H. C. *Chemistry of Food and Nutrition*, 8th ed., Chaps. 4, 5, and 11. New York: Macmillan (1952).

Simoons, F. J. *Eat Not This Flesh: Food Avoidances in the Old World.* Madison: U. Wisconsin (1961).

Tannous, R. I., Cowan, J. W., Rinnu, F., Asfour, R. J., and Sabry, Z. I. "Protein-Rich Food Mixtures for Feeding Infants and Preschool Children in the

Middle East. I. Development and Evaluation of Laubina Mixtures." *Amer. J. Clin. Nutr.*, **17**:143 (1965).

Waterlow, J., and Vergara, A. *Protein Malnutrition in Brazil.* FAO Nutritional Study No. 14. Rome: Food and Agriculture Organization of the United Nations (1956).

Watts, J. H. "Evaluation of Protein in Selected American Diets." *J. Amer. Dietet. A.*, **46**:116 (1965).

Weiss, M. G., and Leverton, R. M. "World Sources of Protein," p. 44, *Farmer's World, The Yearbook of Agriculture.* Washington, D.C.: U.S. Department of Agriculture (1964).

Wohl, M. G., and Goodhart, R. S. *Modern Nutrition in Health and Disease,* Chap. 6. Albanese, A. A., and Orto, L. A. "The Proteins and Amino Acids." Philadelphia: Lea (1964).

World Health Organization Technical Report Series No. 301, *Protein Requirements.* Geneva: World Health Organization (1965).

❧ 9 ❧

Introduction to the Mineral Elements

The relative concentration of the mineral elements which are essential components of the human body will be comprehended better, perhaps, if we make a list showing representative amounts of each present in the organism (see Table 9–1).

TABLE 9–1. MINERAL ELEMENTS IN THE HUMAN BODY

Element	Approximate Amount in a 70-Kg Man Gm
Calcium	1,295
Phosphorus	700
Potassium	245
Sulfur	175
Sodium	105
Chlorine	105
Magnesium	35
Iron	2.8
Manganese	0.21
Copper	0.080
Iodine	0.028
Cobalt Fluorine Molybdenum Zinc Selenium	Very minute quantities

Others reported but functions doubtful

Traces of other elements, e.g., boron and silicon, may not be essential for man although they are probably essential for plants. In addition, other elements have been reported as bodily constituents including aluminum, arsenic, bromine, chromium, lead, nickel, strontium, vanadium, cadmium, barium, and others. Some of these occur naturally in foods; others may have gained access through contamination, but whether they are essential to body structure has not yet been established. The term "trace element" or "microelement" is used in referring to mineral elements which in extremely small amounts play some role in the nutrition of plants and animals.

The development of new methods and instruments for analysis has made it possible to extend our information on the amounts of trace elements in plants used for food. Studies at the New Jersey Agricultural Experiment Station show that specific deficiency symptoms occur in plants due to the absence of or inadequate amounts of various trace elements. For example, with a molybdenum deficiency, the older leaves of cauliflower become long and slender, and with a boron deficiency, black areas have been found in the stem centers of cabbage and cracked areas have been found in celery stems. These studies demonstrate the critical role that trace elements play in plant production. For illustration of molybdenum deficiency, see Figure 11–6.

However, it must be kept in mind that it is the healthy, well-formed plants that have a market value, and with the wide occurrence of these trace elements in the food included in an all-round good diet, it is not likely that a deficiency will occur in human nutrition. In our enthusiasm about the importance of trace elements, we have to be careful not to become victims of the pseudo scientist. Maynard,[1] former Director of the School of Nutrition at Cornell University, sums up our present knowledge as follows: ". . . with the exception of the long-recognized case of iodine, none of the reports which have suggested correlations between soil deficiencies and human diseases have been based on studies or observations which were sufficiently critical to establish any direct relationships. . . ."

The mineral elements of the diet are provided by a great variety of food sources. Since it is possible to produce adverse effects when excessive amounts of a number of the minerals are consumed, it is unwise to indulge indiscriminately in mineral mixtures sold on the market without a prescription.

Mineral Elements as Body Building Material

Quantitatively the mineral elements most prominent in the body are calcium and phosphorus. They chiefly are responsible for the rigidity of the bones and teeth, and serve along with vitamin D to maintain the framework whose value we most appreciate when we see the effect on

[1] Maynard, L. A. "Soils and Health." *J. Amer. Med. A.,* **143**:807 (1950). Review. "Trace Elements in Plants and Soils." *Nutr. Rev.,* **12**:276 (1954).

appearance of poor teeth or of a disease like rickets, in which the mineral deficiency of the bones may result in a hollow chest and poorly developed lungs, to say nothing of the unattractiveness of bowlegs, knock-knees, or flat feet.

The role of mineral elements in the structure and the functions of the human body cannot be well understood without appreciation of the cell, a unit endowed with all the attributes of life.[2] In a cubic inch of normal human blood there are as many as 80 billion cells, red and white, all equipped for special chemical work.

The proteins of the cell nucleus, nucleoproteins, are distinguished by the fact that they contain phosphorus, as an integral part of their structure; hence phosphorus, like iron, which is found in the chromatin of the nucleus, is intimately associated with the fundamental processes of nutrition, sharing in the control of cell activities.

The body of the cell, the cytoplasm as it is called, contains, in addition to protein, mineral salts, water, a substance called lecithin, allied to the fats but having phosphorus as an indispensable element in its composition.

Among cells differentiated for special function are the red corpuscles of the blood, which are the carriers of oxygen to all the tissues and the removers of carbon dioxide arising from the combustion of body fuel. Their power to transport these gases depends on an iron-bearing protein, hemoglobin, and any serious diminution in its amount is accompanied by increased respiration and accelerated heart action in an effort to compensate for the lessened oxygen-carrying capacity of the blood.

The other mineral elements are found variously distributed in the body, chlorine occurring chiefly in the gastric juice; sodium, in the blood and other fluids, combined with chlorine as sodium chloride (common salt); potassium, most abundantly in the protoplasm of muscles and various organs; magnesium, chiefly in the bones but also in muscles and a little in blood; iodine, in the thyroid gland and its product, thyroxine. Copper is very closely associated with iron in animal tissue. It is found in high percentage in the liver, epecially of the newborn infant. Although it does not enter into the structure of hemoglobin, it is essential to its formation. While these elements contribute to the composition of the body, they function more prominently in the regulation of body processes.

Mineral Elements as Regulators of Body Processes

We have seen in the previous discussion that chemical elements which may enter into the structure of the body in very minute quantities are highly important for the maintenance and growth of the cells. In the

[2] For a description of the cell and its relation to body structure as a whole refer to Chapter 8.

regulation of body processes, the amount of an element present in the organism gives no clue as to its significance in the coordination of cell functions. Each element has its own special part to play; two which may be closely related chemically cannot exchange places and may in some of their functions be actually antagonistic to each other. Inasmuch as the role of the mineral salts in vital processes is a matter of their physicochemical relationships, any detailed discussion of their functions leads far into the fields of chemistry and physics, and is beyond the scope of this book. No attempt will be made to do more than discuss briefly some of the more obvious ways in which the mineral elements aid in the regulation of body processes.

In the first place, these elements influence the contractility of muscles. If a muscle is removed from the body and put into a solution containing a suitable mixture of pure salts (particularly calcium, sodium, and potassium chlorides), it will, when stimulated, contract as it would in the body. But if it is put into distilled water (which contains no such salts), it will not respond when stimulated. If the muscle is put into a solution containing sodium and potassium, but not calcium, it will fail to respond; but when calcium is added in suitable amount to the solution, it will respond as at first. Thus the dependence of the muscle on calcium may be demonstrated in the laboratory. It may also be demonstrated by the use of a frog's heart, which can be made to beat or stop as calcium is present or absent from a solution in which the organ has been suspended. So we say the muscles of the heart depend for their rhythmical beat on the nature of the salts in the fluids that bathe them.

In the second place, minerals determine the irritability of nerves. Just as a muscle will not contract normally if suspended in distilled water, so a nerve similarly placed will fail to respond to any stimulus, but when bathed in a suitable salt solution will behave in the normal manner. All the organs regulated by the central nervous system depend for the integrity of their functions not only on the presence of calcium, potassium, magnesium, and sodium in the fluids within the nerve tissues, but on their presence there in just the right proportions.

In the third place, mineral elements control the movement of liquids in the body. Digested food materials must pass freely from the intestine into the blood stream without any blood passing back into the intestine. Also, liquids must pass from the blood into the various organs and tissues, and such a fluid as the gastric juice must be derived from the blood and poured into the stomach. Furthermore, the waste matter of the cells taken away by the blood must be withdrawn from it by the kidneys and discharged in the urine. It is owing to interactions between mineral elements that the cells can bring these things to pass.

As referred to in Chapter 7, the importance of a balance between the various "electrolytes" (that is, mineral elements in body fluids dissociated into ions or electrically charged particles) is recognized as of vital importance in the maintenance of health. The surgeon, for instance, must give attention to the fluid and electrolyte balance to safeguard the survival of the patient undergoing an operation. Cognizance of the role of electrolytes has been one of the factors in the improved prognosis for patients classified as "poor risks" or as elderly citizens.

Mineral elements are also essential to the digestive processes. For example, in the stomach, the gastric juice owes its characteristic acidity to chlorine in the form of hydrochloric acid, upon which the activity of pepsin in digestion depends. In the small intestine, other mineral salts make the secretions alkaline, favoring the digestive processes there, especially the digestion of fat.

Another important function is to keep the blood neutral—neither acid nor alkaline. Here phosphorus (as phosphoric acid) and sodium (as bicarbonate) act as buffers, which means that, when they are present in a solution, considerable amounts of acid or alkali may be added without showing any effect, for these buffers react to dispose of the acid or alkali as such and keep the solution neutral.

Mineral elements take part in the transport of oxygen from the lungs to the tissues and of carbon dioxide from the tissues to the lungs, which makes possible the continued combustion of the fuel foods. As previously pointed out, the power of the iron-bearing hemoglobin of the blood to combine under certain conditions with oxygen and under other conditions with carbon dioxide is fundamental to the process of respiration.

As the mineral elements enter into the composition of every living cell, they determine the vital processes of oxidation, secretion, development, and reproduction. Phosphorus and iron are outstanding examples of such ubiquitous or omnipresent elements.

Mineral elements are essential to the structure of certain complex chemical compounds which profoundly influence the course of metabolism. One conspicuous example is iodine, the element found in the thyroid gland and its products, which has been referred to in Chapter 2 as powerfully influencing the energy metabolism. But this is not all. Without iodine for the proper functioning of the thyroid, normal growth in the young and the maintenance of health in the adult are impossible. The influence on development is strikingly shown in the case of tadpoles; ordinarily they require three weeks to change into frogs; when they are given thyroid, the metamorphosis begins in a few days and is completed so rapidly that there is no time for growth in substance along with the loss of tail and formation of legs, so that the result is pygmy frogs. In the human adult loss of thyroid function results in changes in skin, hair, and facial contours, and other signs that a controlling mechanism is out of order. The part played by minerals in enzyme-catalyzed reactions is of vital significance. Zinc, an integral component of enzymes in the blood cells and pancreas, and molybdenum, a component of an enzyme found in the liver, are major elements in controlling cellular respiration. Other elements, including magnesium, manganese, cobalt, potassium, iron, and copper, are also involved in enzyme activities.

Sulfur

During the past 30 to 40 years our knowledge of sulfur metabolism has been extensively advanced under the leadership of du Vigneaud. Sulfur is a component of body protein occurring chiefly in the amino acids cystine and methionine. The proteins present in the protective surfaces of the body are very rich in these amino acids, and hair, for example, contains 4 to 6 per cent of sulfur. Sulfur in the form of cystine is present in the hormone insulin, essential to normal metabolism of glucose. Sulfur is also a constituent of another chemical regulator of metabolism, glutathione. This latter substance, found and named by Hopkins of Cambridge University in 1921, is present in many body tissues, and is an important factor in the control of oxidative processes in the body. Sulfur is an essential element of the vitamin thiamine, the functions of which will be discussed in Chapter 13. As a constituent part of thiamine and of the respiratory enzyme cocarboxylase and of insulin, sulfur plays a role in the metabolism of carbohydrates. It is also an integral part of coenzyme A.

Sulfur in food is found almost exclusively in the form of protein. Individual proteins differ considerably in their yield of sulfur, but the foods that ordinarily contribute most of the protein of the diet average about 1 gm of sulfur for each 100 gm of protein, or each 16 gm of nitrogen.

As the metabolism of sulfur usually runs somewhat parallel to that of nitrogen in the ratio of about 1 gm of sulfur to 16 of nitrogen (corresponding to 100 gm of protein), we sometimes assume for practical purposes that the sulfur requirement will be met when the protein intake is sufficient to meet the nitrogen requirement. A safer allowance for sulfur would also involve, of course, consideration of the adequacy of the protein quality of the diet, in terms of adequate amounts of the sulfur-containing amino acids.

Sodium and Chlorine

Sodium chloride (common table salt) is the only salt we appear to crave in greater amount than is found naturally in food. The earliest recorded history shows the use of salt by civilized people and suggests that the practice may possibly have developed "at the time man made the transition from a nomadic hunter-fisher, on a roasted meat and milk diet, to an agriculturist on a cereal grain and vegetable diet."[3] Herbivorous animals have long been known to travel great distances, if necessary, to salt licks while, on the other hand, carnivorous animals show little interest in supplementary salt.

The manufacture of salt appears to have originated many centuries ago. Records show that in 2700 B.C. the Chinese obtained salt by solar evaporation of saline waters or by rock salt mining. The Phoenicians apparently were the first to engage in sea salt manufacture in the Mediterranean area. In Greece, slaves were bought and sold with salt, and the good slave was said to be "worth his weight in salt." Through the years, men have been driven to fight, bargain, and travel from place to place to satisfy this great desire for salt. The American colonists also craved salt, and during the early years it was necessary to import it, but soon it was found that salt could be obtained by boiling sea water and this was carried out along the shores of Massachusetts, Long Island, New Jersey, and elsewhere. Later the salt springs of Lake Onondaga in New York and the brine wells along the Kanawha River in West Virginia were developed.[4]

The amount of sodium chloride taken in the form of common salt is far in excess of human requirements for sodium and chlorine. Furthermore, these elements are so widely distributed in food materials that there is little likelihood of shortage of either unless some specially restricted diet is employed over a long period of time or one is working under conditions of excessive heat. The main question is whether or not sodium chloride will be used to excess.

It is reported that the normal adult in the United States has an average daily intake of 7.5 to 18 gm of salt (approximately ⅓ to 1 tbsp) including the sodium and chlorides contained in foods together with those added as salt. In 1948, Osmond and Clements, in a study of 175 households in Australia, reported that the mean daily consumption of table salt per adult male was 5.5 gm. The sodium intake in the United States is about 3 to 7 gm per day, in contrast to that of the Japanese, who often consume 10 to 15 gm daily, part of which comes from soya sauce.

Salt depletion, caused by failure to replace salt losses during excessive sweating, has been observed in men working in hot environments and is characterized by symptoms such as nausea, vomiting, exhaustion, cramps, and respiratory failure. The Food and Nutrition Board of the National Research Council (1963) suggests that workers in hot environments should have free access to water and, if more than 4 liters of water is consumed, extra salt should be provided, approximately 1 gm for each liter of water. In addition to losses in perspiration, sodium depletion may occur

---

[3] Meneely, G. R., Tucker, R. J., Darby, W. J., and Auerbach, S. H. "Chronic Sodium Chloride Toxicity: Hypertension, Renal and Vascular Lesions." *Ann. Intern. Med.*, **39**:991 (1953).

[4] Smith, J. R. "Salt." *Nutr. Rev.*, **11**:33 (1953).

owing to vomiting or diarrhea or urinary losses in patients with kidney disease, or to prolonged use of diuretics.

Diets restricted in sodium are used in a number of conditions, especially those in which water balance is disturbed and development of edema is a problem. Sodium salts are found in greater amounts in the blood and other extracellular fluids than within the cells. Potassium salts, on the other hand, occur in greater concentration within the cells of the soft tissues, the muscles, and other organs and in the blood corpuscles. Together, these salts participate in maintaining water balance and normal osmotic pressure. Fluctuations in water and mineral balance (electrolyte balance) may have dire effects on the viability of the cells.

The possibility that prolonged high intakes of sodium may lead to hypertensive disease in man has been suggested by Dahl and others, based on observations of populations on high and low sodium intakes. Prolonged feeding of high-salt diets to experimental animals does produce hypertension.

In 1958, the American Heart Association published booklets on three different sodium-restricted diets for patients, as prescribed by their physicians. The three diets outlined are the strict 500-mg sodium diet, the moderate 1,000-mg sodium diet, and the mild sodium-restricted diet (2,400 to 4,500 mg of sodium). These diets all permit the consumption of regular milk. If the sodium is reduced below 500 mg, low-sodium milk must be used.

Many foods contain natural sodium. In general, fruits contain very little and meats, poultry, fish, and eggs contain a relatively large amount of natural sodium. Vegetables range from those having very little natural sodium to those containing relatively large amounts. Quantities of food as well as kinds of food must be considered in planning sodium-restricted diets.

Sodium compounds are often added to processed or prepared foods, or are used in medications sold in pharmacies without a prescription. These sodium compounds can be recognized by the consumer because the Federal Food and Drug Administration regulations specify that labels must indicate the presence of added "sodium" or "soda" (sodium bicarbonate).

As there is danger from taking too little sodium chloride, no one should attempt to maintain a low-sodium diet without the supervision of a physician. The popular fad of restricting table salt to lose weight will be disappointing, since the restriction of sodium in this way brings about a loss of water and not tissue. The water is soon replaced in response to thirst.

Pike,[5] on the basis of studies of animals during pregnancy, calls attention to the possible dangers of a low-sodium diet during pregnancy in human beings.

[5] Pike, R. L. "Sodium Intake During Pregnancy." *J. Amer. Dietet. A.*, **44**:176 (1964).

Potassium

Potassium, as previously mentioned, is an essential intracellular constituent. It is abundant in both plant and animal tissues and does not need to be given special consideration in the normal diet. However, a deficiency may occur with prolonged loss of appetite, in fasting, in starvation, in infectious diarrhea in infants, and as a complication in a number of pathological states. Symptoms of the deficiency include over-all muscle weakness, poor intestinal tone (distention), cardiac abnormalities, and weakness of the respiratory muscles.

The Food and Nutrition Board of the National Research Council (1963) states that only limited data on the potassium requirement of man are available. The minimal need has been estimated at 0.8 to 1.3 gm of potassium per day. In the United States diets have been found to contain from 0.8 to 1.5 gm of potassium for every 1,000 calories.

REFERENCES

American Heart Association. *Your Mild Sodium-Restricted Diet; Your Moderate Sodium-Restricted (1000 Milligrams) Diet; Your Strict Sodium-Restricted (500 Milligrams) Diet* (1958).

Bogert, L. J. *Nutrition and Physical Fitness*, 7th ed., Chap. 7. Philadelphia: Saunders (1960).

Clifford, P. A. "Sodium Content of Foods." *J. Amer. Dietet. A.*, **31**:21 (1955).

Dahl, L. K. "Salt, Fat, and Hypertension: The Japanese Experience." *Nutr. Rev.*, **18**:97 (1960).

Food and Nutrition Board. *Recommended Dietary Allowances*. Washington, D.C.: National Research Council (1964).

————. *Sodium-Restricted Diets*. Washington, D.C.: National Research Council (1954).

Review. "Sodium Chloride Intake and Occurrence of Hypertension." *Nutr. Rev.*, **13**:79 (1955).

Sherman, H. C. *Chemistry of Food and Nutrition*, 8th ed., Chap. 12. New York: Macmillan (1952).

Watt, B. K., and Merrill, A. L. *Composition of Foods—Raw, Processed, Prepared*. Washington, D.C.: U.S. Department of Agriculture, Agriculture Handbook No. 8 (1963).

⚘ 10 ⚘

Calcium, Phosphorus, and Magnesium

Current research continues to emphasize the importance of the interrelationship of calcium, phosphorus, and magnesium in the maintenance of skeletal tissues and in numerous metabolic processes. The body is constantly losing some of each nutritionally essential mineral element and it becomes necessary to replace the loss through diet, if health is to be maintained. For the adult, whose tissues are fully formed, it is only necessary to make good these losses; for the growing organism there must be an additional allowance for growth.

In order to administer the diet intelligently, we need to know as much as possible about the requirements for various mineral elements, in both childhood and adult life. For some elements, such as calcium, the amount needed daily is relatively large. And on this account there is possibility of serious shortage, unless food is chosen with discrimination; for others, such as iron, the portion needed day by day is very minute, but the quantities in food materials are also minute, and an intake below the optimum is likely to occur if the matter is left entirely to chance. Practically we shall find that if the requirements for calcium and iron are met, there is relatively little likelihood of the other mineral elements being inadequately furnished, since the foods that supply these elements along with adequate protein also provide the other essential mineral elements. However, in various areas where iodine is deficient in the soil, it needs to be given special consideration, as will be discussed in Chapter 11.

Calcium

SIGNIFICANCE IN NORMAL NUTRITION

Calcium has long been recognized as a major mineral constituent in body-building material, representing 1.5 to 2.0 per cent of the body weight in adults. Approximately 99 per cent of the calcium is found in the bones and teeth. The rigidity of the bony framework of the body is in real contrast to the softness of other tissue and is clearly related to the presence of calcium in the bone. The same is true with regard to the teeth. Not so readily apparent, but of great significance, is the part played by this element in the regulation of body processes. Some of the ways in which it functions have already been mentioned: viz., the control of the contractility of muscles, and particularly the rhythmical beat of the heart; the preservation of the normal response of nerve tissue to stimuli; and the coagulating power of the blood. In addition to these very important functions, calcium is a kind of coordinator among the mineral elements. "Calcium seems to play the role of the gatekeeper, its involvement with and probable attachment to cellular membranes in both animal and plant kingdom suggesting that it helps to regulate ion flux across the cell wall."[1]

In adults, the bones serve as a reservoir of calcium, which can be drawn upon to maintain the level of calcium in the blood with no immediate damage to the bone other than the weakening consequent to withdrawal of some of the supporting calcium phosphate. Bone trabeculae, which contain crystals of calcium compounds, grow from the inner surface of the ends of the bones toward the center of the cavity. This increases the area of bone salt material with which the blood comes in contact as it circulates through the vascular ends of the bones. That adult bone is a dynamic substance and is constantly undergoing reconstruction has been demonstrated by the use of radioactive calcium which makes it possible to trace the pathway of the element as it circulates through the body.

In the young, calcium is needed for the developing bones and teeth. Any deficiency in the calcium supply or any disturbance of the conditions under which the bone is able to store calcium, for example, an inadequate supply of vitamin D, may result in weakened bones, contracted thorax and pelvis, defective teeth, and otherwise stunted growth. Other factors that are known to interfere with the absorption of calcium from the intestinal tract include phytates, oxalates, and fatty acids occurring in certain foods. These substances form partly insoluble calcium complexes. Hypermotility of the intestinal tract may also decrease absorption. On the other hand, lactose and some of the amino acids favor absorption.

In his classic studies on rats, Sherman found that higher levels of calcium in the diet increased the length and density of the skeleton, delayed the onset of degenerative changes, and at the same time provided greater vigor and increased the life span of the rat. In human beings, according to the research of Ohlson and Stearns,[2] a higher calcium intake is generally associated with a greater body height.

---

[1] Comar, C. L., and Bronner, F. (eds). *Mineral Metabolism.* Vol. 2, part A, p. 342. New York: Academic (1964).

[2] Ohlson, M. A., and Stearns, G. "Calcium Intake of Children and Adults." *Federation Proc.*, 18:1076 (1959).

CALCIUM REQUIREMENT OF ADULTS

The calcium requirement has been studied for many years by taking account of the calcium in food, urine, and feces in carefully planned balance studies. The first extensive review was made by Sherman in 1920. The average of 97 experiments indicated that the calcium requirement of adults was about 0.5 gm of calcium per day. Since that time many studies have been published which call attention to a number of problems arising in the determination of the calcium requirement.

Calcium balance studies tend to reflect the previous dietary intake of calcium and to show intermittent fluctuations (losses and gains) of calcium. The utilization of the calcium of ingested food varies tremendously among individuals and may be related in part at least to the composition of the rest of the diet. All the studies show that there is a wide variation in the calcium requirement of adults.

The phenomenon of adaptation and the physiologic state of the individual must be considered in determining requirement. The individual is able to adjust to both high and low calcium intakes within certain limits. A lowering of calcium intake leads to immediate negative balance, but over a period of time more of the dietary calcium is absorbed from the intestine and less lost in the feces so that eventually an individual may establish a positive balance. In a similar way an individual can adjust to a higher level. Thus, it takes a long time to properly establish the calcium requirement by means of balance studies.

In 1963, the Food and Nutrition Board of the National Research Council reviewed the available studies on calcium requirement and reaffirmed the Recommended Daily Allowance of 800 mg for adults of different ages. Authorities do not agree on the optimum level of calcium in the diet, some giving greater emphasis to the ability of the body to adapt to lowered intakes, and others to the importance of higher levels, even above 800 mg, to compensate for losses in urine and sweat. A 1962 study by Consolazio indicated that the loss of calcium in sweat might be appreciable under certain conditions. It is estimated that the average loss for the reference adults might be about 20 mg. The total average calcium losses daily have been estimated at 320 mg. Assuming a 40 per cent absorption a total of 800 mg would be needed to maintain balance.

The calcium requirement of women is greatly increased by pregnancy and lactation. During pregnancy the mother must provide a store of calcium upon which the fetus draws for the development of its skeleton. The 1963 Recommended Daily Allowances for pregnancy include an additional allowance of 500 mg daily during the second and third trimesters. This allowance is intended to provide liberal levels of calcium for the growth of the fetus and is based on the extensive observations of Macy and co-workers, Coons, and others. It is desirable that every woman should continue to have a liberal supply of milk daily through the child-bearing period in order to provide the best calcification for her offspring as well as for her own protection. In cases where the previous diet has not followed a pattern of this kind the practice of taking a quart of milk daily should be started as early in the period of pregnancy as possible. The Food and Nutrition Board (1963) recommends the continuation of the additional 500 mg of calcium daily during the period of lactation.

In 1962, at a Nutrition Meeting in Rome,[3] the Food and Agriculture Organization considered calcium requirements in less developed countries and set a range of 400 to 500 mg as a "safe practical allowance" (see Appendix, Table A–9), in countries where food supplies are not abundant. The adaptation mechanism discussed earlier must be considered in setting a dietary guide for calcium intake for peoples who have been living on a relatively low intake of calcium.

Osteoporosis is the most common metabolic disorder of bone. Lutwak and Whedon estimate that there may be at least 4,000,000 cases of osteoporosis in older people in the United States. The incidence is from four to six times as high in women as in men.

Recent findings suggest a change in the concept of osteoporosis, placing more emphasis on nutritional factors in its etiology. Whedon believes that the significance of calcium intake has generally been disregarded in osteoporosis because the classic concept has been that the disease involved principally the protein matrix of the bone. New evidence has accumulated that calcium deficiency may be a causative factor. If an individual does not have an efficient adaptive mechanism to low calcium intake, calcium will be withdrawn from bone to make good urinary losses and maintain blood calcium levels. Whedon believes that, "Gradually bone resorption, at a rate greater than that of formation, may thus be the principal mechanism through which osteoporosis develops, probably over several decades."[4]

Data accumulated by Nordin in Glasgow, Scotland, suggest "that osteoporosis does not develop in the presence of a high calcium intake but if calcium intake is low, osteoporosis may or may not develop, presumably depending upon whether adaptation to the intake does or does not occur."[5] See Figure 10–1, which shows the relation of calcium intake and x-ray "scores." Lutwak and Whedon were able to obtain positive balance in patients by feeding high levels of calcium over a period of time. The intake at which positive balance was achieved varied considerably, and in most cases was greater than 800 mg per day. An increase in vitamin D intake sometimes improved absorption of calcium in these cases.

[3] FAO Nutrition Meeting Report Series No. 30. *Calcium Requirements.* Rome (1962).

[4] Council on Foods and Nutrition. "Symposium on Human Calcium Requirements," No. IV, Whedon, G. D., and Lutwak, L. *J. Amer. Med. A.,* **185:**588 (1963).

[5] Dallas, I., and Nordin, B. E. C. "The Relation Between Calcium Intake and Roentgenologic Osteoporosis." *Amer. J. Clin. Nutr.,* **11:**263 (1962).

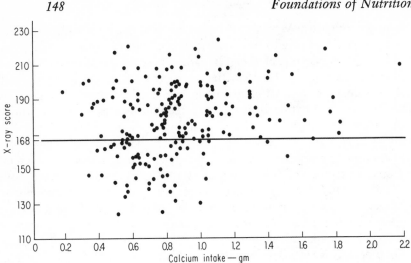

FIGURE 10–1. RELATION BETWEEN CALCIUM INTAKE AND X-RAY "SCORES." Values below the horizontal line represent abnormal scores. Note that most of the dots below the line represent lower intakes of calcium. (*Courtesy of I. Dallas and B. E. C. Nordin. "The Relation Between Calcium Intake and Roentgenologic Osteoporosis." Amer. J. Clin. Nutr., 11:266 [1962].*)

CALCIUM REQUIREMENT DURING GROWTH

In view of the constructive and regulatory functions of calcium, it is important that the growing organism be at all times liberally supplied with this element. The serious handicap of calcium shortage during the period of growth is readily demonstrated in experimental animals. The two rats in Figure 10–2 were of the same litter, weaned from a mother on a normal diet at the age of four weeks and then put, one on a diet inadequate in protein, the other on a diet lacking calcium. That the results of a deficiency of calcium are quite different from those of a shortage of protein is well exemplified by the comparison of these two animals. While both are stunted to the same degree, the low-protein diet permitted more growth of the skeleton and interfered less with health, so the animal on this diet is sleek and slim in contrast to the short, stocky rat on the diet lacking calcium.

The effect of the lack of calcium on the rate of growth will be best appreciated by comparing a calcium-deficient animal's weight record with that of one fed an adequate diet. In Figure 10–3, the animal on the normal diet weighed at the age of 14 weeks more than two and a half times as much as did his litter brother deprived of calcium. The animal on the diet lacking calcium was not only smaller and weaker than its brother on a normal diet, but its fur was rough and thin and it suffered from nasal hemorrhages in addition to severe skeletal deformities.

Such experiments impress upon us the importance of calcium for growth. During the period of growth a white rat, which will have multi-

Figure 10–2. Two Rats Placed at Four Weeks of Age on Restricted Diets and Photographed at the Age of 16 Weeks. The one on the left had only half enough protein; the one on the right was deficient in calcium. Both weighed the same (60 gm). The control (not shown) on an adequate diet weighed 216 gm at this time. Note the short, smooth fur and slender form of the low-protein rat, and the long, bushy fur and very short body of the calcium-deficient rat. (*Nutrition Laboratory, Teachers College, Columbia University.*)

plied its birth weight about 70 times when fully mature, will increase the calcium content of its body about 340 times.

A detailed study of the calcium requirement of children was made by Sherman and Hawley in 1922.[6] Altogether 417 experiments were conducted on 21 healthy children from 3 to 14 years of age. In one series, on three children, 4, 5, and 12 years of age respectively, extending over 48 days, the calcium was kept at different levels in successive periods by changing the amount of milk in the diet, in order to find the daily allowance of milk that would induce the best calcium storage. The relationship between the milk and the calcium storage is shown in Figure 10–4.

[6] Sherman, H. C., and Hawley, E. "Calcium and Phosphorus Metabolism in Childhood." *J. Biol. Chem.*, **53**:375 (1922).

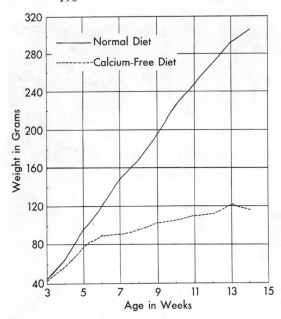

FIGURE 10–3. EFFECTS OF NORMAL AND CALCIUM-FREE DIETS. The upper line represents the growth record of a rat fed an adequate diet from weaning at the age of four weeks; the lower, that of a litter brother fed a diet lacking calcium.

Stearns and Jeans,[7] at the State University of Iowa, gave children, 4 to 12 years of age, diets in which the calcium was adjusted to be equivalent to that in either 1 pt or 1 qt of milk, and found as a rule considerably higher retentions with the larger calcium intake. They also noted that there was better retention when calcium and phosphorus were given together than when some source of calcium was used that did not furnish phosphorus, such as calcium carbonate. Here is seen additional evidence of the practical value of milk, in which these two elements are both well represented. Daniels and her associates[8] at the Iowa Child Welfare Research Station made a careful study of the calcium needs of preschool children. The choice of foods was such that the children receiving a pint of milk daily were getting about as much total calcium as those in the Sherman and Hawley study who received a pint and a half (750 ml) of milk. This was sufficient to give daily retentions of the same magnitude as in the Sherman and Hawley study, mostly between 9 and 12 mg per kilogram.

In summarizing studies bearing on calcium requirement and retention in children, Leitch and Aitken[9] state that there is an endogeneous loss

[7] Stearns, G., and Jeans, P. C. "Utilization of Calcium Salts by Children." *Proc. Soc. Exper. Biol. & Med.*, 32:428 (1934).

[8] Daniels, A. L., Hutton, M. K., Knott, E. M., Wright, O. E., and Forman, M. "Calcium and Phosphorus Needs of Preschool Children." *J. Nutr.*, 10:373 (1935).

[9] Leitch, I., and Aitken, F. C. "The Estimation of Calcium Requirement: A Reexamination." *Nutr. Abstr. & Rev.*, 29:393 (1959).

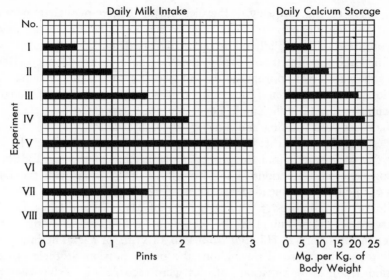

FIGURE 10–4. MILK INTAKE AND CALCIUM STORAGE. This chart shows a series of eight experiments of six days each in which the calcium intake was systematically varied from period to period by changes in the amount of milk. The very definite response to increased milk intake is shown in the above record of calcium storage of a 12-year-old girl.

during growth as well as a growth requirement. Estimates of total requirement are of the order of 250 mg daily in the first year decreasing to between 120 to 160 mg and then increasing again to almost 550 mg during the spurt of adolescent growth. Leitch and Aitken depended for their estimates not only on metabolic balance studies but on records of growth and calcium increment of British children, and also on isotope studies with radioactive calcium.

A recent method that has been developed for estimating calcium status is one used by Williams and Samson,[10] who made bone density measurements determined from x-rays of the little fingers of 32 students, 16 Indian and Pakistani subjects and 16 Americans. Wide variations among individuals were found but there was no correlation between density coefficients, and race, age, sex, weight, or height. The authors suggest that bone density experiments may be a suitable tool for answering problems of calcium requirement for normal growth as well as adult maintenance. In studies with children six to eight years of age Williams and others,[11] using a similar method, found that bone density increases slowly

[10] Williams, D. E., and Samson, A. "Bone Density of East Indian and American Students." *J. Amer. Dietet. A.*, **36**:462 (1960).

[11] Williams, D. E., McDonald, B. B., and Pyle, S. I. "Bone Density and Skeletal Maturation as Indexes of Mineral Status in Children." *Amer. J. Clin. Nutr.*, **14**:91 (1964).

depending on the adequacy of the diet and the degree of skeletal maturation. The body appears to adapt itself to a dietary inadequacy of almost
any nutrient during childhood by retarded growth and development.

The Food and Nutrition Board of the National Research Council (1963)
cites the paucity of appropriate data in assessing the calcium requirement
in infants and children. They state that a daily allowance of 800 mg
calcium should be sufficient to cover the needs estimated by Leitch and
Aitken between the first and ninth years of life. During periods of pre-
pubertal and pubertal growth, retentions of calcium as high as 400 mg
per day may be required for proper mineralization of the rapidly developing skeleton. Retentions of this magnitude are possible with the 1,400
mg of calcium recommended. See Tables A–1 and A–5.

Burke and associates at the Department of Maternal and Child Health,
Harvard School of Public Health, conducted a longitudinal study of the
calcium intake of 125 children from 1 to 18 years of age. The individual
children were followed throughout the major portion of their growth
period. In all 2,707 nutrition histories were recorded. In Table 10–1 the

TABLE 10–1. LONGITUDINAL STUDY OF CALCIUM INTAKE OF CHILDREN ACCORDING TO AGE* COMPARED WITH THE NATIONAL RESEARCH COUNCIL RECOMMENDATION, 1963

	Age Groups yr	Mean Calcium Intake gm per day		NRC Recommended Allowances 1963
		Boys	Girls	
Children	1–3	0.89	0.91	0.8
	3–6	0.97	0.98	0.8
	6–9	1.09	1.07	0.8
Boys	9–12	1.24	—	1.1
	12–15	1.46	—	1.4
	15–18	1.63	—	1.4
Girls	9–12	—	1.19	1.1
	12–15	—	1.21	1.3
	15–18	—	1.17	1.3

* Adapted from Burke, B. S., Reed, R. E., van den Berg, A. S., and Stuart, H. C. "A Longitudinal Study of the Calcium Intake of Children from One to Eighteen Years of Age." *Amer. J. Clin. Nutr.*, **10**: 79 (1962).

findings in regard to the average calcium intake have been grouped according to age and compared with the 1963 Recommendations of the
Food and Nutrition Board of the National Research Council. Wide variations of individual children with regard to age and sex were found. The

average values in all cases (grouped according to age) exceeded the National Research Council 1963 Recommendations except for the girls from 12 to 15 years and 15 to 18 years of age.

FOOD SOURCES OF CALCIUM

For the most part we are dependent on milk and milk products to supply us with calcium. One pint of milk daily for each adult and 2 to 3 cups for children one to nine years of age and 1 qt for older children will meet the daily recommended allowances for calcium. See Table 10–2 for a comparison of foods as sources of calcium.

TABLE 10–2. GRAMS OF FOOD YIELDING CALCIUM APPROXIMATELY EQUIVALENT TO THAT IN ONE CUP OF MILK*

Food	Grams	Food	Grams
Milk, whole	244	Beans, soya, dried	127
Milk, skim, fluid	238	Cheese, Cheddar	38
Milk, evaporated	114	Cheese, cottage, creamed	306
Milk, skim, dry	22	Cheese, Roquefort	91
Yogurt	240	Kale, cooked	238
Bean curd, soya	225		

*288 mg of calcium (based on values in Agriculture Handbook No. 8).

Cheeses are generally considered good sources of calcium but the different varieties vary greatly. See Appendix for calcium values of cheeses (Tables A–4 and A–8).

The availability of the calcium of a number of vegetables has been investigated. It seems safe to say that the calcium of carrots, almonds, kale, Chinese cabbage, cabbage, turnip greens, collards, rutabaga leaves, cauliflower, and broccoli is well utilized. That of spinach, beet greens, and sorrel, because of the oxalic acid present, is, for all practical purposes, not to be counted upon at all. Fruits in general are poor sources of calcium.

Since such a limited number of foods can be relied upon to furnish significant amounts of calcium, the sources of calcium in the diet must be selected with discretion. Certainly there is little danger of excessive intake of calcium from foods. The findings of various dietary surveys in the United States furnish evidence that calcium is likely to be deficient in diets unless adequate amounts of milk are used.

Many investigators have found that people in other lands utilize sources of calcium which we often overlook. In Formosa it was found that the diet of the natives had been reported to be very low in calcium although no evidence of calcium deficiency had been found during a thorough clinical investigation. A study of the foods brought out the interesting fact that millers in Formosa have a practice of adding what they call "stone powder" to the rice during the milling process. The "stone powder" is essentially calcium carbonate and is used to whiten the undermilled rice. This brings the calcium in the cooked rice to about 225 to 450 mg per pound. Since rice is the chief source of calories, a large portion of the calcium needed is obtained in this way.

The soybean and its many products commonly used in China furnish appreciable amounts of calcium. The tortillas used in Latin American countries are prepared from corn treated with lime and thus add more calcium to the diet than might be expected.

The practice of eating small fish including the bones helps to provide calcium in the diets of people in some of the Eastern countries as well as of the Eskimos in Alaska. In Japan it is reported that 8 per cent of the calcium comes from fish.

Sherman stated,

> In the Arctic and in parts of Asia and Africa much bone-calcium is utilized even without the intervention of cookery—by simple mastication of the smaller bones and the soft ends and interiors of the larger ones. Also, in the Orient and in parts of Africa much larger use is made of green leaf foods than in America, and in certain regions not only do the people eat many coarser kinds of leaves than we do, but of the leaves which are too coarse even for them to eat, they eat the ashes. Other previously overlooked sources of calcium are the turbid drinking-waters of some regions and the lime that is often added to the leaves and nuts that are habitually chewed in some parts of the world.[12]

Baker and Mazess[13] reported in 1963 important sources of calcium in the diet of Quechua Indians in the Peruvian Andes that had not been previously recognized and might be missed in diet surveys. Fine powdered ash from rock which contained calcium was eaten in porridge adding an appreciable amount of calcium. Also, a clay earth was used as a sauce for potatoes. Coca was chewed and ashes of stalks were used. In all, the intake of calcium might exceed the National Research Council Recommended Allowance.

Phosphorus

Phosphorus is indispensable for all active tissues of the body (both the skeletal and soft tissue), being involved in cell multiplication and cell movement and the maintenance of the proper liquid content of the

[12] Sherman, H. C. *Chemistry of Food and Nutrition*, 7th ed., p. 261. New York: Macmillan (1946).

[13] Baker, P. T., and Mazess, R. B., "Calcium: Unusual Sources in the Highland Peruvian Diet." *Science*, 142:1466 (1963).

tissues. Organic phosphorus compounds, such as phospholipids, proteins, and energy-transfer enzymes and coenzymes, for example, adenosine triphosphate (ATP), play a role in almost every aspect of metabolism. Depending on ATP-catalyzed reactions, the energy-yielding nutrients are oxidized and their energy liberated at just the rate demanded by the needs of the organism.

Because phosphorus is essential to all body tissues, the growth of new body substance involves the retention of a certain amount, just as it does a storage of protein. The greater part of the retained phosphorus is deposited in the bones along with calcium as calcium phosphate. If conditions during growth are not favorable for the deposition of calcium phosphate in the bones, we have the disease known as rickets, which will be discussed along with vitamin D in Chapter 15. One of the notable advances in the study of rickets was the observation that it is characterized by a low phosphorus content of the blood. After that it was demonstrated that rickets could be produced experimentally by feeding a diet low in phosphorus.

Sherman, in 1920, from consideration of extensive work in his own and other laboratories on the phosphorus requirement of adults, concluded that the adult needs daily an average of 0.88 gm per 70 kg of body weight. He recommended a 50 per cent margin as a "contingency fund" to allow for individual differences in utilization and fluctuation in the amounts found in food and suggested a dietary standard of 1.32 gm of phosphorus per man per day.

An extensive study of the phosphorus requirement of children was made by Sherman and Hawley in 1922. They took 12 children ranging in age from 3 to 13 years to a country home for convalescent mothers, where they could be supervised day and night, and kept account of all food eaten and of all excreta. Some of the children were under this close observation as long as 84 days. From analysis of the data so collected, the authors concluded that the child needs for optimum growth about 1 gm of phosphorus per day up to the age of 14 years. Many additional studies have been made since that time, and the results indicate that the phosphorus allowances should be at least equal to those for calcium in the diets of children.

The Food and Nutrition Board of the National Research Council (1963) suggests that the phosphorus intake should at least equal that of calcium during the period of growth in children and during the latter part of pregnancy and in lactation.

Phosphorus is so widely distributed that the intake of phosphorus in our daily foods usually exceeds that of calcium, except in the case of infants and small children, whose diets are mostly milk. Since it is now well established that a dietary of everyday foods which furnishes sufficient energy, protein, calcium, and iron can also be depended upon to furnish sufficient phosphorus, it is no longer considered necessary, under ordinary circumstances, to calculate the phosphorus.

Magnesium

The adult human body has been found to contain between 20 and 28 gm of magnesium and at least half of this is found in the skeletal tissue. Magnesium is like potassium in that it is an important mineral element in the intracellular fluid of the soft tissue. About 35 per cent of the magnesium present in the serum is apparently bound to protein. The concentration of magnesium in the body at birth is lower than in the adult but rises rapidly. Magnesium activates numerous, important enzymes which split and transfer phosphate groups.

It has long been assumed that because of the wide distribution of magnesium in plant and animal foods, there was little likelihood of an insufficient supply in any ordinary mixed diet. However, it is now appreciated that in a number of conditions a magnesium deficiency may occur. This has been observed principally in alcoholism, in infants with kwashiorkor, and in postsurgical patients on restricted diets.

Seelig,[14] in a 1964 review on the magnesium requirement of adults, postulates that long-term suboptimal intakes of magnesium may play a role in the pathogenesis of cardiovascular, renal, and neuromuscular abnormalities. Rats and dogs fed diets moderately deficient in magnesium exhibit renal lesions, and are more adversely affected by feeding with cholesterol and cholic acid. Primitive people such as the South African Bantu have lower serum cholesterol and higher serum magnesium levels than Europeans. The Europeans are more susceptible to atherosclerosis. However, no correlations between serum magnesium and serum cholesterol levels have been found in the United States.

Shils[15] studied two elderly male subjects who were fed a purified magnesium-deficient diet by tube. After 100 days of depletion one subject exhibited personality changes, gastrointestinal disturbances, gross tremor, and other neurological abnormalities. When magnesium salts were given, these symptoms reverted to normal. The second subject exhibited some neurological symptoms after 55 days. Serum calcium declined as magnesium depletion progressed, indicating an interrelationship between calcium and magnesium metabolism.

A lowering in the magnesium level of the serum in chronic alcoholics has been reported in several studies, particularly if delirium tremens was

[14] Seelig, M. S. "The Requirement of Magnesium by the Normal Adult. Summary and Analysis of Published Data." *Amer. J. Clin. Nutr.*, 14:342 (1964).

[15] Shils, M. E. "Experimental Human Magnesium Depletion. I. Clinical Observations and Blood Chemistry Alterations." *Amer. J. Clin. Nutr.*, 15:133 (1964).

present. Tetany comparable to that associated with low serum calcium has also been reported. Sullivan, Lankford, Swartz, and Farrell[16] investigated 50 alcoholic patients with acute symptoms. Thirty-three of the patients had low serum magnesium levels, and ten of these exhibited delirium tremens, convulsions, stupor, and psychosis. The acute neurological abnormalities were associated with the lowest serum magnesium levels. A marked inability of the kidney to conserve magnesium was demonstrated in some of the alcoholic patients. Flink,[17] in a study of 44 alcoholic patients with delirium tremens, observed the effect of magnesium sulfate therapy. One of the most striking examples of improvement with therapy is shown in the changes in the patient's ability to write. See Figure 10–5, illustrating the writing of one patient receiving therapy.

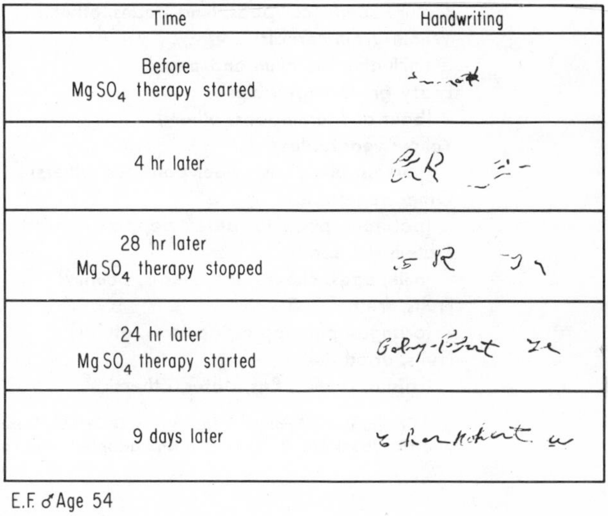

FIGURE 10–5. THE RELATION BETWEEN MAGNESIUM INTAKE AND HANDWRITING IN A PATIENT WITH DELIRIUM TREMENS. Handwriting indicates the patient's degree of tremor and ability to cooperate. (*Courtesy of Dr. E. B. Flink, West Virginia University Medical Center. From the Council on Foods and Nutrition Section, A.M.A. Symposium on "Some Inorganic Elements in Human Nutrition" p. 68 [May 1963] and J. Amer. Med. A., p. 1408 [April 21, 1956].*)

Time	Handwriting
Before Mg SO$_4$ therapy started	
4 hr later	
28 hr later Mg SO$_4$ therapy stopped	
24 hr later Mg SO$_4$ therapy started	
9 days later	

E.F. ♂ Age 54

It has been estimated on the basis of balance techniques that the magnesium requirement of the adult man is between 200 and 300 mg per day. Since the body has a considerable reservoir of magnesium, the depletion of adults is a relatively slow process.[18]

Schofield and Morrell,[19] in studies of girls seven to nine years of age, found them to be in magnesium balance with intakes of 120 to 230 mg

[16] Sullivan, J. F., Lankford, H. G., Swartz, M. J., and Farrell, C. "Magnesium Metabolism in Alcoholism." *Amer. J. Clin. Nutr.*, **13**:297 (1963).

[17] Flink, E. B. "Magnesium Deficiency Syndrome in Man." *J. Amer. Med. A.*, **160**:1406 (1956).

[18] Food and Nutrition Board. *Recommended Dietary Allowances.* Washington, D.C.: National Research Council, Publication 1146 (1964).

[19] Schofield, F. A., and Morrell, E. "Calcium, Phosphorus, and Magnesium." *Federation Proc..* **19**:1014 (1960).

per day. They showed retentions between 10 to 16 mg with no relation to intake.

Magnesium has been recognized as an essential element in nutrition for about 30 years but it is only recently that data on the magnesium content of foods have been available. Tentative data on magnesium have been compiled from Table 5, Agriculture Handbook No. 8 in Table 10–3.

TABLE 10–3. APPROXIMATE MAGNESIUM CONTENT OF FOODS*

Food Groups	Milligrams per 100 gm (approximate range)
Nuts (peanuts, almonds, cashews, others)	200–300
Mature seeds (cowpeas, lima beans, others)	175–250
Whole-grain cereals (including the bran and germ)	150–300
Leafy green vegetables (beet and turnip tops, others)	40–100
Yellow vegetables (carrots, pumpkins, sweet potatoes, others)	15–30
Other vegetables (potatoes, peas, tomatoes, peppers, others)	15–30
Protein-rich foods (milk, eggs, cheese, fish, meats, poultry)	10–40
Fruits, fresh (oranges, pineapples, apricots, others)	10–15
Fruits, dried (raisins, prunes, figs, dates, others)	30–70

* *Composition of Foods.* Washington, D.C.: U.S. Department of Agriculture, Agriculture Handbook No. 8. Compiled and adapted from Table 5, p. 147 (1963).

REFERENCES

Fisher, K. H., and Dodds, M. L. "Calcium Intake of Adolescents and Young Adults." *J. Amer. Dietetic. A.*, **34**:392 (1958).

Food and Nutrition Board. *Recommended Dietary Allowances.* Washington, D.C.: National Research Council, Publication 1146 (1964).

Lutwak, L. "Osteoporosis—A Mineral Deficiency Disease?" *J. Amer. Dietet. A.*, **44**:173 (1964).

Review. "Calcium Metabolism in Osteoporosis." *Nutr. Rev.*, **19**:269 (1961).

Sherman, H. C. "Calcium in the Chemistry of Food and Nutrition." *Nutr. Rev.*, **10**:97 (1952).

———. *Calcium and Phosphorus in Foods and Nutrition.* New York: Columbia U. P. (1947).

———. *Chemistry of Food and Nutrition*, 8th ed., Chap. 14. New York: Macmillan (1952).

Stearns, G. "Human Requirement of Calcium, Phosphorus, and Magnesium." *Handbook of Nutrition*, 2nd ed., Chap. 4. Chicago: American Medical Association (1951).

Thorangkul, D., Johnston, F. A., Kime, N. S., and Clark, S. J. "Adaptation to a Low Calcium Intake." *J. Amer. Dietet. A.*, **35**:23 (1959).

U.S. Department of Agriculture. *Food—The Yearbook of Agriculture 1959*. "Calcium and Phosphorus" by Hathaway, M. L., and Leverton, R. M., p. 112 (1959).

———. *Magnesium in Human Nutrition*. Home Economics Research Report No. 19 (1962).

❧ 11 ❧

Iron, Copper, Cobalt, Iodine, and Other Trace Elements

Iron

The therapeutic value of iron was recognized in prehistoric times but it was not until the eighteenth century that it was discovered to be a constituent of the blood. In 1838, the Swedish chemist Berzelius showed that the red coloring matter of blood was capable of absorbing much oxygen and concluded that this was due to the iron in this pigment. We now know that we have in the adult human body about 25 million times a million red blood corpuscles, owing their color to the iron-bearing protein, hemoglobin, and through its agency the red blood corpuscles transport oxygen through all the intricacies of arteries and capillaries to the innermost cells of every organ and tissue.

In 1889, Bunge reported the case of a young man who developed anemia on a diet of milk only. He also found that mice so fed became anemic, and that although the obvious explanation was the small amount of iron present in milk, the cure was not so simple, inasmuch as the addition of a pure iron salt had but little effect. Since much better results were obtained with egg yolk, Bunge concluded that the difference was due to the peculiar chemical union of the iron with protein in the egg yolk. A few years later Abderhalden,[1] in a critical review of the work of Bunge and others, summarized the knowledge of that period as follows: "The mere fact that the addition of iron to nutriment poor in iron does not have any distinct influence upon the formation of hemoglobin, in no way speaks against the participation of inorganic iron in the synthesis of hemoglobin in the case of normal nutrition, but it indicates that other building material is wanting as well as iron."

For many years the controversy as to the relative value of organic and inorganic iron continued, and it was not until 1927 that it was clearly

---

[1] Abderhalden, E. Textbook of Physiological Chemistry, translated by Hall, p. 398. New York: Wiley (1908).

demonstrated that inorganic iron could be used to form hemoglobin if adequate quantities of copper were also present.

SIGNIFICANCE IN NORMAL NUTRITION

We find iron not only in the hemoglobin of the red blood corpuscles and in the myoglobin of the muscle cells but also in cytochromes and other enzyme systems which are essential for the vital processes of cellular respiration and oxygen transport. Iron has significance out of all proportion to the amount in the body—between 3 and 5 gm. Approximately 75 per cent of this iron is found in the hemoglobin and myoglobin, 16 per cent in the tissues stored as ferritin and hemosiderin, and the rest as transport iron or in enzymes. The intracellular deposits of ferritin and hemosiderin are found in the liver, bone marrow, and spleen.

In 1937, Laufberger, a French scientist, isolated crystalline ferritin from horse spleen. This protein substance was found to contain 23 per cent (dry weight) of iron and has as one of its chief functions that of storage of iron in the liver. This substance furnishes a readily available source of iron which can be mobilized as needed for hemoglobin synthesis. Studies on dogs in which radioactive iron was injected intravenously showed that 80 per cent of the iron administered was recovered in the form of ferritin in the liver.

Early studies on iron absorption using inorganic iron salts showed that ferrous iron was more readily absorbed by human beings than ferric. However, dogs are able to absorb either ferrous or ferric iron equally well. With the advent of radioactive methods our knowledge of iron absorption has been expanded.

Moore, at Washington University School of Medicine, was one of the first to study iron absorption using radioactive iron. He studied the effect of tracer doses on a number of normal individuals for a total of 360 days and found no large excretion of iron from the intestinal tract at any time.

Individuals show considerable variation in the rate of absorption of iron. Differences in age, the extent of iron storage in the body, and the form in which the iron is ingested affect the rate of absorption. During periods of growth or pregnancy the rate of iron absorption is increased. Also, when there is a depletion of iron reserves, as in bleeding, there is an increase in absorption.

Radioactive studies have shown that approximately 10 per cent of the iron in food is absorbed in the normal adult but a slightly higher percentage is absorbed by infants and young children. Iron is absorbed in the small intestine.

Absorption of iron from foods can be increased with the addition of ascorbic acid and influenced unfavorably by the presence of phytates and phosphates in foods. Other factors involved in the absorption and metabolism of iron will be discussed in the sections to follow.

Ferritin also plays a role in the absorption of iron by the mucosa of the intestinal tract. According to a controversial theory of Granick, the mucosa cells apparently contain a protein (apoferritin) that combines with the iron released from the chyme (digested food) in the small intestine, forming ferritin. The iron from the ferritin passes into the blood stream if the blood serum level is low, but if the blood serum level is not sufficiently low, no iron is absorbed from the intestinal tract. This has been described as the "shutter" mechanism of iron absorption.

There are many unsolved problems in connection with the metabolism of iron, and the mechanisms involved need to be further elucidated by research. A discussion of the relationship of iron and copper will be found in the section on copper in this chapter.

IRON REQUIREMENTS OF ADULTS

Early studies of iron requirement involved skill in the use of tedious analytical techniques and covered long periods of observation. The iron in the food ingested by the subjects was compared with that excreted. In 1935 an unusually long study of the iron requirement of adult men was reported by Farrar and Goldhamer[2] of the University of Michigan. One man lived for 316 days on a practically uniform diet, consisting of milk, cream, bread, butter, jelly, shredded wheat, canned grapefruit, and distilled water, and during the last month of this regime maintained iron balance on 5.2 mg of iron daily.

Other investigators using similar techniques have reported iron requirements ranging from 3.7 to 11 mg. From consideration of the data available at the end of the year 1940, Sherman[3] concluded that the average requirement is about 8 mg per day. In 1941, Leverton[4] reported a study on four young women who maintained iron balance on intakes of about 7 mg, while Houghton,[5] in 1942, obtained iron balance in two women on an average intake of just over 4 mg. Moore concluded, as a result of his long-time studies on normal individuals using radioactive iron, that the normal male requires less than 10 mg per day to remain in balance.

It is important that there should be a good margin of safety in a recommended dietary allowance for iron. One reason for a generous surplus is that many minor disturbances in the body cause loss of iron and there are no large reserves to draw upon. Infections, however mild, are a common cause of iron loss, and the individual taking just enough

[2] Farrar, G. E., and Goldhamer, S. M. "The Iron Requirement of the Normal Human Adult." *J. Nutr.*, **10**:241 (1935).

[3] Sherman, H. C. *Chemistry of Food and Nutrition*, 6th ed., p. 288. New York: Macmillan (1941).

[4] Leverton, R. M. "Iron Metabolism in Human Subjects on Daily Intakes of Less Than Five Milligrams." *J. Nutr.*, **21**:617 (1941).

[5] Houghton, D. "The Utilization of Iron from Foods Studied by Two Methods." Dissertation, Columbia University (1942).

to maintain equilibrium may, as Minot,[6] one of the recipients of the Nobel Prize for his work on pernicious anemia, said, "be precipitated into the zone of partial deficiency by the advent of infection." Recent studies emphasize the measurable losses of iron through the skin in perspiration, the hair, the fingernails, and the toenails.

Losses of iron in menstruation have been determined by Leverton and Roberts[7] in a long, well-controlled study of four young college women. They found losses averaging 1.7 to 3.4 mg per day. Moore, on the basis of his studies with radioactive iron, estimated the average menstrual loss to be in the neighborhood of 1 mg per day. He suggested that to compensate for this loss a woman needs to take between 15 and 20 mg of iron per day. According to the Food and Nutrition Board of the National Research Council (1963), ". . . balance studies support the view that equilibrium is maintained on daily intakes of 7 to 11 milligrams of iron in young adult women. The allowance of 15 milligrams daily for adult females is recommended."

A diet which covers the losses of menstruation will go far toward meeting the needs during the early months of pregnancy, because what was formerly lost will be available for the fetus. However, there must be iron not only for its normal development, but to enable it to accumulate a reserve for use during the first few months of life. And there is frequently in pregnancy a decreased secretion of acid in the stomach, which tends to interfere with iron absorption. It has been noted often that many women in the later weeks of pregnancy have a low blood hemoglobin. Some light is thrown on the capacity of the mother to store iron by a study by Coons,[8] at the Oklahoma Agricultural Experiment Station. For 101 days the same diet was eaten, and for 82 days the food was weighed and collections of excreta made. The diet furnished from 18 to 20 mg of iron per day, and storage amounted to from 2 to 6 mg. When wheat germ or wheat germ ash was added to raise the iron intake to 24 to 28 mg, the storage increased, approximating 7 to 9 mg as a rule, but in two different periods it rose to about 11 mg. This study seems to indicate that 20 mg or more per day can be profitably used by pregnant women in the latter half of pregnancy when fetal growth and fetal storage are approaching their maximum. Hahn and associates in 1951 also found that additional iron was of greater importance in the last half of pregnancy. A safe iron allowance for pregnancy and also for lactation would seem to be not less than 20 mg per day, which is the allowance recom-

[6] Minot, G. R. "The Anemias of Nutritional Deficiency." *J. Amer. Med. A.,* **105**:1177 (1935).

[7] Leverton, R. M., and Roberts, L. J. "The Iron Metabolism of Normal Young Women During Consecutive Menstrual Cycles." *J. Nutr.,* **13**:65 (1937).

[8] Coons, C. M. "Some Effects of Cod Liver Oil and Wheat Germ on the Retention of Iron, Nitrogen, Phosphorus, Calcium, and Magnesium During Human Pregnancy." *J. Nutr.,* **10**:289 (1935).

mended by the Food and Nutrition Board of the National Research Council (1963).

Studies of the Bantu in South Africa have shown conclusively that large excesses of iron over long periods of time are undesirable. The Bantu brew their Kaffir beer and cook their food in iron pots and as a result may ingest from 100 to 200 mg daily. This is far in excess of the amount that the body can excrete, and it gradually accumulates in the tissues of the liver, spleen, and pancreas, and eventually in the heart muscle as hemosiderin. This excess of iron precipitates cirrhosis of the liver, diabetes, and heart damage. Among the Bantu, the first signs of the disorders appear in adolescence, and by the ages of 40 to 50 become a serious problem. Undoubtedly other nutritional factors play a role in the development of these conditions, but at the present time the complexity of the factors makes differentiation difficult.

IRON REQUIREMENT OF CHILDREN

The baby comes into the world bearing in its body a special store of iron which serves as a reserve during the early period of life. The percentage in the infant's body at birth is about three times that in the adult's. This store has been regarded as sufficient to compensate for the low iron content of mother's milk through the first few months of life. Many recent studies have shown that, especially with the artificially fed baby, a higher level of hemoglobin is maintained if some special source of iron, such as egg yolk, a special cereal reinforced with iron, or a simple iron salt, is introduced into the diet as early as the third or fourth month. A slight anemia in infants and young children, formerly regarded as unimportant, may slightly retard growth and make the infant more susceptible to infection. When this is coupled with the fact that infection causes a considerable loss of iron, it is easy to see how a liberal intake of iron becomes a real safeguard of health. A notable study of the influence of anemia on infants was made by Mackay[9] in London. During a five-year period over 1,000 babies under her observation were brought by mothers to the clinics of the Queen's Hospital for Children. She found that at five months of age only 10 per cent of the artificially fed and 16 per cent of the breast-fed reached a hemoglobin level of 11 gm per 100 ml, which she considered normal, although according to Elvehjem, Siemers, and Mendenhall,[10] the normal content of the blood of infants between the ages of three months and one year should be between 12 and 13.5 gm. In babies of 12 and 13 months of age Mackay found that 30 per cent of the artifi-

[9] Mackay, H. M. M. *Nutritional Anemia in Infancy with Special Reference to Iron Deficiency.* London: Medical Research Council of Great Britain, Special Report Series No. 157 (1931).

[10] Elvehjem, C. A., Siemers, A., and Mendenhall, D. R. "Effects of Iron and Copper Therapy on the Hemoglobin Content of the Blood of Infants." *Amer. J. Dis. Child.,* **50**:28 (1935).

cially fed and 58 per cent of the breast-fed had reached the level of 11 gm per 100 ml. The infants with the low hemoglobin levels were not suffering from any specific disease, but nevertheless the improvement with iron treatment was marked.

An investigation to discover the best conditions for iron storage in infants was conducted by Stearns and Stinger,[11] who found that at least 0.5 mg per kilogram is necessary to secure any retention, but that it was more regular and considerably greater when from 1.0 to 1.5 mg per kilogram was given, whether the source of iron was eggs, an iron-enriched cereal, or a simple iron salt.

Beal, Meyers, and McCammon, in a study of 28 boys and 31 girls, found that the actual iron intake of infants was about 4 mg daily at the third month of life and reached a maximum of 9 mg at the seventh month. About two thirds of the dietary iron was supplied by commercial baby cereals fortified with iron.[12]

The Food and Nutrition Board of the National Research Council, assuming 10 per cent absorption of iron in infants, recommends for the period of 3 to 12 months an allowance of 8 mg per day or 1.0 mg per kilogram as adequate (1963).

Up to 1930 there had been no effort to determine the iron requirements of the nursery school child. In that year Rose, Vahlteich, Robb, and Bloomfield made a beginning at Columbia University with a study of a two-and-one-half-year-old girl. In 1934 Daniels and Wright,[13] at the Iowa Child Welfare Research Station, made 15 balance experiments on eight children three to six years old; the next year Ascham,[14] at the Georgia Agricultural Experiment Station, reported a study on six children three to six years old; and in 1941, Porter,[15] at Michigan State University, published the results obtained in a study of two three-year-old and two five-year-old children. In these studies totaling 19 children two and one-half to six years of age, there was equilibrium but little or no storage when the iron intake lay between 0.40 and 0.55 mg per kilogram. Significant storage occurred on 0.60 mg per kilogram, but retention was considerably higher when the diet furnished 0.65 to 0.75 mg per kilogram.

These findings are in line with the studies of Rose and Borgeson[16] on a group of 60 nursery school children under observation continually from

[11] Stearns, G., and Stinger, D. "Iron Retention in Infancy." *J. Nutr.*, **13**:127 (1937).

[12] Beal, V. A., Meyers, A. J., and McCammon, R. W. "Iron Intake, Hemoglobin, and Physical Growth During the First Two Years of Life." *Pediat.*, **30**:518 (1962).

[13] Daniels, A. L., and Wright, O. E. "Iron and Copper Retentions in Young Children." *J. Nutr.*, **8**:125 (1934).

[14] Ascham, L. "A Study of Iron Metabolism with Preschool Children." *J. Nutr.* **10**:337 (1935).

[15] Porter, T. "Iron Balances on Four Normal Pre-school Children." *J. Nutr.*, **21**:101 (1941).

[16] Rose, M. S., and Borgeson, G. M. *Child Nutrition on a Low-Priced Diet*. Child Development Monographs No. 17, Bureau of Publications, Teachers College, Columbia University (1935).

6 to 21 months, on a simple, inexpensive diet in which two thirds of the total calories came from milk and cereals and one fifth from fruits and vegetables. One half of the children had an egg added to their diet daily. While the difference in the iron intakes was small, a larger proportion of the children having the eggs had a distinctly better hemoglobin record.

A good deal of our knowledge of iron requirements of older children comes from dietary studies of normal, well-nourished subjects. Koehne and Morell in their studies of girls 6 to 13 years old estimated the iron (in weighed food) over a long time as from 0.37 to 0.53 mg per kilogram. Hemoglobin tests showed that the girls were not anemic. Wait and Roberts found the intake for girls 10 to 16 years of age to range from 0.35 mg per kilogram at ten years to 0.18 at 16 years. Darby and his associates[17] studied the iron absorption in schoolchildren seven to ten years of age. They found the daily intake of iron from dietary records to be about 12 mg. When they fed 2- or 3-mg doses of the radioactive iron, they found 10 to 16 per cent of it in the circulating blood cells. The increased absorption was attributed to the needs for growth. In recent studies Coons and Moyer[18] found that a daily intake of 10 to 11 mg iron provided adequate retention for seven to nine-year-old girls.

Based on their evaluation of all the available data on children, the Food and Nutrition Board of the National Research Council (1963) recommended the daily allowances for different ages as follows: one to nine years, 8 to 12 mg, and 9 to 18 years, 15 mg. See Tables A–1, A–5, and A–7 in the Appendix.

THE ANEMIAS

Many types of anemia are recognized by the medical profession. Of these there are three of special concern to the nutrition student—nutritional or iron-deficiency anemia, pernicious anemia, and hemorrhagic anemia.

Iron-deficiency anemia, commonly called hypochromic anemia, is characterized by a low hemoglobin level. Infants under six months of age may develop this type of anemia unless, as explained earlier in this chapter, the milk diet is supplemented by the third or fourth month with food of high iron value. Infants and children need iron to increase their blood volume, and as Moore[19] suggested, they undoubtedly maintain only a slightly positive iron balance during their period of most active growth.

[17] Darby, W. J., Hahn, P. F., Kaser, M. M., Steinkamp, R. C., Densen, P. M., and Cook, M. B. "The Absorption of Radioactive Iron by Children 7 to 10 Years of Age." *J. Nutr.*, 33:107 (1947).

[18] Coons, C. M., and Moyer, E. Z. "Minor Minerals and B-Vitamins." *Federation Proc.*, 19:1017 (1960).

[19] Moore, C. V. "The Importance of Nutritional Factors in the Pathogenesis of Iron-Deficiency Anemia." *Amer. J. Clin. Nutr.*, 3:3 (1955).

In the report on nutritional status summarized by Morgan[20] the prevalence of lowered hemoglobins in adolescents was noted when less than the recommended allowance of iron was consumed. The iron balance of the young woman through the period of menstruation and childbearing is precarious, and unless the diet is properly safeguarded, an iron-deficiency anemia may develop. A poor diet continued over a period of years or poor absorption may lead eventually to a hypochromic anemia even with normal menstruation. Women between 30 and 50 years of age are most likely to develop this type of anemia which will respond favorably to liberal intakes of iron. Ascorbic acid has been found to increase assimilation of food iron more effectively in cases of iron deficiency than in normal individuals. Adult men and postmenopausal women are less likely to develop a nutritional iron deficiency. Gastrointestinal disturbances, such as diarrhea, deficient gastric secretion, and intestinal disease will interfere with the absorption of iron even though it is present in the food. Iron losses may occur in the presence of intestinal parasites, such as hookworm. In tropical areas the iron loss due to hookworm is appreciable.[21] Iron-deficiency anemia may cause striking alterations in the fingernails with a loss of luster and a flattened or concave appearance, spoken of as "spoon nails" (see Figure 11-1). Also, the skin may become dry and somewhat wrinkled.

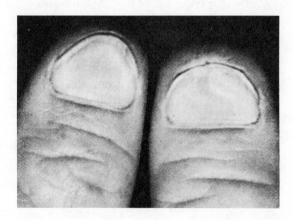

FIGURE 11-1. NAILS OF A WOMAN WITH IRON DEFICIENCY. (*Courtesy of Dr. R. E. Stone, Northwestern University. T. D. Spies. "Some Recent Advances in Nutrition."* J. Amer. Med. A., **167**:*678* [*1958*].)

Pernicious anemia is characterized by a deficiency of the formation of the red blood cells. Because of the prevalence of large cells it is often called *macrocytic* anemia. The hemoglobin is relatively abundant. In 1927 Minot and Murphy announced that the feeding of whole liver was effective in bringing about a remission in pernicious anemia, and Castle demon-

---

[20] Morgan, A. F. (ed.). *Nutritional Status, U.S.A.* Berkeley: California Agricultural Experiment Station Bulletin 769, p. 34 (1959).
[21] Notes. "Iron Loss from Hookworm Infection". *Nutr. Rev.*, **20**:127 (1962).

strated that mixtures of beef muscle and normal human gastric juice would also produce remissions similar to those of liver feeding. Two factors were found to be involved: (1) an intrinsic factor in gastric juice, and (2) an extrinsic factor in foods. Years of research finally led to the discovery of vitamin B_{12} and its effectiveness in pernicious anemia. It is now recognized that pernicious-anemia patients do not produce the intrinsic factor and consequently suffer from impaired absorption of the extrinsic factor, vitamin B_{12}.[22] Subsequently it was shown that folic acid is also requisite for synthesis of hemoglobin. Pernicious anemia and several other varieties of macrocytic and megaloblastic anemias are related to deficient supplies or availability of these two vitamins. This will be discussed further in Chapter 18.

Hemorrhagic anemia results from the loss of a large quantity of blood and can be cured by providing the nutrients necessary to make good the blood loss. In this process liver has been found to be especially effective, and meat in general better than spinach or other vegetables. Whipple and Robscheit-Robbins, in testing various foods for their effectiveness in the cure of anemia induced by bleeding, found the following especially valuable: chicken liver and gizzard, beef liver and kidney, eggs, apricots, and raisins. All of these were superior to spinach, asparagus, and muscle meats.

Moore called attention to the iron requirement of the blood donor. The donation in one year of 500 ml of blood (containing 200 to 250 mg of iron) just about doubles one's iron requirement. The diet of a blood donor should include the foods found effective in the cure of hemorrhagic anemia.[23] In cases where one gives as many as five donations in a year, which is common, there is serious danger of an iron deficiency unless the diet is supplemented with iron salts. The food iron, which is not completely absorbed, is not adequate when the need is so great.

FOODS AS SOURCES OF IRON

Many experiments were undertaken to study the hemoglobin-producing values of food in rats made anemic by milk feeding. The results with whole wheat and oats indicate that the iron of cereals can be efficiently used. Since these foods are very inexpensive sources of iron, even the cheapest diet need not be inadequate in iron. Pye[24] studied the effect of different foods on hemoglobin formation and iron retention in normal rats and found that the iron of whole-wheat flour was about equal in availability to that of ferric chloride. The iron of beef liver gave almost

[22] Review. "Metabolism of Vitamin B_{12} in Pernicious Anemia." *Nutr. Rev.,* **13**: 136 (1955).

[23] McKibbin, J. M., and Stare, F. J. "Nutrition in Blood Regeneration." *J. Amer. Dietet. A.,* **19**:331 (1943); Turner, D. F. "Dietary Recommendations for Blood Donors." *J. Amer. Dietet. A.,* **19**:336 (1943).

[24] Pye, O. F. "The Utilization of Iron from Different Foods by Normal Young Rats." Dissertation, Columbia University (1944).

as good results, and the other foods studied, namely, beef muscle, egg yolk, kale (cooked and uncooked), and spinach (cooked and uncooked), were not quite as satisfactory.

A comparison of the availability of the iron of egg and of wheat bran in a balance experiment on two women, when the amount of iron in the diet was barely sufficient to meet daily requirement, showed equally good utilization of both.[25]

Moore and Dubach,[26] at Washington University in Missouri, studied the absorption of iron from foods in healthy adult subjects by incorporating radioactive iron into the foods. They found that 14 of the 16 subjects absorbed less than 10 per cent of the iron present in eggs, chicken muscle, chicken and rabbit liver, mustard greens, and spinach. This emphasizes the need for generous portions of these foods in our daily diets since they are among the best sources of iron. Further studies need to be made of the effects of mixtures of foods on human subjects. Tables A-4 and A-8 in the Appendix give the approximate iron content of many foods, and Figure 11-2 shows portions of some common foods that yield approximately the same amounts of iron.

Copper

The presence of copper in plants was first recognized in 1816, and about 30 years later a relationship between the copper in plants and the soil in which they were grown was suggested by Deschamps. However, it required another century for its significance in animal nutrition to be clearly established.

Hart, of the University of Wisconsin, and his associates started an extensive investigation in 1924 of the factors influencing hemoglobin formation. It had been recognized by earlier workers that some factor or factors in addition to iron were needed by the rabbit for the synthesis of hemoglobin. It was found that when the ash of lettuce or dried cabbage was fed to an anemic rabbit the nutritional anemia was cured as effectively as when unashed greens were fed. This made it clear that the factor concerned must be inorganic in nature. The pale blue color often noted in some of the ash samples was suggestive of copper salts. The rabbit had been found to be not a wholly satisfactory experimental animal, partly because of its size, and consequently Steenbock, Waddell, Elvehjem, and other workers in the laboratory decided to try the effect of adding copper sulfate in addition to iron to the diet of a single rat which had been made

[25] Vahlteich, E. McC., Funnell, E. H., MacLeod, G., and Rose, M. S. "Egg Yolk and Bran as Sources of Iron in the Human Dietary." *J. Amer. Dietet. A.,* 11:331 (1935).

[26] Moore, C. V., and Dubach, R. "Observations on the Absorption of Iron from Foods Tagged with Radioactive Iron." *Trans. A. Amer. Physicians,* 64:245 (1951).

FIGURE 11–2. FOOD PORTIONS YIELDING APPROXIMATELY EQUIVALENT AMOUNTS OF IRON.*

	Gm		Gm
Lettuce, loose leaf	24	Egg	15
Spinach	11	Bread, whole wheat	15
Cabbage	85	Raisins	10
Tomato	68	Beans, dried	4
Onions	68	Beef, lean	11
Prunes, A.P.	10	Oats, rolled	8
Peas, fresh	18		

* 0.34 mg of iron (based on values in Agriculture Handbook No. 8).

anemic on a milk diet. The hemoglobin response was striking. Similar treatment was tried on other animals, all of which responded in the same way. It was concluded that copper was apparently a contaminant of practically all laboratory iron preparations, and trace amounts of it occurred in most natural food products, for example, dried liver, dried kidney, dried muscle tissue, wheat, and corn. Even as small an amount of copper as 1 μg (microgram) per rat per day gave a measurable response.

That copper alone could play such an important role in animal nutrition was still doubted by Hart[27] and his associates. It was not until they had carried out additional studies using salts of such elements as zinc, cobalt, nickel, germanium, arsenic, manganese, and others that they were finally

[27] Hart, E. B., Steenbock, H., Waddell, J., and Elvehjem, C. A. "Iron in Nutrition. VII. Copper as a Supplement to Iron for Hemoglobin Building in the Rat." *J. Biol. Chem.*, **77**:806 (1928).

convinced that copper alone was effective in the synthesis of hemoglobin and could not be replaced by any other mineral element. Thus, the role of copper in the synthesis of hemoglobin was clearly established.

Studies reported in 1961 showed that a deficiency of copper in the diet of experimental animals leads to a number of abnormalities besides anemia. Defects in bone formation, degeneration of the nervous system, reproductive failure, and changes in the pigmentation and texture of the hair or wool were reported.

Human milk is higher in copper than cow's milk, and it is not likely that a breast-fed infant would suffer from a copper deficiency. Since copper is widely distributed in other foods that are used to supplement the infant's diet, the infant on a cow's milk formula will in all probability be protected against a copper deficiency. It is improbable that a copper deficiency would be a factor in anemia occurring in older children and adults since a diet of even mediocre quality would undoubtedly supply adequate copper. The Food and Nutrition Board of the National Research Council (1963) states that about 2 mg of copper daily in the diet of the adult will meet the requirement. Ordinary mixed diets provide from 2 to 5 mg daily.

Copper has been found to be essential for certain body enzymes. It has also been found to influence the actual absorption of iron when the differences are measured by using radioactive iron instead of inert iron, a technique of extreme sensitiveness. Certain other trace elements, such as molybdenum and zinc, have been found to interfere with the normal utilization of copper. Recent research carried out in Australia shows that the effect of molybdenum on copper metabolism is related to the amount of sulfur in the diet.

Concentrations of from 75 to 150 mg of copper have been reported in the adult human body. The highest concentration was found in the liver, kidney, heart, and brain. The foods known to have the highest amounts of copper in addition to liver and kidney are shellfish, nuts, raisins, and dried legumes. The reader, if interested, may refer to other food sources.[28]

Cobalt

Cobalt was found to be essential in animal nutrition through the investigation of a condition known as coast disease occurring in sheep and cattle. In different localities the same condition was known by other names, bush sickness, pine disease, lakeshore disease, or simply wasting disease. The animals became emaciated, extremely listless, and progressively anemic, and developed a roughness of hair, a scaly condition of the skin, and severe muscular atrophy. This condition was first described in

[28] For a list of common foods as sources of copper see Taylor and MacLeod. *Rose's Laboratory Handbook for Dietetics*, 5th ed. p. 265. New York: Macmillan (1949).

1909 by the Michigan Agricultural Experiment Station, but it was not until 1935–36 that it was shown in Australia and New Zealand to be caused by pasturing on soils low in cobalt and that it could be cured by the administration of cobalt salts.

Ruminants (cows and sheep) apparently have the ability to utilize cobalt in inorganic form, but other animals, including man, apparently must obtain it as it occurs in vitamin B_{12}. This difference is due to the fact that in ruminants the microorganisms (flora) of the rumen can synthesize vitamin B_{12} when enough cobalt is available, whereas in other animals and man the intestinal microorganisms cannot. Rats and chicks, for example, will show a growth response to vitamin B_{12}, but they will not respond to inorganic cobalt.

An excess of cobalt in the diet of rats results in polycythemia, a condition in which the number of red blood cells and the hemoglobin are increased to about one and one-third to one and a half times the normal values. Just how cobalt brings about these results is not known as yet, but it has been stated that the toxic effects of cobalt can be relieved by the administration of ascorbic acid. Polycythemia has also been developed in healthy human subjects by the administration of large amounts of cobalt. Actually these quantities of cobalt are apparently of pharmacological rather than physiological proportions.

Cobalt is like sulfur in having to be obtained in organic form. There is some evidence to show that cobalt is important in the metabolism of sulfur-containing amino acids. Its importance as it occurs in a vitamin will be discussed further in the chapter dealing with vitamin B_{12}.

It is practically impossible to prepare an experimental diet low enough in cobalt to produce a deficiency condition. Whether or not there is a human requirement for cobalt other than as it occurs in vitamin B_{12} is not known. It is not likely that a human dietary would be deficient in cobalt.

Iodine

Iodine has already been referred to as essential to the thyroid gland, which serves as an important regulator of the basal energy metabolism and is an indispensable factor in normal growth. It was not until 1895 that it was shown conclusively that iodine was an essential element in thyroid structure. In 1914, thyroxine was prepared from the gland by Kendall, of the Mayo Clinic, and found to be a substance containing 65 per cent of iodine and having marked physiological properties. Harington, in 1926 and 1927, determined the structure of thyroxine and reported its synthesis.

When Kendall was able to remove iodine from thyroxine and show that the resulting product would not stimulate development, the place of iodine among nutritionally essential mineral elements was no longer questioned. The need for iodine in the normal functioning of the thyroid gland was recognized as its major role in the human organism.

Various species of animals were found to suffer from iodine deficiency; it was estimated in 1916 that about 1 million young pigs were lost annually in Wisconsin. The pigs were born hairless and otherwise defective. In other western states the pig industry was similarly menaced. The mothers appeared normal, but a careful investigation led to the conclusion that iodine starvation of the fetus depressed the activity of the fetal thyroid and caused the arrest of development. When suitable amounts of iodine were administered to the mothers during the gestation period, the hairless condition was prevented and a marked improvement occurred in the vitality of the young pigs. Other farm animals, such as sheep, calves, colts, chickens, and dogs, suffering from goiter, responded favorably to the administration of iodine.

As old as history itself is the incidence of goiter in the human race. Kimball remarked that the *Arthorva Veda*, an ancient Hindu collection of incantations dating from 2000 B.C., contains extensive forms of exorcisms for goiter. It was not until the middle of the nineteenth century, however, that the prevalence of goiter in European countries was made a matter of government investigation. For France alone, a commission appointed in 1864 reported ten years later 500,000 people suffering from goiter and 120,000 cretins and cretinoid idiots. Not only is growth limited in cretinism to the point of dwarfism, with short extremities, large head, an apathetic face, delayed eruption of teeth, and retarded speech, but mental processes are also permanently impaired. In all southern Europe the problem of goiter and cretinism has been of sufficient economic importance to justify national commissions for its investigation.

In the United States there is a wide goiter belt stretching along the Appalachian Mountains as far north as Vermont, westward through the basin of the Great Lakes to the state of Washington, and southward over the Rocky Mountain and Pacific states; but no attempt to prevent human goiter on a large scale seems to have been made previous to 1917. Then Marine and Kimball, reasoning that if goiter could be prevented in animals by administration of iodine, it should be preventable also in the human species, undertook to prove the possibility of such prevention in the public schools of Akron, Ohio. They secured the cooperation of the Superintendent of Schools, the Board of Education, and the County Medical Society, and, in 1917, began a systematic census of the thyroid glands of all the girls from the fifth to the twelfth grades of the elementary schools. The boys were not examined because of the relative infrequency of serious thyroid enlargement in boys. The results are shown in Table 11–1.

As many of these girls as volunteered were given small doses of sodium iodide dissolved in drinking water in a quantity to furnish from 3 to 5 mg

TABLE 11-1. INCIDENCE OF GOITER IN
SCHOOL GIRLS OF AKRON, OHIO IN 1917

State of Thyroid Gland	Number of Girls	Per Cent of Total Number Examined
Normal	1,688	43.2
Slightly enlarged	1,931	49.3
Moderately enlarged	246	6.3
Markedly enlarged	7	0.2
Toxic	39	1.0
Total number examined	3,911	100.0

of iodine twice weekly over a period of a month, and repeated twice yearly. In 1920, as a result of two and one-half years' observations, the investigators reported that of over 2,000 pupils taking the treatment, only five developed thyroid enlargement, while of a similar number not treated, nearly 500 showed enlargement during the same time.

IODINE AND GOITER PREVENTION

This strikingly successful demonstration aroused much interest in goiter prevention both in other parts of this country and abroad. In 1918, Professor Klinger, of Zurich, undertook to carry out similar treatment in three Swiss cantons, Saint Gallen, Bern, and Zurich, with school populations in which the incidence of goiter varied from 82 to 95 per cent. In 1922 a report of the Health Commission of the canton of Saint Gallen gave the following statistics: incidence of goiter among all the schoolchildren of Saint Gallen, in 1919, 87.5 per cent; in 1922, 13.1 per cent. By 1929 there were nine cantons in which only iodized salt was used, and in all but a few of the others it was consumed more or less freely. In the canton of Appenzell the Swiss Goiter Commission reported that after five years there was a total disappearance of congenital goiter and of goiter among young schoolchildren, with a fall of 75 per cent in operations for relief of goiter in adults. There was also a decline in the number of stillbirths and infant deaths due to thyroid deficiency and an average increase of 100 gm in the birth weight.

In this country Michigan has been one of the foremost states in establishing and maintaining a goiter prevention program. In 1928, after four years of educational work on the part of the State Medical Society and the State Board of Health and continued effort on the part of the Wholesale Grocers' Association to bring about the sale of iodized salt exclusively, the schoolchildren were examined in certain districts to see what the effect of the policy had been. In every instance the decline in the incidence of goiter was striking. A resurvey in ten years showed a reduction in the percentage of goiter from 40 to 8. In Midland County, where the original survey had shown fully one third of the children to have well-established goiters and practically every child to have some enlargement, the disease was almost completely stamped out, 90 per cent of the children being reported as normal.

An interesting incident of the survey was the situation in the town of Calumet, where closing of the copper mines in 1932 had thrown two thirds of the families on relief. These families were given only plain bag salt. Furthermore, many of the families who were buying their own groceries were in such financial straits that they, too, bought bag salt because it was cheaper. Thus the use of iodized salt was discontinued through the next three years, with the result that the number of cases of goiter, which had been reduced to a very low figure, became as great as before 1924.[29]

The prevention of goiter has thus been shown to be a nutritional problem. The body has a requirement for iodine to meet daily losses and maintain such a reserve as is necessary for the production of sufficient amounts of the thyroid hormones, thyroxine and triiodothyronine, for health and growth. The current level of salt iodization in the United States is 1 part in 10,000 (100 mg potassium iodide in 1 kg of purified salt). The levels recommended have been shown to have no demonstrable deleterious effects. The added iodide is not to be regarded as a drug but rather as a means of restoring the table salt to something like its natural composition. The Food and Nutrition Board (1963) has recommended federal legislation making mandatory the iodization of salt. Some other nations (Canada, Guatemala, and Colombia) have salt iodization programs which are compulsory. Legislation in a number of other Latin American countries has been passed but has not been put into effect.

With the continued use of iodized salt, the incidence of endemic goiter has been largely eliminated in the United States. Another factor in the decrease of goiter has been the extensive distribution of food supplies grown and produced in all parts of the country and made available in supermarkets almost everywhere, so that the goiter areas are not as well defined as in the past. Although it is no longer a major problem in the United States, this is not true among other populations in the world. In a report published in 1960, Kelly and Snedden state that the number of people with endemic goiter is not known but is probably not far short of 200 million. It is undoubtedly the most prevalent deficiency disease in the world. See Figures 11–3 and 11–4. Goiter, as the survey of the World Health Organization[30] shows in detail, occurs in almost every country of

[29] For further reports see Oleson, R. *Endemic Goiter*, Public Health Bulletin No. 192, Washington, D.C.: U.S. Public Health Service (1929); and Kimball, O. P. "Prevention of Goiter in Michigan and Ohio." *J. Amer. Med. A.*, **108**:860 (1937).

[30] *Endemic Goiter*. Monograph Series No. 44. Geneva: World Health Organization (1960).

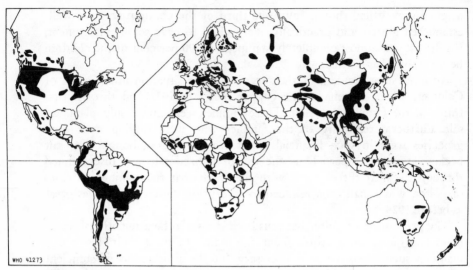

FIGURE 11–3. MAP SHOWING GOITER AREAS OF THE WORLD. (*Photo courtesy of World Health. From "Malnutrition and Disease," p. 38. Geneva* [1963].)

the world although in varying degrees. A reduced incidence of goiter has been found where the iodine content of the water is high, but it must be kept in mind that it is the nature of the food supply that determines the major intake of iodine. Other factors, such as goitrogens in certain areas, have been implicated in the pathogenesis of endemic goiter but the evidence is not clear-cut.

The regular use of iodized salt is especially important during early adolescence and pregnancy. However, Darby[31] states that it is not safe to assume that the world's goiter problem will be solved by education in the use of iodized salt. In many areas of the world where crude salt is used instead of the refined product the stability of the iodine presents a problem. The process of cooking may affect the stability and retention of the iodine. Also, it has been pointed out by Osmond and Clements[32] in Australia that 10 per cent of the children ten years of age in Canberra do not use salt at the table, and 30 to 35 per cent of the children three to four years of age do not use salt at all.

Darby calls attention to the effectiveness in the United States of the administration of iodine either in drinking water or as iodized salt in the prevention and treatment of endemic goiter over a long period of years and cautions that its importance must be constantly kept in mind as a public health measure in order to ensure the continuation of the practice.

[31] *Symposium on Nutrition*, edited by Herriott, p. 238. Baltimore: Johns Hopkins (1953).

[32] Osmond, A., and Clements, F. W. "Goiter Studies. III. The Iodine Prophylaxis of Endemic Goiter." *Med. J., Australia*, **1**:753 (1948).

FIGURE 11–4. A GROUP OF WOMEN SHOWING ENDEMIC GOITER IN A GOITROUS REGION OF GUATEMALA. This photograph was taken in the village of Parramos in the Guatemalan Highlands. Dr. N. S. Scrimshaw, formerly Director of the Institute of Nutrition of Central America and Panama, reported that women with these degrees of goiter were exceedingly common. (*Courtesy of INCAP Photo by Gey.*)

IODINE IN FOOD AND WATER

In an Indian village in the Pemberton Valley of British Columbia there was never any goiter, although Indians living in Minnesota, Michigan, and Wisconsin were as frequent victims as the white inhabitants. Keith, who studied the Pemberton Valley, commented thus on the situation: "Whilst considering the lack of goiter among these Indians I would like to draw attention to the fact that they eat a great deal of salmon. . . and annually cure thousands for winter use. Their pigs also eat dead salmon washed ashore on the gravel banks of the stream. It is quite probable that the Indians and their pigs get enough iodine from the salmon to give their thyroids the necessary quantum of this element."[33] Seafoods are all rich sources of iodine. Von Fellenberg, in Switzerland, found that foods from a goitrous territory contained less iodine than the same kinds from nongoitrous regions. Our knowledge of the iodine content of foods has been limited owing to technical difficulties in determining such minute amounts as are found in common foods. Recently improved methods of iodine analysis have been developed.

Because simple goiter is such a worldwide problem, the Interdepartmental Committee on Nutrition for National Development (ICNND)

[33] Keith, W. D. "Endemic Goiter." *Canad. Med. A. J.*, **14**:284 (1924).

has been making studies of the iodine content of food in nutrition surveys conducted in Vietnam, Thailand, Burma, Malaya, Lebanon, the West Indies, and Latin America.

Vought and London[34] in 1964 reported studies of the iodine content of hospital diets and family diets in the United States. They emphasized the need for a restudy of the iodine values of foods based on current practices of food production, processing, and distribution. They found a wide range of iodine intake in patients and employees at the Clinical Center, National Institutes of Health. Table 11–2 indicates the median iodine values of composites of food groups served in the hospital.

TABLE 11–2. IODINE CONTENT OF COMPOSITES OF FOOD CATEGORIES

Food Groups	Iodine, μg per 100 gm (moist weight)
	median
Seafoods	54.0
Vegetables	28.0
Meat products	17.5
Eggs	14.5
Dairy products	13.9
Bread and cereal	10.5
Fruits	1.8

From the earliest times it was popularly believed that the incidence of goiter was related to the water supply. Chemical evidence of this relationship was afforded by a study of goiter in Michigan in 1924. It was found that localities separated only a few miles varied in percentage of thyroid enlargements in native children from 10 to 100 per cent. One notable instance in percentage of thyroid enlargement was observed between Mount Clemens, which had 26 per cent, and Romeo, 12 miles distant, which had 75 per cent. Mount Clemens had an iodine content in the city water supply of approximately 25 parts per billion, while Romeo water did not contain a trace in 50 liters.

However, it is not the drinking water alone that prevents goiter. In cases of waters containing 10 parts per billion of iodine, 10 qt of water would have to be drunk to get 0.1 mg of iodine, the dose recommended for a schoolchild. The iodine in the water is to be regarded as indicative of

---

[34] Vought, R. L., and London, W. T. "Dietary Sources of Iodine." *Amer. J. Clin. Nutr.*, **14**:186 (1964); "Iodine Intake and Excretion in Healthy Nonhospitalized Subjects." *Amer. J. Clin. Nutr.*, **15**:124 (1964).

the iodine in the soils. Plants growing in the soils are the agency by which it is concentrated for human use. In regions which are nongoitrous, it seems probable that most persons secure sufficient iodine by a liberal inclusion of milk and green vegetables in their diet. Vought and London, in their study of family diets in 1964, found that iodine from water contributed little additional iodine to the total intake.

Fluorine

Fluorine is found in almost all soils, water supplies, plants, and animals in small but varying amounts. Thus it is present as a normal constituent in all diets. The bones and teeth of mammals contain the largest concentrations. There is no convincing evidence that indicates any toxicity of fluoride from ingestion of water fluoridated within the recommended levels in the United States. Even larger amounts, reported recently, indicated that workers in a fertilizer plant exposed for periods up to 25 years to a large continuous administration of fluorine showed no toxic symptoms.[35]

Because fluorine is known to be an integral part of the structure of the teeth and important in the prevention of dental caries it is recognized as essential for optimal health. For a further discussion of the relation of fluorine to the health of the teeth, see Chapter 19.

Other Trace Elements (Manganese, Zinc, Molybdenum, and Selenium)

"Since the above micro elements generally appear to be furnished in adequate quantities by a mixed diet, risks of deficiency in the United States probably are slight. Their use as supplements, without evidence of a deficiency, should be regarded with caution because in each instance injuries occur at high levels of intake, and antagonisms can occur readily."[36] Generous amounts of the trace elements are supplied by green leafy vegetables, fruits, whole grains, and organ and lean meats.

Manganese was recognized as an essential nutrient through experimental work with rats. On a diet of cow's milk supplemented with iron and copper, rats were found to make better growth when manganese was added. Without the manganese there was a delay in sexual maturity, and when the females finally bore young, these were either dead or so weak that most of them did not survive more than a few days. Their bodies contained less than half as much manganese as those of mothers on a similar ration with added manganese. On a strictly manganese-free diet

[35] Review. "Potential Toxicity of Fluorides." *Nutr. Rev.*, **21**:291 (1963).
[36] *Recommended Dietary Allowances*, 6th rev. ed., publication 1146, p. 37. Washington, D.C.: National Research Council (1964).

male rats became completely sterile because of degeneration of their testes
and female rats were unable to suckle their young. Addition of manganese
to their diet resulted in normal development through several generations.

In chickens a manganese deficiency results in a condition known as
perosis (slipped tendon). Also, a low hatchability of eggs laid by hens
whose diets were deficient in manganese has been reported. The embryos
which developed had shortened leg and wing bones and distorted beaks.
Poultry rations commonly contain a manganese salt, which serves as a
protective measure. Manganese has also been found to be an essential
nutrient for swine.

The requirement of manganese in animal nutrition is very low, only
about one tenth that of copper and one one-hundredth that of iron. Certain combinations of other mineral elements may either increase the requirement or decrease its availability. Manganese is present in plant tissues
generally, as well as in those of the animals that eat the plants, so that on
an ordinary mixed diet there seems no likelihood of a deficiency of this
element.[37] Of the manganese present in animal tissues, the highest concentration is in the liver.

Although little is known regarding the role of manganese in human
nutrition, it is recognized as essential. It is known to be bound to proteins
and to activate many enzymes. The daily intake of manganese in adult
human diets has been estimated to be between 5 to 10 mg. Excessive
amounts of manganese are toxic, as has been shown in men mining manganese ore.

Zinc is recognized today as an essential trace element in the nutrition
of man. It is known to be present in a number of enzymes, for example,
carbonic anhydrase in both the red and white corpuscles of the blood; the
pancreatic enzyme carboxypeptidase; and others. It has been found to be
interrelated with the metabolism of copper and molybdenum. Normal
human blood contains about 1 mg of zinc per 100 ml, most of which is
found in the erythrocytes. Traces of zinc are also regularly present in
human tissues, especially in the pancreas.

The effect of a zinc deficiency on the feather growth of chicks will be
observed in Figure 11–5.

In patients suffering from pernicious anemia, an elevation of the zinc
concentration in the blood has been noted as well as an elevation of the
activity of the enzyme carbonic anhydrase. In patients with postalcoholic
cirrhosis an increased urinary excretion of zinc is observed with low
serum zinc levels. Disturbances of zinc metabolism have been noted in a
number of conditions.

Recently a deficiency syndrome observed in young male villagers in
the Kharga oasis area of Egypt has been described by a team from Vander-

[37] For manganese in foods see Taylor and MacLeod. *Rose's Laboratory Handbook
for Dietetics,* 5th ed., p. 265. New York: Macmillan (1949).

A   B

FIGURE 11–5. NOTE THE EFFECT OF A DEFICIENCY OF ZINC ON FEATHER GROWTH
IN THE CHICK. *A.* Normal feathering. *B.* Zinc deficient. (*Courtesy of E. W.
Kienholz, D. E. Turk, M. L. Sunde, and W. G. Migicovsky, University of
Wisconsin, and* J. Nutr., **75:**217 [*1961*], *Fig. 2.*)

bilt University and a U.S. Naval Medical Research unit stationed in
Cairo.[38] They suggest that a mixed iron-zinc deficiency may be responsible
for the clinical manifestations, which include anemia, hypogonadism,
and dwarfism. Low plasma and tissue levels of zinc were found in 16
patients studied. The diet consisted mainly of bread with some seasonal
consumption of fava beans. These patients had no parasitic infections such
as those observed in patients with similar symptoms near Cairo.

There is little likelihood of any deficiency occurring in human nutrition on an ordinary mixed diet since zinc is so widely distributed in
nature. Most human diets contain 10 to 15 mg of zinc per day, which is
probably more than enough to provide for all human needs, even allowing for limited absorption from the gut.

Molybdenum was first recognized as an essential nutrient in 1953
through work on rats which established the fact that molybdenum is required to maintain normal levels of the essential enzyme xanthine oxidase.
The active factor was later isolated from soy flour and from liver, and
found to be a salt of molybdenum. It has been found to be a component
not only of xanthine oxidase but also of aldehyde oxidase and other
enzymes.

The role of molybdenum in soils and plants is significant. See Figure
11–6 for the effect of molybdenum on a cauliflower leaf. Soils vary in
content of molybdenum, many factors affecting its availability. Of the
micronutrients known to be essential for plants, molybdenum is needed
in very minute amounts, and pastures deficient in this element may be

[38] Prasad, A. S., Schubert, A. R., Miale, A., Farid, Z., and Sandstead, H. H. "Zinc
and Iron Deficiencies in Male Subjects with Dwarfism and Hypogonadism but
Without Ancylostomiasis, Schistosomiasis or Severe Anemia." *Amer. J. Clin. Nutr.,*
12:437 (1963).

Figure 11–6. The Effect of Molybdenum on the Growth of the Cauliflower. *A.* Leaf grown on normal soil. *B.* Leaf grown in soil deficient in molybdenum. (*Courtesy of the New Jersey Agricultural Experiment Station and the Climax Molybdenum Co.*)

A   B

in the order of an ounce per acre; thus this small amount in fertilizer may be ample for years.

Apparently most diets contain enough molybdenum to supply the amount needed for the production of xanthine oxidase in the liver. It has been reported that 0.2 to 0.3 μg of molybdenum per rat per day would be adequate to produce a saturation level of xanthine oxidase. Although the human daily requirement for molybdenum has not been established, it is probably considerably less than 0.3 mg per kilogram of body weight.

Molybdenum toxicity has been reported in ruminants under natural grazing conditions and has been found to interfere with copper metabolism. Toxic effects have also been noted in rats, guinea pigs, and rabbits. The condition can be alleviated by giving copper.

Foods considered as good sources of molybdenum include legumes, cereal grains, some dark-green leafy vegetables, and animal organs (liver, kidney, and spleen). To be considered a good source a food should contain 0.6 part of molybdenum per million parts of food. Fruits, berries, and most root or stem vegetables have been found to be relatively poor sources, having less than one-tenth part per million.

Selenium is one of the rarer elements, having properties similar to those of sulfur, the two often occurring together. In 1957, it was discovered to be an essential micronutrient in animal nutrition. It was identified as an integral part of factor 3, an agent found to protect rats against dietary liver necrosis. The liver degeneration is produced by feeding a purified diet, deficient in sulfur-containing amino acids and vitamin E. Factor 3 has since been found to prevent deficiency diseases of different types in mice, mink, chicks, lamb and sheep, calves, and pigs. Its significance in human nutrition is not known.[39]

Selenium in somewhat larger doses is extremely toxic. Selenium poisoning constitutes a public health and agricultural problem in areas such as the north central and southwestern United States because selenium may replace sulfur in cystine and methionine in plants grown in seleniferous soils. The toxicity of selenium compounds varies greatly with the type of compound and the nutritional state of the animal.

REFERENCES

Bogert, L. J. *Nutrition and Physical Fitness*, 7th ed., Chap. 9. Philadelphia: Saunders (1960).

Bothwell, T. H., Seftel, H., Jacobs, P., Torrance, J. D., and Baumslag, N. "Iron Overload in Bantu Subjects." *Amer. J. Clin. Nutr.*, 14:47 (1964).

Cowan, J. W., Najjar, S. S., Sabry, Z. I., Tannous, R. I., and Simaan, F. S. "Some Further Observations on Goiter in Lebanon." *Amer. J. Clin. Nutr.*, 17:164 (1965).

Curtis, G. M., and Fertman, M. B. "Iodine in Nutrition." *Handbook of Nutrition*, 2nd ed., Chap. 6. Chicago: American Medical Association (1951).

Darby, W. J. "Iron and Copper." *Handbook of Nutrition*, 2nd ed., Chap. 5. Chicago: American Medical Association (1951).

Follis, R. H. "Patterns of Urinary Iodine Excretion in Goitrous and Nongoitrous Areas." *Amer. J. Clin. Nutr.*, 14:253 (1964).

Food and Nutrition Board. *Recommended Dietary Allowances*, publication 1146, pp. 17–19 and 34–38. Washington, D.C.: National Research Council (1964).

Food—The Yearbook of Agriculture, 1959. Monty, K. J., and McElroy, W. D. "The Trace Elements." Washington, D.C.: U.S. Department of Agriculture.

Jolliffe, N. (ed.). *Clinical Nutrition*, 2nd ed. Moore, C. V. "Iron Malnutrition," Chap. 9, and "The Essential Trace Elements," Chap. 10; Fertman, M. B. "Iodine Malnutrition," Chap. 11. New York: Harper (1962).

Lang, V. M., North, B. B., and Morse, L. M. "Manganese Metabolism in College Men Consuming Vegetarian Diets." *J. Nutr.*, 85:132 (1965).

McClure, F. J. "Fluorine and Other Trace Elements in Nutrition." *Handbook of Nutrition*, 2nd ed., Chap. 7. Chicago: American Medical Association (1951).

[39] Schwarz, K. "Factor 3, Selenium and Vitamin E." *Nutr. Rev.*, 18:193 (1960).

Review. "Idiopathic Hemochromatosis and Bantu Siderosis." *Nutr. Rev.*, **23**:170 (1965).

Review. "Trace Elements in Plants and Soils." *Nutr. Rev.*, **12**:276 (1954) and **13**:337 (1955).

Schütte, K. H. *The Biology of the Trace Elements. Their Role in Nutrition.* Philadelphia: Lippincott (1964).

Scrimshaw, N. S. "Endemic Goiter in Latin America." *Pub. Health Rep.*, **75**:731 (1960).

Sebrell, W. H., Jr. "Iodine—A Food Essential." *Nutr. Rev.*, **8**:129 (1950).

Vallee, B. L. "The Metabolic Role of Zinc." Council on Foods and Nutrition. *J. Amer. Med. A.*, **162**:1053 (1956).

Wilson, E. D., Fisher, K. H., and Fuqua, M. E. *Principles of Nutrition*, Chaps. 11 and 12. New York: Wiley (1965).

❧ **12** ❧

Vitamin A

Discovery

McCollum gives Dumas, a distinguished French chemist, the credit for being the first scientist to question the adequacy of a diet composed solely of protein, fat, and carbohydrate. In 1871, Dumas, in his paper entitled "The Constitution of Blood and Milk," describes the effects of food on the infants of Paris during the siege by the Germans (1870–71). He tells of the scarcity of milk and eggs and the attempts to prepare an artificial milk for children by emulsifying fat in a sweetened, albuminous solution—a mixture that had disastrous effects. He describes the distress of parents, the premature disease, and the high mortality rate of infants and young children. Saddened by this experience, Dumas drew the conclusion that the artificial milk lacked something essential to life. In this report Dumas for the first time "observed human beings under conditions of dietary restrictions so severe that the results could be interpreted with the accuracy and reliability ordinarily obtainable only in well-controlled animal experiments."[1]

The first experimental evidence that animals could not exist on mixtures of purified proteins, fats, carbohydrates, and mineral salts came from the laboratory of Bunge at the University in Dorpat, Estonia. In 1884 Lunin, one of his pupils, fed mice an artificial mixture of all the components of milk then known, but the animals failed to survive, and he concluded his report thus: "A natural food such as milk must therefore contain besides these known principal ingredients small quantities of unknown substances essential to life." Bunge himself thought the real cause of the nutritional failure was some change in the form of the mineral elements that rendered them incapable of utilization. Although another pupil, Socin, seven years later also became convinced that milk and egg yolk contained un-

---

[1] McCollum, E. V. *A History of Nutrition*, Chap. 14, p. 202. Boston: Houghton (1957).

known substances of special significance for life and growth, surprising as it may be, no systematic search for them was instituted in Bunge's laboratory.

In other parts of the world from time to time men found human diseases that could be cured by changes in diet, and laboratory workers sought animals in which similar diseases could be induced and then cured by the same foods that had proved efficacious for mankind.

Babcock, at the University of Wisconsin, determined to test rations derived from different plant sources to see whether there might be any difference in their nutritive value. With the cooperation at first of Hart and Humphrey and later of Steenbock and McCollum, an experiment was conducted on groups of young heifers, one group being fed a wheat plant ration, another a yellow-corn plant ration, a third an oat plant ration, and a fourth a ration drawn from all three plant sources. For the first year of the experiment there was little to distinguish one group from another, but gradually the corn-fed group grew smoother in the coat and fuller in the barrel, while the wheat-fed group became rough of coat, gaunt and thin, and small of girth. The groups on the oat plant ration and the mixed ration stood intermediate between those on the corn and the wheat.

One of the first persons to appreciate the full significance of adding minute quantities of unknown substances present in natural food appears to have been Hopkins, of Cambridge University. Although he did not venture to print the results of his own experiments until 1912, as early as 1906 he sounded the modern note: "No animal can live upon a mixture of pure protein, fat and carbohydrate, and even when the necessary inorganic material is carefully supplied, the animal still cannot flourish."[2]

Hopkins fed young rats a diet of casein, lard, starch, cane sugar, and mineral salts obtained by mixing equal parts of ash of oats and dog biscuit. When these substances were highly purified, growth was arrested, and decline and death speedily ensued, even though the food intake appeared sufficient. When to the purified ration were added only 2 or 3 ml of milk daily—less than one third of a teaspoon—growth was promptly resumed.

About the same time, Osborne and Mendel in New Haven initiated an investigation of the influence of proteins on nutritive processes. They devised a preparation of milk freed of its casein, albumin, and fat, which they called "protein-free milk." By adding this to mixtures of pure starch, sugar, and fat along with any pure protein to be investigated, they were able to keep white rats alive, but beyond periods of about 100 days there was little or no increase in body weight, although the animals remained for some time in good condition. When whole-milk powder was substituted for the casein and protein-free milk, they were able to bring

[2] Hopkins, F. G. "Analyst and the Medical Man." *Analyst*, **31**:385 (1906).

their animals through two generations. They concluded that the essential difference between the two diets lay in the milk fat. When, accordingly, butter was substituted for lard in the protein-free milk food, growth was promptly resumed and adult size attained.

While these experiments were going on in New Haven, progress in growth control was also being made in Wisconsin. McCollum and Davis, meeting similar difficulties in promoting growth on purified rations, found that resumption of growth occurred promptly when an ether extract of egg or butter was added. Thus two different laboratories, approaching the problem in different ways, simultaneously discovered that there was something in butter fat and egg yolk not found in lard and common vegetable fats which was essential for growth and which could not be manufactured by the animal organism. This substance is now known as vitamin A.

The search for vitamin A in foods went forward by leaps and bounds after 1913. Not only fish-liver oils, eggs, and butter, but also green leaves and yellow parts of plants, proved to be excellent sources. Carrots and sweet potatoes were found to be rich sources, while white turnips and potatoes furnished practically none. In 1919 Steenbock, at the University of Wisconsin, found that yellow corn but not white could be used successfully as the only source of vitamin A in the diet of young rats. He noted the remarkable coincidence in the occurrence of the yellow coloring matter of plants and the success obtained when they were used to furnish vitamin A. Extracting some of the pigment of carrots, known as carotene, he crystallized it, and found that the crystals had vitamin A activity.

In many parts of the world, interest in the relationship between carotene and vitamin A became keen. In Paris, in 1932, a sample of carotene made from spinach 40 years previously and kept in a sealed tube as a museum specimen was brought forth and a portion was fed to vitamin A-deficient rats, with the same success that had attended Steenbock's experiments. At the University of Wisconsin, Hart and some of his co-workers, using chicks, which also require vitamin A, compared the effect of two kinds of plant coloring matter in spinach, one being carotene and the other a related substance known as xanthophyll. All the chicks grew well for about four weeks; then those on the vitamin A-free diet developed severe symptoms of vitamin A deficiency. Growth ceased, feathers became ruffled, a staggering gait developed, then the birds finally appeared drowsy and lay over on one side. In a few days they were dead. Those given xanthophyll were no better off, but those given as little as 0.03 mg of carotene per day grew at a normal rate and remained in excellent health. The difference is shown in Figure 12–1.

Thus evidence accumulated that carotene is the substance out of which the body can manufacture vitamin A, and consequently it is often referred to as provitamin A. Preparation of carotene crystals on a commercial scale has now made them available at low cost.

There are a number of substances differing only slightly in chemical constitution, alpha-, beta-, and gamma-carotene and cryptoxanthin being the most important. All these substances yield vitamin A. Our plant foods generally contain no vitamin A as such, but owe their vitamin A values to their content of provitamin A, while foods of animal origin commonly contain both the vitamin and one or more precursors. We therefore speak of the vitamin A values of foods rather than their vitamin A content. In 1950 three groups of investigators reported the synthesis of beta-carotene.

In 1934 the International unit of vitamin A (and also the United States Pharmacopeia unit) was set at 0.6 μg of pure beta-carotene, and this is

FIGURE 12–1. VITAMIN A DEFICIENCY. The lower chick received 0.03 mg of carotene daily in addition to a basal diet adequate in all respects except vitamin A. It exhibited no vitamin A deficiency and weighed 320 gm at five weeks. The upper chick received 0.25 mg of xanthophyll daily in addition to the basal diet. It developed symptoms characteristic of vitamin A deficiency and weighed only 160 gm at five weeks. (*Courtesy of Professor E. B. Hart.*)

still used for the measurement of carotenes. In 1949 it was also fixed at 0.344 μg of pure all-trans-vitamin A_1 acetate by the World Health Organization (Figure 12–2, *A* and *B*).

When cod-liver oil was discovered to be a rich source of vitamin A, other fish oils were investigated and also found to be rich in this vitamin. Among them, halibut-liver oil proved an easily available source of material from which to isolate the vitamin in pure form. The first step was the preparation of a vitamin A concentrate. This was a slightly yellow, oily substance giving certain well-established tests for vitamin A, and from it Karrer, at the University of Zurich, Switzerland, was able to determine the chemical constitution in 1933. Crystallization of the vitamin was accomplished in 1934 by Holmes, at Oberlin College. He reported a product almost 100 per cent pure having as high as 14,000 times the potency of standard cod-liver oil, but it took nearly three more years to achieve complete success. In the latter part of 1936 he was able to show the first pure, pale-yellow, needlelike crystals of vitamin A,[3] prepared from the liver oil of Atlantic Ocean mackerel, and a little later obtained others from a Japanese fish, *Stereolepis ishingi.* Samples of these crystals were sent to three other laboratories, where their biological activity was found to be about 3,000,000 I.U. per gram. Synthetic vitamin A is now available, methods for synthesizing it having been developed in a number of laboratories (Figure 12–3).

[3] Holmes, H. N., and Corbet, R. "A Crystalline Vitamin A Concentrate." *Science,* **35**:103 (1937).

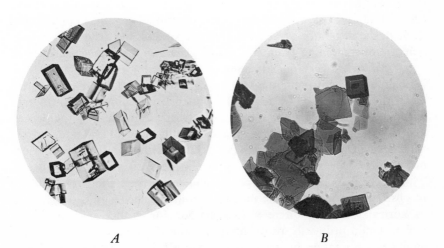

A   *B*

FIGURE 12–2. CRYSTALS OF VITAMIN A ACETATE (*A*) AND OF BETA-CAROTENE (*B*). (*Courtesy of Hoffmann-La Roche, Inc.*)

The Promotion of Growth

As already stated, vitamin A was discovered through the failure of rats to grow for more than 70 to 120 days on inadequate rations. At first there was much irregularity in the time required by different animals to show signs of vitamin A deficiency, but it was soon realized that if the animals placed upon the vitamin A-free diet had been previously fed one rich in it, they continued to grow for a much longer time than those whose former diet had been good in all other respects but low in vitamin A. The upper rat in Figure 12–4 shows the characteristic effects of a diet lacking vitamin A. Typical growth curves for such animals, weaned at the age of four weeks from a mother on an adequate diet and placed on a diet entirely free from vitamin A (Figure 12–5), indicates how growth continues until the vitamin A reserves of the body are exhausted. If the vitamin is not added to the diet when growth ceases, symptoms of deficiency soon become marked and death ensues. The time when growth ceases depends on the vitamin A stored on the prior diet.

Epithelial Tissues

Vitamin A stored in the body is not simply a reserve for some future time of shortage. It is at all times significant for the maintenance of resistance to disease and the development of a high degree of physical vigor. Since 1925 a great deal of experimental evidence has been obtained regarding the character of the changes that lack of vitamin A induces in the various tissues of the body, and it has become very clear that epithelial cells, found in the skin and in the mucous membrane in all its ramifications through the respiratory tract, the digestive system, the genitourinary system, the ducts leading from all sorts of glands, and the inner surfaces of many glands, are very quickly altered by deficiency of this vitamin.

Long before any symptoms of disease are apparent, an examination under the microscope of a few cells scraped from the mucous membrane will disclose the drying and deterioration that are incident to the process known as keratinization; or histological examination of the ducts of the sublingual glands, the sebaceous glands of the skin, or the various lacrimal glands of the eye will show them choked with masses of dead cells which have been thrown off from the mucous surface and have remained to obstruct the passage. The mucous membrane, being thus deprived of its normal secretion, offers a good harbor for chance microorganisms which would ordinarily prove harmless. An adequate vitamin A supply at all times is a means of strengthening the natural defenses of the tissues. After damage due to an inadequate supply has been done, dosing with the vitamin will not guarantee a cure, although it may help to hasten such

FIGURE 12–3. CRYSTALLINE VITAMIN A HIGHLY MAGNIFIED. (*Courtesy of Merck & Co., Inc.*)

FIGURE 12–4. THESE TWO RATS ARE THE SAME AGE. The lower one had an adequate diet, the upper one a diet lacking vitamin A.

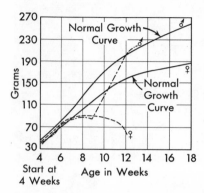

FIGURE 12–5. GROWTH OF RATS ON A VITAMIN A-FREE DIET COMPARED WITH THAT OF RATS OF THE SAME AGE ON A NORMAL DIET. When vitamin A was added to the diet of the male after five weeks' deprivation, it doubled its weight in two and a half weeks. The female, given no vitamin A, and having used up that stored in the liver, lost weight and died.

recovery as the tissues are still capable of. Clausen,[4] of the University of Rochester School of Medicine, studying the influence of vitamin A on infection in infants, found that among 317 under 36 months of age severe infections were twice as frequent in those whose previous diet lacked vitamin A as in those to whose diet it was added in the form of cod-liver oil from the age of three months and also in the form of vegetables containing carotene from the age of six months.

The Respiratory, Alimentary, and Urinary Tracts

The change in epithelial tissue when vitamin A is deficient have nowhere been more clearly demostrated than in the mucous lining of the respiratory, alimentary, and urinary tracts. In the very detailed studies of vitamin A deficiency in China made by Sweet and K'ang, the most frequent symptoms, next to those in the eye, were found in the larynx and the trachea and sometimes even in the bronchi. In studies in this country on infants, Wolbach, of the Harvard Medical School, to whom much of our knowledge of the influence of vitamin A on epithelial cells is due, and Blackfan, a leading pediatrician of the same school, also noted that the earliest appearance of keratinization was in the upper part of the respiratory tract.[5]

These human findings are in agreement with many observations on laboratory animals. As long ago as 1923, Daniels, of the Child Welfare Research Station at Iowa City, observed in a colony of over 400 animals that those on the low vitamin A diets were the ones that manifested respiratory symptoms. Even before there was any evidence of physical breakdown, there was found on autopsy marked congestion of the nasal passages and pus in the middle ear and at the base of the tongue.

If the deprivation of vitamin A is postponed until young rats are two months old, they are less susceptible to xerophthalmia, but more of them

[4] Clausen, S. W. "Nutrition and Infection." *J. Amer. Med. A.*, **104**:793 (1935).
[5] Blackfan, K. D., and Wolbach, S. B. "Vitamin A Deficiency in Infants, Clinical and Pathologic Study." *J. Pediat.*, 3:679 (1933).

show lung infections. In human beings, Getz and Koerner have shown a correlation between a deficiency of vitamin A and the incidence of tuberculosis. The death rate from tuberculosis in Denmark rose early in World War I but declined sharply following the war, when abundant supplies of milk, butter, and meat were again available. Wohl has suggested that in addition to a protein deficiency, the deficiencies of vitamins A and ascorbic acid appear to be in proportion to the extent of the tuberculosis involvement. In 1944, in the survey made in Newfoundland,[6] tuberculosis was prevalent along with indications of poor nutrition. The report of the study made of the Canadian Bush Indians[7] also showed similar relationships.

It must also be remembered in this connection that infection tends to interfere with utilization of the vitamin and to cause depletion of body reserves. Kagen (1955) reported that, in animals, a decrease in plasma levels of vitamin A occurred in infections regardless of the amount of vitamin A stored in the liver. Organisms usually harmless may become harmful if the subject already has a low resistance to infection. Sherman, working with rats, was able to show a good return in health protection when four times the amount of vitamin A needed for the prevention of severe vitamin A deficiency was given. More vitamin A than this was of no additional benefit. As will be discussed later in this chapter, large excesses may be disadvantageous.

In rats sufficiently depleted to lose weight, diarrhea and other signs of digestive disturbance have often been observed, and in monkeys these are sometimes so severe as to cause death before any signs of xerophthalmia appear. One of the physicians at the Peiping Union Medical College described a case of greatly diminished gastric secretion which was restored to normal by the administration of cod-liver oil, and Blackfan and Wolbach reported changes in the epithelium of the alimentary tract of the infants studied by them.

When animals are kept for some time on diets low but not entirely lacking in vitamin A, kidney and bladder stones are frequently found. In chicks, lack of vitamin A affects the kidneys, interfering with the elimination of waste.

McCarrison[8] in India was the first to suggest that certain types of "kidney stone" might occur in human beings on a low vitamin A diet. Undoubtedly, as studies indicate, many factors, probably including vitamin A, are involved in the formation of such urinary calculi.

[6] Adamson, J. D., Jolliffe, N., Kruse, H. D., Lowry, O. H., Moore, P. E., Platt, B. S., Sebrell, W. H., Tice, J. W., Tisdall, F. F., Wilder, R. M., and Zamecnik, P. C. "Medical Survey of Nutrition in Newfoundland." *Canad. Med. A. J.*, 52:227 (1945).

[7] Moore, P. E., Kruse, H. D., Tisdall, F. F., and Corrigan, R. S. C. "Medical Survey of Nutrition Among the Northern Manitoba Indians." *Canad. Med. A. J.*, 54:223 (1946).

[8] McCarrison, R. "A Lecture on the Causation of Stone in India." *Brit. Med. J.*, 1:1009 (1931).

The Skin

China has been an interesting field for the study of vitamin A deficiencies because of the very low vitamin A intake of the poorer people. During the winter and spring of 1928, Frazier and Hu,[9] of the Peiping Union Medical College, observed 15 cases of vitamin A deficiency among young Chinese soldiers, all of whom had xerophthalmia and also a peculiar skin disturbance. Their diets consisted chiefly of rice, maize, millet, white cabbage, and salted vegetables.

The skin was dry and rough, and at the sites of the hair follicles a pimply eruption occurred, spreading over the upper and lower extremities, shoulders, abdomen, chest, and back. There was a typical clogging of the sebaceous glands, so that a dry, firm papule containing a plug of hardened epithelial cells projected above the surface of the skin. Inflammation developed, due to the irritation, and sometimes small ulcers formed. When the patients were put on an adequate diet and given 3 tbsp of cod-liver oil daily, the skin became moist; as the sweat glands began to function again, the papules lost their horny cores, and in the course of four to six weeks the pits so formed gradually shrank and disappeared.

An almost identical report was made by Loewenthal,[10] Medical Officer of the Mulago Hospital, Kampala, East Africa, who found that of 81 prisoners with night blindness or xerophthalmia, 74 had cutaneous eruptions as described above. Upon treatment with 3 tbsp of cod-liver oil daily for nine weeks, with no other change in the diet, 98 per cent of the cases cleared up.

In Ceylon and other areas where the diet of the poor is exceedingly low in vitamin A, the children are afflicted not only with xerophthalmia and night blindness, but also with an inflamed and coarsened condition of the skin known as "toadskin." When this condition is due to a simple vitamin A deficiency, it will clear up on administration of the vitamin.

In the Minnesota experiment conducted by Keys and his associates,[11] the effects of a submarginal intake of vitamin A (1,810 I.U. daily) were reported in 24 of the 31 subjects maintained on a partial starvation diet for 23 weeks. Carotene furnished the chief source of vitamin A since the diet was low in fat. These subjects developed a mild to moderate papular eruption of the skin resembling a vitamin A deficiency. The skin became dry and scaly and the hair lusterless.

[9] Frazier, C. N., and Hu, C. K. "Cutaneous Lesions Associated with Vitamin A Deficiency in Man." *Arch. Intern. Med.*, **48**:507 (1931).

[10] Loewenthal, L. J. A. "A New Cutaneous Manifestation in the Syndrome of Vitamin A Deficiency." *Arch. Dermat. & Syph.*, **28**:700 (1933).

[11] Keys, A., Brozek, J., Henschel, A., Michelsen, O., and Taylor, H. L. *The Biology of Human Starvation*, Vols. 1 and 2. Minneapolis: U. Minnesota (1950).

In the Medical Resurvey of Nutrition in Newfoundland in 1948, Aykroyd and his associates[12] observed a significant reduction (5.2 per cent) in the number of natives showing folliculosis of the skin. This was accounted for by the fortification of the margarine with vitamin A and the distribution of cod-liver oil to 55,000 grade-school children in a quantity sufficient to provide 1 tsp daily to each. Some doubt was expressed regarding the actual ingestion of the cod-liver oil since it was regarded as a product of the fisheries and consequently had less prestige value in Newfoundland. Even greater improvement might have been shown if each child had actually consumed his share of the cod-liver oil. There was also a significant reduction in the incidence of dry, so-called "staring" hair among the children.

Although these studies appear to indicate the curative effect of vitamin A on skin conditions, there is some doubt that vitamin A alone was fully responsible for the improvement reported. It is true that skin conditions similar to those described do not always respond to vitamin A therapy and that other factors (perhaps poor hygiene) are probably involved.

The Eyes

XEROPHTHALMIA

Apparently the oldest reference in history to the eye disease xerophthalmia is found in the Bible. "The Angel said, open the fish, and take the heart and the liver and the gall, and put them up safely. . . . As for the gall, it is good to anoint a man that has whiteness in his eyes and he shall be healed. . . . Tobit also went forth towards the door, and stumbled; but his son ran unto him . . . strake of the gall on his father's eyes. . . . And when his eyes began to smart he rubbed them. And the whiteness pilled away from the corners of his eyes and . . . he saw his son . . . Tobias."[13] This illustrates the possible early recognition of the effectiveness of the topical application of vitamin A, and the rapid absorption in the presence of a substance such as lecithin in gall. Hippocrates is also known to have recommended liver for the curing of night blindness.

Diseases of the eye have afflicted mankind since time began and are mentioned in the ancient medical literature of Egypt, China, and Greece, but the first person of modern times to show a definite connection between xerophthalmia and diet appears to have been a Japanese physician named Mori, who published in German a report of the so-called "Hikan,"

[12] Aykroyd, W. R., Jolliffe, N., Lowry, O. H., Moore, P. E., Sebrell, W. H., Shank, R. E., Tisdall, F. F., Wilder, R. M., and Zamecnik, P. C. "Medical Resurvey of Nutrition in Newfoundland, 1948." *Canad. Med. A. J.*, 60:1 (1949).

[13] Apocrypha. "Tobit." Chapter VI, page 39. Bible, King James Version. Brattleborough, Vermont: Holbrook (1816).

an eye disease of which, at a time of food shortage, he had observed nearly 1,500 cases among children from two to five years of age. This he believed to be due to the lack of fat, as it was curable (if it had not progressed too far) by the administration of chicken livers, fish livers, or eel fat, and also of cod-liver oil, all of which, as we now know, are rich in vitamin A.

The development of the characteristic eye disease known as xerophthalmia in experimental animals on diets deficient in vitamin A was one of the first observations to be reported. In this the lacrimal gland ceases to function; the eyeball becomes dry, and bacteria quickly begin to grow in the conjunctival sac; the lids of one or both eyes become congested, an exudate comes from the inflamed conjunctiva; and soon the swollen, sticky, and scabby lids completely close the eye. If not arrested, the disease eventually attacks the cornea and permanent blindness ensues, unless the animal dies before this stage is reached. The upper rat in Figure 12–4 and the dog in Figure 12–6 show this condition. The relation of the diet to the disease was discovered by Osborne and Mendel in 1921. They found that 50 per cent of their rats on a diet deficient in vitamin A developed typical symptoms of xerophthalmia.

These laboratory experiences with the white rat stimulated inquiry as to the effect of withholding vitamin A from other species of animals, and xerophthalmia has been experimentally produced in dogs, rabbits, mice, horses, swine, guinea pigs, chickens, and monkeys.

In 1917 Bloch,[14] of Copenhagen, had personally observed during the years from 1912 to 1916 many cases of xerophthalmia among children of the Danish poor. The most severe cases were among children about a

FIGURE 12–6. XEROPHTHALMIA IN THE DOG. (*Courtesy of Drs. H. Steenbock, V. E. Nelson, and E. B. Hart.*)

[14] Bloch, C. E. "Eye Disease and Other Disturbances in Infants with Deficiency of Fats in the Food." *J. Amer. Med. A.*, **68**:1516 (1917).

year old, who had been fed chiefly skim milk, along with oatmeal and barley soup, and who were threatened with blindness owing to ulceration of the cornea. As the children were greatly undernourished, whole milk was prescribed together with liberal doses of cod-liver oil. The result was a rapid disappearance of the eye trouble and a complete cure whenever the destruction of the cornea had not gone too far. In 1918, upon the introduction by government action of butter into the dietary of the poorer people, xerophthalmia was practically wiped out of Denmark.

A widespread moderate vitamin A deficiency has been noted in the tropics and subtropics, and in some areas such as Indonesia, parts of east Africa, southern India, and northeast Brazil, severe vitamin A deficiency occurs frequently. When the deficiency is severe, the damage to the eyes is the most tragic effect. If vitamin A is not administered in time, the entire cornea may be destroyed, leaving the victim blind for life. Oomen has aptly expressed his reactions thus: "Xerophthalmia has been the most bitter pill for me to swallow during 18 years of doctor's work in Indonesia. The over and over repeated experience of discovering a child, recently blinded, in the arms of the mother; having to tell her that I now could do nothing more to save its eyesight; remembering that I could have done so with a few spoonfuls of cod liver oil some days ago. . . ."[15]

Young children develop kwashiorkor following the weaning period when their diets tend to be high in carbohydrates and deficient in protein. During this period if the diets are also deficient in vitamin A, xerophthalmia may develop. Oomen studied 6,300 cases in Java and noted a peak incidence of xerophthalmia occurring in children about three years of age and extending through the fourth and into the fifth year. This is approximately two years later than the peak incidence for kwashiorkor. This difference is probably due to storage of vitamin A in the body and the protective effect of the earlier breast feeding. Apparently males are more susceptible to xerophthalmia than females. McLaren,[16] traveling in Guatemala and El Salvador, saw many children with xerophthalmia as a complication of kwashiorkor. See Figure 12–7. Severe xerophthalmia is not common in adults although nursing mothers whose infants have xerophthalmia may develop a mild xerosis and Bitot spots, according to McLaren.

BITOT SPOTS

The French physician Bitot is usually credited with the first description of the conjunctival spot that bears his name but it had actually been described three years earlier by a Russian medical officer. Bitot spots are described as a dry patch of epithelial degeneration raised above the general level of the conjunctiva, sometimes with a foamy surface. These

[15] Oomen, H. A. P. C. "An Outline of Xerophthalmia." *International Review of Tropical Medicine*, Vol. 1, p. 131. New York: Academic (1961).
[16] McLaren, D. S. *Malnutrition and the Eye.* New York: Academic (1963).

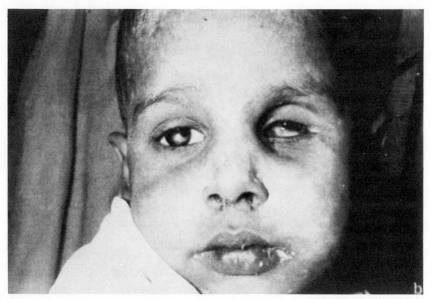

FIGURE 12–7. XEROPHTHALMIA IN A CHILD SUFFERING FROM KWASHIORKOR IN EL SALVADOR. (*With permission of D. S. McLaren from* Malnutrition and the Eye. *New York: Academic Press, Inc. [1963].*)

spots on the "white" of the eye do not interfere with vision, frequently represent a chronic condition, and may or may not respond to vitamin A administration. Their exact cause is not known but they frequently occur in subjects who have definite signs of vitamin A deficiency. Darby and his associates conducted the most extensive investigation of Bitot spots and vitamin A deficiency in connection with the Interdepartmental Committee on Nutrition for National Defense Survey in Ethiopia in 1958–59. Dark adaptation and mean serum vitamin A and carotene levels did not differ for two groups of children, one with Bitot spots and one without.

NIGHT BLINDNESS

Night blindness (nyctalopia or hemeralopia), which is the inability to see clearly in a dim light especially after exposure to an intense one, has been observed wherever xerophthalmia has occurred and probably represents the earliest manifestation of a vitamin A deficiency. Thus, slaves in Brazil, according to an 1883 report, were unable to see when returning from their work after sunset, although strangely enough they had no difficulty in setting out again before sunrise in the morning when it was actually much darker than on the previous evening. According to Mason,[17]

[17] Mason, K. E. "Effects of Vitamin A Deficiency in Human Beings." Article in Sebrell, W. H., and Harris, R. S. *The Vitamins*, Vol. I, Chap. I, Sect. VIII. New York: Academic (1954).

the "impairment of vision in dim light manifests itself as sensitivity to bright light, difficulty in reading unless the light is brilliant, glittering images and dancing specks before the eyes, tendency to stumble or to bump into objects in dim light, and prolonged delay in adaptation from bright to dim light. These defects are much more marked in evening twilight than in the dim light of daybreak."

This condition was demonstrated by Fridericia and Holm in Copenhagen in 1925. The disease was at that time known to be due to an anomaly in the rod cells of the retina, which consisted in inability of visual purple, which is bleached in light, to regenerate quickly. The visual purple in the retinas of normal rats was compared with that of rats given a diet lacking vitamin A. The depleted animals were taken from a dark room and exposed to a brilliant light, by which the visual purple was completely bleached in two hours, the same time required for bleaching in the case of the normal controls. Measurements of the visual purple showed that the time in which the color was completely regained when they were returned to the dark room was very much shorter in the normal animals than in those deprived of vitamin A. Wald[18] in 1938 reported on his outstanding experiments showing that visual purple actually contains an aldehyde called retinal, a derivative of vitamin A which is combined with the protein. In the light visual purple breaks down into the two constituents, and in the dark these recombine into visual purple. See Figure 12–8.

When it was learned that the retina is rich in vitamin A, the value of tests of speed of recovery of the visual purple after exposure to light as a means of detecting vitamin A deficiency began to receive special attention. Using the biophotometer, an instrument developed to measure dark adaptation ability, Jeans and his associates[19] found the greatest incidence of abnormal results in slightly less than 20 per cent of a group of 120 orphanage and other Iowa schoolchildren in the winter, while in late spring the incidence was reduced to 2 per cent in the schoolchildren. The orphanage groups failed to show this seasonal variation.

Other investigators have reported far less consistent results with the biophotometer. However, Jeans called attention to the importance of the technique used and the interpretation of the results. One difficulty is the fact that rod function is affected by many conditions other than vitamin A deficiency. There are currently available only two practical biochemical tests[20] of vitamin A status for population studies. These are blood serum

[18] Wald, G., Jeghers, H., and Aramino, J. "An Experiment in Human Dietary Night Blindness." *Amer. J. Physiol.*, **123**:732 (1938).

[19] Jeans, P. C., Blanchard, E. L., and Satterthwaite, F. E. "Dark Adaptation and Vitamin A." *J. Pediat.*, **18**:170 (1941).

[20] Pearson, W. N. "Biochemical Appraisal of Nutritional Status in Man." *Amer. J. Clin. Nutr.*, **11**:462 (1962).

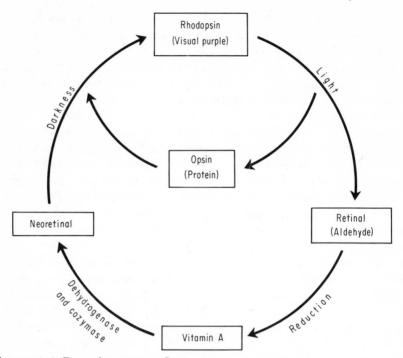

FIGURE 12–8. DARK ADAPTATION CYCLE.

vitamin A and carotene determinations. The Interdepartmental Committee on Nutrition for National Development states that "normal" serum vitamin A values range between 30 and 50 μg per 100 ml of blood. They suggest that vitamin A levels below 10 μg per 100 ml indicate a possible deficiency. Many factors other than vitamin A intake and liver stores affect the blood level, such as infections and presence of parasites. Since most individuals depend on carotene as a source of vitamin A, the serum carotene level must also be measured.

Roels and co-workers[21] made a study of 52 Indonesian boys, aged 3 to 13 years, with vitamin A-deficiency symptoms, 20 of whom had marked eye symptoms and ten slight symptoms. The boys were divided into five groups and given daily supplements including sugar, skim-milk powder, coconut oil, palm oil, and vitamin A acetate to determine the effect of an increase in dietary fat, protein, carotene, and vitamin A on the clinical symptoms. Of the 20 subjects with severe symptoms and ten subjects with slight symptoms initially, those receiving the palm oil and vitamin A supplements were cured of their night blindness after 22 days. Only one boy

[21] Roels, O. A., Djaeni, S., Trout, M. E., Lauw, T. G., Heath, A., Poey, S. H., Tarwotjo, M. S., and Suhadi, B. "The Effect of Protein and Fat Supplements on Vitamin A-Deficient Indonesian Children." *Amer. J. Clin. Nutr.*, 12:380 (1963).

showed improvement in xerophthalmia, while the Bitot spots improved in another boy. There was no improvement in the other groups.

Skeletal Tissues

During growth, continuous remodeling of the skeleton is necessary by removal of bone substances from some sections with new deposition in others, in an organized way. In the presence of an under- or oversupply of vitamin A the balance usually maintained between deposition and resorption of bone is upset. A basic defect in vitamin A deficiency is the dissolution of the cartilage matrix.

An inadequacy of vitamin A in the growing skeleton brings about changes in the skull and spinal column. The resorption of bone is decreased but the deposition continues, resulting in severe deformities.

Equally injurious to growing bone is a large excess of vitamin A, but in a different way. In this case the bone becomes fragile and fractures may occur spontaneously.

The effect of vitamin A on the teeth will be discussed in Chapter 19.

The Nervous System

The effect of vitamin A deficiency on the skull and spinal column in turn causes degenerative changes in the brain, the spinal cord, and the nerves. Early observers of animals deprived of vitamin A noted incoordination, muscular weakness, and paralysis.

In 1932, Elvehjem and Neu, working with day-old chicks on a vitamin A-deficient diet, found that one of the striking results was the development of a staggering gait and paralysis. Similar results were found by Krauss and his associates with rats, as shown in Figure 12–9. They found that after 40 to 50 days over half of the animals showed paralysis in their hind legs and great weakness and wasting of the muscles.

In 1936 Zimmerman and Cowgill found that in rats, adequate doses of carotene given relatively early in the course of the deficiency brought about resumption of normal growth and disappearance of xerophthalmia. However, the signs of the nervous disturbance persisted, which was attributed to the inability of this tissue to regenerate after severe injury.

Reproduction and Lactation

In the classic Wisconsin experiment with rations derived from a single plant source, the most unexpected result was the difference in the reproductive capacity of the cattle on the different diets. Normal young could not be produced on the wheat plant ration; the estrus cycle was delayed and in some individuals never appeared; and in others calves

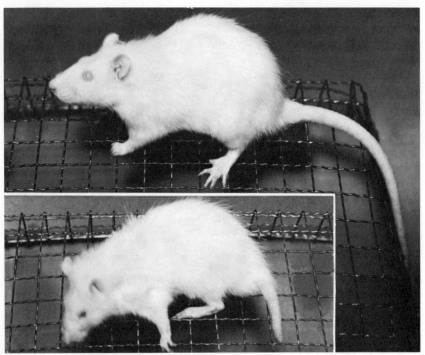

FIGURE 12–9. THESE TWO RATS ARE THE SAME AGE. The upper one had an adequate diet, the lower one a diet lacking vitamin A. The animals are trying to stand on a slanting wire screen. The upper one has no difficulty in spreading its hind legs to maintain its position, but the lower one has paralysis in the hind leg exposed and is unable to use it.

were born prematurely and died. On the corn ration the reproduction cycle was complete, and when yellow-corn grain was substituted for the wheat grain in the wheat plant ration, reproduction again became normal. It was not then known that yellow corn contained vitamin A. In 1924, the Wisconsin experimenters improved the wheat plant ration, correcting its deficiencies by adding 2 per cent of raw cod-liver oil along with other changes, including bone meal, which made a completely adequate ration for reproduction.

Sherman and F. L. MacLeod took two groups of rats from mothers on an adequate diet and fed them diets alike in all respects except that one diet was low and the other high in vitamin A. The diet with the lesser amount of vitamin A proved sufficient for almost normal growth, but not for successful reproduction. The animals receiving the more liberal allowance of vitamin A grew to fully average adult size and reproduced successfully.

Dann, in the Nutritional Laboratory at the University of Cambridge in 1934, found that when the mother's diet was rich in carotene, the amount of vitamin A in the young rat's liver was three times as great as when the mother's diet was lacking in carotene. The liver at birth varies considerably in the total amount of vitamin A present.

Hale in 1935 reported the development of abnormalities in pigs where the maternal diet was just sufficient in vitamin A to allow for the completion of gestation. Death or resorption of the fetus occurred if the diet was not adequate. Warkany and his associates in 1945 reported similar results in rats. They found that when the maternal diet was deficient in vitamin A, the normal development of the eyes, lungs, heart, kidney, testes, and diaphragm of the fetus was interrupted. In 1953 studies[22] showing the prevention of these defects were reported by Warkany's laboratory when vitamin A was given at different times during the developmental period. Further investigation is needed to determine whether a deficiency of vitamin A in human maternal dietaries is ever a cause of congenital malformation.

Metabolic Role of Vitamin A

Prior to absorption, vitamin A ester is hydrolyzed in the intestine. Vitamin A alcohol is esterified mainly with palmitic acid in the mucosal cell. By way of the lymphatic system and blood stream the vitamin A ester is carried to the liver, where it is stored.[23]

Recent studies, as summarized by Wolf[24] in Table 12–1, help us to identify some of the basic metabolic mechanisms of vitamin A, or a "vitamin A complex" of compounds. The number of metabolic reactions in which it takes part, in different forms, as free vitamin A, or as aldehyde or acid, is almost as great as the number of clinical manifestations we have been discussing.

Sources

Vitamin A was first discovered in animal fats (butter, egg yolk, and cod-liver oil). But very shortly the green leaves of alfalfa, cabbage, spinach, and young clover were also found to be good sources (of provitamin A as we now know), and eventually Drummond showed that the cod and other fishes derive their vitamin A from small marine animals, which in turn get it from various minute marine plants, algae, and the like. Thus the dependence of the animal on the plant for vitamin A was established. Now we know that plants have only the provitamin A or carotene. Higher forms of animal life can transform carotene into vitamin

[22] Review. "Malformations Induced by Vitamin A Deficiency." *Nutr. Rev.*, 12:248 (1954).

[23] Review. "Intestinal Absorption of Vitamin A." *Nutr. Rev.*, 22:86 (1964).

[24] Wolf, G. "Some Thoughts on the Metabolic Role of Vitamin A." *Nutr. Rev.*, 20:161 (1962).

TABLE 12–1. METABOLIC ROLE
OF VITAMIN A AND DERIVATIVES

Active Compound	Biochemical Reaction	Clinical Effect
At level of vitamin A or aldehyde only		
1. Vitamin A aldehyde	Reaction with opsin	Vision
2. Vitamin A (or possibly an "active form")	Unknown	Male and female reproduction
At level of vitamin A, aldehyde or acid		
1. Vitamin A (in vitro) Vitamin A or vitamin A acid (in vivo)	Release of proteolytic enzyme	Dissolution of cartilage matrix
2. Vitamin A or "active form," derivable from vitamin A or vitamin A acid	Synthesis of mucopolysaccharides	Stimulation of epithelial mucus secretion
3. Vitamin A or vitamin A acid (or possibly an "active form")	Corticosterone synthesis	Adrenal cortex lesions, loss of glyconeogenesis in deficiency

A, but there are species differences in converting carotenes to vitamin A. It is desirable to speak of the vitamin A value of foods rather than the vitamin A content.

When seeds are sprouted in the absence of light, little, if any, pro-vitamin A (carotene) is produced, but as soon as the sprouts come to light and their tips begin to turn green, provitamin A is rapidly formed. Leaves that do not turn green, such as the inner leaves of lettuce and cabbage, are not nearly so rich a source of the vitamin as the green parts. In general, the thinner and greener a leaf is, the better source it is likely to be.

The storage parts of plants, as thickened roots or tubers, and the endosperm of seeds are relatively poor sources but there is much variation among individual plants; yellow corn is richer than white; sweet potatoes are richer than white ones; and carrots have a higher value than either white or yellow turnips. Of the fruits, apricots, cantaloupes, yellow peaches, and papayas are among the best sources of provitamin A. The oils of certain tropical plants such as the red oil of the palm are quite high in carotene, about 1,000 I.U. per gram.

Whole milk is an important source of preformed vitamin A, as are butter and egg yolk. In some areas the skimmed milk is fortified with vitamin A. Fortified margarine is at least as good a source of vitamin A value as butter.

Preformed vitamin A in the animal is stored in the glandular organs, liver being richest of all. The liver of the seal, the whale, and the polar bear is extremely rich in vitamin A, values from 13,000 to 18,000 I.U. per gram having been reported. However, some reports have indicated a possible toxicity from these livers.

Fish liver oils are among the richest source of preformed vitamin A, but the oils of different fish vary greatly one from another, the cod-liver oil containing about 1,000 I.U. per gram and the halibut and tuna about 50,000 to 100,000 I.U. per gram.

Vitamin A in animal fats loses its potency gradually on exposure to air and more rapidly when thoroughly aerated, especially if the temperature is raised. As it exists in plant tissues as provitamin A, it is not so easily oxidized and withstands ordinary cooking temperatures without marked loss. Table 12–2 shows the comparative vitamin A values of some

TABLE 12–2. FOOD PORTIONS YIELDING VITAMIN A VALUE APPROXIMATELY EQUIVALENT TO THAT IN ONE CUP OF MILK*

Foods	Gm	Foods	Gm
Apricot, dried	3	Liver, calf	2
Carrot	3	Margarine	10
Cheese, Cheddar	26	Milk, whole	244
Egg yolk	10	Spinach	4
Kale	3	Sweet potato	4
Kidney, beef	50	Tomato	38

*350 International Units of vitamin A value.

of our common foods. Additional information regarding the vitamin A value of foods will be found in Tables A–4 and A–8 in the Appendix.

Requirement

The requirement for vitamin A is expressed in International units (I.U.). See page 188 for the discussion of the International unit. The necessity for a liberal supply of vitamin A in the human diet has been established, and we have already seen that requirements are high in periods of rapid growth, in pregnancy, and in lactation.

The two sources of vitamin A in our diets, (1) the preformed vitamin, and (2) the provitamin or carotene, have been discussed. It has been estimated that only one third of the vitamin A in the average American diet occurs as the preformed vitamin, the other two thirds occurring as the provitamin. A great variation in the availability of the carotene has been observed depending on the source and the other substances in the diet. Evidence indicates that carotene is converted into vitamin A in the intestinal wall. For practical purposes it is considered that 2 I.U. of beta-carotene is equivalent to 1 I.U. of vitamin A in man.

The Medical Research Council of Great Britain[25] has reported prophylactic and curative tests on young adults on vitamin A-deficient diets. The adult requirement with a margin of safety suggested in this report was 2500 I.U. of vitamin A. Taking two thirds as carotene and one third as preformed vitamin A, the National Research Council (1963) recommends 5,000 I.U. of vitamin A value per day or 4,000 I.U. from carotene and 1,000 I.U. from preformed vitamin A. In terms of body weight, levels of intake providing 20 I.U. of vitamin A or 40 I.U. of beta-carotene per kilogram of body weight have been found to meet minimal requirements.

Children and pregnant and lactating women have relatively higher requirements for vitamin A than average adults. The allowances recommended for infants and children are liberal in order to provide for growth and adequate body stores. In the second and third trimesters of pregnancy an additional daily allowance of 1,000 I.U. has been recommended. For lactation the additional daily allowance has been increased to 3,000 I.U. above that of the "reference woman." The Food and Nutrition Board of the National Research Council in 1963 proposed the Recommended Daily Dietary Allowances given in Table A–1 of the Appendix.

Hypervitaminosis A

This chapter would not be complete without a word of warning in regard to the possibility of taking too much vitamin A lest in our zeal to keep our stores of vitamin A at the optimum we overdo a good thing. Our readily available vitamin capsules and vitamin A concentrates make it easy to take large amounts of vitamin A, and there are on record in the medical literature many cases where this has happened and toxic effects have resulted. One such case, in a food faddist, is described by Bergen and Roels.[26] If one pays attention to the recommendations of a physician, there should be no danger of getting too much.

When one follows the rules for the selection of an adequate diet, the recommended allowances for vitamin A (5,000 I.U. daily) may be easily attained so that vitamin supplements are not necessary. It is not likely that an excessive level of vitamin A will be obtained from foods alone. It would appear that a diet high in the carotenoids would not lead to hypervitaminosis A. Carotenemia (excess carotene in the blood) may occur but this appears to be a harmless condition although imparting a yellowish tinge to the skin. However, supplements supplying as much as five times

---

[25] Hume, E. M., and Krebs, H. A. (eds.). *Vitamin A Requirement of Human Adults.* London: Medical Research Council, Special Report Series No. 264 (1949).

[26] Bergen, S. S., and Roels, O. A. "Hypervitaminosis A. Report of a Case." *Amer. J. Clin. Nutr.,* **16**:265 (1965).

the daily recommended allowance could be potentially toxic if continued over a period of time.[27]

A great excess of vitamin A in an early period of growth may interfere with normal skeletal development leading to softening and fragility of the bones. Vitamin A intoxication has been found to occur more frequently in infants and young children than in adults. Symptoms are varied depending on the severity of the intoxication and include conditions such as anorexia, skeletal pain, patchy loss of hair, dry skin with ulcerated areas, fissures of the lips, tenderness and swelling in the extremities. Serum vitamin A is abnormally high and even after withdrawal of vitamin A concentrates may continue to be elevated for a period of months. Usually clinical symptoms subside within a short time after withdrawal of the concentrate. In the patient described by Bergen and Roels most of the clinical symptoms disappeared within two months. Hypervitaminosis A has been observed in arctic expeditions after consumption of polar bear, whale, and seal liver, which have been found to be extraordinarily high in vitamin A.

REFERENCES

Beaton, G. H., and McHenry, E. W. (eds.). *Nutrition—A Comprehensive Treatise*, Vol. II, p. 2, I. Dam, H., and Sondergaard, E. "Vitamin A." New York: Academic (1964).

Bourne, G. H. (ed.). *World Review of Nutrition and Dietetics*, Vol. 5. Owen, E. C. "Some Aspects of the Metabolism of Vitamin A and Carotene," p. 133. New York: Hafner (1965).

Butt, H. R. "The Fat Soluble Vitamins A, E, and K." *Handbook of Nutrition*, 2nd ed., Chap. 11. Chicago: American Medical Association (1951).

Darby, W. J., McGanity, W. J., McLaren, D. S., Patson, D., Alemu, A. Z., and Medhen, A. M. G. "Bitot's Spots and Vitamin A Deficiency." *Pub. Health Rep.*, **75**:738 (1960).

Fell, H. B. "The Effect of Vitamin A on Tissue Structure." *Proceedings of the Nutrition Society*, **19**:50 (1960).

Harris, L. J. *Vitamins in Theory and Practice*, 4th ed., Chap. 7. New York: Cambridge U. P. (1955).

Jolliffe, N., (ed.). *Clinical Nutrition*, Chap. 13. Kagan, B. M. "Vitamin A Malnutrition." New York: Hoeber (1962).

McCollum, E. V. "Early Experiences with Vitamin A—A Retrospect." *Nutr. Rev.*, **10**:161 (1952).

McLaren, D. S. "Xerophthalmia." *Amer. J. Clin. Nutr.*, **11**:603 (1962).

———. "Xerophthalmia: A Neglected Problem." *Nutr. Rev.*, **22**:289 (1964).

[27] Council on Foods and Nutrition. "Vitamin Preparations as Dietary Supplements, and as Therapeutic Agents." *J. Amer. Med. A.*, **169**:41 (1959).

McLaren, D. S., Shirajian, E., Tchalian, M., and Khoury, G. "Xerophthalmia in Jordan." *Amer. J. Clin. Nutr.*, **17**:117 (1965).

Review. "The Effect of an Excess of Vitamin A on Membranes in Vitro." *Nutr. Rev.*, **22**:146 (1964).

Roderuck, C. E., Sidwell, V. D., Jebe, E. H., and Eppright, E. S. "Studies of Serum Carotenoids and Vitamin A in Iowa School Children." *Amer. J. Clin. Nutr.*, **13**:186 (1963).

Sherman, H. C. *Chemistry of Food and Nutrition*, 8th ed., Chap. 23. New York: Macmillan (1952).

United Nations Children's Fund. *Children of the Developing Countries.* Cleveland, Ohio: World (1963).

Youmans, J. B. "Deficiencies of the Fat-Soluble Vitamins," *Handbook of Nutrition*, 2nd ed., Chap. 21. Chicago: American Medical Association (1951).

✿ 13 ✿

Thiamine

Discovery

A nerve disease called beriberi was known to the Chinese as early as 2697 B.C. It was widespread in the Orient among the rice-eating peoples particularly in the Malay States, Thailand, Korea, Japan, and the Philippines. That it was not confined to these areas is shown by its occurrence in more recent times in Africa, South America, Norway, different parts of the United States, Labrador, and Newfoundland, where white flour was extensively used. Van Leent in 1873 was apparently the first to infer that beriberi had its origin in the type of diet. He was almost able to eradicate beriberi among the Indian sailors in the Dutch Navy by reducing the ration of rice.[1] In 1872, a young Japanese navy medical officer named Takaki, who noticed the great havoc wrought by beriberi, and unaware of the work of Van Leent, was determined to find the cause and remedy. In 1875, he went to England and entered St. Thomas's Hospital Medical School, where he remained five years. Upon his return he was made Director of the Tokyo Naval Hospital, and began to study everything that might throw any light on the cause of this scourge. He finally came to the conclusion that the disease was of dietary origin, and having been made director-general of the Medical Department of the Navy, he succeeded in obtaining permission from the Japanese Admiralty to make a number of experiments in the service "upon a scale of great magnitude."[2]

In 1882, the "Ruijo," a training ship bearing 276 men, sailed from Yeddo Bay to New Zealand, South America, and Hawaii, and then back to Japan, a voyage lasting 272 days. There were 169 cases of beriberi and 25 deaths before the ship reached Honolulu. Then Takaki sent the "Tsukuba," another training ship, with a similar crew over the same course, but with a better ration, as shown in Table 13–1.

---

[1] Goldblith, S. M., and Joslin, M. A. *Milestones in Nutrition.* 2:259, 281. Westport, Conn.: Avi (1964).

[2] Takaki, K. "The Preservation of Health Amongst the Personnel of the Japanese Navy and Army." *Lancet,* 1:1369 (1906).

TABLE 13-1. DIETS ON THE "RUIJO" AND THE "TSUKUBA"

Food	Diet on the "Ruijo" Weight, oz.	Diet on the "Tsukuba" Weight, oz.
Rice	27.78	22.16
Vegetables	9.56	12.41
Fish	4.85	6.56
Meat	2.18	8.02
Other food (not specified)	—	Milk (condensed) and tea added
Total weight of ration	50.37	78.38

The "Tsukuba" was gone 287 days, but only 14 men had beriberi, and these did not eat their full allowance of the new ration. In 1885, as a result of this experiment, Takaki secured the adoption of a new dietary for the entire Japanese navy, in which the total food was further increased, the rice decreased, wheat and bread added, the vegetables increased, and some milk added.

A few years later, in the Dutch East Indies, Dr. C. Eijkman, director of the hygienic laboratory at Batavia, Java, noted that certain fowls on polished rice diets manifested symptoms curiously like beriberi and began an investigation of the cause. He reported that the disease of the fowls (polyneuritis) was similar to beriberi in man and could be cured by giving rice polishings. His young associate, Dr. Grijns, was the first to interpret correctly (in 1901) the relation between polished rice diets and the etiology of beriberi and concluded that an essential nutrient was removed with the polishing. Eijkman induced the government to order an examination into the influence of rice feeding on human beriberi in the prisons of Java, by which it was shown that only 1 in 10,000 living on unpolished rice acquired the disease, while 3,900 in 10,000 living on polished rice developed it. The work of Eijkman was extended by Grijns, who showed that the antineuritic substance that Eijkman had found in the outer layers and embryo of the rice kernel also occurred in certain beans (*Phaseolus radiatus*).

Such experiences stimulated effort to discover the nature of this antineuritic substance. Several independent investigators within less than a year succeeded almost simultaneously in separating from rice bran and from yeast a substance that would cure the disease when induced in pigeons by feeding polished rice. Of these, Casimir Funk was the first to announce publicly that he had been able to cure, in a few hours, pigeons paralyzed with polyneuritis, by a few milligrams of the crystals that he had prepared from the rice bran (December 1911). He suggested for this substance the name *beriberi vitamine*.

While Eijkman was investigating the antineuritic properties of rice polishings, Hopkins in England was seeking the reason why a very small portion of milk added to a diet of purified proteins, fats, carbohydrates, and mineral salts made the difference between nutritional success and disaster.

Also, in New Haven, Osborne and Mendel were finding repeated instances of the superiority of their "protein-free milk" over a mixture of pure lactose plus pure mineral salts added to their basal diet.

This was also just about the time that Hart, Humphrey, Steenbock, and McCollum published the first report of their investigations in feeding cattle on rations from a single plant source, namely, corn compared with wheat. McCollum and Davis found that the wheat kernel, supplemented with purified casein, a mixture of mineral salts, and butter fat, provided a diet satisfactory for the growth of the young, the maintenance of the adult, and the production of vigorous offspring. But no such success attended the application of the same procedure to polished rice. The animals failed to grow and developed polyneuritis. They then tried replacing part of the rice by milk sugar, with the result that the animals began to grow as soon as it constituted 5 per cent of the ration. If, however, they used highly purified milk sugar, there was no growth. Thinking that something must have been left behind in the water from which the milk sugar had crystallized out, they evaporated this on the food mixture and the ration so reinforced was able to sustain growth.

In 1915 this new growth-promoting food factor was called by McCollum "water-soluble B." He found that pigeons could be cured of polyneuritis by adding to polished rice the same preparation that had been found to induce growth in rats and concluded that a single substance possessed both antineuritic and growth-promoting properties. It soon came to be known as vitamin B. But as the quantitative study of its presence in foods was promptly pursued in many laboratories, various unaccountable irregularities in the results suggested that there must be more than one vitamin. Thus yeast when heated under pressure (autoclaved) lost its power to cure polyneuritis in a pigeon, yet it could still stimulate growth in a rat. It took a number of years for the full significance of such conflicting results to be reconciled, but by 1928 it was finally established beyond doubt that what had been thought a single vitamin was in reality a mixture containing an antineuritic substance, at that time called vitamin B or B_1, and now known as thiamine, and another growth-promoting factor, which was called vitamin G or B_2 and now known as riboflavin.

Crystallization and Chemical Identification of Thiamine

Funk in 1911 prepared a few crystals of what he called the "beriberi vitamine" but could not get sufficient material for further study. It was not until 1926, in Java where Eijkman had made his pioneer studies, that pure crystals, prepared by Jansen and Donath, were used to cure human beriberi. Within a very few years workers in Japan, Germany, and England were also able to obtain crystals which by all biological tests seemed to be identical.

The next step was their chemical analysis. Progress was difficult because of the small amount of material available. Among those actively seeking to solve the problem of chemical structure was R. R. Williams,[3] Chemical Director of the Bell Telephone Laboratories, who made his avocation research upon vitamin B. In the Philippines he had seen beriberi at first hand, and on returning to this country, he labored for nearly 24 years in research which finally led to the development of a method by which he could extract as much as 5 gm of pure crystals from a ton of rice polishings. See Figure 13–1. With sufficient material and able assistance from the Carnegie Institution of Washington, which supplied funds; from the Laboratory of Physiological Chemistry at Teachers College, Columbia University, where much of the work was done; and from the Department of Biochemistry of the College of Physicians and Surgeons of Columbia University the problem of chemical structure was attacked with fresh zeal. A misfortune of earlier years was turned to good account, for sulfur dioxide, which destroyed the vitamin where it was

FIGURE 13–1. CRYSTALS OF THIAMINE. (*Courtesy of Merck & Co., Inc.*)

[3] Williams, R. R. *Toward the Conquest of Beriberi.* Cambridge, Mass.: Harvard University Press (1961).

used as a preservative for rice polish extracts, proved a tool for neatly splitting the molecule into two pieces. One of the pieces contained the sulfur, and this was found to be held in a chemical structure not hitherto found in nature, so that Williams remarked, "It is not difficult to imagine that its discovery may ultimately prove more important in biochemistry than the structure of the vitamin itself."[4] Only the development of new techniques in chemistry made possible the many tests that were necessary for the full identification of both parts of the molecule and of the way in which they are held together.

The next objective was to find a way to synthesize the vitamin. This would not only afford final proof that the structural formula was right but would open the way to commercial manufacture of the vitamin and afford further study of the functions of the vitamin in nutrition. Nearly two years more were spent in this phase of the investigation, and in 1936 the building of the molecule, step by step, was finally accomplished.[5]

Beriberi and Polyneuritis

Beriberi is a disease characterized by changes in the nervous system which have far-reaching effects throughout the whole body. In human beings it has two fairly well-defined forms: dry beriberi (peripheral neuritis) (see Figure 13–2A), in which there is a great muscular wasting, loss of sensation in the skin, and paralysis beginning in the legs and finally extending to the upper portions of the body; and wet beriberi (Figure 13–2B), in which there is a marked edema in the arms, legs (Figure 13–3), and finally the trunk, with great enlargement of the heart, so that death from heart failure is common. The disease develops on diets low but not completely lacking in thiamine. They are usually poor in other respects, so that the uniformity of symptoms observed in laboratory animals does not occur. A great deficiency of thiamine produces the disease rapidly, but a less severe shortage may delay development of acute symptoms for a long time, and slight deficiency gives rise only to subacute symptoms. Beriberi often follows prolonged fevers, especially malaria.

In pigeons deprivation of thiamine results in polyneuritic symptoms in from three to five weeks. There is weakness and general paralysis; sometimes there develops the typical head retraction as shown in Figure 13–4A. In dogs there is a tendency for paralysis to manifest itself in the hind legs. In young rats a characteristic distortion of the spinal column is one of the first symptoms of the nerve involvement resulting from thiamine deficiency (Figure 13–5).

[4] Williams, R. R. "The Vitamin B Adventure." *Amer. J. Pub. Health*, **25**:481 (1935).
[5] Williams, R. R., and Cline, J. K. "Synthesis of Vitamin B₁." *J. Amer. Chem. Soc.*, **58**:1504 (1936).

A   B

FIGURE 13–2. TWO TYPES OF BERIBERI. *A.* This thirty-four-year-old Filipino mother is suffering from "dry" beriberi, although she shows little outward sign of the disease. Note the leanness of the legs. Of her ten pregnancies three resulted in spontaneous abortions; five infants died before reaching three months of age. Only two survive, one an infant, the other nine years of age. *B.* This twenty-two-year-old expectant Filipino mother is suffering from "wet" beriberi. Death from beriberi faces her unborn child. Her hands and feet are already numb and her legs swollen. The pits on her shins have been produced by finger pressure and are characteristic of this type of beriberi. (*Courtesy of Food and Nutrition Research Center, Manila.*)

In human beings it is now realized that thiamine plays an important role in the maintenance of a functionally normal nervous system and that a deficiency of thiamine may be responsible for various forms of nerve disturbance. The ordinary American dietary in which too much prominence was given to artificially refined foods tended, until the "enrichment" of white bread and flour was enforced, to be low in thiamine. If there is any failure of absorption because of unfavorable conditions in the alimentary tract or because of infection, a real deficiency may exist where it is not suspected. A study of 100 cases of human neuritis by Vorhaus and Williams directed attention to the value of thiamine for the well-being of the nervous system. Many of these cases were of long duration and unresponsive to other forms of treatment, but only 10 per cent of the

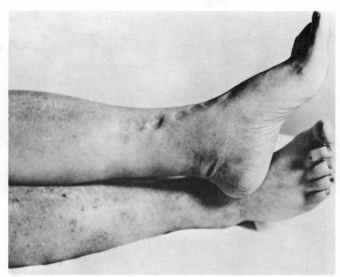

FIGURE 13–3. A CASE OF PITTING EDEMA RESULTING FROM THIAMINE DEFICIENCY. Note the pitting caused by pressure of the fingers. (*Courtesy of Dr. T. D. Spies.*)

patients failed to improve when given 10 mg of pure thiamine daily, and 44 per cent were entirely cured.[6]

The cause of these symptoms in the peripheral nerves was first sought by histological examination of the nerve fibers, but no changes in their structure were found that could account for the severity of the symptoms or the speed with which they could be cured. It is a spectacular effect that one observes when a rat, moribund from inanition and polyneuritis and unwilling to eat, can be revived within two or three hours if given massive doses of thiamine by mouth, and still more dramatic if the vitamin is injected directly into the blood stream, because the recovery may take no more than a quarter or half an hour. It was the successful use of this latter method of curing polyneuritis that aided Williams materially in developing his method of isolating thiamine from rice bran, since at each step of the work tests could be made to see whether the vitamin was in a solution or in the material filtered out.

Such changes are too speedy to involve regeneration of tissue. Hence the solution of the problem had to be sought by study of function. In 1929, Peters, of the University of Oxford, found that pigeons dying of polyneuritis have an increased amount of lactic acid peculiarly localized in the lower parts of the brain. Proof that shortage of thiamine was respon-

[6] Vorhaus, M. G., and Williams, R. R. "Studies on Crystalline Vitamin B." *J. Amer. Med. A.*, **105**:1580 (1935).

A   B

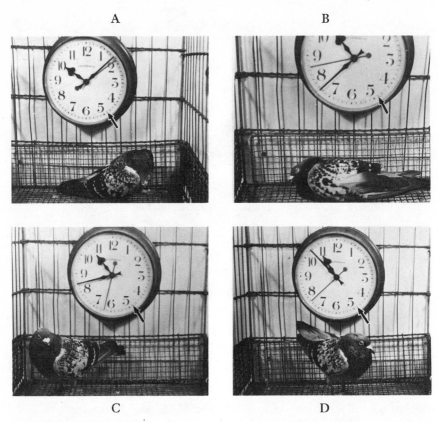

C   D

FIGURE 13–4. RAPID RECOVERY OF PIGEON DEFICIENT IN THIAMINE. The thiamine-deficient pigeon in *A* recovered rapidly following a cerebral injection of thiamine. This recovery took place in less than an hour (*B, C,* and *D*). (*Courtesy of Sir Rudolph Peters from* Biochemical Lesions and Lethal Synthesis; *published with the permission of Pergamon Press, Limited.*)

sible was furnished by injecting it under the skull into the brain where the lactic acid had accumulated. In less than an hour the acute nervous symptoms and excess lactic acid would disappear. See Figure 13–4. The power of the brain tissue to use oxygen when glucose was provided for carbohydrate combustion would be restored. This not only solved the problem of the cause of polyneuritis but also proved that thiamine is a regulator of carbohydrate metabolism. Funk called attention in 1914 to the fact that polyneuritis developed more quickly if the animals were given diets very rich in carbohydrate. Later, various workers reported that thiamine deficiency brings about a drop in carbohydrate tolerance even before nervous disturbances appear. Also it was found that in human beriberi there is an increase in the blood of intermediate products of carbohydrate metabolism which disappear on administration of thiamine.

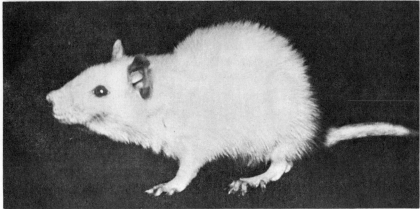

FIGURE 13–5. POLYNEURITIS IN THE RAT. The thiamine-deficient rat (*upper*) shows the typical arched back and hyperextended hind legs. Such rats show spastic gait, turn awkwardly, lose balance and sense of direction. The same rat (*lower*) eight hours after administration of thiamine has normal use of its hind legs and has regained balance. (*Courtesy of The Upjohn Company.*)

Explanation of these changes is found in the work of various investigators, who have established the fact that thiamine forms a compound with phosphoric acid known as thiamine pyrophosphate (TPP or cocarboxylase). Thus thiamine pyrophosphate is the coenzyme of numerous enzyme systems. It functions in carbohydrate metabolism in the decarboxylation of alpha-keto acids such as pyruvic acid. In a thiamine deficiency pyruvate tends to accumulate in the blood and tissues. Utilization of pyruvate is a strategic step in the mechanism of the cycle to provide energy, and thiamine is needed to prevent the failure of the metabolic processes at this point.

The levels of lactic and pyruvic acids in the blood following a metabolic load of glucose and the urinary excretion of thiamine have been used to determine the nutritional status of thiamine. That an early sign of thiamine deficiency can be detected in the red blood cell has been recently discovered. There is a decrease in the activity of an enzyme, the erythrocyte transketolase, the effect of which can be measured to detect a marginal thiamine deficiency. This provides a new diagnostic aid.[7]

BERIBERI IN PRISON CAMPS

Numerous cases of beriberi in Japanese prison camps during World War II afforded an unusual opportunity to observe the characteristics of beriberi. Two exceptionally well-qualified physicians, Dr. Eric Cruickshank and Dr. R. C. Burgess, were fellow prisoners at Changi prison on the Island of Singapore for three and one-half years. This was a large camp at the outset, having a population of about 52,000 British and Australians with a few Eurasian troops. Various lots of prisoners were transferred and others brought in.

These two physicians were in charge of the prevention and treatment of nutritional diseases in the camp. Although there were thousands of cases of beriberi, careful records were kept on 400. The European prisoners observed were well educated and highly cooperative. The three earliest cases developed within a month of imprisonment in men who had histories of previous heavy alcohol consumption. This is an interesting observation because thiamine deficiency is associated with alcoholism probably because of the deficient intake of protective foods.

The highest incidence occurred in those doing the heaviest work, the majority of the prisoners doing physical work for 8 to 12 hours daily. This is in line with the fact that there is a relationship between thiamine and energy expenditure. Loss of appetite appeared to a more or less marked degree as an early symptom. Some men found it difficult to adjust to a diet of plain boiled rice. Intestinal symptoms, such as diarrhea, nausea, vomiting, feeling of distention after eating, and colic, were evident. Neurological symptoms were present in about two thirds of 260 cases in one group of men. Signs of neurological impairment included absence of knee and ankle jerks and arm reflexes, aching pain in the muscles with cramps in the calves, and numbness. Acute cardiac beriberi was observed frequently, but many of these cases were sent to hospitals away from the camp and detailed records were not available to the prison-camp physicians.

CONTROLLED EXPERIMENT IN BATAAN

That the mortality rate of a large population group can be reduced by a slight change in the nutritive quality of the diet was convincingly

[7] Brin, M. "Erythrocyte as a Biopsy Tissue for Functional Evaluation of Thiamine Adequacy." *J. Amer. Med. A.*, **187**:762 (1964).

demonstrated under controlled experimental conditions in the Province of Bataan in the Philippines. This tremendous undertaking was directed by R. R. Williams, who might well be called "the father of the enrichment program." By addition of a premix containing thiamine, niacin, and iron to all of the polished rice produced in one area with a population of 63,000 people, thus ensuring almost exclusive use of this enriched rice as the basic source of calories, the mortality rate due to beriberi was reduced from 263 per 100,000 in 1947–48 to 28 per 100,000 in 1949–50. The rate in 1949–50 is only a small fraction of the lowest annual rate previously recorded in Bataan. The incidence of beriberi in the seven cities in the experimental area was reduced by approximately 90 per cent. The comparison of the mortality rate in the experimental area with that of an adjacent control area having a population of 29,000 is shown in Figure 13–6. The mortality rate remained high in the control zone until enriched rice began to creep in. By 1950, the death rate from beriberi in all of Bataan reached zero.

Although a law was enacted in 1952 to enforce the enrichment of rice in the Philippines, there was opposition among the millers' groups because of personal interests. Even though many attempts have been made to bring about means of enforcement of the law, it has not been possible to do so. R. R. Williams, through this convincing demonstration, had hoped rice enrichment would be applied in areas where beriberi is endemic. However, rice enrichment has not yet had wide application for a number of reasons although it is relatively inexpensive. In areas where there are large numbers of small rice mills, the organization and control of rice enrichment is difficult. In some areas, commercial and political considerations have interfered.

Preventive measures recommended by the Nutrition Committee for South and East Asia include the following: "(a) general improvement of

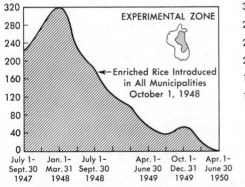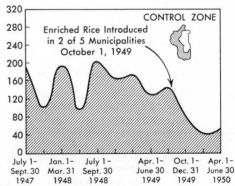

FIGURE 13–6. REDUCTION IN BERIBERI DEATH RATE PER 100,000 POPULATION IN BATAAN. These graphs show the effects of the enrichment of rice on the mortality rate in Bataan from 1947 to 1950 in an experimental and a control zone. (*Courtesy of Food and Nutrition Research Center, Manila.*)

the diet to increase its thiamine content; (b) encouraging the use of un-dermilled rice; (c) encouraging the use of parboiled rice; (d) influencing methods of preparing and cooking rice to preserve its thiamine content to the greatest extent possible; (e) rice enrichment; and (f) the greater use of synthetic thiamine in various ways, apart from rice enrichment."[8]

BERIBERI IN INFANTS

Infantile beriberi is almost always an acute disease of nursing babies whose mothers have a mild chronic form of beriberi. It is characterized by edema, cardiac disturbance, gastrointestinal difficulties, and retarded growth. Over the years it has been common in the Philippines and other rice-eating countries. According to Dr. R. R. Williams,[9] of 25,000 deaths from beriberi in the Philippines, 75 to 85 per cent were deaths of in-fants.

In 1928, Dr. Hoobler[10] observed beriberi in many infants in the tropics. He described the reponse of one of these infants given one-half teaspoon-ful of brewer's yeast concentrate daily for two weeks. This infant changed "from a thin, pale, spastic, restless, whining infant, refusing part of its formula, to a happy, rosy-cheeked, smiling baby whose appetite seemed never to be completely satisfied and whose gain in weight was remarkable." Upon his return to the United States, Dr. Hoobler recom-mended a substance rich in thiamine for infants since he thought there were possibly mild cases of beriberi in the children's hospital wards. To-day babies in the United States are fortunate in having the benefit of cereals enriched with thiamine in their daily diet.

The effect of thiamine on appetite is very striking both at the onset of the deficiency and when the vitamin is administered to a deficient animal. Cowgill and associates,[11] working with dogs, found that a dog would eventually lose the impulse to eat on a thiamine-deficient diet and regain his keen appetite when a dose of thiamine was given either by mouth or by injection. Many factors may affect the appetite, but if it is poor, and the administration of extra thiamine brings about improvement, the con-clusion would seem justified that the anorexia has been due to insufficient intake of the vitamin. Thiamine acts as a regulator or stabilizer of the appetite.

[8] Fifth Report of the Joint FAO/WHO Expert Committee on Nutrition, section 12, "Beriberi" (1958).

[9] Williams, R. R. *Toward the Conquest of Beriberi*, p. 93. Cambridge, Mass.: Har-vard U. P. (1961).

[10] Hoobler, B. R. "Symptomatology of Vitamin B Deficiency in Infants." *J. Amer. Med. A.*, 91:307 (1928).

[11] Cowgill, G. R., Rosenberg, H. A., and Rogoff, J. "Studies in the Physiology of Vitamins. XV. Some Observations of the Effect of Administration of the Antineuritic and Heat Stable Factors on the Anorexia Characteristic of the Lack of the Vitamin B Complex." *Amer. J. Physiol.*, 96:372 (1931).

The Promotion of Growth

The failure of appetite and disturbances of digestion that quickly result from complete deprivation of thiamine inevitably affect growth. If a young rat is weaned from a mother on an adequate diet and then is given in its ration everything needed for growth except thiamine, it will continue to grow only until the small reserve of the vitamin in its body is exhausted, and then it will quickly decline in weight and die. From lack of nourishment the animal will become greatly emaciated and will not live long enough to show very clearly the most characteristic symptom of shortage, polyneuritis. There will, however, be some evidence of this in the distortion of the spinal column and consequent humping of the back which may be seen in Figure 13–5.

A single dose of thiamine concentrate will produce signs of returning health in a very few hours. The animal becomes interested in food and drink, the nervous symptoms are allayed, and the rapidity with which growth is resumed is truly amazing. Growth curves are shown in Figure 13–7. The speedy decline in weight of the animal without thiamine, and its recovery when on the verge of death, are typical of experience with hundreds of animals under similar circumstances.

An interesting report is that of Clements,[12] who stated that whereas infantile beriberi was rare in Australia, cases of partial thiamine deficiency due to an insufficient amount in the mother's milk were not uncommon. In 12 of 150 infants breast-fed to the age of six months he found evidence

[12] Clements, F. W. "Symptoms of Partial Vitamin B₁ Deficiency in Breast-Fed Infants." *Med. J. Australia,* **1**:12 (1942).

FIGURE 13–7. GROWTH CURVES OF RATS ON A THIAMINE-FREE DIET COMPARED WITH THOSE OF NORMAL RATS OF THE SAME AGE. When thiamine in the form of wheat-germ extract was added to the diet, the weight was tripled in less than three weeks.

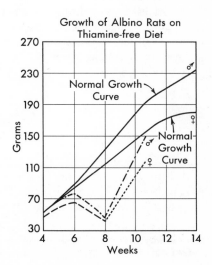

Growth of Albino Rats on Thiamine-free Diet

of such partial deficiency. When the nursing mothers whose milk showed insufficiency of thiamine were given 0.45 mg per day of the synthetic vitamin, the infants showed a prompt increase in rate of growth, and ι ·niting and constipation ceased.

Morgan and Barry of the University of California fed a group of undernourished schoolchildren between 11 and 13 years of age as a part of their school lunch two rolls daily, made with 50 per cent of white flour and 50 per cent of wheat germ, and compared their growth with that of a control group fed the same number of rolls made from white flour only. The increase in weight of the wheat-germ group was approximately three times that of the white-rolls group, and gains in height, though not so striking, were significantly greater in the wheat-germ group. This increase in growth was attributed to thiamine but probably other nutrients in the wheat germ played a role as well. Such studies as this emphasize the need for continued support of the enrichment program.

The Enrichment Program in the United States

In the United States, the enrichment program was launched at the National Nutrition Conference for Defense on May 27, 1941. In 1961, the American people had benefitted by two decades of better health brought about through the enrichment program. Celebrations were held to mark the success of this great new advance in preventive medicine. Thirty states and Puerto Rico at this time had laws requiring the enrichment of white flour and bread including proper quantities of thiamine, riboflavin, niacin, and iron.

> Enrichment, kept up-to-date, can continue to be a most important public health asset. Thanks to the pioneering of scientists such as R. R. Williams and the commercial development of their discoveries, nutrients are available at reasonable cost to tailor-make enriched staple foods to meet the changing needs of the public. Most members of the cereal industry are proud of their role in helping to assure adequate nutrition in the United States. . . .[13]

Sources

Thiamine is found in many common foods but in comparatively small amounts. Oils and fats, cassava (manioc or tapioca), and refined sugar do not have any thiamine. The cereal grains are generally considered our best sources, thiamine usually occurring in the germ and outer layers.

---

[13] Bradley, W. B. "Thiamine Enrichment in the United States." *Ann. New York Acad. Sci.*, **98**:602 (1962).

However, if these grains are highly refined, such as white flour or polished rice, and are not enriched with thiamine, the diets of population groups depending on them as a major source of calories will be very deficient. Before the enrichment program became effective in the United States, it was easy to have an attractive diet adequate in all other essentials but low in thiamine because most people preferred the white bread and refined cereals. The use of enriched bread and cereals along with the whole-grain products has increased the total thiamine in the diet, and if the calories are not too low, the average American diet is likely to be adequate but will probably not have a great surplus of this vitamin. Beriberi occurs in countries where polished rice or cassava furnishes most of the calories.

Next to cereal grains, legumes are the best common source of thiamine. Peas, Lima and soybeans, both fresh and dried, are very good sources. Dried lentils, kidney, navy, and many other varieties of dried beans and peas are good sources. Other vegetable sources contributing thiamine to the diet include spinach, collards, dandelion greens, kale, mustard greens, turnip greens, cabbage, cauliflower, kohlrabi, and okra. Potatoes will furnish significant amounts of thiamine in diets where they make up a fairly large proportion of the calories, as is the case in many European countries.

Fruits as a rule are low in thiamine. However, oranges and grapefruit (fresh, canned, or frozen) contribute considerable thiamine when taken regularly.

Thiamine is not present in large amounts in any of the meats except pork and the glandular organs such as liver, beef heart, and kidney. Fish furnishes less thiamine than beef, lamb, or chicken. In eggs the thiamine is found in the yolk.

The richest natural source of thiamine is dried brewer's yeast. Wheat germ is an excellent source and is now available in most food markets. Soy flour and pecans are also good sources.

Different processes used in the preparation of ready-to-eat cereals affect the thiamine values. Reports show that when cereals are heated dry so that a large surface is exposed to a high temperature, a considerable loss of thiamine occurs. In the cooking of breakfast cereals such as oatmeal or rolled wheat with moist heat at boiling temperature, the loss is insignificant. However, 50 per cent of the thiamine may be lost in the steaming and toasting to which bran is subjected to produce a crumbled breakfast food. Many cereals now have thiamine added in amounts equal to that lost in the processes of preparation. Very little thiamine is lost in the baking of whole-wheat bread. When rice is parboiled, a process in which the rice is soaked in water, then boiled, dried, and milled, much of the thiamine of the whole rice is retained. The commercially processed product is known as "converted rice." Bulgur wheat, another nutritious food, represents man's oldest use of wheat, and has come back into greater use in recent years.

Losses of thiamine in the cooking of vegetables in water that is thrown away are significant. The addition of soda to some vegetables will increase the destruction of the thiamine present.

Dehydrating appears to have little if any effect on the thiamine content of fruits and vegetables. Sun drying of unsulfured fruits may destroy one third to one half of the thiamine, and if the fruits are sulfured, the destruction is increased to from 60 to 100 per cent.

Some foods give evidence of having a thiamine-stabilizing substance. From the above discussion it is apparent that no generally applicable estimate of thiamine losses in cooking is possible.

A few foods have been found to contain substances (probably thiaminases) that prevent the full utilization of the vitamin. Certain varieties of raw fish, clams, and shrimps ingested with meals will reduce the availability of thiamine. This can be counteracted by having generous allowances of thiamine in the diet from other foods.

Figure 13–8 shows portions of some common foods that have the same thiamine value. See Tables A–4 and A–8 in the Appendix for the thiamine values of other foods.

Requirement

The question of what constitutes an adequate intake of thiamine was first investigated by making studies of dietaries on which adults were maintaining good health and children were growing normally. Studies were then undertaken to discover, if possible, a better basis for statements of the requirement. Cowgill and his associates in 1931 found the thiamine requirement closely related to the energy metabolism in experiments on adult dogs changed from a diet rich in thiamine to one deficient in it. When some of the dogs were forced to exercise on a treadmill, signs of thiamine deficiency developed in a much shorter time than in the dogs not exercised. These findings were in line with observations of McCarrison and others that human beriberi is brought on more rapidly in patients who exert themselves physically.

Many studies on human beings to determine the most satisfactory level of thiamine intake were reported during the years 1942 through 1948. Wilder and his associates at the Mayo Foundation reported experiments on a group of 11 women in an institution placed on diets furnishing 0.22 mg of thiamine per 1,000 calories and continued on the diet for 89 to 196 days. They became irritable, quarrelsome, depressed, and uncooperative, lost manual dexterity, became inefficient in their work, and showed increasing forgetfulness. They complained of feet and hands feeling numb, suffered from headache, backache, sleeplessness, constipation, loss of ap-

FIGURE 13–8. FOOD PORTIONS YIELDING APPROXIMATELY EQUIVALENT AMOUNTS OF THIAMINE.*

	Gm		Gm
Tomato juice	100	Pork, loin, med. fat, roasted	5
Orange juice	56	Potato, boiled in jacket	56
Spinach, steamed	63	Oats, rolled, cooked	62
Bran (40%, added thiamine)	13	Egg, cooked in shell	56
Banana, A.P.	150	Peas, cooked	18
Liver, fried	19		

* 0.05 mg of thiamine.

petite, and nausea, and became more and more easily fatigued by very little exertion. Blood pressure, pulse rate, and basal metabolism decreased, while blood sugar was often found to be abnormally high. A prompt fall in urinary excretion of thiamine was observed in every case. When the amount of thiamine in the diet was increased, these symptoms of deficiency gradually disappeared and the subjects reported feeling better. This work was followed by other studies by this same group of investigators.

Melnick reported that women taking 0.7 mg and men receiving 1.0 mg per day gave no evidence of depletion. He found that normal individuals living on diets furnishing 1.0 mg of thiamine daily when given additional thiamine promptly excreted larger amounts in the urine, while deficient subjects on the same additions did not. This was taken to indicate that 1.0 mg was probably sufficient to saturate the tissues and the excess was excreted because it was not needed.

Investigations undertaken by Williams, Oldham, Keys, Najjar and Holt, Hathaway and Strom, Foltz, and Glickman, working in different laboratories, have made important contributions to our knowledge of the thiamine requirement. These studies and others have been reviewed by the Food and Nutrition Board of the National Research Council (1963), and the conclusion drawn was that the minimal requirement for adults is approximately 0.2 mg per 1,000 calories. Doubling this amount will provide a satisfactory level of thiamine under normal conditions. Regardless of the calories, a minimum thiamine intake of not less than 0.8 mg daily has been suggested. The recommended daily dietary allowance for the "reference man" needing 2,900 calories is 1.2 mg and for the "reference woman" needing 2,100 calories is 0.8 mg.

These allowances of thiamine take into consideration the fact that the animal body is capable of storing only a small amount of thiamine. It has been estimated that the adult human body does not contain more than about 30 mg of thiamine. Since the losses in the urine, feces, and perspiration must be replaced if health is to be maintained, the daily intake of thiamine must be adequate. See Tables A–1, A–5, A–6, and A–7 in the Appendix.

Toverud and others in the National Research Council Bulletin 123 reviewed the literature on thiamine needs in maternal and child nutrition through 1950. An increased need for thiamine during pregnancy is indicated but the exact requirement is uncertain. The recommended allowance is 0.2 mg daily above that for the nonpregnant woman for the last two trimesters of pregnancy.

Human milk averages 0.015 mg of thiamine per 100 ml as compared with 0.04 mg in cow's milk. The thiamine level in human milk varies with intake in contrast to a constant level in cow's milk. If the lactating mother secretes 850 ml per day, the total thiamine represented is about 0.13 mg. An allowance of 0.4 mg of thiamine above that for the nonlactating woman is recommended for lactation.

Estimating the thiamine requirement for the human infant on intakes from breast milk, cow's milk formulas, and urinary excretion studies suggests a minimum of 0.2 mg per 1,000 calories, or the same as the adult requirement. This means a recommended allowance of 0.4 mg per 1,000 calories equal to that of the adult.

The same level is recommended for children and teen-agers. For recommendations for pregnancy, lactation, and infants and children, see Tables A–1, A–5, and A–7 in the Appendix.

REFERENCES

Beaton, G. H., and McHenry, E. W. *Nutrition. A Comprehensive Treatise,* Vol. II. Goldsmith, G. A. Chap. 2. "The B Vitamins: Thiamine, Riboflavin, Niacin." New York: Academic (1964).

Elvehjem, C. A. "The Vitamin B Complex." *Handbook of Nutrition,* 2nd ed., Chap. 8, p. 162. Chicago: American Medical Association (1951).

Food and Agriculture Organization. *Rice Enrichment in the Philippines.* Rome: Nutritional Study No. 12 (1954).

Food and Nutrition Board. *Recommended Dietary Allowances,* pp. 20 and 21. Washington, D.C.: National Research Council, Publication 1146 (1964).

Goldblith, S. M., and Joslyn, M. A. *Milestones in Nutrition.* Vol. II, Chap. VII. Westport, Conn.: Avi (1964).

Goldsmith, G. A. *Nutritional Diagnosis.* p. 103. Springfield, Ill.: Thomas (1959).

Horwitt, M. K., Liebert, E., Kreisler, O., and Wiltman, P. *Investigations of Human Requirements for B Complex Vitamins.* Washington, D.C.: National Research Council, Bulletin 116 (1948).

Jolliffe, N. (ed.). *Clinical Nutrition,* 2nd ed. New York: Hoeber (1962).

Toverud, K. U., Stearns, G., and Macy, I. G. *Maternal Nutrition and Child Health. An Interpretative Review.* Washington, D. C.: National Research Council, Bulletin 123 (1950).

Williams, R. R. "Food Fortification in the Orient." *Nutr. Rev.,* **12**:289 (1954).

———. "Recollections of the Beriberi-Preventing Substance." *Nutr. Rev.,* **11**:257 (1953).

———. *Toward the Conquest of Beriberi.* Cambridge, Mass.: Harvard U. P. (1961).

Youmans, J. B. "Deficiencies of the Water-Soluble Vitamins." *Handbook of Nutrition,* 2nd ed., Chap. 22, p. 533. Chicago: American Medical Association (1951).

❧ 14 ❧

Ascorbic Acid

Discovery

Once again the hands of time are turned back many centuries to the period when scurvy was a constant menace to sailors, soldiers, and explorers, and at intervals swept over great areas of land, especially in northern regions where people had to subsist for a large part of the year on a diet consisting mainly of grain products and meat or fish. The French crusaders are reported to have suffered greatly from it in the thirteenth century. On Jacques Cartier's second voyage to Newfoundland in 1535

> . . . he wintered near an Indian village, Stavacona, in Quebec. Both the Indians and his crew were afflicted with scurvy. Between December and the middle of March, 25 men from his crew died, and the rest were so sick that recovery was despaired of except for three or four. Cartier noticed an Indian whole and sound who had been very ill with scurvy ten or twelve days earlier. He asked the Indian how he had healed himself and was told that he had taken the juice and sap of the leaves of a certain tree called "Ameda." At Cartier's request, the Indian had branches brought and showed how the bark and leaves should be boiled together and the resulting decoction taken every other day. So successful was the remedy that all Cartier's crew were speedily completely cured, and the narrator goes on to say: "It wrought so well, that if all the physicians of Montpelier and Louaine had been there, with all the drugs of Alexandria, they would not have done as much in one yere as that tree did in sixe days, for it did so preuaile, that as many as used it, by the grace of god recouered their health." He explains that the "Ameda" is thought to be the sassafras tree, but this incident occurred in the middle of March at a season when "our captaine" was walking from his boat to the shore upon the ice at the time he saw the Indian who had been healed, so the "Ameda" could not have been a deciduous tree. Lind believed it to be the American spruce.[1]

In 1747, this same Dr. Lind, who was a surgeon in the British navy, conducted a most interesting experiment to compare various articles of

[1] Appleton, V. B. "Spruce Beer as an Antiscorbutic." *J. Home Econ.*, 13:604 (1921).

diet as to their antiscorbutic properties, using as subjects 12 sailors sick with scurvy on board the "Salisbury" at sea. They had one diet common to all, water gruel sweetened with sugar in the morning, fresh mutton broth often for dinner; at other times light puddings, boiled biscuit with sugar, etc., and for supper, barley and raisins, rice and currants, sago and wine, or the like. The men were divided into pairs. One pair had each a quart of cider daily; another, a spoonful of vinegar three times a day. Two of the worst had half a pint of sea water every day; two others had each two oranges and one lemon; two others had a most amazing compound of seeds, gums, etc., with a drink of barley water acidulated with tamarinds. The result of this nutrition experiment was that in six days "the most sudden and visible good effects were perceived from the use of the oranges and lemons." He recommended that thereafter lemon juice evaporated to a syrup should be carried in all ships for the safeguarding of the sailors, and in 1795 regular administration of lemon (called lime) juice was prescribed in the British navy, wherefore British sailors are today familiarly known as "limies." With the introduction of the potato into northern Europe scurvy greatly decreased on land, extensive outbreaks occurring only when crops failed or other misfortune deprived the people of their usual food.

Scurvy was considered a disease of adults, and the recognition of it as a dietary disease was far from universal a hundred years after the rule was made for its prevention in the British navy. In 1878 a famous English physician connected with the London Hospital for Sick Children, Dr. Cheadle, described three cases of scurvy in children under three years of age. Dr. Cheadle had made the Northwest Passage, sailing from Liverpool to Quebec in 1862, and hence had traveled across the American continent to the Pacific coast. On these wanderings he "learnt much about adult scurvy, small-pox, starvation, massacres and hairbreath adventures." Returning to London, he found the doctors groping in darkness for the cause of the dreadful condition of the gums of certain children and recognized that it was scurvy. Then he asked, why did these children, of all the number in the hospital, become scorbutic? An inquiry into the diet showed that one child for eight months had had only oatmeal, rusks, and water with a little mutton broth; another for three months had lived on bread and butter with a one-seventh share in a pint of milk together with a patent infant food; the third had been weaned at two years of age and then been fed bread, butter, and tea with occasionally some sausage and a little brandy and water. Dr. Cheadle's answer to his own question was "potatoes," which most children of the poor were fed after they were weaned. His treatment consisted of unboiled milk with mashed potatoes beaten up in it, raw meat, and the juice of two oranges.

Five years later another great English physician, Sir Thomas Barlow, published a classic paper "On Cases Described as 'Acute Rickets' which are Probably a Combination of Scurvy and Rickets, the Scurvy Being an Essential and the Rickets a Variable Element." Among the symptoms noted in one of the children were an excessively pale, sallow complexion, flabby muscles, and a tendency to shriek when approached due to a "deep-seated pain connected with the bones." Hemorrhages into the muscles and under the periosteum of the bones of the legs were noted. Two teaspoonsful of orange juice were given daily, and in three days there was a notable change, and in eight weeks this child could stand upright with a little support, "was of ruddy color and his skin and muscles had become quite firm." The conclusion was reached that while the disease had occurred in rickety children, the characteristic symptoms were not due to rickets at all, but were "truly scorbutic."

Systematic Study of Antiscorbutic Foods

At the close of the nineteenth century it was known from practical experience that certain foods would cure scurvy, and various untenable theories had been proposed to account for the antiscorbutic power of these foods. In 1907 Holst and Frölich of the University of Oslo, stimulated by the success of Eijkman and others in producing experimental polyneuritis in pigeons by a faulty diet, undertook similar experiments in the hope of finding the causes of ship beriberi. Instead of pigeons they used guinea pigs and found to their surprise that, when fed polished rice, these developed, not beriberi, but *scurvy*. Further investigation showed that a diet of grain plus cabbage, dandelion, carrot, potato, or other fresh vegetable prevented the disease. They found that certain foods such as cabbage, and cauliflower lost their antiscorbutic property on heating or drying, while some others, such as potatoes, remained antiscorbutic after cooking. Fürst, working in the same laboratory, investigated dried peas, lentils, and almonds, and found that they resembled cereals in their lack of the antiscorbutic substance, but that when soaked and allowed to sprout they developed antiscorbutic properties. Uncertainty arose partly from the fact that it was found impossible to induce scurvy in rats.

The rat's immunity to scurvy was explained by the discovery that rat livers are antiscorbutic even when the animals have subsisted for a long time on a scorbutic diet. When the livers of such rats were fed to guinea pigs very ill with scurvy, the symptoms promptly disappeared and the animals gained rapidly in weight.

Hess and Unger in 1918 showed that the antiscorbutic substance could be extracted from orange juice and would cure scurvy when given by injection directly into the blood stream. By 1920 the evidence was sufficiently clear and Drummond proposed that this antiscorbutic substance be called vitamin C.

Isolation and Identification of Ascorbic Acid

In 1921, at the Lister Institute in London, Zilva succeeded in making a preparation of this easily destroyed vitamin which would keep for several months if protected from air and light. For eight years (1921–1929) Zilva pursued his researches, getting still more concentrated solutions of vitamin C and learning more about its properties. These researches brought one immediate practical return in connection with the British Air Route Expedition to Greenland in 1930–31. For over six months (October to May) one member of the party was isolated from the regular base and had to subsist, after the first month out, mainly on the sledging ration, consisting of pemmican, margarine, sugar, chocolate, cocoa, pea flour, and oats plus a casein preparation for additional protein with occasionally a teaspoonful of condensed milk. To guard against malnutrition, he added daily about 1 gm each of dried yeast and of a mineral salt mixture such as is used in laboratory studies, and one dessertspoonful of a lemon juice concentrate prepared by Zilva. Every second day he also included a dessertspoonful of cod-liver oil. On a ration thus fortified, although forced to reduce the sledging ration by one half as supplies began to run low, and although snowed up completely in his hut from the last of March to the beginning of May, he was able when relieved to ski about one mile unaided to the relief camp, and his teeth and gums remained in good condition so that he "could throughout bite hard uncooked food without discomfort."

In 1931, King and Waugh[2] succeeded in obtaining crystalline preparations of the vitamin (see Figure 14–1) from lemon juice that protected guinea pigs from scurvy when they received 0.5 mg per day. Publication followed in the spring, 1932, and their work was promptly confirmed by E. K. Nelson in the Department of Agriculture. They also obtained a sample of hexuronic acid from E. C. Kendall at Mayo Clinic prepared by an independent method from adrenal glands and found it to have identical properties and a protective potency when 0.5 mg was fed to guinea pigs. Also, apparently it was identical with a preparation obtained several years earlier at Cambridge University by Szent-Györgyi and described as a "hexuronic acid."

Often in research, independent lines of investigation suddenly converge and many perplexing problems in several fields are thereby illuminated. This was so in the case of vitamin C. Research on the nature of biological oxidations, and especially of respiration in the leaves of plants, led to the discovery by Szent-Györgyi, at that time working in England at the

[2] Waugh, W. A., and King, C. G. "Isolation and Identification of Vitamin C." *J. Biol. Chem.,* **97**:325 (1932).

FIGURE 14–1. CRYSTALS OF
ASCORBIC ACID. (*Courtesy
of Professor C. G. King.*)

University of Cambridge, of a substance in the cortex of the adrenal
gland which he identified as hexuronic acid. L. J. Harris, at Cambridge,
suggested that the hexuronic acid might be related to vitamin C, on the
basis of publications from other laboratories. Zilva, however, reported that
the product was not identical with vitamin C. Svirbely, who had worked
with King at the University of Pittsburgh in attempts to isolate the vitamin, joined with Szent-Györgyi during the winter of 1931–32 and tested
a sample of the acid that had been prepared from adrenal glands. In
April 1932, they reported protection of scurvy in guinea pigs when fed
1 mg per day. Svirbely and Szent-Györgyi then succeeded in preparing a
large quantity of the vitamin from paprikas and supplied it to a number
of organic chemists for study of its molecular structure. Other workers
were eager to extend these findings.

Crystals from lemon juice, adrenal glands, and red peppers were found
to agree in antiscorbutic value. Chemists in Europe and America attacked
the problem of chemical structure and synthesis. In 1933, Haworth in
England and Karrer and Reichstein in Zurich established the structure and
published the correct formula. Commercial synthesis followed, and ascorbic acid became the first pure vitamin available to the public by large-
scale industrial synthesis starting with glucose as the raw material. In 1939,
the name ascorbic acid was adopted by the Council on Pharmacy and
Chemistry of the American Medical Association and became the official
designation for this antiscorbutic vitamin.

Since the isolation of ascorbic acid in pure crystalline form, it has been shown that the adrenal gland of a normal guinea pig is very rich in ascorbic acid, but that the gland of a severely scorbutic animal contains practically none, The rat and the dog cannot be made scorbutic because they manufacture sufficient ascorbic acid to maintain an adequate store of this vitamin in the adrenals.

Experimental Scurvy in the Guinea Pig

For scientific study of any disease an experimental animal is necessary in order that conditions may be controlled and only one factor in a situation be varied at a time. A first step in the discovery of ascorbic acid was the observation in 1895 by Smith, of the Rockefeller Institute for Medical Research, that guinea pigs kept on a diet of oats and no fresh vegetables developed a hemorrhagic disease. As has been pointed out earlier in this chapter, Holst and Frölich produced scurvy in guinea pigs in 1907 by feeding them restricted diets. However, it was not until 1918 that Cohen and Mendel demonstrated that scurvy could be produced at will in guinea pigs by simply controlling the diet. They prepared a soybean cracker that contained all the then-known essentials of an adequate diet for guinea pigs.

At first their appearance was satisfactory. On about the tenth day, however, they exhibited a tenderness of the wrist and ankle joints, though they were still eating well and gaining in weight. Then the conditions became more severe. The joints swelled to twice or three times the normal diameter and spontaneous fracture of the wrist occurred in one animal. Appetite diminished and a sharp nutritive decline ensued.[3]

These are today recognized as characteristic symptoms of scurvy. If a healthy young guinea pig weighing about 300 gm is placed on a diet free of ascorbic acid, it continues to grow for about two weeks, then loses weight rapidly, and dies in from 26 to 34 days (Figure 14–2). When the weight begins to fall steadily, the joints become tender and swell, the animal becomes relaxed and weak as shown in Figure 14–3, and frequently, because its gums and jaws are sore, it will lie down with the side of its face on the floor of its cage in a typical "face-ache" position. The jawbones suffer from absorption and appear eroded, the gums are spongy and bleeding, the teeth become loose and take irregular positions. The roots are absorbed, and when the jaw is removed from the body and cleaned, the molars easily fall out (see Figure 19–2 in Chapter 19).

When tissues or organs are low in ascorbic acid, their respiratory activity is markedly decreased, showing that ascorbic acid is essential to the

[3] Cohen, B., and Mendel, L. B. "Experimental Scurvy of the Guinea Pig in Relation to the Diet." *J. Biol. Chem.*, **35**:425 (1918).

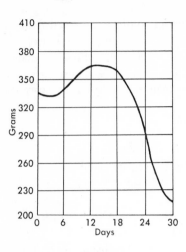

FIGURE 14–2. EFFECTS OF A SCORBUTIC DIET. Guinea pigs weighing 300 to 350 gm placed on a scorbutic diet continued to grow for about 15 days, then lost weight rapidly and died of scurvy in from 26 to 34 days. The curve is the average of ten guinea pigs on a diet lacking ascorbic acid. (*Courtesy of Professor H. C. Sherman and Miss S. L. Smith.*)

complex interplay of enzymes and oxidizable materials involved in the combustion of the fuel foods. Even more easily observable than the relationship to tissue respiration is the influence that ascorbic acid exerts on the structure of tissues. The widespread degenerative changes all over the body in scurvy have been found by Wolbach, Howe, Bessey, and others to be caused for the most part by the failure in the production

FIGURE 14–3. THE LOWEST ANIMAL IS NORMAL. The two upper ones show characteristic positions of the scorbutic guinea pig.

of collagen. This inability to produce the intercellular material, collagen, according to Wolbach is the underlying cause of the following:

1. Hemorrhages which may occur anywhere in the body.
2. Profound changes in the structure of the teeth and gums.
3. Changes in the growing ends of bones with beading and other deformities that in earlier times were mistaken for rickets.
4. The falling apart of bones owing to loss of supporting cartilage.
5. Enlargement of the heart.
6. Degeneration of muscle fibers generally, causing extreme weakness and even death.
7. Anemia due to failure of the tissues that form red blood cells and loss of blood by hemorrhage.
8. Loss of calcium through degeneration of the bone matrix so that it is no longer able to retain the mineral salts and the bones become so soft that they break spontaneously.
9. The degeneration of the sex organs.

In fact, the lack of ascorbic acid is the cause of such widespread disorganization that it is amazing that scurvy can be latent for so long a time before the onset of pain and occurrence of marked outward symptoms. It is also surprising how rapidly improvement follows the administration of the vitamin if it is given before the condition has advanced too far. In 24 hours formation of new "cement" material has been demonstrated in both bones and soft tissues.

Over the years the guinea pig has proved to be the most satisfactory of the experimental animals for the study of scurvy and the early testing of ascorbic acid in foods (Figure 14–4). Most animals are able to synthesize ascorbic acid, the exceptions being the guinea pig, the primates,

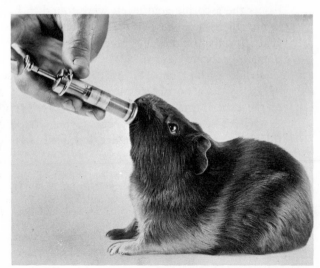

FIGURE 14–4. A GUINEA PIG BEING FED A MEASURED AMOUNT OF ORANGE JUICE. This shows an earlier method of testing the ascorbic acid in foods. (*Courtesy of Dr. H. Goss.*)

and man. Recently, it has been reported that the fruit-eating bat and the bulbul bird, both native to India, require a dietary source of ascorbic acid. It is of interest to note that most of the signs of ascorbic acid deficiency in the guinea pig have been observed in human beings.

Recent work by King and associates at Columbia University demonstrated, by the use of glucose and its derivatives, labeled by the use of radiocarbon, that ascorbic acid is synthesized from glucose in animals that do not have dietary requirement.

Ascorbic Acid and Wound Healing

As long ago as 1769 it was recorded in the report of Anson's voyage that "the scars of wounds which had been for many years healed were forced open by this virulent distemper" (scurvy). Pirani and Levenson,[4] of the United States Army Medical Nutrition Laboratory in Chicago, in 1953, demonstrated a similar condition occurring in guinea pigs reared on an adequate diet. When they weighed 450 gm, an incision 4 cm in length was made in each animal and allowed to heal for six weeks. At this time half the animals were placed on a diet free of ascorbic acid and the other half remained on the control diet. Those on the scorbutic diet developed signs of scurvy within 17 to 18 days and severe symptoms by the twenty-sixth day, when swelling, herniation, and hemorrhages were noted in the scars of the deficient pigs. No such changes occurred in the controls. In 1959, Abt, von Schuching, and Roe[5] reported the rupturing under pressure of healed abdominal incisions in guinea pigs after they had been placed on scorbutic diets. The scar tissue and muscle were found to contain a higher concentration of ascorbic acid when they were compared with the nonscar skin and muscle. In a sample of human old scar tissues the ascorbic acid levels were found to be 64 per cent greater than in normal tissue. These studies demonstrate clearly the need for ascorbic acid not only for normal healing of a wound but for the maintenance of previously formed scar tissue.

Crandon, Lund, and Dill[6] in 1940 reported a study of the development of scurvy in a normal human being. Crandon himself was the subject of the experiment, living on a scurvy-producing diet for 6 months and 18 days. The first signs of scurvy, hemorrhagic areas around the hair follicles of the legs, did not develop until after he had lived on this diet

[4] Pirani, C. L., and Levenson, S. M. "Effect of Vitamin C Deficiency on Healed Wounds." *Proc. Soc. Exper. Biol. & Med.*, 82:95 (1953).

[5] Abt, A. F., von Schuching, S., and Roe, J. H. "Connective Tissue Studies. II. The Effect of Vitamin C Deficiency on Healed Wounds." *Bull. Johns Hopkins Hosp.*, 67:105 (1959).

[6] Crandon, J. H., Lund, C. C., and Dill, D. B. "Human Experimental Scurvy." *New England J. Med.*, 223:353 (1940).

for five months. During the fourth and fifth months he experienced slight lassitude and was easily fatigued but marked fatigability did not develop until the sixth month. When he had been on the diet for three months, a 2½-in. cut was made in the lower part of his back. In 11 days the wound had healed quite normally, but when another cut was made on the other side of his back, after six months on the diet, no healing had taken place in ten days. The subject was then given daily 1 gm of ascorbic acid intravenously for ten days in succession while continuing on the scurvy-producing diet. Satisfactory healing of the wound resulted, and a new incision made directly across the healed area also healed normally. The ascorbic acid level of the plasma fell to zero in 42 days and that of the white cells in 122 days. Similar observations were reported by the British Medical Research Council[7] of experimental scurvy in a group of volunteers (see Figure 14–5).

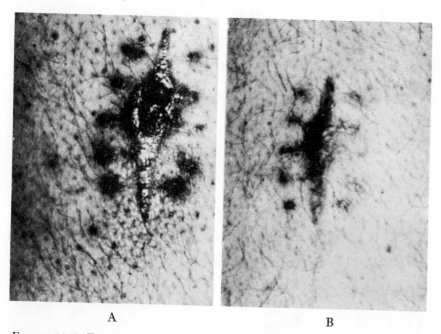

A   B

FIGURE 14–5. EFFECTS OF ADMINISTRATION OF VITAMIN C. *A* shows scar of excised wound with no progress of healing for two months. *B* shows scar of excised wound in *A* after 71 days of vitamin C administration. The wound has completely healed. (*With permission of the Controller of Her Britannic Majesty's Stationery Office. From Bartley, Krebs, and O'Brien (eds.). Vitamin C Requirement of Human Adults [1953].*)

[7] Bartley, W., Krebs, H. A., and O'Brien, J. R. P. (eds.). *Vitamin C Requirement of Human Adults*. London: Medical Research Council, Special Report Series No. 280 (1953).

As a result of such experiments and the observations of others on surgical cases, it is suggested that a deficiency of ascorbic acid may be a cause of the delay or failure of some human wounds to heal and that the diets of surgical patients should be planned to furnish higher amounts of ascorbic acid. Coon[8] studied 130 patients maintained postoperatively on fixed daily intakes of ascorbic acid. Assuming that postoperative recovery was benefited by the maintenance of tissue saturation, he found that 150 to 200 mg of ascorbic acid daily was necessary to maintain tissues at or near the saturation level in 95 per cent of a surgical population, if a blood level of 0.4 mg per 100 ml is considered as adequate. The individual variation in the level of ascorbic acid in the blood of subjects preoperatively may have affected the response to different intakes of ascorbic acid postoperatively.

Changes in the Bones

In 1923, a comprehensive study of rickets undertaken in New Haven, under the auspices of the Children's Bureau, revealed a number of instances in which unsuspected scurvy was discovered by means of x-ray examinations. Since then, bone changes in scurvy have been studied in great detail, particularly by Park[9] of Johns Hopkins University. Rickets is a disease of the entire bone; scurvy affects the growing ends. In rickets, the bone tends to bend; in scurvy, to break. The ribs show beading at their junction with the breast bone exteriorly resembling rickets (Figure 14–6). The disturbance of growth renders the junction weak, and nature tries to compensate by broadening the opposing surfaces of the junction. The

[8] Review. "Intake and Tissue Levels of Ascorbic Acid in Surgical Patients." *Nutr. Rev.*, **20**:328 (1962).

[9] Park, E. A., Guild, H. M., Jackson, D., and Bond, M. "The Recognition of Scurvy with Especial Reference to the Early X-Ray Changes." *Arch. Dis. Child.*, **10**:265 (1935).

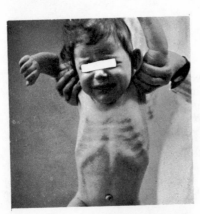

FIGURE 14–6. A CASE OF SCORBUTIC ROSARY IN AN INFANT. (*Courtesy of Dr. Rustin McIntosh. From Jolliffe, Tisdale, and Cannon. Clinical Nutrition. New York: Paul B. Hoeber, Inc. [1950].*)

cartilage cells continue to grow at the end of the shafts until severe scurvy develops, but the activity of the bone-forming cells is arrested and there is no increase in thickness of the bone. Furthermore, the bone already formed begins to grow thin as the cells can no longer hold the mineral salts. The regions in which these changes are greatest are the ones which in health are the site of most active development. The middle ribs become especially fragile at their anterior ends because of their exceedingly rapid growth and, under strain, give way.

One of the most characteristic changes is the occurrence of hemorrhages at various points in the bone itself, in the marrow or under the periosteum. Subperiosteal hemorrhages develop only when the involvement of the bone has reached an advanced stage. They originate at the ends of the bone and extend toward the middle. When the bone begins to give way, and fractures occur, the periosteal blood vessels are torn and the blood escapes under sufficient pressure to loosen the periosteum, which is more easily detached in scurvy than in health.

In studies of the boys in Christ's Hospital in 1918–22, one of the results of the deprivations of the war years was found to be the increased number of fractures, which decreased again as soon as the diet was improved. While this was attributed to low vitamin D and calcium, there was also an increase in the incidence of "rheumatism" during the same years, which fell off as sharply as the fractures when the diet was improved. Rheumatic-like pains may sometimes arise from an inadequate supply of ascorbic acid.

Changes in the Teeth

A discussion of the significance of ascorbic acid in the maintenance of dental health will be found in Chapter 19.

Changes in the Blood Vessels

The hemorrhages so characteristic of scurvy are due to the failure of the intercellular cement substance in the walls of the blood vessels, so that the capillaries become fragile and rupture under strains that would ordinarily have no effect. Since the changes in the capillaries are among the earliest to occur, it was thought that a capillary test might be developed based on the application of different degrees of pressure on the skin. It is now recognized that these tests are not specific for scurvy, but they have demonstrated the effectiveness of ascorbic acid in helping to strengthen the blood vessel walls. Göthlin described the recovery of a 12-year-old country girl who had typical scorbutic gums. They were swollen, spongy, and red, and some of her teeth were slightly loose. "I shall never forget how this little girl with the dull, tired, resigned expression of face, through five weeks of intensive treatment with orange juice awakened, so to speak, how her movements became livelier and her eyes grew bright, and how her looks showed what pleasure she got out of life."[10]

Grusin and Kincaid-Smith,[11] in 1954, reported finding 30 cases of scurvy in adults among the South African Bantu. In every patient hemorrhage was found in the muscles of the lower limbs which was accompanied by pain in the legs. Twenty-four showed a bleeding tendency and/or hypertrophic gums. Both legs were affected in 20 of the patients, and invariably the hemorrhage was found in the calf of the leg; in 10, the hemorrhage was more generalized, affecting the entire calf. Paradoxically, the disease appeared more frequently in the spring and summer when fruit and green vegetables were more plentiful and inexpensive, probably owing to the poor food habits of these individuals. More men than women developed scurvy and it was rarely found in children.

Thomson in Scotland in 1954 reported finding 100 cases of florid scurvy in the general hospital in Glasgow during a period of 15 years. Only six of these patients were women. Fifty-two of these patients reported that they lived alone or in lodging houses where they did their own cooking. Eighty were found to have sheet hemorrhages in the lower limbs (see Figure 14-7 for a case of this kind) or widespread subcutaneous extravasation of blood either spontaneous or following minor trauma. Eighty-two showed moderate or severe anemia. Complete recovery following treatment occurred in 95 patients. Thomson suggested that there are almost certainly several minor cases never seen by the doctor for each case that comes under medical care and that subclinical scurvy may cause a good deal of the vague general ill health wrongly attributed to "old age".

Resistance to Infection

As previously discussed, ascorbic acid is concerned with factors that hold cells together in specialized tissues and organs, and thus its withdrawal means widespread distintegration. It would be strange if under such circumstances bacteria of many sorts did not find ready access to organs and tissues and aid in their deterioration. Hess called attention to the fact that in infants one of the striking and important symptoms of scurvy is susceptibility to infection. Latent scurvy has been induced in guinea pigs and the animals' resistance to infection has been tested by

---

[10] Göthlin, G. F. "A Method of Establishing the Vitamin C Standard and Requirements of Physically Healthy Individuals by Testing the Strength of Their Cutaneous Capillaries." *Skandinav. Arch. für Physiol.*, **61**:225 (1931).

[11] Grusin, H., and Kincaid-Smith, P. S. "Scurvy in Adult Africans." *Amer. J. Clin. Nutr.*, **2**:323 (1954).

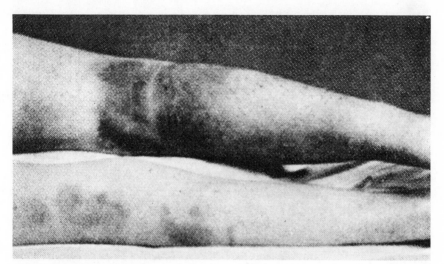

FIGURE 14–7. HEMORRHAGE INTO TISSUES OF MAN WITH SCURVY. (*Courtesy of R. E. Stone, Northwestern University; from T. D. Spies, "Some Recent Advances in Nutrition,"* J. Amer. Med. A., **167**:677 [*1958*].)

dosage with various microorganisms. Inoculation with 1,000 million pneumococci was fatal to all those with the limited ascorbic acid intake, while those with a liberal supply were quite resistant. Experiments with other common types of bacteria have given similar results, showing how important a liberal supply of this vitamin is for full protection.

Several tests of the power of guinea pigs to resist the tubercle bacillus have shown that in the scorbutic animal tuberculosis develops more rapidly than in the nonscorbutic. These studies aroused interest in the possible relation of ascorbic acid to human tuberculosis, and it is thought that it may be advantageous in this disease to increase the level of ascorbic acid in the diet.

Increased resistance to a bacterial toxin due to ascorbic acid has been demonstrated by King and Menten, who gave guinea pigs two different dosages and then injected diphtheria toxin four times within 29 days. Before there were any signs of scurvy, animals on the lower ascorbic acid intake averaged three times as much loss in weight. It was further found that in addition to greater injury to the tissues, the toxin caused a definite loss of ascorbic acid from the adrenals, pancreas, kidneys, and liver.

More recently, studies have been conducted to show the effect of injury and infection on the requirement of ascorbic acid in guinea pigs in the germ-free state as opposed to the usual contaminated state when placed on a scorbutic-producing diet. The germ-free animals survived longer (44 days versus 27 days for animals in the conventional group). They had a better growth rate, higher body weight, greater food consumption, fewer hemorrhages into the joints, more osteogenesis, and more hematopoiesis. In explanation, it was suggested that the intestinal organisms may have a requirement for ascorbic acid and that the alteration of ascorbic acid in the gut may bring about a depletion of ascorbic acid in the entire body more rapidly in the conventional group of animals than occurs in a germ-free animal.[12]

Other Functions of Ascorbic Acid in Human Nutrition

Ascorbic acid is involved in many metabolic processes. It has an important role in the oxidation of the amino acids phenylalanine and tyrosine, in conversion of the vitamin folacin to its active form, folinic acid, in the regulation of the respiratory cycle in mitochondria and microsomes of the cell, and in the development of odontoblasts and other specialized cells. It exerts a marked sparing action on the requirements of members of the vitamin B complex probably because of a change in the intestinal flora. It is involved in the utilization of certain mineral elements such as, calcium, phosphorus, iron, and copper. It seems to have some protective mechanism in the prevention of the oxidation of certain enzymes. It is important in maintaining adrenal integrity. The administration of adrenocorticotropic hormone reduces adrenal ascorbic acid concentration. Almost any stress, if severe and prolonged, causes a decrease in the concentration of ascorbic acid in the adrenal and other tissues.

Sources

Ascorbic acid is produced by the plant in the process of its growth. It is not present in dry mature seeds, but develops as soon as they begin to sprout. It is abundant in actively functioning and succulent fresh green leaves where, as Szent-Györgyi has shown, it is essential for the respiration of the plant. Old-time remedies for scurvy, such as fir tops, pine needles, water and garden cresses, juices of scurvy grass, nettles, burdock, dandelions, field daisies, and turnips, as well as oranges and lemons attest the wide range of vegetable sources discovered by man in the past. It must be noted, however, that many decoctions were boiled so long that it is probable that they owed their chief value to the orange or lemon juice which was frequently added. An old writer, who commends lemon juice as "precious remedy and well tried," also suggests that when lemon or orange juice cannot be obtained, "nitre dissolved in vinegar" or water acidulated with nitric acid may be substituted. Today we know that it would be futile to place hope in the latter. We have substituted scientific knowledge for tradition.

[12] Review. "Scurvy in Germ-Free Animals." *Nutr. Rev.*, **21**:159 (1963).

As a general preventive of scurvy in the temperate zones in the past the potato undoubtedly has held first place. Hess wrote in 1921:

> It is hardly exaggeration to state that in the temperate zones the development or nondevelopment of scurvy depends largely on the potato crop. In Ireland, when the potato has failed, scurvy has developed. The same thing has been true in Norway. . . . This is attributable in part to the fact that the potato is an excellent antiscorbutic, but to a greater extent because it is consumed during the winter in amounts that exceed the combined total of all other vegetables.

Scientific investigation has shown that ascorbic acid is very irregularly distributed in food materials and also very easily destroyed. It is necessary to know the conditions under which a food has been secured, the processes to which it has been subjected in preparation for the table, as well as its original store of the vitamin, to determine its practical value as an antiscorbutic. Fresh raw cabbage contains more ascorbic acid than fresh raw potato, but there is little loss in cooking the potato whereas the cabbage rapidly loses its antiscorbutic value when it is cooked too long. The parsnip, popular in parts of Canada, is another root vegetable that compares favorably with the potato as a source of ascorbic acid.

Apples vary greatly with variety. Storage results in considerable loss, most of the vitamin having disappeared after nine months in an ordinary cellar, and about one fourth after six months in cold storage. Cooking destroys much of what is present in the raw flesh, so that applesauce is not an antiscorbutic, as a man found to his sorrow who undertook to live on milk, whole-grain cereals, and applesauce when in financial straits, and after a time became a patient in a hospital and was diagnosed as a case of scurvy. Raw apples, eaten skin and all, in generous quantities, undoubtedly provided protection in many a country home in the days before the cause of scurvy was so well understood, and before oranges and tomatoes were so readily available as protective foods. An interesting result of the search for new sources of ascorbic acid in England and in Scandinavian countries was the discovery that some varieties of rose hips are rich in this vitamin and practical to use.

Animal foods are less satisfactory sources of ascorbic acid. Eggs have none. The concentration in liver is usually somewhat higher than in muscle. The amount in fresh raw milk depends on the diet of the cow, but in practice varies less with the season than is generally supposed.

When milk is pasteurized to destroy microorganisms, the amount of ascorbic acid lost will depend on the conditions under which the heating is conducted. Traces of copper from equipment rapidly catalyze oxidative destruction of the vitamin. Milk brought rapidly to the boiling point, held there two minutes, and quickly cooled, loses less than that pasteurized for 20 minutes at 165° F. Since ascorbic acid is so important for the welfare of the infant, it has become a routine practice to give all infants some food of high antiscorbutic value, such as orange juice, instead of trying to depend on milk for this vitamin. Human milk has been found to be two to three times as rich as cow's milk.

Heating, drying, and aging have all been shown to be factors in the destruction of ascorbic acid, but operate differently with different foods, and time, temperature, and other factors contributing to oxidation should be considered. Unless one has specific knowledge of the ascorbic acid content of foods, generally it is best to establish a habit of eating regularly some food or foods of high antiscorbutic value. The regular consumption of not less than one-half cup of orange juice in the daily diet is a protective measure of great value, even when potatoes and other fruits and vegetables are included, and nothing short of imperative when food shortage or economic stress forces dependence on milk and cereals for most of the ration.

For the full conservation of our food resources, it is necessary that certain amounts be frozen, canned, concentrated, or dehydrated. Some kinds, such as milk, orange juice, and lemon juice, have been commercially dried with little if any loss of antiscorbutic value. However, recent reports show that fresh cooked potatoes contain two and a half to five times more ascorbic acid than the various forms of the reconstituted dehydrated products. This is "food for thought" when it is predicted that by 1970, 50 per cent of the potato crop will be consumed in the processed form. Vegetables are likely to lose less in commercial canning than in ordinary home cooking. Fresh market vegetables may lose as much as half their ascorbic acid by the time they reach the city consumer, 24 to 48 hours after gathering. One of the advantages of a home garden lies in the possibility of using the vegetables as soon as they are gathered. Vegetables preserved by commercial quick freezing lose practically no ascorbic acid while in the frozen state, but are subject to the same losses between picking and freezing. They also lose their ascorbic acid quickly when they are thawed and should be cooked before they are entirely thawed out. For the conservation of ascorbic acid the cooking of vegetables should be done as quickly as possible in small amounts of water, and the juices retained whenever feasible.

The many varieties of citrus fruits have long been recognized as the most dependable sources of ascorbic acid throughout the year in the markets of the United States. However, in many of our markets certain tropical fruits that are good sources of ascorbic acid are appearing more commonly, such as the mango and papaya. The guava is another tropical fruit with a high ascorbic acid content but is not yet as commonly used here.

An extremely rich source of ascorbic acid is the acerola, known as the West Indian cherry, which has an average potency of ascorbic acid 30 times that of orange juice.[13] Asenjo and his associates, at the School of Tropical Medicine in Puerto Rico, first reported the high potency of the acerola in 1946. The acerola tree has apparently grown wild in Puerto Rico for over 2,000 years and it took eight years of experimentation to develop this variety of cherry as a cash crop. One cherry will provide the recommended daily allowance for ascorbic acid.

In 1963, Bradfield and Roca[14] in a study of Peruvian foods, reported a fruit known as camu-camu, which grows on a bushlike tree along the rivers of the Amazon Basin. When mature the fruit is a burgundy red in color, weighs 6 gm on the average, and contains one or two seeds. Sixty-two samples studied during a period of three years gave a mean total ascorbic acid value ranging from 1,755 to 2,994 mg of ascorbic acid per 100 gm of pulp. When it is prepared as a fruit drink or jelly, the ascorbic acid values are still extremely high. This interesting fruit from the jungle area of Peru is one of the best sources of ascorbic acid thus far reported.

Nature has taken care of man with a wide variety of sources of this tremendously important vitamin from the northern countries to the tropics. Great strides have been made in ferreting out the sources in different locales.

Other good available sources of ascorbic acid are tomatoes, fresh peppers, broccoli, collards, spinach, various melons, and berries (particularly strawberries and lingonberries) in season. Table 14–1 shows a selection of common foods having approximately the same content of ascorbic acid. For a more complete listing of the ascorbic acid values of foods see Tables A–4 and A–8 in the Appendix.

Requirement

In making recommendations for the 1963 Daily Dietary Allowances for ascorbic acid the Food and Nutrition Board of the National Research Council based their decision on the following:

> . . . (a) providing a safe margin above intakes known to protect against severe or mild signs and symptoms of scurvy; (b) the quantity (average 4 milligrams per liter) supplied to infants by human milk when the mother's intake of vitamin C is characteristic of good diets; (c) human and animal intakes that maintain specific functions such as wound healing, enzyme activity, cellular proliferation, and resistance to common stresses such as moderate exposure to bacterial toxins and low temperatures; (d) variations in serum, urine, and tissue concentration that result from different intakes; and (e) comparative studies in nutrition, includ-

[13] Values as high as 80 times that of orange juice have been reported.
[14] Bradfield, R. B., and Roca, A. "Camu-Camu—A Fruit High in Ascorbic Acid." *J. Amer. Dietet. A.*, **44**:28 (1964).

TABLE 14–1. FOOD PORTIONS
YIELDING APPROXIMATELY EQUIVALENT
AMOUNTS OF ASCORBIC ACID*

Food	Gm	Food	Gm
Banana	300	Pepper, green	16
Broccoli spears, cooked	22	Potato, boiled	122
Cabbage, raw	43	Strawberries	34
Grapefruit juice	53	Tomato	88
Orange juice	44	Tomato juice	124

*20 mg of ascorbic acid.

ing animals that require vitamin C for protection from scurvy (guinea pigs, primates, and the Indian fruit bat) and animals that maintain a "normal" concentration of the vitamin by tissue synthesis.[15]

The recommended allowances are three to six times as high as the minimal amount needed to prevent gross signs of scurvy through a period of several months in babies, children, and adults. "There is evidence, however, that intakes to preserve optimal health under common forms of stress are much higher than minimal supplies." The recommended daily dietary allowances for the "reference man" and the "reference woman" have been set at 70 mg of ascorbic acid, with allowances of 100 mg for pregnancy (second and third trimester) and lactation. For recommendations for other individuals, infants, and children, see Tables A–1, A–5, and A–7, in the Appendix.

These are not actually saturation levels since even higher intakes have been reported to provide for higher concentrations in the tissues. In general, the lower the intake of ascorbic acid, the smaller is the amount found in the blood and urine, and when the intake is raised gradually, a level is found at which there is a large increase in the amount found in the urine, and at the same time the amount in the blood reaches a level not increased by further additions, these being largely excreted. The body is then thought to be in a state of saturation as to ascorbic acid. There is not complete agreement as to whether it is necessary to keep the body saturated, but there seems to be no doubt that amounts considerably in excess of those only sufficient to prevent scurvy or other signs of ascorbic acid deficiency are needed for the maintenance of good health.

Pye, Taylor, and Fontanares[16] studied the effect of different levels of ascorbic acid, namely, 2, 4, 6, and 8 mg per day, throughout the life of

[15] Food and Nutrition Board. *Recommended Dietary Allowances*, p. 24. Washington, D.C.: National Research Council (1964).

[16] Pye, O. F., Taylor, C. M., and Fontanares, P. E. "The Effect of Different Levels of Ascorbic Acid in the Diet of Guinea Pigs on Health, Reproduction, and Survival." *J. Nutr.*, **73**:236 (1961).

guinea pigs. The females receiving 8 mg of ascorbic acid daily were significantly superior to those on the lower levels in terms of the number of pregnancies per female, the total number of young, and the living young. They also had a somewhat longer reproductive period. The total birth weight of the young was greater and their survival period tended to be longer.

Studies of the ascorbic acid status of human beings in the United States have shown that many persons are living on diets too low in this vitamin. Cooperative research investigations appear to indicate a greater need of vitamin C for males after age 12 than for females. Both the tissue content, indicating the past dietary history, and the blood serum, showing the recent custom, reflect the intake of ascorbic acid. "Changes during adolescence and menopause appear to exert stresses which affect the utilization of this vitamin and may increase the need for it in the diet. About a third of the men and boys and a somewhat smaller proportion of women and girls had blood levels indicating an unsatisfactory status as to ascorbic acid."[17]

REFERENCES

Beaton, G. H., and McHenry, E. W. (eds.). *Nutrition. A Comprehensive Treatise*, Vol. II, Chap. 4, Woodruff, C. W. "Ascorbic Acid." New York: Academic (1964).

Bourne, G. H. (ed.). *World Review of Nutrition and Dietetics*, Vol. I, Chap. 3, p. 63, King C. G., and Becker, R. R. "The Biosynthesis of Vitamin C (Ascorbic Acid)." New York: Hafner (1959).

Food and Nutrition Board. *Recommended Dietary Allowances*. 6th rev. ed. Washington, D.C.: National Research Council, Publication 1146 (1964).

Goldblith, S. A., and Joslyn, M. A. *Milestones in Nutrition*, Vol. 2, Chap. 8. Westport, Conn.: Avi (1964).

Harris, L. J. *Vitamins in Theory and Practice*, 4th ed., Chap. 5. New York: Cambridge U. P. (1955).

Jolliffe, N. (ed.). *Clinical Nutrition*, Chap. 20. New York: Hoeber (1962).

King, C. G. "Early Experiences with Ascorbic Acid—A Retrospect." *Nutr. Rev.*, 12:1 (1954).

———. *Handbook of Nutrition*, 2nd ed., Chap. 9. "Vitamin C." Chicago: American Medical Association (1951).

Lind Bicentenary Symposium, *Proc. Nutr. Soc.*, 12:201 (1953).

Youmans, J. B. "Deficiencies of the Water-Soluble Vitamins." *Handbook of Nutrition*, 2nd ed., Chap. 22, p. 562. Chicago: American Medical Association (1951).

[17] Agnes Fay Morgan (ed.). *Nutritional Status U.S.A.*, Bulletin 769, p. 105. Berkeley: California Agricultural Experiment Station (1959).

❧ 15 ❧

Vitamin D

Rickets

It is thought that rickets first appeared as a menacing disease in the great towns in the low countries of Northern Europe, although it probably existed in England before the days of the Romans. Its prevalence in severe form in the British Isles led to its being called early in the seventeenth century the "English disease." The first treatise on the subject by an English author was written in Latin and published for the degree of Doctor of Medicine at Leyden in 1645 by Daniel Whistler. The great classic on the subject appeared in 1650, also in Latin by an English physician who was for over 30 years "Professor of Physic" at Cambridge, Sir Francis Glisson.

For two centuries after Glisson its cause remained a mystery, and as it is a disease which does not cause death but only makes life miserable, it did not excite much interest in times when many other miseries abounded. It was recognized as a disease of the bones, in which, as one writer quaintly said, "The head waxeth too great, whilst the legs and lower parts wain too little." The state of knowledge even in the latter part of the nineteenth century was empirical rather than scientific, as will be indicated in the following excerpt from an old household guide, *Information for Everybody*, bearing the date of 1874.

As the cause of this disease is an absence of the mineral salts, the natural remedy for the case would seem to be to give the system those salts of which it stands in need, namely, the phosphates of lime and soda. The cure, however, cannot always be effected by these means alone, . . . the restoration to health can only be attained by a steady and gradual system of dietetics and regimen. The first indispensable requisite is change of air, and if possible, to the seaside; . . . an abundance of milk, and a full, rich diet—animal and vegetable—with fruit; the patient in this instance being enjoined to eat the rind or skin as well as the fruit, and when the digestion is good, water-cresses, radishes, salad, and any crude vegetable in which the mineral salts are in their natural abundance. . . . Though the diet and regimen are the chief agents required in the treatment of rickets, some medicine is necessary. . . . In the first place, cod liver oil, on account of the nitrogen or animalizing principle it contains, has been greatly recommended in this disease, and there can be no doubt that in cases of much debility it may be given with very great effect.

Apparently little heed was paid to cod-liver oil as a specific for rickets for another quarter of a century. In 1909, Schabab, of the Children's Hospital in Petrograd, took a four-year-old child who had been rachitic since it was a year and a half old, unable to stand or walk, and administered cod-liver oil with the result that in two months the child was normal. Up to this time it had been customary to give phosphorus with the cod-liver oil, and any good effects had been attributed to the phosphorus, but this and other experiments of Schabab made it clear that the oil itself was responsible.

In 1917 new interest was aroused in cod-liver oil therapy in this country by Hess and Unger, who noted the very high incidence of rickets among Negro babies in New York City and sought to test the efficacy of cod-liver oil as a preventive measure. Over 90 per cent of these babies had the disease, the infant mortality rate being the highest in the city, and respiratory diseases, to which rickets is a predisposing cause, played a large role in the death reports. From December to June, cod-liver oil was given to about 50 babies. Of 32 children who received oil for six months, all but two were fully protected; of 12 who received it for only four months, five were found to show symptoms of rickets; and 16 who received none were all rachitic. The report of this work "gradually spread throughout the district, and the ordinary symptoms of rickets became the common knowledge of the mothers, who often brought their babies for consultation with the request that cod-liver oil be administered"; and shortly afterward the New York City Department of Health established a rickets clinic in connection with its baby welfare station, where cod-liver oil could be dispensed at cost.

There was an acute outbreak of nutritional disorders of bones not only in children but also in adults in Germany, Austria, and Poland at the close of World War I. In Vienna the disease was particularly bad, and this city became the seat of the investigations of Dalyell and Chick sent by the Lister Institute of London to study the situation. Between January and May (1920) over six hundred persons applied for help, of whom about one third were chosen for special study. Most of the patients were middle-aged or elderly people who had been living on a diet restricted to bread and vegetables mainly, with small amounts of flour and sugar— no milk, meat, eggs, butter, or other fat. Their disease corresponded closely in character to rickets, which was also so widely prevalent that every child in Central Europe was said to have been rickety at that time. In rickets there is a failure to deposit calcium and phosphorus in the growing bone. In the corresponding disease of adults, called osteomalacia, the bones soften as the calcium and phosphorus already deposited there are withdrawn and excreted. Osteomalacia is extremely rare in adults other than pregnant women who get very little sunshine. However, the patients mentioned above who were on starvation rations, were particularly vulnerable to avitaminosis D and responded to cod-liver oil therapy.

Experimental Rickets

Findlay, in 1908, at the University of Glasgow, produced rickets in a group of puppies in laboratory cages on a milk and porridge diet. (See example of rickets in a puppy in Figure 15–1.) Inasmuch as another group allowed to run in the open did not contract rickets, he thought that muscular exercise was the explanation of the difference. In 1917, McCollum and Simmonds observed that many rats on a cereal diet developed beaded ribs and other skeletal deformities which suggested rickets. The diet was the sole determining factor in the etiology of the lesions, since the entire colony of approximately 2,000 animals lived under identical conditions except for their food.

While these observations were being made in Baltimore, Mellanby in Great Britain succeeded in inducing rickets in puppies by means of various faulty diets, such as bread or other cereal food with a little whole milk; or bread and a little separator milk, with linseed oil to replace the milk fat. When cod-liver oil was substituted for other fat in

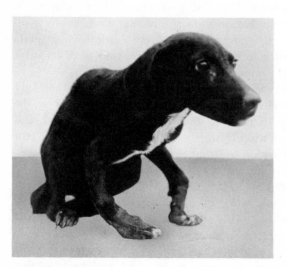

FIGURE 15–1. A RACHITIC PUPPY. (*Courtesy of Professors H. Steenbock and E. B. Hart.*)

the rachitic diet, the disease was prevented; since cod-liver oil was by that time (1919) known to be rich in vitamin A, Mellanby concluded that this vitamin must be antirachitic as well as growth-promoting.

Inasmuch as rickets is a disease in which the bones are deficient in calcium, it was thought that administration of calcium should cure it. However, this was disappointing and rickets sometimes developed when children were fed liberally on cow's milk, rich in calcium.

A little later the Johns Hopkins investigators also evolved a rickets-producing diet low in phosphorus and made the further observation that butter fat, while preventing the disease that results from shortage of vitamin A, did not satisfactorily modify the pathological condition of the skeleton; "if anything, it was intensified, probably as a result of the slight stimulation given by the butter fat to the growth of the bone."

On the other hand, when cod-liver oil was added to the diet there were no signs of rickets. Within the year (1921) this difference between butter fat and cod-liver oil was explained. Hopkins had pointed out in 1920 that if oxygen were allowed to pass through a heated fat, any vitamin A it contained would be destroyed, and very shortly McCollum in Baltimore, Steenbock in Madison, and Coward and Drummond in London reported that cod-liver oil so treated lost its growth-promoting power but retained its antirachitic property. The vitamin was recognized as a substance distinct from vitamin A by McCollum and his associates in 1922 and given the name vitamin D.

Rickets and Sunlight

In the earlier clinical studies of rickets, lack of sunlight, overcrowding, poor ventilation, and prolonged indoor confinements of infants in the wintertime were thought to be contributing factors. In 1890, Palm, an English physician in Japan, became interested in the geographical distribution of rickets, being struck with its absence in Japan "as compared with its lamentable frequency among the poor children of the large centers of population in England and Scotland." In Glasgow it was almost universal, and in London the situation was not much better. Palm had read Hirsch's *Handbook of Historical and Geographical Pathology* (1886), in which it was said of rickets,

In amount and severity of type it stands in a definite relation to climate. Countries with a cold and wet climate, subject to frequent changes of weather, such as Holland, many parts of England, the north German plain, the mountainous regions of central and southern Germany, and the plains and mountainous districts of northern Italy, if they are not the exclusive seats of rickets are at all events its headquarters.

He sent out a questionnaire to various medical missionaries in China and Tibet because he thought,

> If we find the disease to be unknown where the diet and sanitary surroundings are even worse than in places where the disease prevails, we can no longer regard them as prime factors in producing the disease.

The reports, mostly from rural regions, told of poverty, of poor food, of filthy streets, and of utter absence of sanitation, but no rickets. The air was generally dry and stimulating, with much sunshine, people living out of doors, the children practically naked and rarely weaned before three years of age. Palm suggested as a result of his study that "sunlight is essential to the healthy nutrition of growing animals and that a deficiency of it characterizes the localities or conditions of those who suffer from rickets and is the most important element in the aetiology of the disease."

Refined methods of diagnosis were made possible by use of the x-ray, and many children who would not have been classified as rachitic by the earlier clinicians were added to the list of the afflicted. Hess and Unger found that fully three fourths of the bottle-fed and half the breast-fed babies of New York City showed at least slight signs of rickets in March, the time of year when the disease reached its peak.

In 1921 it was demonstrated by Hess, Unger, and Pappenheimer in New York and by Shipley, Park, Powers, and McCollum in Baltimore that rickets in rats fed a rickets-producing diet could be prevented by daily exposure to direct sunlight, and Hess and Unger found further that the low inorganic phosphate characteristic of the blood serum of rachitic infants could be raised to the normal level by daily sun baths. For an illustration of the effect of sunlight on chickens, see Figure 15–2.

It did not take long to discover through studies on young children that there is a seasonal tide of blood phosphorus which is directly related to the amount of sunshine at different times of the year. This led to the application of "artificial sunlight" by means of a carbon arc lamp and to the realization that it is the ultraviolet rays that are curative of rickets. Artificial light is also used for the prevention of rickets (see Figure 15–3). The fact that these shorter rays do not penetrate dark clothing or pigmented skin explained further some of the irregularities in the occurrence of rickets, especially the high susceptibility of Negro infants.

Light and Vitamin D

How the same effect could be secured by such diverse means as (1) direct sunlight, (2) cod-liver oil, (3) a ration carefully balanced with regard to calcium and phosphorus, and (4) ultraviolet light was a mystery. The solution was found in 1924 when almost simultaneously

FIGURE 15–2. EFFECTS OF SUNSHINE. These two chicks are the same age and were fed the same diet, but the upper one was kept in a dark room, while the lower had plenty of sunshine. (*Courtesy of Dr. Harry Steenbock.*)

Hess in New York and Steenbock and Black in Wisconsin showed that liver, lung, and muscle tissue from irradiated rats would promote bone calcification in rachitic rats while that from nonirradiated rachitic animals would not. The irradiation of food was tried next, and it was found that the success of irradiation depended on a substance occurring in minute quantity in the oils of seeds including cereal grains and in vegetable oils such as olive, peanut, and cottonseed, known as phytosterol; or in a closely related substance in animal fats, called cholesterol. The chemical search for the pure vitamin in activated cholesterol led to the identification of another chemically related substance associated with cholesterol, called ergosterol. It is found in largest amounts in ergot, from which it gets its name, and in yeast.

Pure ergosterol was irradiated and found to have a vitamin D activity 200,000 to 700,000 times that of cod-liver oil. It was found to be curative for rats in doses of 0.0001 mg. The identification of ergosterol as a substance from which vitamin D could be made was announced in 1927 by Rosenheim and Webster and also by Windaus and Hess. Irradiated ergosterol was made available to the public as a concentrated solution in oil known as viosterol.

Activated ergosterol was found to contain at least half a dozen substances. It was "a complex resinous mixture" resisting all efforts at crystallization. Finally in 1930 Bourdillon, with Askew and other associates in London, was able to produce small amounts of a crystalline sub-

FIGURE 15–3. YOUNG CALVES SHARE THE BENEFITS FROM A SUN LAMP. (*Courtesy of Westinghouse Electric Corp.*)

stance which was named calciferol (see Figure 15-4). Meanwhile Windaus, who at the University of Göttingen had engaged in the study of cholesterol for many years, was also giving his attention to the search for pure vitamin D and in 1931 he reported the isolation of two crystalline substances protective for a rat in a dosage of about 0.000003 mg, one of which was subsequently identified as the calciferol of the English investigators, now known as vitamin D_2. The other was the same substance in combination with another that was physiologically inactive. Pure calciferol has an antirachitic potency of 40,000 I.U. per milligram.

Further investigation revealed that not only ergosterol and cholesterol but other closely related compounds could be made antirachitic by irradiation. Gradually it became apparent that vitamin D is not a single substance, but a group of closely related compounds. New compounds with vitamin D activity were developed, so that many are now known to the chemist. The two most important forms are vitamin D_2 (calciferol) and vitamin D_3 (a form obtained from fish-liver oil). The latter is believed to be the form that is produced when the skin is irradiated with ultraviolet rays.

The Prevention and Cure of Rickets

Although rickets is a disease affecting the whole body, its most characteristic symptom is a failure of the bones to calcify properly, with

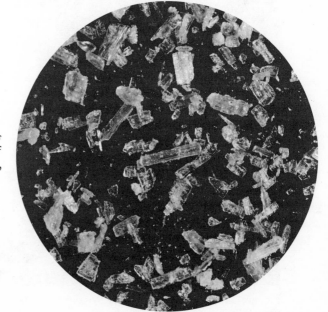

FIGURE 15-4. CRYSTALS OF VITAMIN D_2. (*Courtesy of Distillation Products, Inc., Rochester, N.Y.*)

resulting deformities. The first defect to appear is the so-called "rachitic rosary"—a row of beadlike protuberances down each side of the chest where the bones of the ribs join the costal cartilages (Figure 15–5). The chest fails to develop normally, the ribs are thrust forward, forming a pigeon breast, and the lung space is contracted, interfering with deep, full respiration. The ends of the long bones become enlarged, especially at wrists and ankles. Calcium phosphate is not deposited in the normal way. The evidence of rickets is seen at the junction of the shaft of the bone with its head, called the epiphysis. In the normal bone this junction is a straight, clear line; in the rachitic bone it is ragged if not wholly obscure (Figure 15–6). The cartilage of the epiphysis is not converted into bone, but persists and increases, and there is an irregular enlargement of the soft tissue. The lacelike bony structures in the end of the shaft, called trabeculae, are poorly developed, giving further signs of the inability of the body to store calcium and phosphorus. They are normal reservoirs of calcium and phosphorus where any surplus is stored and from which these elements are withdrawn if needed elsewhere. Rickets is defined as severe when all tendency toward healing is absent and bone destruction predominates over bone formation.

A normal calcium and phosphorus metabolism depends on many factors, especially (1) the ability of the body to absorb these minerals from the food; (2) the supply of enough of each element to meet the require-

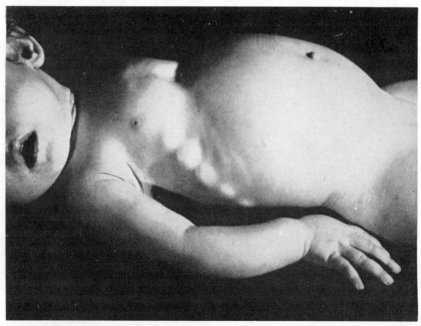

FIGURE 15–5. A CASE OF RACHITIC ROSARY IN AN INFANT. (*Courtesy of Dr. Norman Jolliffe.*)

ments of growth; and (3) the amount of vitamin D supplied. Since calcium and phosphorus are the materials on which the growth and maintenance of normal bone so largely depend, it is easy to see that they must be furnished in sufficient amounts to get the best results. Normal infants on a diet of milk, even when showing no symptoms of rickets, retain more calcium and phosphorus from the food and grow better if given additional vitamin D. Thus Daniels and some of her associates at the Iowa Child Welfare Research Station found that giving vitamin D to babies on milk formulas increased the phosphorus retention to three or four times what it had been on the milk only, and calcium retention was markedly improved. It is very evident that in human beings vitamin D helps to conserve calcium and phosphorus even when both are fed in the liberal amounts in which they occur in milk. Thus the current practice of fortifying milk with vitamin D is advantageous.

The best diet to prevent or cure rickets is one in which liberal calcium and phosphorus are kept in favorable relationship with a moderate and regular supply of vitamin D. It can be supplied directly through the action of the ultraviolet rays of sunlight upon the skin; through the use of some food naturally rich in the vitamin, such as halibut-, cod-, or other fish-liver oil; or through the use of a food that has been fortified either by irradiation or by addition of a vitamin D concentrate.

Rickets, although not a problem in the United States, is a disease prevalent in many parts of the world including Japan, Africa, India, and

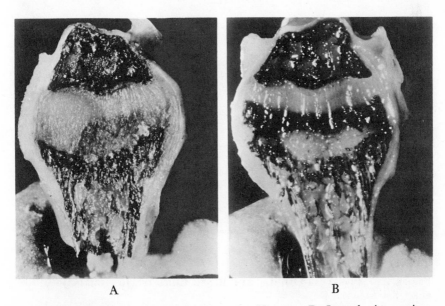

A   B

FIGURE 15–6. EFFECTS OF ADMINISTRATION OF VITAMIN D. Lengthwise sections of leg bones (*A*) of rat with rickets, and (*B*) showing line of new bone formed after administration of vitamin D. (*Courtesy of E. R. Squibb & Sons.*)

Egypt, and it can be severe in undernourished infants. A recent study carried out by Aboul-Dahab and Zaki in Egypt emphasized the association of rickets with other deficiency diseases, such as marasmus.[1] Paradoxically, it is recognized as a widespread disease in the tropics and subtropics where there is no shortage of sunlight. See Figure 15–7 for a child with rickets in South Africa. Rickets is common in tropical cities such as Calcutta, because sunlight does not penetrate into the areas where the children live. Also, children may be kept indoors most of the day. In some areas mothers may carry children on their backs wrapped tightly so that their little bodies are almost completely covered with clothing or blankets.

Vitamin D and the Teeth

The eruption of the teeth is delayed by rickets and it is common for a rachitic child to have only one or two teeth by the end of the first year.

A further discussion of the role of vitamin D in the health of the teeth will be found in Chapter 19.

Hypervitaminosis D

The danger of excessive doses of vitamin D was recognized when enormous amounts of 100,000 I.U. or more were administered in

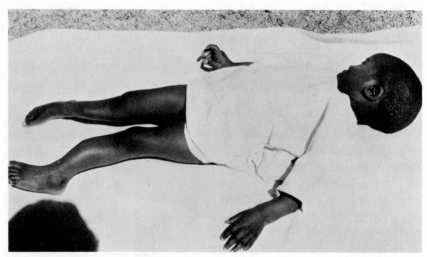

FIGURE 15–7. FIVE-YEAR-OLD RACHITIC BANTU CHILD IN HOSPITAL IN JOHANNESBURG, SOUTH AFRICA.

[1] Aboul-Dahab, Y. W., and Zaki, K. "Studies on Rickets and Malnutrition in the Undernourished Child." *Amer. J. Clin. Nutr.*, **13**:98 (1963).

cases of rheumatoid arthritis, psoriasis, tuberculosis, and other diseases. The effects of an overdosage resemble those of an overdosage of parathyroid hormone with symptoms of anorexia, nausea, vomiting, excessive urination, and thirst. Calcium may be withdrawn from the bones and deposited in soft tissues such as the heart, kidney, lungs, and blood vessels. The effects are reversible if the administration of vitamin D is withdrawn in time.

The syndrome of infantile hypercalcemia has been reported in some infants receiving five to ten times the recommended allowance in association with a generous intake of calcium. A high incidence (over 200 cases in a two-year-period) was reported from Great Britain associated with intakes as high as 4,000 I.U. daily mainly in fortified infant foods.[2] Improvement follows a reduction in vitamin D and calcium intake. In evaluation of vitamin D intake all vitamin D-fortified foods in the diet must be taken into account.

Sources

In general, foods cannot be depended upon to provide significant amounts of vitamin D except those which are fortified. Among the natural sources, fish-liver oils are the most potent, 1 tsp of cod-liver oil containing the recommended 400 I.U. and percomorph oil many times as much. One drop of many fish-liver oils is sufficient, especially those which are enriched with vitamin D. At least 22 different species of fish have more vitamin D in the liver oil than does cod, the liver of the bluefin tuna ranking the highest with 600 times the potency of standard cod-liver oil. The oily flesh of fish such as herring, mackerel, salmon, and sardines may be rich sources. The fish roe is also a good source.

Vitamin D milk is available in fresh, in evaporated, and sometimes in dry form. As has been stated, 1 qt of fresh milk is standardized to contain 400 I.U. of vitamin D. Vitamin D milk is produced by adding crystalline vitamin D or vitamin D concentrate, or by the exposure of the milk to ultraviolet light. None of these processes impairs the flavor of the milk.

Although muscle meats contain no vitamin D, the liver of animals contains small amounts. Eggs contain small and variable amounts, the yolk being the chief source.

Requirement

It has been established that 300 to 400 units daily will provide maximum retention of calcium in infancy when the calcium intake is adequate. A recommendation of 400 I.U. has been made for both breast-

[2] Wohl, M. G., and Goodhart, R. S. (eds.). *Modern Nutrition in Health and Disease*, 3rd ed., p. 362. Philadelphia: Lea (1964).

fed and formula-fed infants. Rickets develops more readily in premature infants because of their rapid growth rate and delay in exposure to sunlight. The administration of as little as 100 to 250 units daily has been found adequate. For maximum calcium retention during growth throughout the school years and adolescence, 400 I.U. is recommended. This is the quantity that is provided by 1 qt of vitamin D milk.

The adult requirement for vitamin D is not known but is small enough to be supplied by the average diet and occasional exposure to sunlight. For persons who have little or no exposure to sunlight because of occupation, religion, or other factors, a small amount of vitamin D is desirable. Available evidence indicates that 400 units daily is probably adequate for pregnancy and lactation.[3]

REFERENCES

Beaton, G. H., and McHenry, E. W. (eds.). *Nutrition. A Comprehensive Treatise*, Vol. II, Chap. 1, p. 20, "Fat-Soluble Vitamins. II. Vitamin D." New York: Academic (1964).

Bills, C. E. "Early Experiences with Fish Oils—A Retrospect." *Nutr. Rev.*, 13:65 (1955).

Bourne, G. H. (ed.). *World Review of Nutrition and Dietetics*, Vol. 2, Chap. 8, p. 187. Engfeldt, B., and Hjertquist, S. O. "Vitamin-D Deficiency and Bone and Tooth Structure." New York: Hafner (1960).

Davidson, S., Meiklejohn, A. P., and Passmore, R. *Human Nutrition and Dietetics*, Chaps. 29 and 30. Baltimore: Williams & Wilkins (1959).

Goldblith, S. A., and Joslyn, M. A. *Milestones in Nutrition*, Vol. 2, Chap. 5. "Vitamin D." Westport, Conn.: Avi (1964).

Harris, L. J. *Vitamins in Theory and Practice*, 4th ed., Chap. 6. New York: Cambridge U. P. (1955).

Jeans, P. C. "Vitamin D." *Handbook of Nutrition*, 2nd ed., Chap. 10. Chicago: American Medical Association (1951).

Jolliffe, N. (ed.). *Clinical Nutrition*, Chap. 14. Park, E. A. "Vitamin D and Rickets." New York: Hoeber (1962).

Sherman, H. C. *Chemistry of Food and Nutrition*, 8th ed., Chap. 24. New York: Macmillan (1952).

Stearns, G. "Early Experiences with Vitamin D in the Nutrition of Infants and Children—A Retrospect." *Nutr. Rev.*, 12:193 (1954).

Youmans, J. B. "Deficiencies of the Fat-Soluble Vitamins." *Handbook of Nutrition*, 2nd ed., Chap. 21. p. 514. Chicago: American Medical Association (1951).

[3] Food and Nutrition Board, *Recommended Dietary Allowances*. Washington, D.C.: National Research Council, Publication 1146 (1964).

❧ 16 ❧

Riboflavin

Discovery

For years, reports of the complexity of "water-soluble vitamin B" puzzled investigators. For example, it was found that rats would not grow normally if large amounts of rolled oats were the only source of vitamin B. Yet the addition of only a little (5 per cent) brewer's yeast, heated until it would no longer cure polyneuritis in a pigeon, brought about normal rat growth. It was quite apparent that the autoclaved brewer's yeast added something necessary for the rat which the oats lacked.

An experiment by Sherman and Axtmayer in 1927 helped to clear the confusion arising from various results with heated (autoclaved) and unheated yeast, and from using different kinds of food as the source of vitamin B. They fed one group of rats a vitamin B-free diet to which 0.8 gm daily of ground whole wheat was added, and no growth resulted. Another group was given the same amount of autoclaved yeast with no more success. To a third group of animals they gave 0.8 gm of a mixture of the two in equal parts. Much better growth resulted. It was evident that each food material furnished something the other lacked for growth.

From these and numerous other researches it was established beyond doubt by 1928 that there was an antineuritic vitamin B (B_1) and another growth-promoting vitamin that was incapable of curing polyneuritis, designated vitamin G (also known as B_2). These two vitamins are called thiamine and riboflavin, respectively.

In the Department of Chemistry of Columbia University, Booher by 1933 had achieved a high concentration of vitamin G from whey powder, so that the final product had 2,000 times the riboflavin activity of the original milk. It was adequate for growth when fed in conjunction with a concentrate of thiamine.

Meanwhile another line of investigation had opened new vistas. It had been known since 1879 that there were in plant and animal tissues water-soluble, yellowish pigments having a greenish fluorescence, but no one had given any particular attention to their possible function. In 1914, in a paper from the University of Missouri, Palmer and Cooledge wrote:

> The natural yellow color of cow's milk is caused by two entirely dif-
> ferent kinds of pigments; the principal one of the two pigments is found
> in milk fat. It has recently been found by one of us to be a mixture
> of carotin and xanthophylls, principally carotin, which are transmitted
> to the milk fat from the green feeds of the cow. The secondary or minor
> pigment has not been identified. Its presence in the milk is largely
> masked by the white color of the caseinogen and is only seen in the whey
> which remains after the caseinogen has been coagulated. The pigment
> is then seen imparting the usual greenish color to whey.[1]

The "carotin" we recognize, of course, as the carotene of today, the precursor of vitamin A. Little did these authors dream that both pigments were vitamins!

It was approximately 20 years later before the "lactochrome's" biological significance began to be understood. In 1932 Warburg and Christian, in Berlin, reported investigations of the "yellow oxidation enzyme" which plays an important part in cell respiration. The yellow pigment was isolated from whey and egg white in pure crystalline form, 0.06 gm of crystals being obtained from about 750 gal of milk, by Kuhn and others at the University of Heidelberg. Analysis showed that it belonged to a group of compounds known as flavins. These crystallize in yellow-brown needles which, when dissolved in water, give a yellow solution with a greenish-yellow fluorescence. According to the substance from which they were extracted, they were called lactoflavin, ovoflavin, etc.

The fact that growth was stimulated by very small quantities suggested that it was a water-soluble vitamin belonging to the vitamin B group. Subsequent work made it clear that this water-soluble, yellow pigment was vitamin G. In 1935 the synthesis of riboflavin was accomplished almost simultaneously by Kuhn and associates in Germany and Karrer and associates in Switzerland. See Figure 16–1.

The dermatitis described by Goldberger in 1926 in rats as a thickening of the skin, cracking, and desquamation, leaving a denuded, pale pink, glistening skin, has since been shown to be due to a deficiency of both riboflavin and pyridoxine. This points out the difficulty in obtaining at that time clear-cut deficiency symptoms of a single factor.

In 1931, Day, of the University of Arkansas, reported that on a ribo-flavin-deficient diet rats developed a cataractlike condition of the eyeball. Other investigators reported similar conditions in other species of animals but it has not been proved that this lesion is specific for riboflavin.

[1] Palmer, L. S., and Cooledge, L. H. "Lactochrome—The Yellow Pigment of Milk Whey." *J. Biol. Chem.*, **17**:251 (1914).

FIGURE 16–1. CRYSTALS OF RIBOFLAVIN. (*Courtesy of Merck & Co., Inc.*)

Ariboflavinosis

In 1938, Sebrell and Butler,[2] of the National Institutes of Health, United States Public Health Service, published the first description of proved riboflavin deficiency in human beings, a condition for which they proposed the name ariboflavinosis. Their subjects were 18 women who, on a diet extremely low in riboflavin, developed cracking of the skin at the corners of the mouth and an oily dermatitis around the folds of the nostrils, conditions that could be made to disappear only by giving riboflavin. When riboflavin was discontinued the cheilosis, as the cracking of the skin at the angles of the mouth is called, reappeared, but treatment with riboflavin caused it to disappear again, proving conclusively that the condition was due to riboflavin deficiency, since no other additions that were tried had any effect. A more detailed account of this

[2] Sebrell, W. H., and Butler, R. E. "Riboflavin Deficiency in Man." *Pub. Health Rep.,* **53**:2282 (1938).

work was published in 1939.[3] Since these reports by Sebrell and Butler, several others have appeared confirming and extending their findings, Sydenstricker and his co-workers[4] found this condition of cheilosis in a group of hospital employees who had developed it in spite of being free to choose their food from an adequate institutional dietary. A study of their freely chosen food intakes, however, revealed the fact that their consumption of milk, eggs, and green vegetables was so low as to make their diets deficient in riboflavin, thus accounting for the cheilosis and the oily dermatitis as well as eye disturbances. Still another symptom which has been described as a result of riboflavin deficiency is a specific type of glossitis, an abnormally smooth condition of the tongue caused by a flattening of the tiny protuberances (papillae) of its surface and accompanied by a change of its color to purplish-red.[5] This condition also responds promptly to the addition of riboflavin to the diet.

Sydenstricker and co-workers conducted another study of the effects of riboflavin deficiency on the eyes of 47 human subjects, among them the hospital employees already referred to. The symptoms found were a dislike of light (photophobia); watering, itching, and burning of the eyes; swelling, soreness, and a feeling of roughness in the eyelids; eyes easily fatigued; and dimness or blurring of vision. When the eyes were examined by means of the slit lamp used by ophthalmologists, an ingrowing of capillaries into the cornea was found, the extent of the damage depending on how long the deficiency had existed. This condition of superficial vascularizing keratitis, as it is called, responded to the administration of riboflavin but not of thiamine, ascorbic acid, vitamin A, or nicotinic acid. They noted that it occurred in their subjects along with the skin manifestations of riboflavin deficiency previously described— cheilosis, oily (seborrheic) dermatitis, and glossitis—and that all four symptoms responded to administration and withdrawal of riboflavin, although the eye symptoms regularly appeared first. It must be kept in mind that the eye lesions of ariboflavinosis have been subject to considerable controversy. It is now believed that corneal vascularization is not always specifically due to riboflavin deficiency but may be precipitated by many types of trauma and infection. Indeed, as is emphasized by many investigators, the nutritional significance of any clinical sign must be evaluated in conjunction with other factors that may influence the condition.

[3] Sebrell, W. H., and Butler, R. E. "Riboflavin Deficiency in Man." *Pub. Health Rep.*, **54**:2121 (1939).
[4] Sydenstricker, V. P., Sebrell, W. H., Cleckley, H. M., and Kruse, H. D. "The Ocular Manifestations of Ariboflavinosis." *J. Amer. Med. A.*, **114**:2437 (1940).
[5] Kruse, H. D., Sydenstricker, V. P., Sebrell, W. H., and Cleckley, H. M. "Ocular Manifestations of Ariboflavinosis." *Pub. Health. Rep.*, **55**:159 (1940).

Spies and associates observed ariboflavinosis in children as shown in Figure 16–2.

Riboflavin Deficiency in Experimental Animals

Warkany in 1940 reported that female rats maintained on a diet deficient in riboflavin produced young showing congenital skeletal malformations, which included shortening of the mandible, tibia, fibula, radius, and ulna; fusion of the ribs, sternal centers of ossification, fingers, and toes; and cleft palate. These conditions developed in 30 per cent of the young of the riboflavin-deficient rat mothers. Further studies of the effect of specific vitamin deficiencies were stimulated by Warkany's findings. Some deficiencies do not disturb the development of the embryo, but some, like riboflavin deficiency, cause malformations more or less serious. The type of defect occurring depends on the specific vitamin concerned and the degree and duration of the deficiency. This interesting research has been carried out on various species of animals but its application to human nutrition has not yet been established.

Extensive investigations of the effects of riboflavin on general health and vigor were conducted by Sherman and Ellis, who found that when parallel groups of rats were fed on graded levels of riboflavin intake, beginning with one that supported normal growth and apparently good health, successively more liberal levels resulted in more rapid growth,

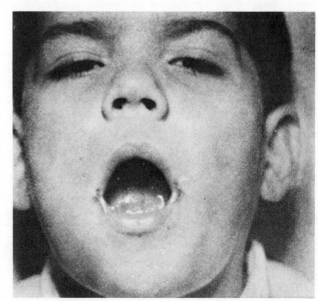

FIGURE 16–2. BOY WITH RIBOFLAVIN DEFICIENCY. (*Courtesy of R. E. Stone, Northwestern University; from T. D. Spies, "Some Recent Advances in Nutrition," J. Amer. Med. A.,* **167**:676 [*1958*].)

earlier maturity, better vigor as shown by ability to bear young, postponement of the signs of senility, and "enhancement of nutritional well-being," or, as McCollum has aptly said, "preservation of the characteristics of youth." Animals fed more riboflavin than the amount just required for normal growth not only lived longer but had a longer period of adult vigor and a relatively short period of senility.

Riboflavin deficiency has been studied in a variety of animals including the rat, mouse, hamster, dog, pig, and monkey, all of which exhibit skin changes. In the rat, the fur becomes uneven, with areas of alopecia and encrustation of red-brown pigment. The skin is scaly and the eyes are affected (See Figure 16–3A). When a riboflavin-deficient rat is given an oral supplement of a riboflavin solution, the response is dramatic in growth as well as appearance (see Figure 16–3B).

Sources

In most of the foods that contain riboflavin, it is associated with other members of the vitamin B complex. The richest sources of riboflavin are dried yeast, liver, kidney, and dried skim milk. Muscle meats (beef, lamb, and veal) contribute very little in comparison to the organ meats. Egg yolk is about twice as rich as egg white when compared on the amount in 100 gm. Milk, whether whole or skim, is doubtless the most important source of riboflavin. Cheddar cheese is also a good source.

Among vegetable foods, dark-green leaves are the best sources, such as spinach, kale, collards, broccoli, Brussels sprouts, and others. Cereal grains are only fair sources, including the enriched products. Most of the riboflavin is concentrated in the germ.

Heating does not readily destroy this vitamin; consequently, canned foods are about as rich as the original food before preservation. Meat will lose 15 to 30 per cent of its riboflavin during the processes of braising, roasting, or boiling. Three fourths of the riboflavin in milk may be destroyed if it remains in direct sunlight for three and one-half hours. Riboflavin values for foods are given in Tables A–4 and A–8 in the Appendix. See Table 16–1 for a comparison of foods having the same amounts of riboflavin.

Requirement

Riboflavin is involved in protein and energy metabolism functioning as a coenzyme or active prosthetic group of flavoproteins which play a role in tissue oxidation and respiration. Bro-Rasmussen,[6] of the

[6] Bro-Rasmussen, F. "The Riboflavin Requirements of Animals and Man and Associated Metabolic Functions." *Nutr. Abstr. & Rev.*, **28**:369 (1958).

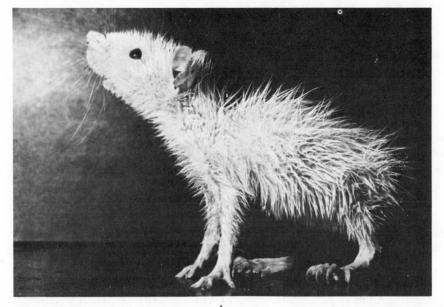

A

B

FIGURE 16–3. RIBOFLAVIN DEFICIENCY. *A* shows rat after ten weeks on a ribo-flavin-deficient diet, while *B* shows control on the same diet plus an oral supplement daily of synthetic riboflavin solution. (*Courtesy of Nutrition Laboratory, Teachers College, Columbia University.*)

**TABLE 16-1. APPROXIMATE AMOUNTS OF
FOOD YIELDING RIBOFLAVIN EQUIVALENT TO
THAT IN ONE EGG***

Foods	Gm	Foods	Gm
Almonds, shelled	16	Liver, beef, fried	4
Beans, Lima, cooked	150	Milk, evaporated	44
Beef round, lean	79	Milk, whole	88
Beets, raw	300	Peanuts, shelled	115
Cheese, cottage	54	Peas, dried	52
Egg	50	Spinach, cooked	107
Kidney, raw	6		

* 0.15 mg of riboflavin (based on values in Agriculture Handbook No. 8).

National Vitamin Laboratory in Copenhagen, made a thorough review of the riboflavin requirements of animals and man. He concluded that the riboflavin requirements are more closely related to energy expenditure than to protein intake. With this in mind the National Research Council has computed the 1963 allowances as 0.6 mg of riboflavin per 1,000 calories.

To prevent clinical signs of deficiency the minimum requirement appears to be approximately 0.3 mg per 1,000 calories for adults. When the riboflavin intake was less than 0.75 mg per day (0.2 to 0.3 mg per 1,000 calories), lesions such as those of angular stomatitis and dermatitis were observed in population groups. As emphasized by the National Research Council, such physical lesions are not specific and may vary with the individual and his environmental stresses.

Urinary excretion of riboflavin during pregnancy has been used to estimate the riboflavin requirement. It was observed on a constant intake of riboflavin that the excretion of riboflavin fell as the period of pregnancy progressed, indicating an increased need. The critical level of riboflavin intake during pregnancy is estimated to be about 0.7 mg of riboflavin per 1,000 calories. To meet these needs, the National Research Council recommends an additional 0.3 mg of riboflavin daily during the last two trimesters of pregnancy. See Tables A-1 and A-5.

An interesting study of 370 pregnant women in Israel[7] demonstrated the importance of the use of flour enriched with riboflavin for low-income groups. An earlier study of pregnant women living in the same area and of similar economic status who did not have enriched flour had shown a widespread incidence of ariboflavinosis. The average

[7] Poznanski, R., Brzezinski, A., and Guggenheim, K. "Value of Flour Enrichment to Pregnant Israeli Women." *J. Amer. Dietet. A.*, **40**:120 (1962).

intake of riboflavin in the 370 pregnant women receiving the enriched flour was 1.5 mg of riboflavin, or approximately the recommended allowance. Of this, 0.55 mg of riboflavin was provided by the enriched flour. Clinical examination of the women revealed no confirmed case of ariboflavinosis.

The recommended allowance during lactation provides for an increase of 0.6 mg riboflavin daily above that of the reference woman. Human milk furnishes about 0.6 mg of riboflavin per 1,000 calories. Cow's milk contains three to four times as much riboflavin as human milk. The daily recommended allowance for infants and children is 0.6 mg per 1,000 calories.

REFERENCES

Beaton, G. H., and McHenry, E. W. *Nutrition. A Comprehensive Treatise*, Vol. II, Chap. 2. Goldsmith, G. A. "The B Vitamins: Thiamine, Riboflavin, Niacin." New York: Academic (1964).

Elvehjem, C. A. "The Vitamin B Complex." *Handbook of Nutrition*, 2nd ed., Chap. 8, p. 166. Chicago: American Medical Association (1951).

Food and Nutrition Board. *Recommended Dietary Allowances*. Washington, D.C.: National Research Council, Publication 1146 (1964).

Goldsmith, G. A. *Nutritional Diagnosis*. Springfield, Ill.: Thomas (1959).

György, P. "Early Experiences with Riboflavin—A Retrospect." *Nutr. Rev.*, 12:97 (1954).

Jolliffe, N. (ed.). *Clinical Nutrition*, Chap. 17. Goldsmith, G. A. "Riboflavin Malnutrition." New York: Hoeber (1962).

Review. "Riboflavin Deficiency and Anemia in Man." *Nutr. Rev.*, 23:197 (1965).

Warkany, J. "Congenital Malformations Induced by Maternal Dietary Deficiency." *Nutr. Rev.*, 13:289 (1955).

Youmans, J. B. "Deficiencies of the Water-Soluble Vitamins." *Handbook of Nutrition*, 2nd ed., Chap. 22, p. 544. Chicago: American Medical Association (1951).

❧ **17** ❧

Niacin (Nicotinic Acid)

Pellagra

By 1914 pellagra, a disease which had been more or less prevalent in certain sections of Europe for 200 years, had become widely prevalent in the southern states. Goldberger decided to find out its cause. This decision was timely, for in 1915 over ten thousand persons died of the disease in the United States, and by 1917–18 two hundred thousand were suffering from it.

The symptoms of pellagra are many and varied, but among the most typical is a skin eruption which at first resembles sunburn, but later becomes dark and makes the skin rough and scaly. It attacks only certain parts of the body surface, particularly the backs of the hands in adults and of the feet in children. Other parts not infrequently at-tacked are the sides or front of the neck, the face, elbows, and knees. Another marked peculiarity is its tendency to appear at about the same time on both sides of the body. If the back of one hand or one cheek is affected, the corresponding part on the opposite side is involved also. See Figure 17–1. Accompanying the skin eruption are soreness of the mouth and redness of the tongue, indigestion and diarrhea, and dis-turbance of the nervous system leading in some cases to insanity. The mortality records tell the smallest part of the misery it entails, due to lowered physical and mental standards and reduced capacity for the enjoyment of life. The poor man was always the chief victim, but the limitation of the disease to rather clearly defined geographical areas indicated that other factors besides poverty were involved. In Great Britain the endemic disease of the poor was rickets; in the Far East, beriberi; in the cotton mill villages of the South and in southern rural districts of the United States where cotton was practically the only crop, it was pellagra.

The first scientific description of the disease was written by a Spaniard named Casal and published in 1735. He noted the very poor diets in the pellagrous districts of Andalusia and attributed the disease to faulty

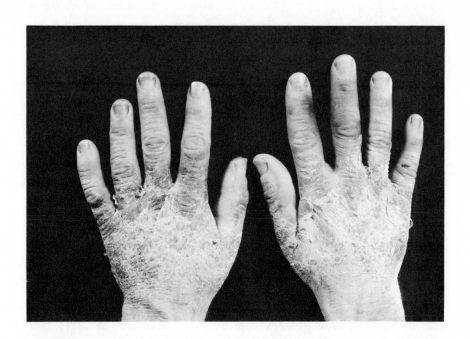

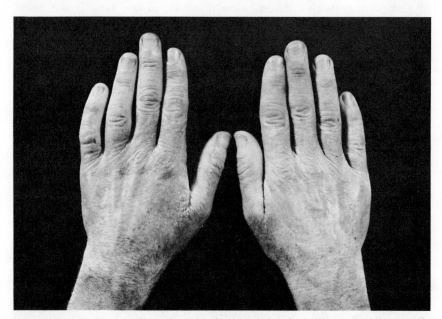

FIGURE 17–1. PELLAGRA. Appearance of the hands of a pellagra patient on admission to a hospital (*upper*) and after three weeks of treatment with niacin (*lower*). (*Courtesy of Professors J. M. Ruffin and D. T. Smith, Duke University School of Medicine, Durham, N.C.*)

nutrition. A few years later it was recognized and named in Italy, pellagra being an Italian word meaning rough skin. Subsequently it was identified in France, Hungary, Rumania, Turkey, and Greece. In 1845 a French physician, Dr. Roussel, wrote a treatise on pellagra in which he, too, pointed out that it is a nutritional disease and recommended broth, meat, milk, eggs, and fish as the best cure. At the close of World War I pellagra broke out in Egypt in camps for Armenian refugees and for prisoners of war. Dr. Wilson of Cairo, who studied the diets, thought them too low in protein and cured the victims by the addition of meat and milk to their high-cereal diets.

Experimental Pellagra

In the parts of the South where pellagra was becoming a scourge in 1914, as has been stated, the main agricultural crop was cotton and the people subsisted on foods bought in the local groceries, mainly cornmeal and grits, white flour, polished rice, sugar, molasses, and fat pork. In mill villages there were no butcher shops or dairies and even in the rural districts few persons kept any cows, poultry, or other live-stock. A survey made by Goldberger convinced him that "the suspicion of pellagra may with confidence be dismissed in one who is a habitual milk drinker and meat eater," but he determined to put the matter to the test, and to see whether pellagra could be induced in healthy men by dietary measures.

He selected for his experiment the farm of the Mississippi State Penitentiary where there was a camp well isolated from the surrounding communities (to rule out the possibility of bacterial infection) caring for some 70 to 80 convicts. On promise of a pardon from the governor of the state, 12 men volunteered to serve as subjects (later one was dismissed), and at the beginning of February 1915, they were quartered in a small screened cottage and kept under guard day and night. Until April 19 they had the usual prison fare and there were no signs of pellagra. They were then put on an experimental ration consisting chiefly of cornmeal and grits, cornstarch, white flour, rice, cane syrup and sugar, sweet potatoes, and pork fat, with exceedingly small amounts of turnip greens, cabbage, and collards. The average protein intake was only 6 per cent of the total calories and from 80 to 97 per cent of the total protein came from the cereal foods. Six men developed symptoms that were deemed sufficient to justify a diagnosis of pellagra by November 1. No one in the camp not on the volunteer squad showed any sign of the disease. In concluding the investigation Goldberger said:

In relation to the study of pellagra this study suggests that the dietary factors to be considered as possibly essential are (1) an amino acid deficiency, (2) a deficient or faulty constitution of the mineral supply, possibly, but doubtfully, (3) a deficiency of the fat soluble vitamine intake, and perhaps (4) an as yet unknown (vitamine?) factor. As to which or what combination (or combinations) of these constitutes the specific pellagra-producing dietary defect or defects remains to be determined.[1]

Studies on human subjects in certain asylums in which pellagra recurred regularly showed that addition to the diet of purified protein alone was without effect, but that dried brewer's yeast was able to give good protection in doses of about 2 oz daily, and that an extract of yeast free from protein was equally effective. These results were interpreted at that time to rule out an amino acid deficiency as the cause of pellagra. Continuing their investigations, Goldberger and his associates in 1926 established the fact that yeast which, because of heating, had lost its antineuritic property still contained a substance active in curing pellagra. They named this then-unknown substance the P-P (pellagra-preventive) factor. When riboflavin (present in the heated yeast) became available in pure form, experiments on dogs were immediately carried out to determine whether it was the P-P factor. By this time there was general agreement that the condition in dogs known as blacktongue was closely analogous to pellagra in the human being. Blacktongue was produced in dogs by the typical diet of pellagrins; in fact, the dogs of pellagrous families were frequently found to be suffering from blacktongue, doubtless because they were fed the table scraps of the family. In studies of Sebrell, Hunt, and Onstott riboflavin was found to be entirely ineffective in experimental blacktongue in dogs,[2] and administration of the pure substance to a number of pellagra patients proved that it alone was not capable of inducing a cure. However, Sebrell and his group rightfully suspected that a multiple vitamin deficiency was involved in alleviation of all the symptoms of pellagra.

In the late summer of 1937, Elvehjem and his associates at the University of Wisconsin announced that they had succeeded in both preventing and curing blacktongue in dogs by administration of either nicotinic acid or its amide. Nicotinic acid had been crystallized earlier but had not been recognized as a vitamin. See Figure 17–2. These substances were promptly tried in cases of human pellagra and found to give truly spectacular results, beneficial effects being seen within 24 to 48 hours even when the disease had progressed to the stage of producing mental derangement. Thus the identity of the P-P factor was finally established. Because the name "nicotinic acid" associates this compound

[1] Goldberger, J., and Wheeler, G. A. *The Experimental Production of Pellagra in Human Subjects by Means of Diet.* Washington, D.C.: Hygienic Laboratory, U.S. Public Health Service, Bulletin No. 120 (1920).

[2] Sebrell, W. H., Hunt, J. D., and Onstott, R. N. "Lactoflavin in the Treatment of Canine Blacktongue." *Pub. Health Rep.,* **52**:235 (1937).

FIGURE 17–2. CRYSTALS OF NICOTINIC ACID (NIACIN). (*Courtesy of Parke, Davis and Co.*)

with the nicotine of tobacco and this was considered undesirable for a food constituent, another name for the compound was sought. Of those proposed, the name *niacin* (*ni* for nicotinic, *ac* for acid, *in* for vitamin) was chosen and was adopted by the United States Food and Drug Administration, but the term "nicotinic acid" is still used in the scientific literature. The amide of the acid, nicotinamide, is also used in the treatment of pellagra. The name "niacin" is commonly used to cover the group.

The dog was used as the experimental animal in all the early work in the study of pellagra, but as highly purified rations were developed that could be supplemented with the B complex vitamins, it was found that the growing chick also needs niacin for optimum growth and for prevention of chick blacktongue.

FUNCTIONS OF NIACIN

Niacin functions in metabolism chiefly as a component of two coenzymes, called coenzyme I (or cozymase) and coenzyme II, which are essential for normal oxidation of carbohydrate in the body, in glycolysis and tissue respiration. It has been found that these catalysts are markedly reduced in amount in the tissues of dogs suffering from blacktongue.

Studies of the end products of niacin metabolism in the urine of human subjects have shown that the amino acid tryptophan is converted to niacin in the body. It is interesting that the vitamin pyridoxine, functioning as a coenzyme, is necessary in this conversion. This has also been found to occur in several species of animals and in microorganisms. Rats ordinarily get all the niacin they need from that synthesized by intestinal bacteria, but on diets containing large amounts of corn they fail to grow normally and show other signs of niacin lack. If either niacin or tryptophan is given in small amount with these diets, symptoms of niacin deficiency do not appear. Corn contains very little free niacin, and its chief protein, zein, is a very poor source of tryptophan. The diets high in corn are therefore low in both available niacin and its precursor, tryptophan.

Spies reported occurrence of latent or mild pellagra in infants and children who did not show the usual symptoms of pellagra but were weak and failed to grow. Treatment with niacinamide brought about improvement in these children. Niacin has also been shown to have a favorable effect in cases of poor appetite and of digestive disturbances.

It has been reported by physicians that while niacin cures pellagra, they find that many of their pellagra patients need, in addition, thiamine or riboflavin or both. Spies found a number of patients who were given the three vitamins and still were not entirely well. He then administered the vitamin pyridoxine and saw improvement. Also, it has been found that the anemia in blacktongue of dogs is apparently complicated by a simultaneous deficiency of folacin. Results such as these have led to the suggestion that perhaps we should think of pellagra as a multiple-deficiency disease rather than as being due to a specific deficiency of niacin. It is obvious that a diet producing pellagra made up largely of corn bread, syrup, and fat pork would be deficient in a number of essential nutrients.

SOURCES

Niacin values (preformed only) of foods will be found in Table A–4 in the Appendix. The best sources of niacin are liver, lean meat, poultry, yeast, fish, peanuts, beef heart, and whole wheat. Dried legumes contribute significant amounts. Fruits and vegetables are poor sources as are also cheese, eggs, and milk. Table 17–1, tabulated from the agriculture Handbook No. 8, gives the values of preformed niacin and potential niacin equivalent values of food groups in the national food supply. It will be noted that some of the foods low in preformed niacin have a relatively high value in terms of niacin equivalent, which includes the niacin formed from tryptophan.

Since nicotinic acid is a very stable compound, ordinary cooking processes cause very little destruction of it, and therefore losses in cooking are practically negligible if the cooking water is used. Niacin, thiamine, riboflavin, and iron are being added to our highly milled cereals, thus compensating for the removal of these nutrients in the milling process.

TABLE 17–1. PREFORMED NIACIN AND POTENTIAL NIACIN EQUIVALENT VALUE OF NATIONAL PER CAPITA FOOD CONSUMPTION PER DAY, 1960*

Food Group	Tryptophan mg	Niacin† from Tryptophan mg	Preformed Niacin mg	Niacin Equivalent mg
Dairy products	320	5.3	0.6	5.9
Eggs	99	1.6	0.0	1.6
Meat, poultry, fish	417	7.0	10.2	17.2
Dry beans, peas, nuts	56	0.9	1.3	2.2
Vegetables and fruits	76	1.3	3.4	4.7
Grain products	220	3.7	4.5	8.2
Miscellaneous	—	—	0.1	0.1
Total	1,188	19.8	20.1	39.9
Allowance for tryptophan‡	500			
Adjusted total	688	11.5	20.1	31.6

*U.S. Department of Agriculture. *Composition of Foods.* Agriculture Handbook No. 8. Table 9, p. 169 (1964).
† Assumes 60 mg tryptophan converted to 1 mg niacin.
‡ Needed for other body functions.

Requirement

As previously discussed, it is well established that tryptophan is a source of niacin for man and thus the dietary requirement is influenced by the quantity and type of dietary protein. Animal protein contains approximately 1.4 per cent, and vegetable protein 1 per cent, tryptophan. Studies of Goldsmith and co-workers and of Horwitt of the administration of tryptophan in normal subjects indicate that on the average 60 mg of dietary tryptophan is equivalent to 1 mg of niacin.

Goldsmith and her associates have reported[3,4] investigations carried out on human beings to determine the requirement for niacin. Two different diets were used, one high in corn and the other high in wheat, each furnishing approximately 200 mg of tryptophan, little more than the minimum human requirement for this amino acid, and 5 mg of niacin. Each of three subjects on the corn diet showed characteristic signs of niacin deficiency after about 50 days on the diet. Of three subjects on the wheat diet, one showed typical niacin deficiency at the end of

[3] Goldsmith, G. A., Sarett, H. P., Register, U. D., and Gibbens, J. "Studies of Niacin Requirement of Man. I. Experimental Pellagra in Subjects on Corn Diets Low in Niacin and Trytophan." *J. Clin. Invest.*, 31:533 (1952).

[4] Goldsmith, G. A., Rosenthal, H. L., Gibbens, J., and Unglaub, W. G. "Studies of Niacin Requirement in Man. II. Requirement on Wheat and Corn Diets Low in Tryptophan." *J. Nutr.*, 56:371 (1955).

80 days, a second developed amenorrhea, herpes of the lip, and slight redness of the tongue papillae, while the third showed lassitude and depression as the only clinical effects. The time it took for pellagra to develop and the severity of it seemed to be related to the intake of niacin and tryptophan per unit of body size on both diets, but these investigators decided that this relationship might not be the complete explanation of the differences between the clinical and laboratory findings on the two diets. In a review (1964) Goldsmith,[5] discussing factors that may influence niacin requirements, cites the possibility of an amino acid imbalance when the niacin and tryptophan content of the diet is low. Summarizing the results of the investigations of the Goldsmith group and the Horwitt group, it is concluded that body stores of the vitamin approach adequacy when the diet furnishes about 9 mg of niacin equivalents per day. The recommended allowance (1963)[6] in niacin equivalents is 6.6 mg per 1,000 calories. The minimum requirement for niacin (including that formed from tryptophan) to prevent pellagra averages 4.4 mg per 1,000 calories with an absolute daily minimum for adults of 8.8 mg if the calorie consumption is less than 2,000 calories. In the United States diets usually supply 500 to 1,000 mg or more of tryptophan daily along with 8 to 17 mg of preformed niacin, making a total of 16 to 33 mg of niacin equivalents, which is well above the recommended allowance.

During pregnancy Wertz and co-workers (1958) observed an increased conversion of tryptophan to nicotinamide. The level of the metabolite N^1-methylnicotinamide (N^1-Me) in the urine increases about 40 per cent from the first to the third trimester, and then returns to prepartum values in the eighth postpartum week. For pregnancy an increased allowance of 3 mg each day is recommended during the last two trimesters. See Table A–1. During lactation an additional allowance of 7 mg niacin equivalent is recommended. An average of 0.17 mg niacin and 22 mg tryptophan per 100 ml is found in human milk, or about 0.5 mg niacin equivalent or 7 mg equivalent for each 1,000 calories.

If a breast-fed infant receives 850 ml (600 calories) of mother's milk, he has an intake of about 4.5 mg niacin equivalent per day. Studies of Holt with human infants on a synthetic diet lacking niacin indicated that the niacin needs will be met if the diet contains 15 per cent casein (6 mg niacin equivalent). A level of 10 per cent casein (4 mg niacin equivalent) will not be sufficient. The recommended allowance for infants and children is 6.6 mg niacin equivalent per 1,000 calories.

[5] Goldsmith, G. A. "The B Vitamins: Thiamine, Riboflavin, Niacin," Chap. 2 in *Nutrition. A Comprehensive Treatise,* edited by Beaton, G. H., and McHenry, E. W., Vol. II. New York: Academic (1964).
[6] Food and Nutrition Board. *Recommended Dietary Allowances.* Washington, D.C.: National Research Council (1964).

Although intakes of this magnitude are customary in the United States and pellagra is no longer a problem even in the southeastern United States, pellagra is found in a number of areas throughout the world. The Interdepartmental Committee on Nutrition for National Defense, which has conducted many nutrition surveys throughout the world, recommends the determination of the urinary metabolite N^1-Me as a practical means of assessing niacin status.

De Lange and Joubert[7] made an assessment of the nicotinic acid status of population groups in South Africa. They determined urinary metabolites of niacin collected from 12 apparently healthy, well-fed white adults. The metabolite ratios were correlated with the known niacin and tryptophan intake. These ratios were then used to compare the metabolites in the urine of white and Bantu primary schoolchildren. They found higher ratios of the metabolites, 2-pyridone to N^1-Me, in the urine of the white children than in the Bantu children among whom pellagra is prevalent. The diet of the Bantu is largely cereal with a high percentage of whole ground or lightly milled maize (corn).

Prevention of Pellagra

Those who have worked intensively on the relation of nicotinic acid to human pellagra have called attention to the importance of education in the control of the disease. In the United States a number of field studies made before the discovery of the part played by nicotinic acid proved that pellagra could be controlled through education and diet. In 1932 Stiebeling and Munsell, of the U.S. Department of Agriculture, investigated the food supply of 73 South Carolina farm families and its relation to the incidence of pellagra, dividing them into two groups: (1) 44 families in an unsatisfactory economic situation, members of which were suffering from pellagra or were in imminent danger of doing so; and (2) 29 families whose economic condition indicated that they could maintain themselves in a better state of nutrition than the other group. To each of the families in the first group some kind of pellagra-preventing food was furnished, dried or evaporated milk, wheat germ, cured lean pork, canned tomatoes, or pure dry yeast being chosen for the purpose. Periodic examination of these 44 families for pellagra revealed that the incidence and severity of the disease were less than in former years and much less than in unaided families of similar resources.

Wheeler and Sebrell, of the U.S. Public Health Service, also in 1932, concluded from their studies that under institutional conditions, where

[7] De Lange, D. J., and Joubert, C. P. "Assessment of Nicotinic Acid Status of Population Groups." *Amer. J. Clin. Nutr.*, **15**:169 (1964).

the diet can be controlled, the problem of pellagra can be eliminated. They said,

> By a few simple and comparatively inexpensive additions to the daily menu, one state institution for the insane, the largest in the South and second largest in the country, has reduced the annual death rate from pellagra from 6.2 per cent of all inmates to as low as 0.1 per cent, this in spite of the fact that during the same time deaths from this cause for the state at large increased almost 100 per cent. . . . Except under extremely reduced resources, its conspicuous presence in any community in which the diet is subject to regulation by central authority can no longer be justified.

And further, regarding the pellagrous districts in the country at large they made this significant statement:

> In looking for cases of pellagra, the home surrounded by evidence of a good garden, or a cow or two, a few pigs and some poultry may as well be passed up, for the chances are less than one in a thousand that pellagra will be found. On the other hand, the home surrounded only by last year's cotton patch will always bear watching.[8]

This statement, made in 1932, was interestingly supported by the results of a survey, reported in 1941, of two adjacent localities in the Kentucky mountains, one of which, a rural community, was found to be free of pellagra, while in the other, a coal mining community, pellagra was endemic. Kooser and Blankenhorn,[9] looking for an explanation of this striking difference between two groups of similar economic level, found that the rural group, in which pellagra had formerly been endemic, had been so influenced by the teaching of the Frontier Nursing Service nurses concerning the relation of food to health that they had planted gardens and were keeping cows and chickens, while in the mining district, where no such service had been available, only insignificant gardens were found. The greatest differences in food consumed by the two groups were found to be in the amounts of milk and eggs, the families in the rural area using much more of each because they produced them for themselves.

The results of these investigations enable us to say with assurance that any one item in the following list will furnish full pellagra prevention per person for one day:

[8] Wheeler, G. A., and Sebrell, W. H. "The Control of Pellagra." *J. Amer. Med. A.,* **99**:95 (1932).

[9] Kooser, J. H., and Blankenhorn, M. A. "Pellagra and the Public Health: A Dietary Survey of Kentucky Mountain Folk in Pellagrous and Non-pellagrous Communities." *J. Amer. Med. A.,* **116**:912 (1941).

One quart of milk or buttermilk	One pound of fresh or
One pint of evaporated milk	canned collards or
One-third to one-half pound of	kale or
dried skim milk or	green peas or
lean meat or	turnip greens
canned salmon or	Two to three pounds of
peanut meal or	fresh tomatoes or
wheat germ	canned tomatoes or
	tomato juice

Any combination of fractional parts of these individual items could, of course, be made; for example, 1 pt of milk (half the amount listed) and 3 or 4 oz of lean meat consumed in one day would give the desired protection.

It is obvious, in terms of our present-day knowledge of the importance of niacin equivalents and additional B complex vitamins, why these foods are so important.

REFERENCES

Elvehjem, C. A. "Early Experiences with Niacin—A Retrospect." *Nutr. Rev.*, 11:289 (1953).

———. "The Vitamin B Complex." *Handbook of Nutrition*, 2nd ed., Chap. 8, p. 169. Chicago: American Medical Association (1951).

Food and Agriculture Organization of the United Nations. *Maize and Maize Diets* (1953).

Gillman, J., and Gillman, T. "Malnutrition and Pellagra in South Africa." *Nutr. Rev.*, 5:353 (1947).

Goldberger, J. "Pellagra: Its Nature and Prevention." *Pub. Health Rep.*, Reprint No. 461, pp. 481–88 (1918).

Jolliffe, N. (ed.). *Clinical Nutrition*, Chap. 18. Spies, T. D. "Niacinamide Malnutrition and Pellagra." New York: Hoeber (1962).

Parsons, R. P. *The Trail to Light* (A Biography of Goldberger). Indianapolis: Bobbs (1943).

Sebrell, W. H. "Joseph Goldberger." *J. Nutr.*, 55:3 (1955).

Sherman, H. C. *Chemistry of Food and Nutrition*, 8th ed., Chap. 20. New York: Macmillan (1952).

Sydenstricker, V. P. "The History of Pellagra, Its Recognition as a Disorder of Nutrition and Its Conquest." *Amer. J. Clin. Nutr.*, 6:409 (1958).

Terris, M. (ed.). *Goldberger on Pellagra*. Baton Rouge: Louisiana State U. P. (1964).

Wohl, M. G., and Goodhart, R. S. (eds.). *Modern Nutrition in Health and Disease*, Chap. 11, p. 380 by Horwitt, M. K. Philadelphia: Lea (1964).

❧ 18 ❧

Other Vitamins

Continuing research on the sources and functions of the vitamins has brought to light numerous additional factors playing a role in the infinitely complex organization of the living body. In this chapter a number of these will be discussed briefly, although the significance of some of them in the human organism has still not been completely clarified.

The fat-soluble vitamins E and K are discussed first. All the remaining vitamins in this chapter are classified as water-soluble and are members of the vitamin B-complex group.

Vitamin E (Tocopherols)

DISCOVERY

The first positive indication that a diet which would enable an animal to grow to maturity in apparently excellent health might still be inadequate for reproduction was furnished in 1920 by Mattill of the State University of Iowa, who was seeking an answer to the question: Is milk, which so admirably meets the needs for growth of the young, a food that will furnish all dietary requirements through the whole life span? Young rats were found to prosper till they approached maturity (at the age of about two months), when they grew somewhat more slowly and failed to reproduce. Various additions to the diet were tried without success, and the investigators were at a loss for an explanation. This was furnished in 1922 by Evans of the University of California. Investigation with a highly purified ration, thought to be adequate in everything but vitamin A, revealed that it could not be made satisfactory for reproduction even when much vitamin A in the form of cod-liver oil was added.

The animals raised on this diet had every appearance of health, being "of splendid size, sleek-coated and active," but they bore no young.

They would exhibit normal estrus cycles, breed, ovulate, and conceive, but something would happen to the placenta which resulted in the death of the fetus. Careful work with wheat embryo revealed a remarkable potency, only ¼ gm daily being needed to restore normal fertility. Evans concluded that there was a special fertility factor and it soon came to be known as vitamin E.

Evans and his associates, in 1935, obtained from wheat germ oil a crystalline compound that was potent for the prevention of sterility. To this they gave the name alpha-tocopherol.[1] Since the identification of alpha-tocopherol, three other naturally occurring substances have been found, beta-tocopherol, gamma-tocopherol, and delta-tocopherol, which are similar to vitamin E. Many synthetic compounds are now known which are chemically related to these tocopherols and exhibit vitamin E activity. See Figure 18–1.

FUNCTIONS

Vitamin E deficiency has been produced in many different laboratory animals, but manifestations of the deficiency are diversified. For example, as discussed above, vitamin E deficiency in the rat results in sterility.

FIGURE 18–1. CRYSTALS OF VITAMIN E PALMITATE. (*Courtesy of Distillation Products, Inc., Rochester, N.Y.*)

[1] Evans, H. M., Emerson, O. H., and Emerson, G. A. "The Isolation from Wheat Germ Oil of an Alcohol, α-Tocopherol, Having the Properties of Vitamin E." *J. Biol. Chem.*, **113**:319 (1936).

Also, creatinuria and other effects occur on a diet totally deficient in vitamin E. Muscular dystrophy occurs in rabbits, encephalomalacia in chicks, and anemia in monkeys. Dinning[2] and associates developed vitamin E deficiency in monkeys by feeding purified diets for six months to three years. The monkeys developed nutritional muscular dystrophy, becoming weak and losing skeletal muscle. A few weeks after the onset of dystrophy the animals were frequently unable to get up. Vitamin E therapy resulted in spectacular recovery, if it was begun soon enough. All the vitamin E-deficient monkeys developed a macrocytic anemia with very low red cell counts. It would appear that the anemia is caused by a lack of some specific maturation factor in the bone marrow, possibly interrelated with the functions of folic acid and vitamin B_{12}. In 1962[3] a study was conducted on 12 anemic infants in Jerusalem, Jordan, treated with vitamin E. In addition to the improvement in the anemia, the accompanying creatinuria was decreased in the infants. The typical history of the infants was that of a healthy child until about five months of age, at which time growth failure, febrile or diarrheal disease, and edema or other symptoms appeared to alarm the mother. She had frequently made unsuitable changes in the diet restricting the infant to rice water or other thin gruel, diluted condensed milk, and tea. The mothers themselves had had poor diets for years. The infants exhibited protein-calorie malnutrition along with the anemia. The authors recommend that tocopherol be considered in areas where protein-calorie malnutrition is prevalent.

Creatinuria found in patients with cystic fibrosis of the pancreas and some kinds of biliary cirrhosis respond to the administration of vitamin E. Ceroid (brownish-red) pigment has been observed in increased amounts in children with cystic fibrosis as well as in celiac disease and sprue when a vitamin E deficiency has been suspected.

Vitamin E deficiency has been identified in human beings conditioned by disease and malabsorption and having existed on very inadequate diets for a period of time. However, vitamin E administration in cases of human sterility, muscular dystrophy, and heart disease has proved disappointing and of no avail.

SOURCES

Vitamin E is widely distributed in common foods. The amounts needed under normal conditions are certainly small, and its very wide distribution in food materials ensures a considerable intake. It occurs in the

[2] Dinning, J. S. "Vitamin E Responsive Anemia in Monkeys and Man." *Nutr. Rev.*, 21:289 (1963).

[3] Majaj, A. S., Dinning, J. S., Azzam, S. A., and Darby, W. J. "Vitamin E Responsive Megaloblastic Anemia in Infants with Protein-Calorie Malnutrition." *Amer. J. Clin. Nutr.*, 12:374 (1963).

greatest richness in the oils of wheat germ, corn, cottonseed, and soybean, but is found in abundance in legumes, green leaves, whole grains, eggs, liver, butter, margarine, and most vegetables. The average daily intake for the adult man has been estimated to be about 14 mg of d-alpha-tocopherol.

REQUIREMENT

As stated by the National Research Council (1963), it is difficult to make any recommendation other than that the tocopherol require-ment will vary between 10 and 30 mg a day for adults. Various factors may affect the requirement, such as the intake of polyunsaturated fatty acids and the presence of selenium and other nutrients. In their anti-oxidant functions there is considerable overlap in the activities of selenium and tocopherol. More information concerning the antioxidant needs of the body and the role of vitamin E is also needed. A level of 0.5 mg per kilogram, the amount usually obtained from human milk, has been suggested as a requirement for infants.

Vitamin K

DISCOVERY

In 1934 Dam and Schonheyder, two Danish investigators, described a deficiency disease they had produced in chicks (see Figure 18–2) which resembled scurvy in that subcutaneous and intramuscular hemorrhages developed but which was not prevented or remedied by addition of ascorbic acid to the diet. The outstanding feature of the disease was the ease with which hemorrhage occurred. It was not long before Dam

FIGURE 18–2. CHARACTERISTIC HEMORRHAGE RESULTING FROM DEFICIENCY OF VITAMIN K. (*Courtesy of E. R. Squibb & Sons.*)

and his associates in Denmark and Almquist and Stokstad in this country had obtained evidence that this disturbance in the blood-clotting power was due to the lack of a vitaminlike factor which Dam named vitamin K, thinking of it as a vitamin regulating blood coagulation, *koagulation* in Danish. It was found that the decrease in coagulability of the blood was due to a lowered content of prothrombin, one of the substances required for normal blood clotting. By 1939 two vitamins K had been isolated, K_1 from alfalfa and K_2 from putrefied fish meal. These two vitamins are known to be derivatives of the chemical compound naphthoquinone. It is not known as yet in what form the vitamin must exist to carry out its functions in the body. The two vitamins are so much alike in activity that they are commonly referred to simply as vitamin K. Many chemically related compounds have been synthesized and tested for their antihemorrhagic activity, and one of these is marketed under the name of menadione.

FUNCTIONS

The precise mode of action of vitamin K in prothrombin formation by the liver is unknown. Vitamin K may be concerned in stimulating oxidative phosphorylation. If there is an injury to the liver, the concentration of prothrombin in the blood is decreased. If, in such cases, the liver damage is severe, administration of vitamin K is usually without effect.

If there is a lack of bile in the intestines and interference of fat absorption occurs, as in obstructive jaundice, chronic diarrhea, or colitis, for example, vitamin K is not adequately absorbed and prothrombin is lowered. Since the recognition of vitamin K the death rate during operations in these cases has been greatly reduced by the use of the vitamin with bile salts. A small amount of vitamin K brings about a very rapid response in the prothrombin level.

Another condition that has been greatly benefited by the use of vitamin K is the low plasma levels of several coagulation factors in the prothrombin complex commonly found in the blood of newborn infants, predisposing them to hemorrhage resulting in death. There are many reports in the medical literature of striking success in reducing the death rate from hemorrhage in newborn infants by giving vitamin K either to the mother prior to the birth of the baby or to the baby immediately after birth. Excessive doses of synthetic vitamin K are undesirable since they have resulted in the breakdown of red blood cells in the rat and other toxic conditions in the human infant.

SOURCES

There is evidence that vitamin K may be synthesized by microorganisms normally present in the intestines, so that small amounts may be obtained in this way. The vitamin is so widely distributed among different kinds of food that there seems to be little likelihood of a dietary deficiency. The green leafy vegetables, tomatoes, cauliflower, egg yolk, soybean oil, and liver are all good sources of this vitamin.

REQUIREMENT

According to the National Research Council,[4] "A daily allowance for vitamin K cannot be established because of the wide but inconsistent distribution of the vitamin in the diet and the variability of intestinal flora and absorption activity from person to person."

Vitamin B_6

DISCOVERY

The term "vitamin B_6" was originally applied by György, in 1934, to a factor essential for rats which was distinct from the vitamins B_1 and B_2. Lack of it in the diet of the rat resulted in a specific dermatitis or acrodynia. In 1938 a crystalline compound (see Figure 18–3) which was found to cure these symptoms was isolated almost simultaneously in five different laboratories, and in 1939 Harris and Folkers reported that they had synthesized it. The name pyridoxine was given to the compound and it was called either vitamin B_6 or pyridoxine.

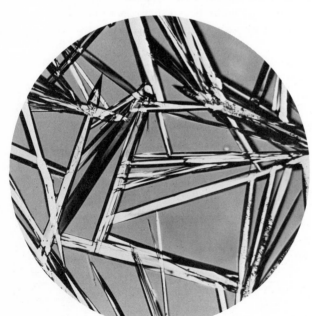

FIGURE 18–3. CRYSTALS OF PYRIDOXINE. (*Courtesy of Merck & Co., Inc.*)

[4] *Recommended Dietary Allowances*, 6th rev. ed., p. 45. Washington, D.C.: National Research Council (1964).

In 1942 Snell and his associates reported that both rats and human beings converted pyridoxine to one or more substances having greater potency for promoting the growth of lactic acid bacteria than pyridoxine itself. This led to the synthesis of two compounds, pyridoxal and pyridoxamine, which were found to be highly active for lactic acid bacteria. Since all three of these compounds occur naturally, the term "vitamin B_6" is used as a collective term for the group.

FUNCTIONS

Vitamin B_6 has been found essential for normal nutrition in all animals investigated, although different species show different effects of a deficiency of the vitamin. Rats develop a dermatitis (see Figure 18–4); in dogs and swine severe anemia results; hamsters show marked changes in the hair coat, as do cattle; and monkeys exhibit a variety of effects, among them, fissuring of the epithelium of the hands and feet, severe anemia, and sclerotic lesions in the arteries.

The first attempts to produce vitamin B_6 deficiency in human beings were unsatisfactory owing to difficulties in removing all three forms completely from the diet. However, Vilter and his associates (1956) reported production of the deficiency in man by feeding deoxypyridoxine, a chemical analogue of pyridoxine, or antivitamin, that inhibits its activity. The most common sign observed was a seborrheic dermatitis occurring about the eyes, in the eyebrows, and at the angles of the mouth. Other results were changes in the tongue and membranes of the mouth very much like those occurring in pellagrins, and cheilosis, conjunctivitis, and angular stomatitis such as are seen in riboflavin-deficient subjects.

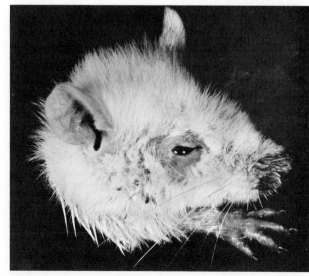

FIGURE 18–4. RAT SHOWING EFFECTS OF VITAMIN B_6 DEFICIENCY. (*Courtesy of Merck & Co., Inc.*)

Treatment with pyridoxine, pyridoxal, or pyridoxamine, either orally or parenterally, was effective in clearing up these symptoms.

Vitamin B_6 is involved in the metabolism of amino acids, fats, and carbohydrate. There are 20 or more recognized enzymes which require pyridoxal phosphate as coenzyme. Vitamin B_6 plays a specific role in the metabolism of tryptophan. In a deficiency of pyridoxine abnormal metabolites of tryptophan are formed. One of these, xanthurenic acid, is excreted in excessive amounts in the urine. This serves as the basis of a load test of tryptophan to determine the pyridoxine status.

The excretion of urinary oxalate is increased in vitamin B_6 deficiency and has been implicated in the formation of kidney stones. Pyridoxine has also been studied in relation to the impairment of the production of circulating antibodies. Hodges and co-workers[5] studied six volunteer prisoners; two were on control diets, two were on pyridoxine-deficient diets, and two were given pyridoxine antagonists. The four deficient subjects showed gastrointestinal disturbances and skin changes. However, the formation of antibodies against tetanus and typhoid was only slightly impaired. A continuation of this study with subjects on a combined deficiency of pantothenic acid and pyridoxine showed definite impairment of antibody response along with a lowering of gamma globulin in the blood.

Hyperirritability and convulsions have been observed in infants on intakes of less than 100 μg of vitamin B_6. Such serious neurological abnormalities in pyridoxine deficiency can be explained by the role of pyridoxine in brain metabolism, which is currently under investigation.

A rare familial condition, probably an inborn error of metabolism, has been described in which excessive amounts of pyridoxine appear to be required to prevent convulsions.[6]

Although the role of pyridoxine in fatty acid and cholesterol metabolism has been extensively studied over a period of years, the nature of the relationship has not been clarified.

Requirement

Studies conducted in Sauberlich's[7] laboratory have provided the best evidence at present of the human requirement of vitamin B_6. Young, healthy adult men, aged 18 to 22 years, served as subjects. They were placed on a liquid-formula diet sufficient in all known nutrients except vitamin B_6. One group received 30 gm of protein and a second group

[5] Hodges, R. E., Bean, W. B., Ohlson, M. A., and Bleiler, R. E. "Factors Affecting Human Antibody Response. IV. Pyridoxine Deficiency," page 180; and "V. Combined Deficiencies of Pantothenic Acid and Pyridoxine." *Amer. J. Clin. Nutr.*, 11:187 (1962).

[6] Review. "Pyridoxine Dependency in Siblings." *Nutr. Rev.*, 22:199 (1964).

[7] Baker, E. M., Canham, J. E., Nunes, W. T., Sauberlich, H. E., and McDowell, M. E. "Vitamin B_6 Requirement for Adult Men." *Amer. J. Clin. Nutr.*, 15:59 (1964).

100 gm of protein. The rate of pyridoxine depletion was directly related to protein intake. It was concluded that the optimal daily vitamin B_6 requirement for subjects on a high protein intake appeared to be 1.75 to 2.0 mg per day, while subjects on a low protein intake appeared to have a requirement of 1.25 to 1.5 mg per day. The tentative recommended allowance suggested by the National Research Council (1963), 1.5 to 2.0 mg for the adult, provides a margin of safety on protein intakes of 100 mg or more and under ordinary conditions of stress. Although increased excretion of xanthurenic acid has been observed in pregnancy, it is not clear that this is related to pyridoxine requirement. The vitamin B_6 requirement for infants has been generally accepted at 0.4 mg per day.

SOURCES

For determination of vitamin B_6 in foods three procedures have been used, chemical, biological, and microbiological. Recent work has demonstrated the unreliability of these methods, but a newer method combining chromatographic separation and yeast assay appears to be promising in analyzing foods. Vitamin B_6 occurs widely in both animal and plant products and is not likely to be deficient in human diets. Analyses by the Food and Drug Administration of the vitamin B_6 foods selected to represent moderate-cost diets of boys 16 to 19 years of age indicate daily intakes from 2.2 to 2.9 mg.

Liver, yeast, rice bran, milk, cereals, legumes, meats, and fresh vegetables are good sources of the vitamin. See Table 18–1.

TABLE 18–1. VITAMIN B₆ CONTENT OF SOME COMMON FOODS*

(Micrograms per 100 gm of edible portion)

Foods	µg	Foods	µg
Milk, cow's	65–73	Peanuts	300
Milk, human	3.5–22	Split peas	190–400
Milk, dried (nonfat)	50–56	Cabbage	290
Eggs	22	Cauliflower	20
Beef, round	400	Peas	50–190
Beef, kidney	390–1,020	Potatoes	160
Beef, liver	710–810	Spinach	83
Ham, fresh	330–580	Tomatoes	70
Ham, smoked	190	Turnips	100
Fish, salmon	110–130	Apples	26
Corn	250–570	Bananas	300
Oats	190–250	Oranges	80
Wheat, whole	270–410	Yeast, dried, brewer's	3,930
Wheat, germ	1,030–1,120		

* Compiled from various sources indicating approximate values for comparison.

Pantothenic Acid

DISCOVERY

Pantothenic acid was identified in 1933 by R. J. Williams as a substance essential to the growth of yeast. The name pantothenic is derived from the Greek, meaning occurring everywhere. Williams gave the acid this name because of its widespread occurrence in living tissues of all kinds, which seemed to him to indicate that it must be of fundamental importance. In 1939 Elvehjem and his co-workers at the University of Wisconsin and Jukes of the University of California, working independently of each other, demonstrated that the "chick dermatitis factor" which they had been trying to identify was evidently pantothenic acid. The synthesis of the acid was accomplished in 1940. See Figure 18–5 for crystals of calcium pantothenate.

FUNCTIONS

When rats are placed on diets low in this vitamin, they fail to grow normally and are found, on autopsy, to have suffered injury to the cortex of the adrenal glands. Graying of the hair has been observed on these diets when black rats were used and restoration of color when the missing vitamin was introduced into the food mixture. Many studies on the graying of hair in human beings have shown that the administration of

FIGURE 18–5. CRYSTALS OF CALCIUM PANTOTHENATE. (*Courtesy of Hoffmann-La Roche, Inc.*)

pantothenic acid is ineffective. The vitamin is so widely distributed in foods that a deficiency is not likely.

Experiments have shown that, in dogs, the deficiency of pantothenic acid is characterized by a sudden collapse of the animals, which on autopsy reveal fatty livers and abnormalities in the intestines. Disturbances of the nervous system have been found in chicks and pigs on deficient diets. In all animals thus far studied a deficiency of this vitamin has resulted in severe disturbances followed by death.

Ralli has reported that pantothenic acid is apparently important in offsetting stress conditions in human subjects. She found that large doses (10 gm per day for six days) of calcium pantothenate cleared up some of the blood and urinary disturbances resulting from immersing young men in cold water. Glusman and Vernon have reported independently a possible relationship of pantothenic acid to the "burning feet syndrome" seen in Japanese prisoners of war. In another study of this condition Gopalan reported improvement in ten patients treated with calcium pantothenate.

It has been difficult to produce a pantothenic acid deficiency in human subjects. In 1959, Hodges and his associates studied the syndrome in man by the use of a semisynthetic diet and a pantothenic acid antagonist. The deficiency was characterized by fatigue, headache, nausea, abdominal cramps, vomiting, parasthesias, muscle cramps, and impaired coordination.

It is recognized that pantothenic acid is a part of coenzyme A. This enzyme is involved in the release of energy during carbohydrate utilization and is needed for the synthesis and the breakdown of fatty acids, sterols, and steroid hormones. It has also been shown to be involved in the formation of other compounds in the body, including the amino acids.

SOURCES

Liver, eggs, dried yeast, wheat germ, and bran have been found to be especially good sources of the vitamin; skim milk, broccoli, cauliflower, sweet potatoes, tomatoes, and molasses were classified as good sources. Of the canned foods studied, fish products were the best, while asparagus, corn, and peas were only fair sources. In the cooking of meats a loss of one third of the vitamin took place, but only slight losses occurred in the cooking of vegetables. A loss of 57 per cent of the vitamin in wheat may take place in the manufacturing of patent flour. See Table 18–2.

REQUIREMENT

In a study reported by Mangay Chung and others,[8] adequate "high-cost" and adequate "low-cost" diets, patterned after food plans suggested

[8] Mangay Chung, A. S., Pearson, W. N., Darby, W. J., Miller, O. N., and Goldsmith, G. A. "Folic Acid, Vitamin B$_6$, Pantothenic Acid and Vitamin B$_{12}$ in Human Dietaries." *Amer. J. Clin. Nutr.*, 9:573 (1961).

TABLE 18-2. PANTOTHENIC ACID
IN SOME COMMON FOODS*

(Micrograms per gram of edible portion)

Foods	μg	Foods	μg
Milk, whole	3.23	Walnuts	9.70
Milk, skim	3.75	Beans, green	2.02
Cheese, cottage	2.80	Broccoli	12.87
Eggs, whole	15.75	Cabbage	2.80
Beef, rib	5.42	Carrots	2.72
Beef, liver	93.36	Kale	12.88
Lamb, leg	8.86	Lettuce	3.63
Ham	6.94	Onions	1.68
Cornmeal	5.93	Potatoes	4.05
Oats	12.13	Spinach	3.12
Rice, white	6.40	Sweet potatoes	9.35
Wheat	10.95	Tomatoes	3.14
Navy beans	12.08	Avocados	11.35
Lentils	14.99	Bananas	3.06
Split peas	21.16	Oranges	2.21
Almonds	5.78	Pineapples	1.75
Cashews	11.62	Yeast, dried, brewer's	99.24

* Source: U.S. Department of Agriculture Handbook No. 97 (1956).

by the U. S. Department of Agriculture, and a "poor" diet were analyzed for folic acid, vitamin B_6, pantothenic acid, and vitamin B_{12}. On the average, the adequate "high-cost" diet was found to contain 16 mg of pantothenic acid and the adequate "low-cost" diet 14 mg. The "poor diet" was grossly inadequate in calories, protein, thiamine, riboflavin, and niacin. The "poor" diet was patterned after actual menus recorded in a study of pregnant women at Vanderbilt University. It was found to contain 6 mg of pantothenic acid.

Considering intake studies such as the one described and investigations dealing with urinary excretion of pantothenic acid in normal adults, it seems likely that 10 mg per day of this vitamin will satisfy human requirements.

Folacin (Folic Acid)

DISCOVERY

In 1945, Day and his associates reported evidence that a substance previously unknown was required by the monkey. They proposed calling it vitamin M (for monkey). Other workers, because it was found in green leaves, called it folic acid. When it was isolated in pure form and its formula established, it was found to be pteroylglutamic acid. See Figure 18–6. Also some forms that are combinations of pteroylglutamic acid with other compounds are known to occur. All these forms may be referred to as the folic acid group. The American Institute of Nutrition has now adopted the name folacin for folic acid or pteroylglutamic acid.

FUNCTIONS

It has been found that folic acid is required for normal growth and blood formation in the chick, fox, mink, and monkey. Rats and dogs do not require it in the diet under conditions of normal activity of intestinal bacteria.

Folic acid deficiency results in a failure of red cell formation in the bone marrow, glossitis, and gastrointestinal disturbances. In the macrocytic anemias (those characterized by blood cells enlarged in size and fewer in number than normal), which occur rather commonly in infants and pregnant women and in sprue, and other malabsorption syndromes, folic acid proves effective. Persons with scurvy and infants on diets of milk exclusively may develop macrocytic anemia because of folic acid and ascorbic acid deficiency.

When synthetic folic acid became available, it was tried on pernicious anemia patients with striking effect on the macrocytic anemia but with no effect on the neurological condition. Anemias due to lack of iron do not respond to folic acid treatment.

FIGURE 18–6. CRYSTALS OF FOLIC ACID. (*Courtesy of Hoffmann-La Roche, Inc.*)

Folic acid deficiency in the chick also results in abnormal feather pigmentation. It is thought that this may be the result of abnormal metabolism of the amino acid tyrosine due to the folic acid deficiency, since it is known that folic acid as well as ascorbic acid is involved in tyrosine metabolism. Ascorbic acid is important for the maintenance of folic acid in the reduced form through enzyme activity.

The functions of the coenzymes formed from folic acid are basic in the intermediary metabolism and involve the transfer of single carbon units in intracellular synthesis. Vitamin B_{12} appears to be involved to a very important degree in reactions necessary for the activity of the folic acid coenzymes.

Folic acid is readily absorbed by the gastrointestinal tract and is stored principally in the liver.

SOURCES

The first attempts to determine the folic acid content of foods yielded unsatisfactory results because of ignorance of the bound forms of the vitamin which necessitate liberating the folic acid by certain enzymes in order to obtain the total amount. In 1951, however, Toepfer, of the U.S. Department of Agriculture, presented the results of determining the folic acid content of a large number of foods by improved quantitative methods. His results indicate that fresh, green, leafy vegetables, kidney, liver, whole grains, nuts, and fresh green vegetables such as asparagus, green beans, and peas may be considered good sources while most other foods are only fair or poor sources of the vitamin.

Recent chromatographic studies are attempting to provide further data on the folic acid compounds in individual foods in order to arrive at a better estimate of the folic acid activity in diets.[9]

REQUIREMENT

The dietary requirement for folic acid is not definitely established; it appears that part of the requirement may be met as a result of the activities of intestinal bacteria.

Davidson and Jandl (1959)[10] discuss the measures that can be used to estimate the daily allowance for folic acid. A hematogical response is induced in persons with sprue by as little as 0.025 mg of crystalline folic acid daily; 0.25 mg induces response in persons with macrocytic anemia caused by dietary deficiency of folic acid. A daily intake of 0.05 mg prevents depletion of serum folic acid.

[9] Santini, R., Brewster, C., and Butterworth, C. E. "The Distribution of Folic Acid Active Compounds in Individual Foods." *Amer. J. Clin. Nutr.*, **14**:205 (1964).

[10] Davidson, C. S., and Jandl, J. H. "Editorial: On the Daily Allowance for Folic Acid." *Amer. J. Clin. Nutr.*, **7**:711 (1959).

Pregnant patients with cirrhosis of the liver have higher requirements, and their diets should be planned to include foods rich in folic acid.

Folacin activity in the daily American diet, based on food tables now in use has been calculated to be between 160 and 190 micrograms. The data presented by Butterworth and co-workers, show that only about 11 per cent of this activity is from pteroylglutamic acid. It is not known what per cent of the folacin requirement can be met by other compounds with folacin activity present in the diet.[11]

Since it is possible for an undiagnosed pernicious anemia patient to obtain an undesirable excess of folic acid by dietary supplementation, the sale without prescription of vitamin preparations suggesting levels greater than 0.1 mg (100 μg) per day is prohibited (*Federal Register.* July 20, 1963).

Vitamin B$_{12}$ (Cyanocobalamin)

DISCOVERY

Minot and Murphy in 1926 reported finding that in their clinical practice pernicious anemia responded to treatment with whole liver or an extract of it. This announcement stimulated research in a number of laboratories on the fractionation of liver extracts with the object of isolating the active component. Finally, in 1948, Smith and Parker in England and Folkers and his associates in the United States reported simultaneously the isolation of a crystalline red substance (see Figure 18–7) containing cobalt and phosphorus and which was effective in pernicious anemia. It was named vitamin B$_{12}$. In clinical tests daily dosages as small as one- to five-millionths of a gram injected intramuscularly were effective in arresting the neurological disturbances in pernicious anemia as well as in restoring the blood to a normal condition. The presence of cobalt in this compound was of special interest because it had already been established that pasturing ruminants on soils low in cobalt resulted in the disturbances referred to as the coast disease in Australia and New Zealand (see Chapter 11).

In 1955, the structural formula of this complicated molecule was announced. One molecule of this compound is known to contain 63 atoms of carbon, 90 of hydrogen, 14 of oxygen, 14 of nitrogen, one of phosphorus, and one of cobalt. With the exception of protein molecules, this molecule appears to be the heaviest and most complex thus far found in nature.

Early in the studies of liver feeding in pernicious anemia it was found that mixtures of beef muscle and normal gastric juice brought about the

[11] Review. "Folacin Activity in U.S. Diets." *Nutr. Rev.,* **22**:142 (1964).

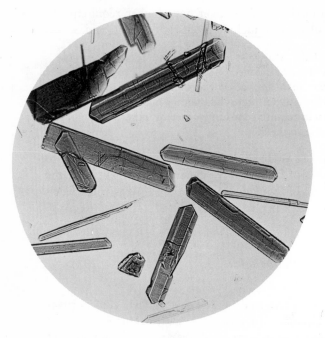

FIGURE 18–7. CRYSTALS OF
VITAMIN B$_{12}$. (*Courtesy of
Merck & Co., Inc.*)

same improvement in the blood picture as the liver. The gastric juice of
anemia patients would not act in this way. This led to the conclusion that
two factors were involved—an intrinsic factor in normal gastric juice and
an extrinsic factor present in food. The efficacy of vitamin B$_{12}$ in treatment of pernicious anemia established it as the extrinsic factor. In 1960,
it was established that the intrinsic factor is a mucoprotein enzyme
secreted by the stomach. This enzyme appears to remove vitamin B$_{12}$
from the protein combination in which it occurs in foods.

FUNCTIONS

Pernicious anemia typifies the deficiency state of vitamin B$_{12}$. This
deficiency is due to a genetically controlled lack of the intrinsic factor in
stomach secretions. These individuals may develop, along with the anemia,
symptoms such as sore tongue, paresthesias, and signs of degeneration of
the spinal cord. A vitamin B$_{12}$ deficiency may at times occur in persons
living entirely on vegetables and in cases of malabsorption.

This vitamin has been reported to have growth-promoting activity for
some microorganisms and for animals under controlled conditions (see
Figure 18–8). A number of reports in the literature over a period of years
indicated that a vitamin B$_{12}$ deficiency might be involved in the growth
failure of children. However, both negative and positive findings have
been reported showing inconclusive results. To answer this question,
Scrimshaw and his associates in 1959 conducted a carefully controlled
study in Guatemala. The experimental subjects included 278 preschool-

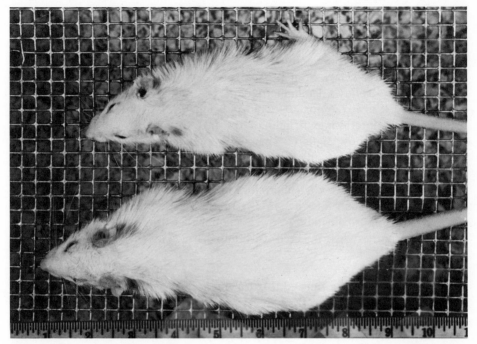

FIGURE 18–8. TWO RATS—LOWER NORMAL, UPPER SHOWING VITAMIN B₁₂ DEFICIENCY. (*Courtesy of Merck & Co., Inc.*)

and schoolchildren who had existed on diets very low in animal protein and whose growth was retarded two to four years. After 18 months in which some children received vitamin B_{12} six days a week and others placebos, it was concluded that "vitamin B_{12} supplementation is without effect on the nutritional status of children from technically under-developed areas whose growth and development is retarded."[12]

Evidence has been obtained that vitamin B_{12} plays a part along with choline and folic acid in the metabolism of the amino acid methionine. Vitamin B_{12} is necessary for the normal function of all types of cells but especially those of the bone marrow, the nervous system, and the gastro-intestinal tract. Its chief importance appears to be in nucleic acid and folic acid metabolism, although it probably is involved in protein, carbo-hydrate, and fat metabolism.

SOURCES

The vitamin is not present in significant amounts in ordinary foods of vegetable origin. The richest food sources of those that have been tested

[12] Scrimshaw, N. S., Munox, J. A., Tandon, O. B., and Guzmán, M. A. "Growth and Development of Central American Children. II. The Effect of Oral Administration of Vitamin B_{12} to Rural Children." *Amer. J. Clin. Nutr.*, 7:180 (1959).

are kidney, liver, eggs, milk, and muscle meats. Various seaweeds have been reported to be rich sources. It is suggested that these algae may be the source from which marine animals such as clams, oysters, other mollusks, and fish obtain the comparatively large amounts found in them. Various milks have been assayed for their content of the vitamin, giving results as follows (millimicrograms per milliliter): rat, 13.0; ewe, 7.0; cow, 2.3; sow, 1.7; goat, 0.9; human being, 0.3. The low results for human milk are interesting in light of the fact that breast-fed infants are not known to show signs of vitamin B_{12} deficiency. This doubtless means either that the infant's requirement is low or that it is born with stores that are adequate until the time comes for supplements. There is considerable evidence that microflora in the intestinal tract can furnish significant amounts of vitamin B_{12} to the host. One pint of cow's milk contains approximately 1 μg, an amount that produces good hematological response when injected daily into pernicious anemia patients.

REQUIREMENT

It is currently estimated that for the normal individual, a diet providing 3 to 5 μg of vitamin B_{12} per day (with an absorption of about 1 to 1.5 μg) will satisfy the requirement. If body stores of vitamin B_{12} have been depleted, a diet providing 15μg per day should gradually replenish them. The average American diet apparently satisfies these requirements. The study of "high-cost," "low-cost," and "poor" diets referred to in the discussion of pantothenic acid (see page 291) reported 31, 16, and 2.7 μg of vitamin B_{12}, respectively, for these diets.

Biotin

DISCOVERY

Biotin was first isolated in 1936 by Kögl and Tonnis in Holland. See Figure 18–9. Through the cooperative efforts of two laboratories, those of duVigneaud at Cornell University Medical College and György at Western Reserve University School of Medicine, its structure was established in the fall of 1942 and its synthesis accomplished in the spring of 1943.

FUNCTIONS

Recognition of biotin as a dietary essential resulted from studies of a condition produced in rats when they were fed diets containing high amounts of raw egg white. These animals developed a severe dermatitis, skin hemorrhages, edema, signs of nervous disturbances, and some anemia, and suffered complete loss of hair. If the egg white was cooked, no injury developed. It was found in the course of these studies that feeding very large amounts of the vitamin B complex prevented this condition

FIGURE 18–9. CRYSTALS OF
BIOTIN. (*Courtesy of Dr.
Vincent du Vigneaud and
the* Journal of Biological
Chemistry.)

and also cured it when it had developed. It was discovered that egg white contains avidin, a protein that has the property of uniting with biotin to form a product that cannot be absorbed from the intestines. Avidin thus brings about the same result as a biotin-deficient diet. Nielsen and Elvehjem found that feeding an amount of biotin in excess of that which unites with the avidin cured the "egg white" injury.

Dr. Sydenstricker and his co-workers at the University of Georgia Medical School fed four human volunteer subjects a diet low in biotin and high in egg white but complete in all other known essentials. Dermatitis developed on hands, arms, and legs, some changes in the tongue occurred, nervous symptoms very similar to those seen in thiamine deficiency appeared, loss of appetite resulted, and a peculiar grayish pallor of the skin developed. The hemoglobin content of the blood and the number and size of red blood cells decreased. Prompt relief of all symptoms was brought about by administration of a concentrate of biotin. These observations indicate that biotin plays a role in normal human nutrition. It apparently plays an important part in intermediary metabolism, having been recognized as a coenzyme in several processes.

SOURCES

It is found widely distributed in food materials. Egg, liver, kidney, yeast, most fresh vegetables, several fruits, and milk have been reported as good sources.

REQUIREMENT

"Daily needs are provided by diets containing 150–300 micrograms of biotin. This amount is provided by the average American Diet."[13]

Choline

Choline has been known for many years as a part of lecithin, one of the phospholipids. That choline has a specific relation to the metabolism of fat has been demonstrated in rats as well as dogs. In addition to fatty livers, Griffith has also noted in rats on choline-deficient diets the occurrence of hemorrhages in the kidneys and the eyes, enlargement of the spleen, and a decrease in size of the thymus gland. Several investigators have reported that on choline-deficient diets rats, dogs, and chicks fail to grow normally.

Direct evidence of disease in man due to choline deficiency is lacking. It is probably important in human nutrition but not an essential dietary constituent because the body can form it from other compounds, particularly methionine.

Inositol

Inositol, a component part of the well-known substance phytin, is a sweet-tasting, crystalline substance which in the animal body is found in muscle. It also occurs in brain tissue, red blood cells, and eye tissues.

It has often been listed among the B-complex vitamins. It has been reported to be required for proper nutrition and the growth of certain animals. Its significance in human diets is not known.

REFERENCES

Butt, H. R. "Fat-Soluble Vitamins A, E, and K." *Handbook of Nutrition*, 2nd ed., Chap. 11. Chicago: American Medical Association (1951).

Elvehjem, C. A. "The Vitamin B Complex." *Handbook of Nutrition*. 2nd ed., Chap. 8, pp. 173–96. Chicago: American Medical Association (1951).

Food and Nutrition Board. *Recommended Dietary Allowances*. Washington, D.C.: National Research Council, Publication 1146 (1964).

Food—The Yearbook of Agriculture 1959. McCollum, E. B., and McCollum, E. V. "Vitamins A, D, E, K," p. 130; Goldsmith, G. "Vitamins of the B Complex," p. 139. Washington, D.C.: U.S. Department of Agriculture.

Harris, L. J. *Vitamins in Theory and Practice*, 4th ed., Chaps. 8, 9, 10, and 11. New York: Cambridge U. P. (1955).

[13] *Recommended Dietary Allowances*. Washington, D.C.: National Research Council (1964).

"International Symposium on Vitamin B_6." *Science,* **146**:674 (1964).

Johnson, B. C. "Dietary Factors and Vitamin K." *Nutr. Rev.,* **22**:225 (1964).

Krehl, W. A. "Pantothenic Acid in Nutrition." *Nutr. Rev.,* **11**:225 (1953).

Lepkovsky, S. "Early Experiences with Pyridoxine—A Retrospect." *Nutr. Rev.,* **12**:257 (1954).

Leverton, R. M. "Nutritional Well-Being in the U.S.A." *Nutr. Rev.,* **22**:321 (1964).

Mattill, H. A. "Vitamin E." *Nutr. Rev.,* **10**:225 (1952).

Peterson, W. H. "The Folic Acid Story—Reminiscences." *Nutr. Rev.,* **12**:225 (1954).

Review. "Vitamin B_{12} and Growth of Children." *Nutr. Rev.,* **18**:45 (1960).

Tower, D. B. "Pyridoxine and Cerebral Activity." *Nutr. Rev.,* **16**:161 (1958).

Youmans, J. B. "Deficiencies of the Fat-Soluble Vitamins." *Handbook of Nutrition,* 2nd ed., Chap. 21, pp. 257–532. Chicago: American Medical Association (1951).

❧ 19 ❧

Nutrition and Dental Health

Dental caries is the most prevalent disease in the United States involving an estimated 97 to 98 per cent of the population at some time in their lives. Other dental diseases, such as periodontal disease, and malocclusion, are widespread throughout the United States. It is reported that 68 million Americans suffer from periodontal disease, which is an even greater cause of tooth loss in adults than tooth decay. Dental caries is defined as inflammatory destruction affecting the enamel, dentine, and cementum with secondary infection of the pulp. The periodontal membrane, composed of fibers attached to the root and lining the cement of the tooth, helps to hold the tooth in place. It is subject to degenerative or destructive disease, which is called periodontal disease or periodontoclasia.

The Causes of Dental Disease

Early theories stressed that the susceptibility of the teeth to dental caries was largely a matter of the quality of the teeth at the time they are formed during prenatal life and in early childhood. These theories were questioned by later research emphasizing the importance of the oral environment in dental decay throughout life. In current thought it is appreciated that the etiology of a disease is rarely simple and that many factors are usually involved. In dental caries, a variety of factors, such as an individual's inheritance, the presence or absence of fluorides in drinking water, the type of diet in terms of nutritive value, the amount and kind of carbohydrate, the consistency of the food, and the oral flora, are all known to play a role.

Research with germ-free animals has given clear-cut evidence that caries is produced by bacterial activity in the mouth. Germ-free rats do not develop caries on diets which are usually cariogenic (caries-produc-

302

ing). But if the germ-free animal is contaminated with microorganisms, caries develops rapidly. Also, in the oral environment the type and volume of saliva may have an influence on dental decay.

When food debris and calculus (tartar) are allowed to accumulate at the gum line and between the gum and tooth surfaces, the gums may become irritated and infected. This continual irritation causes swelling and recession from the neck of the tooth so that the periodontal membrane becomes affected. Infection and destruction of this membrane, resulting in disintegration of the surrounding bone, lead to the loss of the tooth. Many influences affect the health of the gum and the periodontal membrane.

Population Surveys of Dental Conditions

Dental surveys, discussed by Russell and associates,[1] have been conducted in many areas of the world. It is difficult to find any consistent correlation between nutritional status in a population group and the prevalence of dental caries. Undoubtedly, this is due to many variables in addition to the differences in nutrient intake in each situation. Diets of different population groups differ in the amount of fermentable carbohydrates, the consistency of the foods, stickiness and texture. The differences in ethnic strains, habits of living, dental practices, all complicate the situation and make it difficult to identify specific causes.

The prevalence and characteristics of periodontal disease are more closely related to nutritional status, but again it is difficult to identify consistent relationships. In Alaska, it was observed that men in more remote villages had a lower incidence of DMF (decayed, missing, filled) teeth. Generally, a lower incidence of caries is observed in primitive people, but not always.

A low incidence of caries in parts of Ecuador and in Ethiopia was associated with higher intakes of fluoride. The descendants of the Inca Indians living in the southern Sierra had the lowest incidence of caries in the population groups studied in Peru. In Vietnam dental caries incidence was only slightly higher than in Ethiopia. If caries-prevalence levels in these countries were low by United States standards, the prevalence and severity of periodontal disease were very high. In Vietnam periodontal disease was universally found with heavy deposits of calculus in the mouths of almost every person over 12 years of age. The Vietnamese diet is generally soft in consistency with highly milled rice as a staple, and marginal nutritional deficiencies were found.

[1] Russell, A. L., Littleton, N. W., Leatherwood, E. C., Sydow, G. E., and Greene, J. C. "Dental Surveys in Relation to Nutrition." *Pub. Health Rep.*, **75**:717 (1960).

Development and Structure of the Tooth

Many nutrients play a role during the development of the tooth. The tooth is formed of three layers of calcified tissue, chiefly calcium phosphate but with small amounts of calcium carbonate, magnesium phosphate, calcium fluoride, and traces of other mineral salts. The pulp cavity, containing blood vessels and nerves, is covered by the dentine. Where the tooth is exposed, the dentine is covered with enamel but the submerged roots have a layer of cementum (Figure 19–1). The cementum resembles very closely cortical bone in composition. The dentine, hard and dense, has almost 75 per cent mineral salts, while the enamel, still harder and more dense, contains almost 98 per cent mineral salts. An organic matrix similar to that of bone is found in dentine and cementum. Enamel bears a unique position within the family of hard tissues because it is composed of densely packed rods and prisms of mineral salts, devoid of cellular and vascular elements. Yet the seemingly solid enamel prisms are surrounded by a honeycomb network of organic matter. The ameloblasts, which compose the enamel organ and which originate from the oral epithelium, are undoubtedly important in the development of the enamel. The dentine matrix has neither cells nor blood vessels, but even in its bulkiest form, the ivory of the elephant tusk, is in cellular communication with the internal odontoblasts which line the pulp cavity. The odontoblasts play an important role in the development of dentine.

Calcium, Phosphorus, and Magnesium

Studies on the mineral composition of the teeth show considerable variation within so-called normal values. About 36 per cent of the

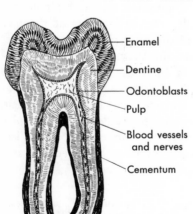

Enamel

Dentine

Odontoblasts

Pulp

Blood vessels and nerves

Cementum

FIGURE 19–1. A DIAGRAM SHOWING IN CROSS SECTION THE RELATIONSHIP OF PARTS IN A TOOTH.

enamel and 27 per cent of the dentine is composed of calcium, while the average phosphorus content of the enamel is 17 per cent and of the dentine 13 per cent. The percentage of magnesium in the enamel is only about 0.4 and in the dentine 0.8. The ratio of calcium to phosphorus is very important during the developmental stage in determining the composition of the enamel and the dentine. In studies with cotton rats a low calcium : phosphorus ratio in the diet during tooth development resulted in changes in the mineral composition, making the teeth more susceptible to dental decay. The relationship of these findings to human situations is not known.

An early effect of magnesium deficiency in animal experiments is shown by the atrophy of both the odontoblasts and the ameloblasts. Both the enamel and the dentine show abnormal development.

The effectiveness of soluble dietary phosphates in the prevention of experimental dental caries is being actively investigated at the present time. The mechanism by which various organic and inorganic phosphorus-containing compounds reduce the incidence of caries in experimental animals is not known, and the effectiveness of these compounds in human beings has not been demonstrated.

As Sognnaes states, defective tooth structure, so common in man, may arise from faulty construction during growth. Teeth are very susceptible to metabolic injury before development is complete, and rings or lines of inadequate mineralization or hypocalcification are detectable under the microscope. Once formed, teeth, unlike bone, are not normally involved in lifelong reconstruction nor do they contribute to the mineral pool of the body.

Vitamin A

The outstanding researches of Wolbach of Harvard University and Howe of the Forsyth Dental Infirmary in Boston have made it clear that vitamin A exercises a very definite control over tooth development.[2] When rats are placed on a diet lacking vitamin A, their teeth become chalky, white, and brittle, owing to the loss of the enamel with its orange-colored pigment and the exposure of the dentine. The development of the enamel is controlled by the enamel organ, the complex structure of epithelial origin, which begins to degenerate as soon as vitamin A is withheld. The formation and maintenance of the dentine depend on the odontoblasts, a single layer of very active cells arranged in an orderly row between the pulp and the dentine and sending filaments into both. The changes in the enamel organ affect the odontoblasts first on the side

---

[2] Wolbach, S. B., and Howe, P. G. "The Incisor Teeth of Rats and Guinea Pigs in Vitamin A Deficiency and Repair." *Amer. J. Path.*, 9:275 (1933).

opposite to the enamel organ, and the dentine on that side becomes thin and defective while increasing on the other side, so that the tooth in cross section becomes much distorted. Eventually all the odontoblasts shrink and shrivel, and the dentine as well as the enamel becomes strikingly defective. These findings were confirmed and extended by Schour, Hoffman, and Smith.[3]

The health of the teeth is affected not only by these controlling organs within the structure of the tooth itself but also by the soft tissues in which they are embedded, upon which proper position in the jaw and freedom from bacterial invasion of the gums to a very considerable degree depend. In England Lady Mellanby studied for many years the effect of vitamin A on the teeth of rats and puppies, and her conclusion with regard to vitamin A follows:

> It is of fundamental importance to include vitamins A and D in the diet during the early developmental period if the periodontal tissues are to resist disease. A large supply of these vitamins during a later period even from the fifth month onwards, does not compensate for a deficiency during the earlier period. Vitamin A in very large doses may prevent the spread of the pathological condition.[4]

Reviewing the effects of vitamin A deficiency on the teeth, Bessey and Wolbach concluded that "in all probability, vitamin A deficiency during the formative period of teeth outranks in the human being all other vitamin deficiencies in importance."[5]

As discussed in Chapter 12, vitamin A deficiency disorganizes normal developmental and remodeling changes in the bone during growth. Shaw[6] points out that these effects on bone growth are of interest in the field of dentistry and orthodontics in children. The disproportionate development of the teeth and the bones in the face and the jaws of some children suggests alterations in vitamin A metabolism which warrant investigation.

Ascorbic Acid

In the days when the Roman soldiers were campaigning on the Rhine, they suffered, after the campaign had lasted two years, from loosening of the teeth, and a remedy was discovered in the eating of a

[3] Schour, I., Hoffman, M. M., and Smith, M. C. "Changes in the Incisor Teeth of Albino Rats with Vitamin A Deficiency and the Effects of Replacement Therapy." *Amer. J. Path.*, 17:529 (1941).

[4] Mellanby, M. *Diet and the Teeth*, Part II, p. 31. Medical Research Council. Special Report Series No. 153. London: His Majesty's Stationery Office (1930).

[5] Bessey, O. A., and Wolbach, S. B. *The Vitamins*, p. 46. Chicago: American Medical Association (1939).

[6] Shaw, J. H. "Nutrition in Relation to Dental Medicine," Chap. 20, p. 667 in Wohl, M. G., and Goodhart, R. S. *Modern Nutrition in Health and Disease*. Philadelphia: Lea (1964).

native plant thought by modern writers to be some variety of sorrel. Swelling and bleeding of the gums and progressive loosening of the teeth have always been accounted characteristic symptoms of human scurvy, and in their early researches Holst and Frölich noted the same symptoms in guinea pigs. But actual changes in the structure of the tooth itself were first reported in 1916 by Jackson and Moore, who noted hemorrhages in the pulp of the teeth in guinea pigs. Soon after, in 1919, Zilva and Wells showed that scurvy produced great changes in the teeth of both guinea pigs and monkeys and discovered that the tooth is one of the first parts of the body to be affected by any shortage of ascorbic acid. They found that when the mildest degree of scurvy could barely be detected on post-mortem examination, profound changes in tooth structure had already taken place.

In this country Howe was also actively engaged at this time in studying the effects of diet on teeth, and he described changes not only in the gums and pulp, but also in the enamel and dentine, that could be cured by addition of orange juice to the diet. Zilva and Wells had noted that the odontoblasts of the teeth of scorbutic guinea pigs became disorganized, and their work was soon extended by Höjer of Sweden. In 1924 he found that when not enough ascorbic acid was given to promote growth, but only that small amount which would arrest decline in weight for several weeks, changes could still be detected in the teeth by the second week, while on a completely scorbutic diet they appeared within a week. The first change occurs in the odontoblasts, which make the nutritional connection between the pulp of the tooth and the dentine. When ascorbic acid is not entirely lacking in the diet but is present in too small quantity, the odontoblasts, which ordinarily stand in a row side by side like the pickets of a fence, lose their orderly arrangement and change their character. They shrink away from the dentine, which in turn begins to degenerate, becoming liquefied and later being replaced by "secondary dentine," which is more like bone than like the original dentine. There is also injury to the pulp, sometimes resulting in large hollows filled with fluid. In the guinea pig about twice as much ascorbic acid is needed for complete tooth protection as for the prevention of the ordinary signs of scurvy.

A study by Fish of the Royal Dental Hospital, London, and Harris of Cambridge University showed that the enamel-forming cells (ameloblasts) are not affected as soon as the odontoblasts or by as mild a degree of scurvy, but that when the disease is severe, "they either disappear altogether or become hard and shriveled so that even if the animal is cured there never will be any enamel on that section of the tooth which was forming when the disease was at its height."

The cementum, which covers the part of the tooth embedded in the jaw, is secreted by cells (cementoblasts) that undergo degeneration, so that no cementum is produced, and its place is taken by a scar tissue with calcium deposits similar to that laid down to protect the pulp (secondary dentine). In short, deficiency of ascorbic acid appears to affect all cells concerned with the laying down of the hard tissues—dentine, enamel, cementum, and the bone of the jaw. See Figure 19–2. Crampton in 1947 suggested a bioassay method for ascorbic acid based on the growth of the odontoblast cells of the incisor teeth of young guinea pigs.

Just how all these findings apply to human teeth is not yet entirely clear, but they have served to emphasize the far-reaching role of nutrition in tooth health. No animal except the monkey has been found sufficiently like the human being in tooth structure and food requirements to serve as a satisfactory testing agent. Westin, in collaboration with Höjer, studied 18 cases of human scurvy and reported degeneration of the odontoblasts and changes in pulp, dentine, and cementum similar in many respects to those observed in guinea pigs' teeth. The extensive studies of Lady Mellanby on the relation of the structure of the teeth to dental disease and especially as a factor in dental caries, while largely conducted on dogs, which do not get scurvy and hence give no direct evidence regarding the role of ascorbic acid, indicate very strongly a definite relationship between poor tooth structure and susceptibility to caries, and the relationship of ascorbic acid to every kind of tooth-building cell justifies emphasis on ascorbic acid as a factor in tooth health and development.

In the survey *Nutritional Status, U.S.A.*, prevalence and causes of dental caries in high school boys and girls were investigated in five western areas. Findings on ascorbic acid were summarized, and it was stated that ascorbic acid intake affects the condition of the gums when the diets of children are on the borderline of adequacy. However,

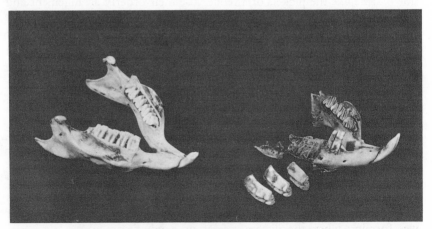

FIGURE 19–2. THE JAWS OF TWO GUINEA PIGS. The one on the left is from an animal fed plenty of ascorbic acid; the one on the right, from a scorbutic animal. The deterioration of the jawbone has permitted the molar teeth to fall out. (Nutrition Laboratory, Teachers College, Columbia University.)

ascorbic acid does not produce measurable improvement in children already in good vitamin C status.[7]

Vitamin D

That vitamin D plays an important role in the prevention of dental caries was demonstrated by McBeath and Zucker[8] of Columbia University in a study extending over four years in nine different orphanages in and near New York City. The subjects, over 800 in all, ranged in age from 6 to 14 years. It was established that the incidence of dental caries was seasonal, the greatest number of new cases appearing in late winter and early spring and the smallest number during the summer. Giving graded amounts of vitamin D (as vitamin D milk, in which the vitamin D was of animal origin) resulted in graded prevention. Of the three amounts given (250, 400, and 800 I.U. daily), only the highest entirely prevented an increase in new cases of caries during late winter and early spring. The two lower dosages had significant effects, however, with more protection resulting from the use of 400 units than of 250. When these investigators tried improving the diet by simply adding protective foods or increasing the amount of ordinary milk in the diet, no other source of vitamin D being given, they found some reduction in new cases of caries but not equal to that seen when the vitamin D milk was given. When they reversed the control and experimental groups during two successive years in 100 cases, they found the results reversed, indicating, they thought, that "individual susceptibility to caries was negligible compared to the effect of nutritional factors."

Of interest in connection with these findings are those of East and his associates,[9] who, using data on the incidence of dental caries in children collected by the American Dental Association and the U.S. Public Health Service along with the records of the United States Weather Bureau giving the annual hours of sunshine in the localities in which the children lived, found that in the regions where the hours of sunshine were highest, the number of cases of caries in every instance was lowest. Also, they found that groups living in zones that had an average winter temperature below 30° F. had a higher incidence of caries than those living where the mean winter temperature was higher, and, in accord with this, the children living in the North showed more caries than those living in the South.

[7] Morgan, A. F. (ed.). *Nutritional Status, U.S.A.* Berkeley: California Agricultural Experiment Station Bulletin 769, p. 84 (1959).

[8] McBeath, E. C., and Zucker, T. F. "The Role of Vitamin D in the Control of Dental Caries in Children." *J. Nutr.*, 15:547 (1938).

[9] East, B. R. "Mean Annual Hours of Sunshine and the Incidence of Dental Caries." *Amer. J. Pub. Health*, 29:777 (1939). East, B. R., and Kaiser, H. "Relation of Dental Caries in Rural Children to Sex, Age, and Environment." *Amer. J. Dis. Child.*, 60:1289 (1940).

Lady Mellanby observed that when Sir Edward Mellanby's puppies developed rickets, their teeth were seriously affected, and she began the investigation mentioned earlier in this chapter of the factors controlling normal tooth development in dogs. She found that young puppies fed diets lacking in vitamin D showed delay in the eruption of the permanent teeth; the enamel was irregularly formed and poorly calcified, the surface being pitted and grooved; the jaw bones were thickened and the teeth irregularly arranged. The dentine also was irregularly calcified, and the tissue at the margin between tooth and gum was abnormal in its development.

In 1927, the Medical Research Council of Great Britain, greatly impressed by Lady Mellanby's findings on dogs, decided to support her in an investigation of the effect of vitamin D on the teeth of children. Three institutions in the neighborhood of Birmingham were chosen, caring for 835 children from 2½ to 16 years of age. At one of them there was added to the diet 1½ oz daily of syrup (treacle); at another, 1½ tbsp of olive oil was added; and at the third, the children under eight years of age each received 1 tbsp of cod-liver oil, and those who were older, 1½ tbsp. Thorough dental examinations were made every six months for two years. At the final inspection it was found that while the actual number of carious teeth had approximately doubled at the institutions where syrup and olive oil were fed, it had increased by only one half in the third group, where cod-liver oil was given. It appears to be well established that defects in tooth structure do occur in rickets although they may be difficult to distinguish from injuries caused by deficiency of vitamin A or ascorbic acid. In children suffering from rickets dentition is commonly delayed.

Fluorine

In 1916, McKay[10] reported that the factor causing mottled enamel of the teeth was due to something present in the water supply during the period of tooth development. He came to this conclusion after an examination of 6,873 individuals in 26 communities or rural districts. At that time the methods for water analysis were of no help in finding the unknown element that was likely to cause this mottled condition of the teeth. It was not until 15 years later, in 1931, that three separate laboratories[11] published evidence showing that high levels of fluorides in

[10] McKay, F. S. (in collaboration with Black, G. V.). "An Investigation of Mottled Teeth." *Dent. Cosmos*, **58**:627–44, 781–92, 894–904 (1916).

[11] Smith, M. C., Lantz, E. M., and Smith, H. V. *The Cause of Mottled Enamel, a Defect of Human Teeth.* Tucson: U. of Arizona Experiment Station Technical Bulletin No. 32 (1931); Churchill, H. V. "Occurrence of Fluorides in Some Waters of the United States." *J. Indust. & Engin. Chem.*, **23**:996 (1931); Velu, H. "Dystrophie Dentaire des Mammifères des Zones Phosphatées (Darmous) et Fluorose Chromique." *Compt. Rend. Soc. de Biol.*, **108**:750 (1931).

the water were evidently responsible for the dull, chalky, white blotches and frequently unglazed appearance on the surface of the teeth, known as mottled enamel. See Figure 19–3. As this condition progressed, the teeth became stained and developed a characteristic brown color. Eventually, the enamel became pitted.

Extensive studies followed to ascertain the level of fluorides in drinking water in many parts of the United States, the findings of which helped to establish pertinent facts. Drinking water having a fluoride content of 2.5 ppm (parts per million) and above was found to result in fluorosis of a disfiguring degree, and the incidence and severity of the fluorosis increased as the levels approached 10 to 20 ppm. In localities where these very high levels were found, almost all the natives had severe dental fluorosis. When the fluoride content of the water was as low as 1 ppm, a low incidence of dental caries was found. A high incidence of dental caries was found among children growing up in communities where the fluorine in the drinking water was less than 0.5 ppm. This pointed out that too little fluorine tended to cause dental caries, a little prevented dental caries, while too much caused the unsightly mottled enamel.

In Colorado Springs, Colorado, drinking water, which had been obtained from the same source for 75 years, was found to have a natural fluorine content of 2.4 ppm. The teeth of 400 persons, ten years of age and older, who had lived continually in Colorado Springs, were examined. In the older group of inhabitants, that is, those between 40 and 44 years of age, an average of 0.61 tooth per person was found to be decayed or filled in contrast to an average of 10.2 teeth per person in the United States as a whole. No harmful symptoms that could be traced to the higher fluorine content of the water were noted except fluorosis.

Under normal conditions bones and teeth have been found to contain some fluoride, and where the intake of fluoride is high, retention of fluoride in the body is increased, but when the amount ingested is low,

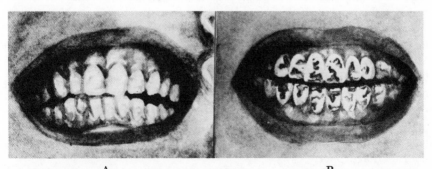

A   B

FIGURE 19–3. FLUOROSIS. *A* shows a mild degree of fluorosis; *B* a severe degree. (*From* Public Health Reports, *Vol. 50* [*1935*].)

little is retained. The fluorine content of the enamel of sound teeth has been reported to be higher than that of the enamel of carious teeth. In mottled teeth the enamel was found to be two or three times as high in fluorine as in sound teeth.

These findings paved the way for many more surveys of the fluorine content of water in different locations and the effects on teeth, the results of which established the fact that fluorine in drinking water at a level of 1 ppm was the most desirable level for the control of dental caries.

During 1945 and 1946, long-term studies of the artificial fluoridation of drinking water were started in several experimental communities. Grand Rapids, Michigan, the first city in the world to initiate such a program, started it in January 1945. The city of Aurora, Illinois, having a water supply with a natural fluoride content of 1.2 ppm was used for comparison. Periodic examinations of the teeth of the children living continuously in Grand Rapids were conducted. Ten years of continuous fluoridation of the water supply showed a reduction in the decay of permanent teeth of from 76 per cent in six-year-olds to 29 per cent in the 16-year-old group. In 1945, Aurora had about two thirds less tooth decay than Grand Rapids. At the end of the ten-year period the incidence of tooth decay in the two cities was found to be approximately the same.

In April 1945, another convincing study was started in Newburgh, New York, and in the city of Kingston, just 38 miles away. In both cities the drinking water had an extremely low fluorine content. The water of the city of Newburgh was treated with fluoride to bring the content of fluorine to the level of 1 ppm, while the water of the city of Kingston remained untreated. Periodic examination of the schoolchildren was continued for ten years. On the tenth anniversary of the initiation of the program, Dr. David B. Ast, Director of Dental Health, New York State Department of Health, reported an average of 58 per cent reduction in the decayed, missing, or filled teeth (DMF) among the children of Newburgh as compared with those in the city of Kingston, where the water was not fluoridated. The six- and seven-year-old children in Newburgh who had always had fluoridated water showed an improvement in dental health of about 69 per cent. No adverse effects of the fluorine were found among the children participating in the study. Currently, about 900 communities are known to have had fluoridated water for ten years or longer. The experience of these communities gives clear-cut evidence that fluoridation is an effective public health measure against dental decay. See Table 19–1. There is also some evidence to suggest that fluoridation may help to prevent malocclusion (irregularly positioned teeth that do not function properly).

As previously cited, many communities have high levels of fluoride in their natural water supply. Abnormalities other than mottled enamel have not been identified in surveys in communities with levels as high as

TABLE 19–1. IMPROVEMENT IN DENTAL DECAY
OBSERVED IN SOME FLUORIDATION STUDIES

Location of Study	Years of Observation	Age Groups	Reduction in Dental Decay,* (per cent)
Brantford, Ontario	7	6	59
		7	70
		8	52
		9	46
		13	33
Evanston, Illinois	4	6	74
		7	56
		8	35
Grand Rapids, Michigan	8	6	71
		7	53
		8	49
		9	48
		13	40
Newburgh, New York	10	6–7	69
		10–12	52
		13–14	48
		16	41

* Decayed, missing, and filled teeth (DMF).

8 ppm in the water supply. For example, a survey was conducted in two Texas towns, Bartlett with 8 ppm of fluoride in the water and Cameron with essentially none. Some residents of Bartlett had severely mottled enamel, but there were no other unfavorable health effects observed. Of course, no one likes the unsightly appearance of fluorosis, and in areas where the water supply has 2.5 ppm or higher, steps need to be taken to treat the water through the development of a new source of supply, dilution, or removal of fluorides.

Other factors, such as diet and hereditary tendencies, also play an important role in the prevention of tooth decay and must not be overlooked. But the evidence of the beneficial effects of established levels of fluorides in drinking water now available from these carefully controlled studies is convincing and should alleviate any fear of disastrous effects from the fluoridation of drinking water. Table 19–2 gives the rating on fluoridation by state.

Other Factors Influencing Dental Health

Some of the earlier studies suggesting rather definite findings have more recently been under criticism since many contributing factors

TABLE 19-2. RATING BY STATES
ON FLUORIDATION

Percentage of Population with Public Water Supplies with Natural or Controlled Fluoridation*

		Per Cent			Per Cent
1	Maryland	93.2	26	Texas	34.1
2	Rhode Island	87.6	27	Kansas	32.9
3	New Mexico	85.4	28	Wyoming	32.6
4	Wisconsin	81.9	29	Alabama	29.2
5	West Virginia	76.9	30	Connecticut	28.9
6	Missouri	76.2	31	Montana	27.8
7	Illinois	72.0	32	Michigan	26.7
8	Indiana	70.5	33	South Carolina	25.2
9	Iowa	70.1	34	Vermont	24.1
10	Colorado	69.4	35	Florida	23.8
11	North Dakota	68.1	36	Mississippi	21.0
12	Minnesota	66.9	37	Louisiana	16.7
13	Virginia	65.7	38	Washington	15.6
14	Alaska	62.4	39	New York	14.0
15	Kentucky	60.5	40	Oregon	13.1
16	North Carolina	52.7	41	Hawaii	12.7
17	Delaware	51.9	42	California	11.4
18	Oklahoma	49.8	43	Nebraska	9.8
19	Arkansas	49.6	44	Maine	9.2
20	Tennessee	47.7	45	Massachusetts	8.0
21	Idaho	45.0	46	New Jersey	7.8
22	Pennsylvania	43.1	47	Arizona	7.7
23	Georgia	39.9	48	New Hampshire	4.1
24	South Dakota	39.8	49	Nevada	3.7
25	Ohio	39.2	50	Utah	3.1

*U.S. Department of Health, Education, and Welfare (1963).

were not then recognized, and consequently they were not controlled.

At present additional factors are being investigated that may have a possible influence on dental health in some situations. Other mineral elements and amino acids, such as lysine, may be found to have some relation to dental problems.

PYRIDOXINE

Monkeys maintained on a diet deficient in pyridoxine developed dental caries within 16 to 56 months. The teeth of these deficient animals were reduced in size and altered in shape. Decalcification of the incisors often exposed the dentine. The gingivae were swollen and inflamed. The effect of increased levels of pyridoxine in reducing caries on hamsters and rats has also been demonstrated.[12] Hillman and associates[13] studied the effect of pyridoxine supplements on dental caries in 540 women during the period of pregnancy. The subjects were of mixed ethnic background from the ward maternity service, and the diets were uncontrolled. The subjects receiving the pyridoxine supplements appeared to have a more favorable caries experience showing, on the average, a smaller increase in the DMF rating.

The Dietary Regimen in Dental Health

CARBOHYDRATES IN THE DIET

Of all the components of the diet, carbohydrate is the one that appears most closely related to the oral flora and the growth of the acid-producing microorganisms that initiate tooth decay. The kind of carbohydrate also makes a difference. Studies in Sweden conducted in a mental institution revealed that sucrose fed in solution did not have as deleterious an effect on the teeth as when fed as sticky caramels or toffees. Sugar in chocolate was intermediate in effect. In general, starches and cereals in various human and animal studies were not found to be as caries-producing in effect, but the fineness of the milling, as in rice, seems to make some difference. It is interesting that a reduction in dental caries incidence is associated with wartime rationing of sugar in World Wars I and II.

Thus limitation in sugar intake would seem to be important on two counts: (1) its relationship to the oral flora, and (2) its "empty calories," which tend to "dilute" the nutritive value of the diet.

During the developmental stage of the teeth it is clear that an adequate diet is essential for the best formation of the jaw and the oral cavity and the health of the teeth and other oral tissues. All four food groups should be represented with a reliable source of vitamin D. In the selection of foods, attention to those foods that require vigorous mastication is desirable. Fresh fruits, fruit juices, and milk should be encouraged as between-meal snacks in place of sticky, high-carbohydrate foods.

REFERENCES

Comar, C. L., and Bronner, F. *Mineral Metabolism—An Advanced Treatise,* Vol. 1, Part B, Chap. 15. Sognnaes, R. F. "Dental Aspects of the Structure and Metabolism of Mineralized Tissues." New York: Academic (1961).

Council on Foods and Nutrition. "Symposium on Nutrition in Tooth Formation and Dental Caries." *J. Amer. Med. A.,* **177**:304 (1961).

[12] Review. "Pyridoxine and Dental Caries—Animal Studies." *Nutr. Rev.,* **21**:145 (1963).

[13] Hillman, R. W., Cabaud, P. G., and Schenone, R. A. "The Effects of Pyridoxine Supplements on the Dental Caries Experience of Pregnant Women." *Amer. J. Clin. Nutr.,* **10**:512 (1962).

Editorial. "Fluoridation of Public Water Supplies." *J. Amer. Med. A.*, **186**:64 (1963).

Graves, J. *Keeping Your Teeth Healthy*. New York: Public Affairs Committee, Inc. Public Affairs Pamphlet No. 363 (1964).

Hard, M. M., Esselbaugh, N. C., and Jacobson, F. L. "Bone Density and Dental Caries." *J. Amer. Dietet. A.*, **47**:274 (1965).

Review. "Attitudes Towards Fluoridation." *Nutr. Rev.*, **22**:291 (1964).

———. "Bone Density and Fluoride Ingestion." *Nutr. Rev.*, **19**:198 (1961).

———. "Pyridoxine and Dental Caries—Human Studies." *Nutr. Rev.*, **21**:143 (1963).

———. "Dietary Phosphates and Dental Caries." *Nutr. Rev.*, **21**:60 (1963).

———. "Metabolism of Fluorides." *Nutr. Rev.*, **19**:259 (1961).

———. "Phosphates and Experimental Dental Caries." *Nutr. Rev.*, **21**:315 (1963).

Shaw, J. H. "Nutrition in Relation to Dental Medicine," Chap. 20. Wohl, M. G., and Goodhart, R. S. *Modern Nutrition in Health and Disease*. Philadelphia: Lea (1964).

Sognnaes, R. F. (ed.). *Advances in Experimental Caries Research*. Washington, D.C.: American Association for the Advancement of Science (1955).

Tank, G. "Recent Advances in Nutrition and Dental Caries." *J. Amer. Dietet. A.*, **46**:293 (1965).

Tank, G., and Storvick, C. A. "Caries Experience in Children One to Six Years Old in Two Oregon Communities (Corvallis and Albany). 2. Relation of Fluoride to Hypoplasia, Malocclusion, and Gingivitis." *J. Amer. Dent. A.*, **70**:100 (1965).

Toverud, G., Cox, G. J., Finn, S. B., Bodecker, C. F., and Shaw, J. H. *A Survey of the Literature of Dental Caries*. Washington, D.C.: Food and Nutrition Board, National Research Council (1952).

❧ **20** ❧

Food Selection and the Recommended Dietary Allowances

Race Experience Does Not Ensure Good Nutrition

Experience has taught the human race a great deal of practical value about diet, but it is no guarantee of an ideal one. Some people with no scientific knowledge of nutrition are so situated as to be well nourished on their natural diet. McCarrison cited isolated peoples in the Himalayas, whom he found remarkably vigorous, although living on what would seem to be a much restricted diet. He said:

> For nine years of my professional life my duties lay in a remote part of the Himalayas, where there are located several isolated races, far removed from the refinement of civilization. Certain of these races are of magnificent physique, preserving until late in life the characters of youth; they are unusually fertile and long lived and endowed with nervous systems of notable stability. Their longevity and fertility were, in the case of one of them, matters of such concern to the ruling chief that he took me to task for what he considered my ridiculous eagerness to prolong the lives of the ancients of his people, among whom were many of my patients. The operation for senile cataract appeared to him a waste of my economic opportunities, and he tentatively suggested instead the introduction of some form of lethal chamber designed to remove from his realms those who by reason of their age and infirmity were no longer of use to the community.[1]

These people lived on a very frugal diet, consisting of apricots, which they sun-dried for winter use, vegetables, and goat's milk; goats were the only livestock, and while butter was made from the milk, goat's meat was eaten only on feast days.

Mellanby described another isolated group on the Island of Lewis in the Hebrides, whose houses were unsanitary, being windowless and full

[1] McCarrison, R. "Faulty Food in Relation to Gastro-Intestinal Disorders." *J. Amer. Med. A.*, **78**:1 (1922).

of smoke, and whose children got comparatively little sunlight; yet the death rate of their infants was very low and rickets practically unknown. Their diet consisted mainly of milk, oatmeal, potatoes, turnips, and fish. A staple article of diet was cod's head, stuffed with a mixture of oatmeal, milk, and cod livers. Such a diet would seem very limited to an average American, yet was capable of a great saving of infant lives. Many other peoples throughout the centuries, and currently, have not been able to obtain or select an adequate food supply as well as these examples might imply.

An example of a primitive people who managed to survive and maintain themselves on foods available years ago is the American Indian. Many tribes depended on hunting and on foods now unavailable, such as buffalo meat and bone, to provide nutritive essentials. When civilization brought changes, the American Indians found it hard to adjust to practices now needed for survival in regard to either nutrition or sanitation. Hence these peoples, economically deprived, developed serious health problems and the life span shortened. In selecting foods made available in the white man's culture, such as white flour and sugar, their diets became increasingly unbalanced. Now the U.S. Public Health Service has a special Indian Health Program in an attempt to improve the health practices of the Indians. Nutrition education has an important role to play within this over-all program.

Review of the Essentials of an Adequate Diet

The advances in the science of nutrition have given us the tools for planning adequate diets and thus have freed us from the dangers of "hit or miss" eating. In previous chapters we have considered the essentials of an adequate diet and have found that they may be stated under five headings:

1. Energy to meet the daily expenditure; with surplus for storage only when actually needed for growth or to build up an underweight adult.

2. Protein in sufficient quantity to replace daily nitrogen loss, and to supply a liberal and complete assortment of indispensable amino acids, especially during growth.

3. Mineral elements of many kinds, each with its own special function for which no other can be substituted, and all related to the regulation of life processes as a whole.

4. Vitamins, serving as regulators of metabolism and controlling the processes involved in maintenance, growth, and reproduction.

5. Water, not only an important constituent of the body, but essential in the regulation of body processes.

These dietary essentials may be conveniently summarized according to their main functions in the following way:

1. Food as a source of energy or fuel for the body machine:

Carbohydrates
Fats
Proteins

2. Food as a source of material for the development and maintenance of body structure:

Proteins
Mineral elements
Vitamins
Water
Carbohydrates and fats (in some metabolic activities)

3. Food as a means of coordinating and otherwise regulating body processes:

Amino acids
Mineral elements
Vitamins
Water
Carbohydrates and fats (in some metabolic activities)

The Recommended Dietary Allowances

The requirement for each of the nutrients known to be essential in human nutrition have been discussed in the earlier chapters and reference has been made to the Recommended Dietary Allowances suggested by the Food and Nutrition Board of the National Research Council.

The first Recommended Dietary Allowances for specific nutrients were presented at the National Nutrition Conference called by President Roosevelt in May 1941. Prior to this, a special committee of the Food and Nutrition Board of the National Research Council had as their responsibility the recommendation of the amounts of the various nutrients that should be provided for both the armed forces and the general population.

Previously some standards had been suggested for certain nutrients by a number of workers. Sherman had proposed standards for protein, calcium, phosphorus, and iron for adults; Lucy Gillett had set up calorie standards for children based on food intake records; and the Technical Commission of the Health Committee of the League of Nations had defined the food requirements of different categories of the population including heavy physical work, pregnancy, and lactation. Individual investigators had suggested requirements for different nutrients based on their research, which was often conflicting. The committee, having reviewed all evidence on requirements, formulated a tentative set of values for the various nutrients for different ages and conditions. Before adoption, they were again reviewed by a large group of nutrition specialists throughout the United States.

The first edition of Recommended Dietary Allowances was published in 1943 and revisions were made in 1945, 1948, 1953, 1958, and 1963. The allowances are intended to serve as goals in planning food supplies and as guides for the interpretation of food consumption records of groups of people.

> The allowances are designed to afford a margin of sufficiency above average physiological requirements to cover variations among essentially all individuals in the general population. They provide a buffer against the increased needs during common stresses and permit full realization of growth and productive potential; but they are not to be considered adequate to meet additional requirements of persons depleted by disease or traumatic stresses. On the other hand, the allowances are generous with respect to temporary emergency feeding of large groups under conditions of limited food supply and physical disaster.[2]

The Recommended Daily Dietary Allowances, Revised 1963, will be found in the Appendix, Table A–1. Comparative dietary standards for adults developed by other countries and by FAO will be found in the Appendix, Table A–9. These will be discussed in Chapter 28.

Comparing the Contribution of Foods with the Recommended Allowances

Our knowledge of the nutritive values of food is the result of the labors of many investigators in this field. We now have extensive tables (see reference list in Chapter 5) giving the results of hundreds of thousands of analyses of food materials for protein, fat, carbohydrate, water, mineral elements, and vitamins. With the establishment of nutrition laboratories in many countries, our knowledge of the composition of foods in other parts of the world has been greatly extended.

To the beginner food composition tables may seem somewhat confusing to interpret because the values are expressed in so many diverse units. However, it is mathematically possible for practical purposes to establish a common denominator that will be helpful in studying relationships. When all the nutritive values of foods and the recommended daily allowances for nutrients are expressed in a common unit (the share), it is possible to make comparisons quickly. Thus the contribution of one food

[2] *Recommended Dietary Allowances,* 6th rev. ed. Washington, D.C.: A Report of the Food and Nutrition Board, National Academy of Sciences, National Research Council. Publication 1146, p. v (1964).

can be easily compared with those of another. Also, one can see at a glance how one food (or a dietary) contributes in satisfying the recommended allowances.

THE MATHEMATICAL DERIVATION OF THE SHARE

The Food and Nutrition Board of the National Research Council has recommended 2,900 calories as the daily energy requirement of the "reference" man in the United States. The feasibility of thinking of the energy values of foods in terms of standard or 100-calorie portions has long been recognized. Each 100 calories would then be one twenty-ninth of the day's allowance.

Let us now think of a 2,900-calorie diet as made up of 29 such portions or 29 shares. As we have already seen (Table A–1 in the Appendix), the other allowances recommended for the "reference" man, aged 18 to 35 and weighing 70 kg, are as follows:

Protein, 70 gm for the 70 kg man, or 2.41 gm per 100 calories
Calcium, 0.8 gm, or 0.028 gm (28 mg) per 100 calories
Iron, 10 mg, or 0.34 mg per 100 calories
Vitamin A, 5,000 I.U., or 172 I.U. per 100 calories
Thiamine, 1.2 mg, or 0.041 mg per 100 calories
Riboflavin, 1.7 mg, or 0.058 mg per 100 calories
Ascorbic acid, 70 mg, or 2.41 mg per 100 calories

In an adequate diet we may think of each 100 calories as constituting a cross section of the day's ration and carrying its own share of each of the above-mentioned nutrients. We may then call one twenty-ninth of the daily allowance of each nutrient one share of that nutrient. The values for each of these would then be as follows:

> One share of energy   = 100 calories
> One share of protein   = 2.41 gm
> One share of calcium   = 28 mg (0.028 gm)
> One share of iron   = 0.34 mg
> One share of vitamin A   = 172 I.U.
> One share of thiamine   = 0.041 mg
> One share of riboflavin   = 0.058 mg
> One share of ascorbic acid = 2.41 mg

The dietary allowances for all age levels given in Table A–1 (Appendix) can now be expressed in shares simply by dividing the recommended amount of each nutrient by the value of one share of that nutrient. Share values for niacin have not been suggested because if a dietary furnishes adequate amounts of the other essentials, it will undoubtedly provide sufficient niacin or its precursor, tryptophan. Vitamin D is not included in the tabulation because the requirements for other than infants, children, and pregnant and lactating women have not been established. Also, it occurs in relatively small amounts in only a few common foods so that fish-liver oils or concentrates of them or specially treated food such as vitamin D milk must be depended upon as sources.

The "reference" man thus needs 29 shares of each nutrient to meet the daily Recommended Dietary Allowances. Using the share value of each dietary essential, one may easily calculate the daily Recommended Allowances in shares for the "reference" woman. In Table A–1 in the Appendix the allowances recommended for the "reference" woman are as follows:

Calories	2,100	Vitamin A	5000 I.U.
Protein	58 gm	Thiamine	0.8 mg
Calcium	0.8 gm	Riboflavin	1.3 mg
Iron	15 mg	Ascorbic acid	70 mg

If the above values are divided by the share value of each nutrient, the recommended allowances for the "reference" woman in shares are as follows:

Calories	21	Vitamin A	29
Protein	24	Thiamine	20
Calcium	29	Riboflavin	22
Iron	44	Ascorbic acid	29

This has been worked out for all ages and individuals and tabulated in Table A–5 in the Appendix, giving the Recommended Dietary Allowances expressed in shares.

To obtain the share values for a given food, the calories, weights in grams, or milligrams, or International Units given in Table A–4 can be divided by the share value for each nutrient. One cup of whole milk (item no. 1), as given in Table A–4, has the following nutritive values:

1 Cup Milk

Calories	160	Vitamin A	350 I.U.
Protein	9 gm	Thiamine	0.08 mg
Calcium	288 mg	Riboflavin	0.42 mg
Iron	0.1 mg	Ascorbic acid	2 mg

Dividing the above values by the value of one share for each nutrient, the nutritive value for 1 cup of milk expressed in shares will be as follows:

1 Cup of Milk (Expressed in Shares)

Calories	1.60	Vitamin A	2.0
Protein	3.7	Thiamine	2.0
Calcium	10.3	Riboflavin	7.2
Iron	0.3	Ascorbic acid	0.8

These values appear as item no. 1 in Table A–8 in the Appendix. The share values have been computed in the same way for each of the food items listed in Table A–4 and have been tabulated in shares in Table A–8 ready for use in the calculation of diets and in graphic comparisons.

A graphic presentation can be made showing the contributions from 2 cups or 1 pt of milk toward the daily Recommended Allowances for the "reference" man and the "reference" woman (see Figure 20–1). It will be noted at a glance that 1 pt of milk contributes over two thirds of the calcium recommended daily for the "reference" man and woman. It also contributes about one half of the riboflavin recommended each day for the "reference" man and two thirds of the riboflavin recommended for the "reference" woman.

In Chapter 21 share graphs showing the comparative values of different foods will be found in Figures 21–1, 21–2, 21–3, 21–4, and 21–7.

In Chapters 22, 23, 25, 26, and 27 daily dietaries have been worked out in shares and compared with the recommended allowances. It would be easy to make a graphic presentation of the totals of each of these dietaries compared with the recommended allowances. For further details of the advantages of using shares in calculations and presenting food values graphically see Taylor's *Food Values in Shares and Weights*.

It is well to keep in mind that should the need arise, shares can be converted back to weights merely by multiplying by the appropriate share value.

Of course, there are situations in which it is desirable to use the nutritive values of foods as expressed in Table A–4 in the Appendix. It will be noted in this table that in addition to the values for which there are recommended allowances, other nutritive values are included such as water, fat, fatty acids, and carbohydrates. It is important to have all these values for use in connection with the many different types of nutrition problems in which nutrient intakes must be calculated.

Minimum Daily Requirements

The United States Food and Drug Administration has established Minimum Daily Requirements of specific nutrients to be used primarily in connection with legal labeling requirements of foods and vitamin preparations. They cover only the major vitamins and minerals. For legal reasons, the levels chosen are such that intakes below this minimum standard would produce demonstrable deficiency signs. These minimum values should not be confused with the Recommended Dietary Allowances of the Food and Nutrition Board of the National Research Council, which have been discussed in this chapter. If the label on a package of cereal or other food states the percentage of a nutrient that a serving of

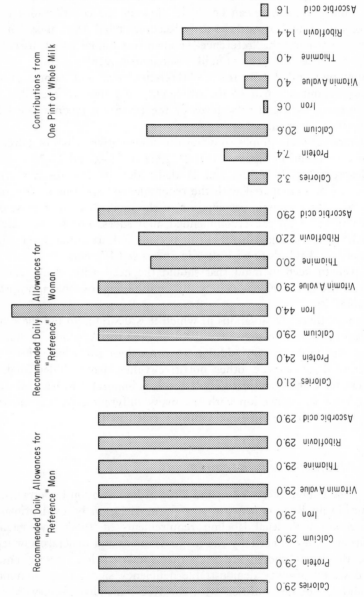

FIGURE 20–1. CONTRIBUTIONS OF ONE PINT OF MILK TOWARD THE DAILY RECOMMENDED ALLOWANCES FOR THE "REFERENCE" MAN AND THE "REFERENCE" WOMAN (IN SHARES).

the product will supply, it refers to the minimum daily requirement (MDR) unless indicated to the contrary. See Table A–11 in the Appendix.

REFERENCES

Beaton, G. H., and McHenry, E. W. (eds.). *Nutrition—A Comprehensive Treatise.* Young, E. G. "Dietary Standards," Chap. 5; Cuthbertson, D. P. "Food Selection," Chap. 8. New York: Academic (1964).

Bosley, B. "Nutrition in the Indian Health Program." *J. Amer. Dietet. A.,* **35**:905 (1959).

Engel, R. W. "1963 Recommended Dietary Allowances." *J. Amer. Dietet. A.,* **44**:91 (1964).

Food and Nutrition Board. *Recommended Dietary Allowances.* Washington, D.C.: National Academy of Sciences, National Research Council, Publication 1146 (1964).

League of Nations. "Report by the Technical Committee on Nutrition." *Bull. Health Organ. League of Nations,* **7**:461 (1937).

Phipard, E. F. "Role of the Recommended Allowances in Assessing Diets." *J. Amer. Dietet. A.,* **36**:37 (1960).

Roberts, L. J. "Beginning of the Recommended Dietary Allowances." *J. Amer. Dietet. A.,* **34**:903 (1958).

Sherman, H. C. *The Nutritional Improvement of Life.* New York: Columbia U. P. (1950).

Stiebeling, H. K., and Leverton, R. M. "Problems in Human Nutrition," p. 558, *Farmer's World, The Yearbook of Agriculture, 1964.* Washington, D.C.: U.S. Department of Agriculture.

Taylor, C. M. *Food Values in Shares and Weights,* 2nd ed. New York: Macmillan (1959).

Taylor, C. M., and MacLeod, G. *Rose's Laboratory Handbook for Dietetics,* 5th ed. New York: Macmillan (1949).

Watt, B. K., and Merrill, A. L. *Composition of Foods—Raw, Processed, Prepared.* Washington, D.C.: U.S. Department of Agriculture, Agriculture Handbook No. 8 (1963).

❧ **21** ❧

Contributions to the Diet Made by Food Groups

One only needs to step into a large supermarket to appreciate the great variety and abundance of foods available to the American housewife. Without some guide to food selection the quantity of foods of all kinds attractively displayed is almost overwhelming. Unless one has a plan for a well-balanced diet, one is in danger of "hit and miss" choices leading to possible inadequate nutrition.

Today's consumer is the victim of high-pressure salesmanship at every turn and is presented with a bewildering number of facts and fallacies which are frequently misleading. This makes a simple food guide imperative if an adequate diet is to be attained.

Surveys of the American diet continue to show that many individuals each day select foods that fail to meet the Recommended Dietary Allowances and thus may be jeopardizing the opportunity to achieve the benefits of buoyant health. Interestingly enough, lack of money for food is not usually the reason for poor choices. It may be a failure to appreciate fully the relationship between good nutrition and health or it may be a lack of knowledge of the basic rules of good food selection.

FOODS GROUPED ACCORDING TO NUTRITIVE VALUE

Many foods are quite similar in their chemical composition and nutritive properties and may be considered in groups. If selections are made daily from each group in quantities recommended, it is possible to attain an adequate diet.

1. *Milk*, of all single food materials, contains the greatest assortment of nutritive substances and constitutes the foundation on which an adequate diet can most safely and most easily be constructed.

2. *Meat, fish, poultry, eggs, legumes, and nuts* are of prime significance for their yield of proteins of good to excellent quality. Meats, eggs, and legumes are good sources of iron; meats and eggs, of riboflavin. The yield of other minerals and vitamins varies with the different members of the group.

326

3. *Vegetables and fruits* are of greatest significance for their mineral constituents and vitamins. Both are irregularly distributed, but if such foods are taken in large enough quantities and embrace a wide range of varieties, there is a good chance of safety, provided a serving of a dark-green and/or a yellow vegetable and a citrus fruit are included each day. Only certain members of the group are good sources of calories, and still fewer of proteins.

4. *The grains* are primarily sources of energy, and secondarily of protein, not always adequate by itself, but when properly supplemented, of great practical value. Only if whole grain or "enriched" does this class of foodstuffs become important for minerals or vitamins. Their most significant contributions are thiamine and iron. They lack vitamin A and ascorbic acid and contain relatively smaller amounts of riboflavin.

5. *Fats* are primarily sources of calories in concentrated form. In certain cases they are also carriers of vitamin A and other fat-soluble vitamins. For their importance in the diet in other connections, see Chapter 6.

6. *Sugars and other carbohydrates,* like fats, are sources of calories. Pure sugars contribute nothing else. For further discussion of carbohydrates in the diet, see Chapter 6.

In the following sections the nutritive values of these various food groups are discussed in more detail. There are a number of ways in which foods can be grouped so that if a selection is made from each group an adequate diet will be achieved. The four essential groups suggested by the U.S. Department of Agriculture are the following: (1) milk, cheese, and ice cream, (2) meat, poultry, fish, (3) vegetables and fruits, and (4) bread and cereals. By following this plan many people have been guided to the selection of a more adequate diet.

In Canada, five groups of food have been worked out for their national food guide, the five groups serving their needs better than the four groups. The five groups are as follows: (1) milk, (2) fruits, including citrus and tomatoes, (3) vegetables, green and yellow, and potatoes, (4) breads and cereals (one serving of whole grain daily), and (5) meat and fish, including poultry, liver, eggs, cheese, and dried beans and peas.

The five food groups that have been worked out by the Department of Health for use in Puerto Rico are as follows: (1) milk, fresh, evaporated, or dried, (2) meat, fish, eggs, and legumes, (3) yellow and green vegetables, sweet potato, and calabaza (pumpkin), (4) fruit, fresh domestic including citrus, papaya, mango, banana, acerola, and pineapple, and (5) rice, kidney beans, codfish, sugar, lard, fat, and coffee (foods familiar to Puerto Ricans).

In the *Guide to Good Eating* (1963) suggested by the Food and Nutrition Center in the Philippines, six food groups listing foods available in the country are included. Group I consists of leafy and yellow vegetables such as squash leaves and flowers as well as the "fruit," mustard greens and carrots, along with various leafy vegetables available in the Philippines.

Group II consists of vitamin C-rich foods such as cashew, guava, papaya, and other tropical fruits, as well as the citrus, melons, and tomatoes.

Group III consists of other fruits and vegetables such as okra, pineapple, jackfruit, avocado, granada, and many others.

Group IV consists of fat-rich foods such as butter and margarine, coconut, coconut milk and oil.

Group V consists of protein-rich foods such as all kinds of whole milk, meat, fish, or poultry, eggs, dried beans, and nuts.

Group VI consists of rice and other energy foods such as bread and root vegetables.

The menu pattern suggested is listed below.

FILIPINO MENU PATTERN

Breakfast

Any fruit in season
Enriched rice or bread
Protein dish (meat, fish or poultry)
Beverage

Lunch or Supper

Protein dish
Vegetable
Enriched rice
Fruit or dessert

A SAMPLE MENU FOR A DAY CONTAINING FOODS FROM EACH OF THE BASIC SIX FOOD GROUPS

Breakfast

Banana (or any fruit in season)
Halaan omelet
Enriched rice
Soybean beverage with milk

Lunch

Fish sinigang (silinyasi, kangkong, sitaw, tomatoes, kalamansi)
Sauteed alamang (alamang, tomatoes, lard, garlic, onion)
Enriched rice
Fruit in season

Supper

Picadillo (ground pork and beef, malunggay leaves, tomatoes, lard, garlic, onion)
Ampalaya guisado (ampalaya, lard, garlic, onion, tomatoes, egg)
Enriched rice
Fruit in season

Each of these plans, if carefully followed, will assure an adequate diet. In planning such guides for a particular population group, foods selected for each group must be chosen from those (1) available, (2) of high nutritive value, (3) in keeping with native likes and dislikes, and (4) within the income level of the mass of the population. Other countries have worked out food group plans to fit their food supply, economy, diet patterns, and cultural background.

Milk and Cheese

The value of milk in improving a diet was clearly demonstrated by the classic four-year experiment in an institution for poor English boys, 6 to 11 years of age, reported by Mann,[1] in 1926. One group received the regular diet of the institution only; six others received supplementary food, as follows: (1) a pint of milk daily, (2) sugar equivalent in calorie value to the pint of milk, (3) New Zealand butter to give the same number of calories as the milk, (4) unfortified margarine equivalent to the butter, (5) edible casein furnishing only 65 extra calories, (6) ¾ oz daily of fresh water cress. The group on the regular diet gained, during the four-year period, an average per year of 3.85 lb and 1.84 in. Extra protein in the form of casein made practically no difference in weight or height. Extra calories in the form of sugar or margarine made no difference in height and increased weight only a very little; the group on water cress and butter made a better showing, but the milk group gained 6.98 lbs and 2.63 in.

This work led the Department of Health for Scotland to undertake a series of extensive studies of the influence of milk consumption on the growth of school children in the years 1927–30. The results substantiated Mann's findings, even when only ¾ pt of milk daily was furnished each child for four months. The report by Leighton and McKinlay, in 1930, of a study of 20,000 children 5 to 12 years old in Lanarkshire, 10,000 of whom had a milk supplement, concluded with these significant words:

> The results, read along with the results of the previous Scottish test, are conclusive on the main issue. They demonstrate that the addition of milk to the diet of children has a striking effect in improving physique and general health and increasing mental alertness. They suggest also that, apart from its own food value, milk enables the other constituents of the ordinary diet to be fully utilized as growth factors.[2]

During the last week or two of the test the various head teachers of the schools were asked to submit in writing their general impressions of the effect on the children. They spoke of "an increase in the bloom of their cheeks and the sleekness of their skins," and one went so far as to

---

[1] Mann, H. C. Corry. *Diets for Boys During the School Age,* Preface. Medical Research Council, Special Reports Series, No. 105. London: His Majesty's Stationery Office (1926).

[2] Leighton, G., and McKinlay, P. L. *Milk Consumption and the Growth of School Children,* pp. 2 and 3. London: His Majesty's Stationery Office (1930).

say, "In the playground buoyancy and pugnacity are developing to an alarming extent."

These classic studies have stimulated milk distribution programs in many parts of the world. In Libya, in 1955, FAO and UNICEF started a school milk distribution program which included over 60,000 children. It was reported after one year that the school attendance increased particularly in rural areas, absences due to illness decreased significantly, and teachers noted a steadily increasing alertness among the children.

These and other studies have served to emphasize the importance of milk in the diet, not only of the child, but also of the adult. No other food can so well serve as the foundation of an adequate diet, because no other reinforces it at so many points. It is for this reason that the term "protective food" is aptly applied to milk.

A quart of whole cow's milk yields 640 calories. Drinking a single glass of whole milk at each meal adds about 480 calories a day. Thus it can be readily seen that whole milk, although providing nothing to chew, is not insignificant as body fuel.

In contrast, 1 qt of nonfat fluid (skim) milk yields only 360 calories and offers an excellent means of cutting total calories, particularly those from fat, when this is necessary. The energy value of other kinds of milk will be found in Tables A–4 and A–8 in the Appendix.

A quart of milk yields protein of the highest quality because of its excellent assortment of essential amino acids. From every point of view milk is an economical source of protein. Its protein is produced at less expense than that of meat or eggs. The milk cow has been reported to be more than three times as efficient in transforming the protein of its feed into milk protein as are beef cattle or sheep in the production of protein as meat.

Milk enhances the nutritive value of bread and other cereal proteins by adding those essential amino acids such as lysine and tryptophan in which cereal proteins are relatively poor. Experiments in feeding the lowest amount of protein capable of maintaining nitrogen balance in the adults have shown that less protein is required when milk is practically the sole source than when meat is so used, and that proteins derived half from bread and half from milk furnish a mixture that is utilized with the same economy as milk alone.

In milk are found all the different kinds of mineral elements needed in nutrition. Milk ash strongly resembles in its composition the ash of the body of the newborn young.

The importance of milk as a source of calcium for the growing child has already been discussed at length, and the desirability of an adequate amount of milk daily to ensure the best storage of calcium in the body has been emphasized. Shortage of calcium does not affect growth as quickly as shortage of calories, protein, or some of the vitamins. It is therefore possible for a child to grow up "calcium poor." Normal development during growth demands a steady increase in the store of body calcium, and this cannot be achieved without a dietary program that ensures a liberal daily supply.

While phosphorus is less likely to be deficient in the dietary than calcium, since it is present in a wide variety of food materials, the necessity of a liberal supply of phosphorus still makes the contribution of milk significant. When the calcium requirement is met through the use of milk, we know that the phosphorus requirement is also covered. Although milk is not as rich in iron as in calcium or phosphorus, the iron present is in a form that can be absorbed and utilized.

Whole milk in the amount recommended yields a good portion of the vitamin A for normal growth and, with additions from other foods, such as liver, butter, or margarine, and eggs, makes a substantial contribution to the preformed vitamin A content of the diet, which is desirable for periods of rapid growth in childhood or for special demands such as pregnancy and lactation in the adult. Milk is a fairly good source of thiamine but is much less dependable as a source of ascorbic acid. It is one of the best sources of riboflavin whether whole or skimmed. When taken in quantities recommended, it furnishes a large proportion of the daily allowance.

The addition of vitamin D to milk is a sound public health measure and offers protection against rickets for the infant and young child. The fortification of milk with vitamin D can be credited to a large extent for the decline in the incidence of rickets in recent decades.

Evaporated milk is widely used because of its convenience and economy, and, in the case of infants, because of its ease of digestion, owing to the fine flaky curds formed in the stomach. Vitamins A and D are not materially altered by the processes employed in the evaporation of milk, and evaporated milk is generally fortified with vitamin D. Thiamine is likely to be reduced by about 25 per cent. Any destruction of ascorbic acid is not a serious matter since it is customary to give infants and children orange juice or some other supplement for this vitamin. Evaporated milk is pure cow's milk minus about 60 per cent of its water and is not to be confused with sweetened condensed milk, which is preserved by the addition of a large amount of cane sugar.

Powdered milk is made from either whole milk or skim milk. Both are excellent products from the nutritional standpoint and, prepared by modern methods, retain the food values of the original whole or skim milk, except the ascorbic acid. The vitamin A removed in the production of skim milk must be provided by other good sources of this vitamin in the diet. The instant skim milk powder is inexpensive and easy to mix and, when reconstituted, has such good flavor that its use is increasingly popular.*

In recent years special attention has been given in many countries to increasing the consumption of milk because of the growing appreciation of the importance of milk in safeguarding the health of infants, children, and expectant and nursing mothers. Shipments of nonfat dry milk under the Food for Peace program reached approximately 750 million lb in 1963 sent to some 80 countries and territories. The government of Japan alone has imported more than 100 million lb of nonfat dry milk yearly for the school lunch program. The Japanese nutritionists credit the milk program as one of the factors responsible for the general increase in height and weight of the Japanese schoolchildren. While cows produce 90 to 95 per cent of the total milk supply in the world, the milk of other cattle is also consumed, such as goats, sheep, buffalo, caribou, camels, donkeys, and yaks.

CHEESE

Of the cheese manufactured in the United States the major portion is of the Cheddar variety, commonly called "American" cheese. A pound of such cheese contains the casein and fat of a gallon of milk, together with traces of whey retained by the curd. It has about one fourth of its calories in the form of protein and the other three fourths in the form of fat. The milk sugar is mostly withdrawn in the whey or changed to lactic acid in the ripening process. The calcium, phosphorus, and iron of the milk are retained in the cheese and also a large part of vitamin A and riboflavin.

Such a concentration of the most important nutritive elements of milk in a food of excellent keeping qualities entitles cheese to a place in the diet that is not always fully appreciated. Its strong flavor precludes its use in many of the ways in which milk is practical and makes it more akin to meat in regard to its place on the menu. As a substitute for meat it gives a much better return in nutritive value for the money expended and is particularly valuable as a source of calcium in the diet of adults who have not acquired the habit of using milk freely. From 3 to 4 oz of cheese (except cottage cheese) will furnish enough calcium for an average man for one day.

Because of its flavor cheese is often regarded as a condiment and is served with other foods merely to add zest to a meal. It should be remembered, however, that cheese is a concentrated food and is properly used in the diet much as meat would be. Because of its texture and its

* Fluid nonfat milk may be fortified with vitamin A in some areas in the United States, but at present it is not legal to add vitamin A to the nonfat dried milk powder. However, vitamin A may be added to the nonfat dried milk powder, for additional protection, for use in the developing countries.

high proportion of fat calories to total calories, it is digested best when used with bread or other cereal foods. It is interesting to realize that cheese is thought to have been used as a food for over 4,000 years.

A comparison of the nutritional contributions of different cheeses can be made by examining the data in Tables A–4 or A–8. In Figure 21–1 the contributions to the diet of milk and cheese are graphically illustrated. It would be of interest to make a share graph showing a comparison of the contributions of whole milk with other milk products listed in Table A–8.

Meat, Fish, Poultry, Eggs, Dried Legumes, and Nuts

Milk has been described as an outstanding source of protein. However, meat, fish, poultry, eggs, dried legumes, and nuts are grouped together as our chief sources of protein in terms of the quantity of protein present.

MEAT, FISH, AND POULTRY

In 1963 the world production of meat, on the increase since 1951, reached a record high of 112 billion lb, 38 per cent above the 1951–55 average. About 50 per cent of the world meat supply in 1963 consisted of beef, 41 per cent of pork, and 9 per cent of lamb, mutton, goat, and horse meat. The United States led in meat production with 31 billion lb, while the Soviet Union was second with 15 billion. Annual per capita consumption of beef in the United States has risen from 55 lb in 1938 to 93 lb in 1963; total meat consumption per capita was 167 lb in 1963.*

According to the study of American family dietaries by the U.S. Department of Agriculture in 1955, an average of 31 per cent of the food money was spent on meat, poultry, and fish. Is the expenditure of so much money for meat wise? Does it help to guarantee to the American people adequate diets? The only way to answer these questions is to study carefully the nutritive value of the principal flesh foods. In connection with the prevailing market meats, beef, veal, mutton, lamb, and pork, we may also discuss poultry, game, fish, and shellfish, since nutritionally they have the same characteristics. For the most part, Americans eat muscle tissue to the exclusion of other parts of the animal. Oysters and sardines are the only animal foods of any considerable importance in which the whole body is consumed. This is in marked contrast to the habit of carnivorous animals and of people living chiefly on animal food, none of whom let any part go to waste.

---

* These per capita consumption figures are based on national averages adjusted from disappearance or use of foods in the marketing system. They are not estimates of foods actually ingested by the consumer. Dietary studies provide the latter kind of information.

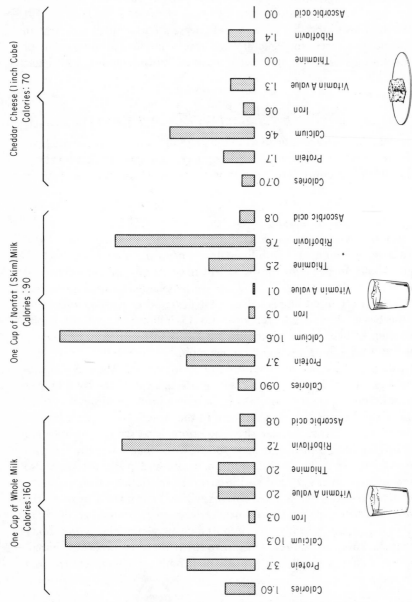

FIGURE 21–1. COMPARATIVE CONTRIBUTIONS TO THE DIET MADE BY WHOLE MILK, NONFAT MILK, AND CHEDDAR CHEESE (in SHARES).

All kinds of flesh foods contain protein and usually fat; the fat varies greatly in amount with the species of animal and also, in the case of the larger creatures, with the cut. The amount of fat chiefly determines the proportions of other substances, the fat-free flesh being quite uniform in composition.

The proteins of meats of all kinds are much alike in furnishing a good assortment of essential amino acids, and hence are capable of supporting growth, though they are in no way superior to milk and egg proteins. Quantitatively, lean meat is conspicuous for its high yield of protein, but any increase in fatness quickly changes the proportion of protein to total calories.

The amount of any mineral element in meat or fish is more or less proportional to the amount of protein present rather than to the total calories. Lean meats are therefore richer in mineral elements than fat meats. Meats, poultry, and fish (with the exception of canned salmon) resemble the cereal grains in being deficient in calcium and rich in phosphorus. Internal organs, such as the heart, brain, liver, and kidney, are much richer in iron than muscle tissue. Strictly lean meats and eggs are much alike in their contributions of iron to the diet.

As sources of vitamins, it is necessary to consider separately muscle meats and glandular organs. Muscle meats are fair to good sources of thiamine and riboflavin. Pork is an outstanding source of thiamine but not quite so good a source of riboflavin. Beef heart is an excellent source of thiamine and riboflavin. Liver, including that of beef, calf, pork, lamb, and chicken, is an excellent source of vitamin A and riboflavin. The small amount of ascorbic acid found in glandular organs is mostly destroyed in cooking.

From the foregoing it is evident that, aside from total calories, the most significant contributions of meat to the average dietary are protein, iron, and riboflavin, and, in the case of pork, thiamine.

The contributions to the diet made by two eggs, 3 oz of lean beef, and 3 oz of salmon steak are compared in Figure 21–2.

There is an increasing awareness today of the importance of fish in the diet and an appreciation of the part it may play in future planning, as the following quotation from Finn[3] indicates. "It is estimated that only a fraction of one per cent of the food consumed by human beings is fish from the oceans and seas although these cover more than 70 per cent of the surface of the earth. The vast expanse of the oceans and seas which occupy about 90 million square miles suggests that it should be possible to obtain greatly increased quantities of food from this source and this thought is supported by the knowledge that the sea is, acre for acre, about as productive as arable land." Only 2 per cent of the American food

[3] Finn, D. B. *Fish—The Great Potential Food Supply*. World Food Problems, No. 3. Rome: Food and Agriculture Organization of the United Nations (1960).

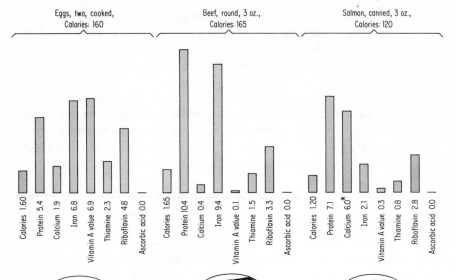

FIGURE 21–2. COMPARATIVE CONTRIBUTIONS TO THE DIET MADE BY EGGS, BEEF, AND CANNED SALMON (IN SHARES).

dollar, as reported in 1955, was spent for fish. In light of its low fat content, the quality of its protein, and its availability, it can be highly recommended as an economical food.

Chicken and turkey, sold in parts as well as whole, have increased in popularity with the American housewife. They have a large proportion of bone to lean but may usually be considered less expensive sources of protein of good quality than other meats.

EGGS

In making a selection from available sources of protein it is wise to pay attention to other growth-promoting substances that may be secured incidental to the protein. From this point of view, the egg is a good choice, and especially the yolk, which is rich in all substances necessary for growth, except calcium and ascorbic acid. The chief protein of the egg yolk (ovovitellin) resembles casein of milk in its amino acid content and so does that of the white (ovalbumin). Both are therefore complete proteins independently capable of supporting growth and valuable in bringing to full efficiency proteins of lower value, such as the cereal proteins.

The mineral elements of the egg are mainly found in the yolk. The iron in egg yolk compares very favorably in quantity with that in other foods that may be considered significant sources of iron.

The white of the egg is a rich source of riboflavin but contains no thiamine. The yolk is rich in vitamin A, is a good source of thiamine and riboflavin, but has no ascorbic acid. Eggs cannot be regarded as a substitute for milk, but may be advantageously used in addition to it. They admirably reinforce milk as to iron.

DRIED LEGUMES AND NUTS

The dried legumes include dried beans of all kinds, dried peas, lentils, soybeans and soya products, and also soups that are mostly legumes. They are inexpensive sources of proteins and other nutrients such as iron and thiamine.

In many parts of the world where sources of animal protein are scarce, dried legumes combined with rice make a fairly good basis for a nutritionally adequate diet when supplemented with good sources of vitamin A and ascorbic acid.

Nuts are often regarded as a mere adjunct to the dietary to be nibbled between courses at dinner, to add interest to afternoon tea, or to be eaten between meals for pure amusement. Thus used they may prove disturbing to digestion or furnish calories in excess of body needs, for they contain chiefly protein and fat and digest rather slowly, and their fuel value is very high. About half an ounce of almost any one of our common nuts is sufficient to yield 80 to 100 calories.

The proteins of nuts of various kinds, including almonds, coconuts, peanuts (ground nuts), and pecans, have been found to be adequate for growth, and chemical analyses of individual proteins from some of these have shown an amino acid assortment rather similar to that of meat and soybeans. Peanut flour, made from the press cake left after the extraction of the peanut oil, has been found an excellent supplement to the proteins of wheat. In the United States peanut butter is one of the popular ways of using peanuts.

As sources of mineral elements, nuts as a class are not of much importance in the amounts generally eaten. They are a better source of iron than of calcium, the cashew nut being relatively high in iron. Among nuts for which we have analyses, almonds and filberts are outstanding in regard to calcium. Nuts are poor in vitamin A and the oil pressed from them is practically devoid of it.

Table 21–1 shows changes in our food supply making differences in the sources of protein from food groups.

Vegetables and Fruits

Vegetables and fruits vary so greatly in nutritive value that no general statement is applicable to all. They may be any part of a plant—leaf, stem, bulb, tuber, root, seed or seed pod, blossom, or fruit. Like parts tend to be similar in composition. Some fruits, flowers, leaves, and stems, such as tomato, cauliflower, lettuce, cabbage, asparagus, and celery, are low in calories. Fleshy roots, bulbs, and tubers, being storage parts of the

**TABLE 21–1. CHANGES IN SOURCES OF
PROTEIN IN OUR FOOD SUPPLY***

Sources of Protein	1909–13	1956–58
	Per Cent of Total	Per Cent of Total
Dairy products, including butter	18	26
Eggs	5	6
Meat, poultry, fish	29	35
Total from animal products	52	67
Dry beans and peas, nuts	4	5
Flour and cereal products	36	20
Other foods	8	8
Total from nonanimal products	48	33
Total from all foods	100	100

* U.S. Department of Agriculture.

plant, contain energy-yielding carbohydrates either as starch, as in the white potato, or as sugar, as in the carrot, or as both, as in the sweet potato. They are also a good source of minerals and vitamins. Seeds are higher in energy value than other storage parts and, when mature and dry, resemble the cereal foods but are better sources of proteins. Consequently, they are grouped with meats, poultry, and fish.

Many of our most popular vegetables are native to the Americas. Potatoes originated in the valleys of the Andes mountains in South America, where over a hundred varieties were known. It is probable that the Spaniards introduced the potato to Europe. Potatoes were apparently first cultivated in the United States in New Hampshire in 1719 from stock brought from Ireland and consequently called the "Irish" potato.

Potatoes have often been maligned as a starchy vegetable high in calories, but actually they are a good source of ascorbic acid, thiamine, and iron. They are not higher in calories than many other foods, about three fourths of the weight of the potato being water. Potatoes are bland in flavor, are easily digested, and might desirably be included in the daily diet. The sweet potato is higher in calories and, being a deep-yellow vegetable, furnishes considerable vitamin A.

Tomatoes also originated in South America, but like the potato, they are grown the world over in favorable climates. Botanically the edible portion of the tomato is a fruit, but the tomato is considered a vegetable because of the way in which it is used.

As sources of mineral elements vegetables are of great importance. Along with those elements that need special consideration, such as calcium and iron, we obtain from these foods a number of other trace elements, such as iodine and copper, which, although present in minute quantities, are of real significance.

Vegetables and fruits are not so rich in calcium that they may be depended on, in the quantities ordinarily eaten, to furnish sufficient amounts of this element. Also, it is necessary to take account of losses incurred in cooking and to keep in mind that the calcium of some of the leafy green vegetables is not available due to the presence of oxalic acid (see Tables A–4 and A–8 in the Appendix). As sources of iron, the green vegetables are extremely important foods, as are the dried fruits, apricots, prunes, raisins, and figs.

Heat alone does not affect the mineral content, but when a food is cooked in water, a considerable portion of the mineral salts may dissolve in the water. To reduce these losses to a minimum the smallest amounts of water possible should be used and the cooking water should be saved for use in soups, gravies, vegetable juice cocktails, and other appropriate ways if possible.

One of the best reasons for including vegetables and fruits in the diet is to ensure a liberal supply of vitamins. Knowledge of the vitamin content of raw foods of this class and of the changes brought about by storing, cooking, canning, drying, quick and flash freezing, freeze drying, etc., is therefore necessary for the intelligent planning of dietaries. Cooking may cause considerable loss of some of the vitamins, especially thiamine and ascorbic acid. In general, the shorter the time of cooking, the smaller is the loss. One of the advantages of quick-frozen foods is that cooking time is reduced, quick-frozen vegetables requiring only one half to two thirds as much time as the fresh vegetables. Cooking without defrosting has been found to reduce vitamin losses. The freezing process itself brings about little, if any, loss of vitamins. The blanching required before freezing is probably responsible for the major losses that occur. In general, it is true that canning of foods causes no greater loss of vitamin values than the usual home-cooking methods. It has been reported that exclusion of light during cooking conserves riboflavin. Dehydrating fruits and vegetables causes a considerable loss of the vitamins. It is of interest to note that the commercial practice of treating some fruits with sulfur dioxide to prevent darkening during the drying process tends to conserve some of the vitamins. Tables A–4 and A–8 in the Appendix give the nutritive values of most of the common vegetables and fruits.

The richest plant sources of vitamin A are dark-green leaves such as spinach, kale, turnip and beet tops, and mustard greens. These can be used interchangeably in the diet. Other green vegetables, such as green peas and green string beans, make significant contributions although they are not as rich. Bleached leaves, such as the inner leaves of cabbage and head lettuce, have much less than similar leaves when green. Seeds, roots, and tubers generally contain little vitamin A, but the yellow root vegetables, like carrots and sweet potatoes, are excellent sources.

Thiamine is present in a great many fruits and vegetables. Few vegetables are weight for weight as rich as whole-grain or enriched cereals. Peas and beans, both fresh and dried, are good sources of thiamine. In plants thiamine seems to be concentrated in the seeds and not in the leaves, quite the reverse of what is true for vitamin A and ascorbic acid.

Ascorbic acid is obtained almost exclusively from vegetables and fruits, and it is so irregularly distributed and so easily destroyed that one must know definitely whether the vitamin occurs in the food material in question and also in each instance the effect of storing, canning, cooking, freezing, or drying. Cabbage is an excellent antiscorbutic when raw but may lose much of its value in the process of cooking; tomatoes, on the other hand, lose but little in the short time required for cooking, and canned tomatoes or juice may be considered a staple antiscorbutic.

The citrus fruits, especially oranges and grapefruit, not only have a relatively high content of ascorbic acid in the fresh state, but retain their antiscorbutic property when concentrated. Lime juice is about half as rich as lemon juice, but although both are good sources, they are used in comparatively small amounts.

Green vegetables eaten raw vary greatly in their antiscorbutic values. For example, weight for weight, raw green peppers furnish more than ten times as much as escarole. Mature seeds have little or no ascorbic acid, but when sprouted, seeds are an important source in some parts of the world. See Chapter 14 for a fuller discussion of the fruits and vegetables as sources of ascorbic acid.

Riboflavin is formed in the growth of the green plant. Seeds, roots, and tubers are relatively poor in this vitamin. Spinach and other dark-green leafy vegetables are good sources of riboflavin.

Contributions to the diet made by three common vegetables are shown graphically in Figure 21–3 and by three common fruits in Figure 21–4.

Bread, Flour, and Cereals

Wherever we have agriculture, we have the cultivation of grain. Seventy per cent of the entire harvested acreage of the world is used to grow grain, which was more than ½ acre per capita in 1963. Grain affords a staple article of diet, which can be placed in reserve for seasons of scarcity, and one whose keeping qualities and ease of marketing make it relatively cheap. For half the people of the world rice is the chief article of diet. For over 1 billion people in Asia it provides 80 to 90 per cent of the daily calorie intake. Corn is the staple article of the diet of the populations of Romania, Mexico, Venezuela, and Guatemala, and of the

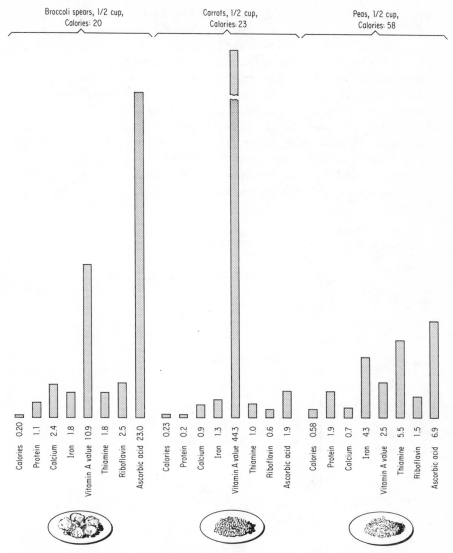

Broccoli spears, 1/2 cup,
Calories: 20

Carrots, 1/2 cup,
Calories: 23

Peas, 1/2 cup,
Calories: 58

Calories	0.20
Protein	1.1
Calcium	2.4
Iron	1.8
Vitamin A value	10.9
Thiamine	1.8
Riboflavin	2.5
Ascorbic acid	23.0
Calories	0.23
Protein	0.2
Calcium	0.9
Iron	1.3
Vitamin A value	44.3
Thiamine	1.0
Riboflavin	0.6
Ascorbic acid	1.9
Calories	0.58
Protein	1.9
Calcium	0.7
Iron	4.3
Vitamin A value	2.5
Thiamine	5.5
Riboflavin	1.5
Ascorbic acid	6.9

FIGURE 21–3. COMPARATIVE CONTRIBUTIONS TO THE DIET MADE BY COOKED BROCCOLI, CARROTS, AND PEAS (IN SHARES).

Negroes and poor whites of the southern United States. In the average American diet about one fifth of the calories are derived from cereals.

Seldom is the intact kernel of grain used as food by man in any considerable amount. It is not easy to eat dry whole grains. From time immemorial they have been ground, crushed, or otherwise treated to break up or remove the bran coats. With the increase of trade and the shipping and storing of grain foods, there has grown up the practice of removing the germ, because it is here that insects tend to deposit their eggs, and this makes it unfit as human food. Also, the oil of the germ is altered during storage and this spoils the flavor of the cereal.

In the United States since 1941, programs for the enrichment of white flour, white bread, cornmeal or grits, macaroni and noodle products, rice, and processed food cereals have been put into effect. Any flour labeled "enriched" must contain per pound 13.0 to 16.5 mg of iron, 2.0 to 2.5 mg of thiamine, 1.2 to 1.5 mg of riboflavin, and 16 to 20 mg of niacin or niacinamide. Optional with the producer, the flour may also be enriched with calcium to make the content of this element 500 to 625 mg per pound and with vitamin D to make the content of this vitamin 250 to 1,000 U.S.P. units per pound. The standards for the enrichment of other specified

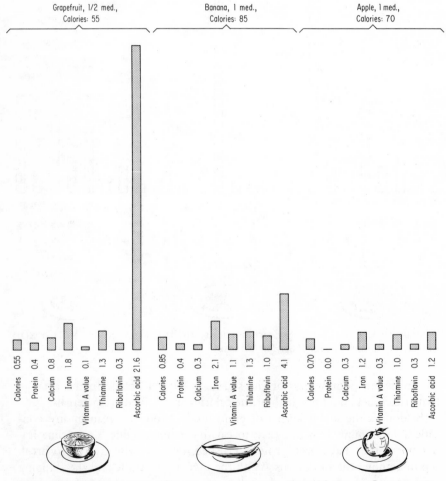

FIGURE 21–4. COMPARATIVE CONTRIBUTIONS TO THE DIET MADE BY GRAPEFRUIT, BANANA, AND APPLE (IN SHARES).

food products will be found in Table 10, page 171, of *Composition of Foods—Raw, Processed, Prepared,* Agriculture Handbook No. 8, U.S. Department of Agriculture (1963). Although enrichment is not compulsory in all states, it has been well supported by industry.

As stated in Chapter 13, by 1961, 30 states and Puerto Rico had laws requiring the enrichment of white flour and bread. The practice of flour enrichment has been adopted in a number of countries in different areas around the world. In some situations the enrichment of flour is mandatory and in others it is voluntary. That dramatic health benefits from enrichment are possible is graphically presented in Figure 21–5, showing the decline in the mortality rates in Newfoundland over a six-year period following the enrichment of flour and the fortification of margarine with vitamin A in 1944.

Since the uncooked cereal foods are all very low in moisture content and have great similarity in chemical composition, they have much the same energy value, approximating 1,650 calories per pound. The weight of a 100-calorie portion (dry) is close to 1 oz, although the space occupied by 1 oz will differ with the coarseness of the material, from 3 tbsp of whole-wheat flour to 2⅛ cups of puffed wheat, or 1 large shredded-wheat biscuit. When a cereal is cooked, there will be variation in weight as well as measure, the dry cereal swelling from two to five times its volume, due to the amount of water absorbed.

From 8 to 12 per cent of the calories in cereal foods are derived from protein. In their analysis of 92 American dietaries in 1917, Sherman and Gillett found that grain products contributed 38 per cent of the total calories and 36 per cent of the protein. From the years 1910 to 1955 the U.S. Department of Agriculture records on food consumption show a steady decline in the average per capita consumption of grains (see Figure 21–6). With the increase in the percentage of protein from other foods

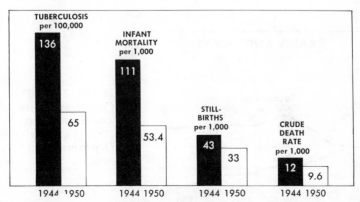

FIGURE 21–5. DECLINE IN MORTALITY RATES IN NEWFOUNDLAND COINCIDENT WITH FLOUR ENRICHMENT (1944–50). (*Courtesy of the National Vitamin Foundation, Inc.*)

since 1910 the per cent of the protein from cereals in the American diet has been greatly reduced.

We have already seen, in the discussion of protein in Chapter 8, that individual cereal proteins differ in their amino acid assortment, that several kinds of proteins are found in one grain, and that the proteins of bran and germ tend to supplement those of the endosperm. Laboratory experimentation has shown that the proteins of wheat, oats, maize, rye, and barley are about equally efficient in promoting and supporting growth. None of them is quite equal in value to an equivalent weight of the complete proteins that we find in milk, eggs, or meat, but all of them can be made highly efficient by combination with relatively small amounts of milk.

While there is much similarity in the energy and protein values of cereal foods, including highly refined flour and white bread, there is great diversity in their yield of mineral elements. Much of this is due to milling, since the outer coats of the grains contain most of the mineral matter. The cereal foods, even when made from the whole grain, are deficient in calcium.

The less money available for food, the more dependence there will be on the cereal foods. Therefore, those yielding iron should be regularly chosen, as they can be made the carriers of this essential element with little or no extra cost. Studies of children's dietaries make it quite evident that no very economical diet for a child can be liberally supplied with iron without the use of cereal foods (including breadstuffs) that contain it, that is, the whole-grain or enriched forms.

Whole grains, like other seeds, are relatively poor in vitamin A and are entirely lacking in ascorbic acid and vitamin D and contain only small amounts of riboflavin.

On the other hand, both germ and bran are excellent sources of thiamine. The germ is about four times as rich in this vitamin as whole-

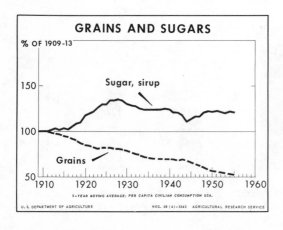

FIGURE 21-6. PER CAPITA CONSUMPTION OF GRAINS AND SUGARS FROM 1910 TO 1955. (*Courtesy of the U.S. Department of Agriculture.*)

wheat flour. It may be safely used where the cellulose of bran is objectionable. It may easily be added to the diet of growing children in various ways. Many cereal breakfast foods on the market now contain added wheat germ or vitamins in amounts sufficient to restore those lost in milling and processing. The actual amounts are stated on the package. Since milk is rich in riboflavin, in which cereals are low, and whole grains are such an excellent source of thiamine, in which milk is not as rich, we have another good reason for saying that the best foundation for an economical diet is a combination of milk and whole-grain or enriched cereals. See Figure 21–7 for a graphic comparison of cereals.

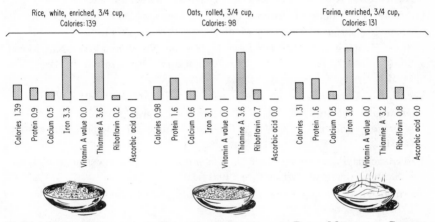

FIGURE 21–7. COMPARATIVE CONTRIBUTIONS TO THE DIET MADE BY COOKED PORTIONS OF ENRICHED RICE, ROLLED OATS, AND ENRICHED FARINA (IN SHARES).

REFERENCES

Agricultural Experiment Station, University of Wisconsin. *Milk as a Food throughout Life*. Madison: Bulletin 447 (1954).

Arrington, L. R. "Foods of the Bible." *J. Amer. Dietet. A.*, **35**:816 (1959).

Cowgill, G. R. "Improving the Quality of Cheap Staple Foods." *Handbook of Nutrition*, 2nd ed., Chap. 28. Chicago: American Medical Association (1951).

Editorial. "Relation of Vitamin D Milk to Incidence of Rickets." *J. Amer. Med. A.*, **148**:1227 (1952).

Eheart, M. S., and Gott, C. "Conventional and Microwave Cooking of Vegetables. Ascorbic Acid and Carotene Retention and Palatability." *J. Amer. Dietet. A.*, **44**:116 (1964).

Farmer's World. The Yearbook of Agriculture, 1964. Murray, K. L. "Grain, A Basic Food," p. 118; Mehr, S. "Fruit of the Earth," p. 126; Cook, A. C. "Growing and Using Vegetables," p. 138; Bishop, D. R. "Meat Production and Trade," p. 146; Strobel, D. R., and Crockett, S. L. "Milk and Dairy Products," p. 155; Shapiro, S. "Fisheries of the World," p. 161. Washington, D.C.: U.S. Department of Agriculture.

Food and Agriculture Organization of the United Nations. *Better Utilization of Milk.* Rome (1949).

——. *Rice and Rice Diets* (1948). *Maize and Maize Diets* (1953). *Rice Enrichment in the Philippines* (1954).

Food, The Yearbook of Agriculture, 1959, Chap. VI, "Food." Washington, D.C.: U.S. Department of Agriculture.

The Good in Your Food. New York: Super Market Institute, Inc. (1960).

Home and Garden Bulletin No. 57. *Getting Enough Milk.* Washington, D.C.: Agricultural Research Service, U.S. Department of Agriculture (1957).

Howe, P. E. "Foods of Animal Origin." *Handbook of Nutrition,* 2nd ed., Chap. 26. Chicago: American Medical Association (1951).

Kon, S. K. *Milk and Milk Products in Human Nutrition.* FAO Nutritional Study No. 17. Rome: Food and Agriculture Organization of the U.N. (1959).

Lee, F. A. "Nutritional Value of Frozen Foods." *Nutr. Rev.,* 9:1 (1951).

Maynard, L. A., and Nelson, W. L. "Foods of Plant Origin." *Handbook of Nutrition,* 2nd ed., Chap. 25. Chicago: American Medical Association (1951).

Miscellaneous Publication No. 870. *The Food We Eat.* Washington, D.C.: U.S. Department of Agriculture (1961).

Sherman, H. C. *Foods: Their Values and Management.* New York: Columbia U.P. (1946).

Taylor, C. M. *Food Values in Shares and Weights,* 2nd ed. New York: Macmillan (1959).

Taylor, C. M., and MacLeod, G. *Rose's Laboratory Handbook for Dietetics,* 5th ed. New York: Macmillan (1949).

U.S. Department of Agriculture. *Conserving the Nutritive Values in Foods.* Home and Garden Bulletin No. 90. Washington, D.C.: Agricultural Research Service (1963).

——. *Vegetables—Consumer Quality, Yield, and Preparation.* Home Economics Bulletin No. 17. Washington, D.C.: Agricultural Research Service (1962).

Watt, B. K., and Merrill, A. L. *Composition of Foods—Raw, Processed, Prepared.* Washington, D.C.: U.S. Department of Agriculture, Agriculture Handbook No. 8 (1963).

Williams, R. R. "Food Enrichment." *Agric. & Food Chem.,* 2:770 (1952).

Wolgamot, I. H., and Fincher, L. J. *Milk and Its Products—Facts for Consumer Education.* Washington, D.C.: Home Economics Research Branch, Agricultural Research Service, U.S. Department of Agriculture (1954).

≥ **22** ≥

Adequate Diet for Adults

In the merging of many ethnic groups, this country has achieved a widely varied diet. Nearly every nation of the world has contributed its unique dishes, and in many instances those once exotic foods have become part of our daily diet, widely available on the shelves of stores. Such items as spaghetti, pizza, chow mein, enchiladas, kippers and shishkebab remind us of our dietary debt to other countries.[1]

Even in our smaller cities and towns the fruit and vegetable markets carry items from many parts of the world, which refrigeration and air transportation have made possible. Foreign restaurants abound where typical national meals can be obtained on request.

Since the thirties, eating out has grown in popularity, and the U.S. Department of Agriculture studies of city families indicated that by 1955 nearly one fifth of the food and beverage expense was for food away from home. This expense included meals in restaurants, cafeterias, drug stores, in-plant lunchrooms, diners, coffee shops, and drive-in restaurants. This trend of eating out has continued. Through the thirties it was common practice for workers to carry dinner pails or lunch boxes to work, but by 1955 in-plant feeding had become a 3-billion-dollar business, with about 23 million meals being served each working day.

Ready-prepared meals such as TV dinners can be purchased on the way home and within minutes are ready to eat. Many adults living alone welcome the convenience of foods of this kind, and with the improvement in the quality of the foods used, both the flavor and nutritive value are now more acceptable. The dinners usually include a green or yellow vegetable and potatoes along with meat, fish, or poultry, and thus provide a well-balanced meal.

The purpose of this chapter is to show how one may apply knowledge of requirements of the various dietary essentials and of the nutritive values

[1] *How American Buying Habits Change*, Chap. V. "Meals, Menus, and Market Baskets." Washington, D.C.: U.S. Department of Labor (1959).

of common food materials to formulate a workable scheme for daily living, avoiding the problem of perpetual calculation or worry about food selection and at the same time avoiding eating according to the whim of the moment regardless of future welfare. Every person should have a simple program to care for routine food needs systematically and effectively. In this chapter dietary programs will be planned to show how to meet the needs of adults differing in (1) age, (2) degree of activity, (3) amount of money available for food, (4) food preferences and customs, and (5) cooking facilities.

Planning a Diet for the "Reference" Man

A good diet at a moderate cost can be easily planned by referring to the four food groups in Chapter 21 and making a list of essential foods needed each day as given below:

1 pt milk
½ to ¾ cup orange, grapefruit, or tomato juice or their equivalent in fresh fruit
½ to ¾ cup of green or yellow vegetable
1 potato
1 egg daily or at least 3 or 4 per week
4 to 5 oz of meat, poultry, or fish
4 to 6 slices of whole-wheat or enriched bread or equivalent
Other foods such as cereals, fats, sweets, and additional vegetables and fruits to meet the calorie requirement.

As previously pointed out, milk is a protective food of unique importance for calcium and riboflavin, and a significant source of protein. Even in an adult diet, therefore, an adequate amount of milk should be included at all times—preferably a pint a day. This may be at least in part nonfat milk or buttermilk. Milk is a very economical source (see Figure 22–1 *A* and *B*) of calcium, riboflavin, and protein, and the nonfat dry skim milk is a particularly good buy. Green and yellow vegetables yield good returns of vitamin A value for the money spent, as do tomatoes and citrus fruits of ascorbic acid. Potatoes are inexpensive sources of iron and thiamine.

The amount of eggs, meat, poultry, and fish to be used is determined partly by cost. As can be seen in Figure 22–2 (*A* and *B*), meats are relatively expensive in comparison with their nutritive return. Also note in Figure 22–2 (*A* and *B*) that dried beans, peas, and nuts are inexpensive sources of protein and iron. The foods from the cereal grains are also economical items in the diet, and the proportion used depends largely on the amount of money available for food. As much as one half of the total

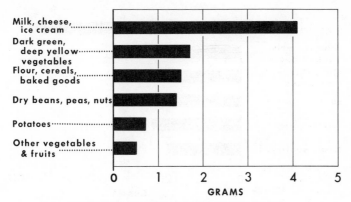

A

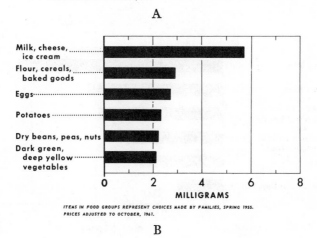

B

FIGURE 22–1. CONTRIBUTIONS OF FOOD GROUPS OF (*A*) CALCIUM YIELD AND (*B*) RIBOFLAVIN YIELD FOR ONE DOLLAR. (*Courtesy of U.S. Department of Agriculture.*)

calories of an adequate diet for an adult may be secured from this group of foods.

SUGGESTIONS FOR MENU PLANNING

Suggestions for the making of an attractive menu can be summarized as follows:

1. Conceive of the whole day as a unit, rather than the individual meal.

2. Endeavor to distribute the protein, fat, and carbohydrate throughout the day, so that no meal will have a striking preponderance of one kind of fuel foodstuff. For example, fried potatoes and pie in one meal concentrates the fat.

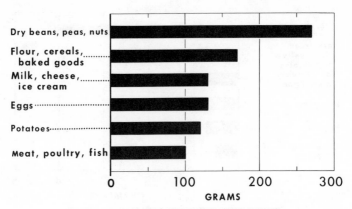

ITEMS IN FOOD GROUPS REPRESENT CHOICES MADE BY FAMILIES, SPRING 1955.
PRICES ADJUSTED TO OCTOBER, 1961.

A

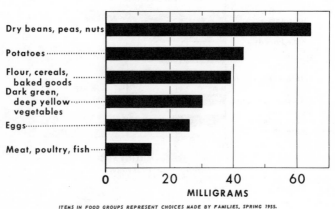

ITEMS IN FOOD GROUPS REPRESENT CHOICES MADE BY FAMILIES, SPRING 1955.
PRICES ADJUSTED TO OCTOBER, 1961.

B

FIGURE 22–2. CONTRIBUTIONS OF FOOD GROUPS OF (*A*) PROTEIN YIELD, AND (*B*) IRON YIELD FOR ONE DOLLAR. (*Courtesy of U.S. Department of Agriculture.*)

3. With the exception of a few such staples as bread, butter, and milk, try to avoid serving any food in the same form twice in the same day, and serve it preferably only once in any form.

4. Try to avoid serving any food that gives character to a dish twice in the same meal, even in different forms. Do not, for instance, select tomato soup and tomato salad for the same meal.

5. At each meal, seek contrasts between successive courses, a bland course being followed by a more highly flavored course, and vice versa, to give a pleasing rhythm.

6. In each course pay attention to flavor, color, form, and texture. There are esthetic values in crisp crackers with soup, a green lettuce leaf on a salad plate, a red cherry on a rice pudding, a gelatin jelly turned from a graceful mold, a slice of lemon with a serving of fish, and other combinations that exhibit pleasing contrasts.

7. As the number of courses increases, decrease the number of dishes and size of the servings in each.

Using the food guide and the suggestions for menu planning, meals such as the following can be worked out.

A DAY'S MENUS FOR THE "REFERENCE" MAN

Breakfast	Luncheon
Orange juice	Apricot nectar
Rolled oats, cooked	Tuna fish salad
(with milk and sugar)	Bread and margarine
Toast, with margarine and jam	Lemon meringue pie
Coffee with milk and sugar	Milk to drink

Dinner

Broiled chicken
Potato, boiled
Broccoli spears
Cole slaw
Rolls and margarine
Orange sherbet, cookie
Coffee

The list of foods with amounts needed for this 2,900-calorie diet for one day for the "reference" man is given in Table 22–1. The contributions of the foods have been calculated in shares, and the totals of each nutrient have been compared with the Recommended Daily Allowances in shares (see Table A–5). It will be noted that the diet as planned provides a liberal margin of safety for each nutrient except calories. By glancing over the contributions of the different foods furnishing each nutrient, one can quickly identify the significant sources.

Although the menus planned for this particular day do not include an egg as such, some egg has been used in food preparation, and it is assumed that the menus on other days would provide three or four eggs in the week.

Considerable variation in selection of foods within the four food groups is possible, but a knowledge of food values is helpful in making the most desirable choices. This is particularly true in the selection of fruits and vegetables.

TABLE 22–1. A DAY'S DIETARY FOR THE "REFERENCE" MAN

			Shares							
Foods	Measure	Calo-ries	Calo-ries	Pro-tein	Cal-cium	Iron	Vita-min A Value	Thia-mine	Ribo-flavin	Ascor-bic Acid
Milk, whole	1 cup	160	1.60	3.7	10.3	0.3	2.0	2.0	7.2	0.8
Milk, nonfat (skim)	1 cup	90	0.90	3.7	10.6	0.3	0.1	2.5	7.6	0.8
Tuna fish	3 oz.	170	1.70	10.0	0.3	4.7	0.4	1.0	1.7	0.0
Chicken, broiled	5 oz.	190	1.90	13.9	0.5	6.9	0.9	2.2	4.7	0.0
Broccoli spears, cooked	½ cup	20	0.20	1.1	2.4	1.8	10.9	1.8	2.5	28.0
Celery, diced	⅓ cup	5	0.05	0.1	0.5	0.3	0.5	0.3	0.2	1.2
Coleslaw	½ cup	60	0.60	0.2	1.0	0.8	0.5	0.8	0.5	7.3
Lettuce	1 large leaf	5	0.05	0.2	0.6	1.1	2.8	0.4	0.4	1.9
Potato, boiled	1	105	1.05	1.2	0.4	2.4	0.0	3.3	0.9	9.1
Apricot nectar	½ cup	70	0.70	0.2	0.4	0.8	6.9	0.3	0.2	1.5
Orange juice	6 oz.	83	0.83	0.6	0.6	0.5	2.2	4.0	0.4	34.9
Bread, white, enriched	4 slices	240	2.40	3.2	2.4	7.2	0.0	6.0	2.8	0.0
Bread, whole wheat	2 slices	110	1.10	1.6	1.6	3.0	0.0	3.0	1.0	0.0
Rolls, enriched	2	230	2.30	2.4	2.0	4.2	0.0	5.6	2.4	0.0
Oatmeal, cooked	¾ cup	98	0.98	1.6	0.6	3.1	0.0	3.6	0.7	0.0
Margarine, (or butter)	3 tbsp.	300	3.00	0.0	0.3	0.0	8.1	0.0	0.0	0.0
Mayonnaise	1½ tbsp.	165	1.65	0.0	0.2	0.5	0.3	0.0	0.3	0.0
Lemon meringue pie	1 piece	305	3.05	1.7	0.6	1.8	1.2	1.0	1.7	1.7
Orange sherbet	¾ cup	195	1.95	0.6	0.8	0.0	0.5	0.4	0.8	1.3
Cookie	1	120	1.20	0.4	0.3	0.6	0.1	0.3	0.2	0.0
Sugar	2 tbsp.	90	0.90	0.0	0.0	0.0	0.0	0.0	0.0	0.0
Jam	2 tbsp.	110	1.10	0.0	0.2	1.2	0.0	0.0	0.4	0.0
Coffee		00	0.00	0.0	0.0	0.0	0.0	0.0	0.0	0.0
Totals from diet		2,921	29.21	46.4	36.6	41.5	37.4	38.5	36.6	88.5
Recommended daily allowances		2,900	29.00	29.0	29.0	29.0	29.0	29.0	29.0	29.0

Planning a Diet for the "Reference" Woman

Following the same guide rules for the selection of foods and suggestions for menu planning, suitable menus for one day are suggested below for the "reference" woman needing 2,100 calories.

A DAY'S MENUS FOR THE "REFERENCE" WOMAN

Breakfast

Grapefruit
Puffed wheat, enriched (with milk)
Poached egg on toast
Margarine
Coffee with milk and sugar

Luncheon

Oyster stew with oyster crackers
Fruit cocktail
Gingerbread
Tea (if desired)

Dinner

Pork chop with applesauce
Sweet potato
Spinach
Lettuce with French dressing
Bread and margarine
Ice milk
Coffee

In looking at the menus it will be observed that although milk for drinking is not listed, a full pint of milk is included in milk for the cereal and coffee and in the oyster stew and ice milk.

The list of foods with amounts and calculations of the nutritive values expressed in shares is given in Table 22–2. When the totals for each nutrient in this dietary are compared with the Recommended Daily Allowances, it will be noted that each nutrient is generously provided. In the case of calories there is only a small surplus since it is not desirable to have an excess.

TABLE 22–2.   A DAY'S DIETARY FOR THE "REFERENCE" WOMAN

			Shares							
Foods	Measure	Calo-ries	Calo-ries	Pro-tein	Cal-cium	Iron	Vita-min A Value	Thia-mine	Ribo-flavin	Ascor-bic Acid
Milk, whole	1 cup	160	1.60	3.7	10.3	0.3	2.0	2.0	7.2	0.8
Ice milk	¾ cup	214	2.14	2.8	7.8	0.5	1.7	1.7	5.3	0.6
Egg, cooked	1	80	0.80	2.5	1.0	3.2	3.4	1.3	2.6	0.0
Oyster stew	1 cup	200	2.00	4.6	9.6	9.7	3.7	3.3	7.1	0.0
Pork chop	1	260	2.60	6.6	0.3	6.5	0.0	15.8	3.1	0.0
Lettuce	¼ head	15	0.15	0.4	0.8	1.7	2.2	1.8	1.2	3.0
Spinach, cooked	½ cup	20	0.20	1.1	3.0	5.9	42.4	1.7	2.2	10.4
Sweet potato, baked	1	155	1.55	0.8	1.6	2.9	51.8	2.5	1.2	10.0
Applesauce	¼ cup	58	0.58	0.1	0.1	1.0	0.2	0.3	0.1	0.3
Fruit cocktail	½ cup	98	0.98	0.2	0.4	1.5	1.1	0.5	0.3	1.1
Grapefruit	½	55	0.55	0.4	0.8	1.8	0.1	1.3	0.3	21.6
Bread, white, enriched	2 slices	120	1.20	1.6	1.2	3.6	0.0	3.0	1.4	0.0
Muffin, enriched	1	140	1.40	1.7	1.8	2.4	0.3	2.0	1.9	0.0
Oyster crackers	20	90	0.90	0.8	0.2	1.2	0.0	0.0	0.0	0.0
Gingerbread	1 slice	175	1.75	0.8	1.3	3.8	0.3	1.5	1.0	0.0
Wheat, Puffed	¾ cup	35	0.35	0.5	0.1	1.2	0.0	1.3	0.4	0.0
Margarine	1½ tbsp	150	1.50	0.0	0.2	0.0	3.9	0.0	0.0	0.0
French dressing	1 tbsp	60	0.60	0.0	0.1	0.3	0.3	0.0	0.0	0.0
Sugar	1 tbsp	45	0.45	0.0	0.0	0.0	0.0	0.0	0.0	0.0
Coffee		0	0.00	0.0	0.0	0.0	0.0	0.0	0.0	0.0
Totals from diet		2,130	21.30	28.6	40.6	47.5	113.4	40.0	35.3	47.8
Recommended Daily Allowances		2,100	21.00	24.0	29.0	44.0	29.0	20.0	22.0	29.0

The recommended allowance for the "reference" woman for iron is considerably higher than that for the "reference" man. This calls for special attention to the iron values in foods. It will be of interest to look at the foods in this dietary that make outstanding contributions of iron.

In a 2,100-calorie diet the sugar must be kept at a minimum since it contributes calories only and is a good example of a food containing so-called "empty calories."

The vitamin A value in the diet on this particular day is quite high since the menus provide for both a green and a yellow vegetable. Since vitamin A can be stored in the liver, a surplus such as appears in this dietary may help to make up an inadequate amount on another day. There may be considerable variation in the nutritive values of the food selected from day to day, and always in making a judgment of nutritional adequacy the intake over a period of several days to a week must be taken into account.

Seasonal foods are not as much of a factor as they were in the past because of technological advances in the preservation of foods and improved marketing facilities and practices. However, fresh fruits and vegetables purchased out of season may not be economical buys. Even for the low-income family the variety of foods is much more bountiful than it was at the beginning of the century.

Planning a Diet for a Sedentary Adult

The plans so far suggested have been for persons leading a life in which most of the working day is spent in at least moderate muscular activity, such as walking and lifting fairly heavy materials. But in a modern city, one may ride to work, sit all day at one's desk, or engage in no muscular activity greater than standing or walking slowly about from time to time, having luncheon in the building in which one works, riding home at night, sitting down to dinner, and afterward spending the evening sitting, whether reading at home, attending the theater, or looking at television. How many calories are spent under such circumstances? And what changes in the program are required to adapt it to the lower calorie expenditure? Suggestions for estimating the calorie requirement for different types of activities are given in Chapter 3. The problems of weight control will be considered in Chapter 23. A practical way of checking on a suitable calorie intake is to observe weight changes at regular intervals.

It should be kept in mind that when the calories are reduced, the other dietary essentials must at the same time be kept at a high level (see Table A–6 in the Appendix). A review of the dietary planned for the "reference" man will help one to see how the calories can be reduced. For example, replacing the lemon meringue pie with a low-calorie fruit dessert will lower the calories without affecting the total nutritive value significantly. The sugar and jam can be omitted and the number of slices of bread reduced. A few changes similar to these will help in lowering the calories for the "reference" woman. For a 1,200-calorie dietary see Chapter 23, on weight control.

Food for the Adult at Minimum Cost

Many individuals who are struggling to maintain themselves are faced with the problem of how to attain a diet of optimum nutritive value at low cost. Economizing on food is only one of the many ways in which expenses may be cut, and the cost of food can be reduced to an amazingly low level without lowering the standards of health, provided the food is chosen wisely. In fact, it is possible for one to live on an even higher nutritional level than formerly. In other words, it is not the size of the food budget that determines the nutritive quality of the diet but the wisdom with which one selects food.

Food costs include many items besides just the cost of the raw materials, such as the cost of fuel, rental, service, profit, and depreciation. Rooms with cooking and refrigerator privileges command more rent than similar rooms without such privileges. However, the additional rent is usually small compared with the money saved by preparing one's own food. Even when one chooses to eat in self-service cafeterias or automats, the outlay is still greater than the cost of the food in the open market.

Students or others having rooms with these special privileges just mentioned can live fairly well from a nutritional standpoint on an allowance of $1.25 to $1.50 a day for the raw materials at present city prices.* If two persons join forces, they can purchase food for less than twice this by careful buying. With two to share the responsibility, time can be saved in marketing and food preparation, and meals can be made more interesting because the purchasing can be done to better advantage. Also, a good companion with whom to enjoy one's meals is often just the incentive needed to make meals interesting.

If one has a room without refrigerator and cooking privileges, the problem of keeping food is a great drawback. The choice of foods meeting these specifications is so limited that it is probably necessary to have at least one meal in a cafeteria or in a neighboring restaurant. Casseroles with adequate calories as well as other nutrients should be chosen, such as meat and vegetable stews, Spanish rice, macaroni and cheese, meat-and-potato hash, baked beans, and hot soups, especially the creamed vegetable or kidney bean soups. The breakfast and supper will have to be very simple. Only those foods which can be used in the same day or those which will keep for a couple of days at room temperature should be purchased.

* These food costs for unattached adults are based on New York City food prices (1964–1965).

Certain important protective foods should be included daily and chosen from the standpoints of quantity, nutritive quality, and cost. Milk, of course, should head the list since no other food will give the same nutritive returns for so little money. A quart a day is a good amount to buy because it can be divided between the two meals to be eaten at home. If one prefers to save still more money, a large can of evaporated milk can be purchased in place of the fluid milk since the nutritive quality is nearly the same. One can also use the instant skim-milk powder provided he has some other adequate source of vitamin A. Probably a 1 lb loaf of bread will be enough for two days unless one is engaging in more than the usual amount of activity and needs additional calories to maintain weight. There are several varieties to choose from: whole wheat, white enriched, rye, cracked wheat, or raisin bread. A small jar of peanut butter or occasionally a glass of jelly or jam can be purchased and will keep for some time without refrigeration. One can of orange juice, grapefruit juice, or tomato juice purchased every other day will provide the ascorbic acid required, or if fresh oranges fit the budget, they can be used, and occasionally an apple, banana, or other available fresh fruit can be substituted. Since the orange is far superior to the apple and the banana as a source of ascorbic acid, it would be wise to favor oranges in choosing fresh fruit. For a little more variety, raisins, dried prunes, and apricots can be purchased since they can be washed and eaten dry or soaked in a little water until they soften sufficiently to be eaten. Soaking overnight should be long enough to make them palatable. If they can be purchased in small enough quantity and at a sufficiently low price, fresh vegetables that need no cooking, such as tomatoes, cabbage, carrots, and onions, may be used. However, one must not allow himself to carry these tempting foods to his room unless he feels sure that they can be eaten before spoiling. Remember always that there is no allowance on a limited budget, in fact on any budget, for the wasting of food. A metal container of some kind should be obtained which will hold the food to be stored and keep it clean and sanitary. For additional suggestions for cutting food costs, see Table A–20 in the Appendix.

For the older adult who lives alone some adjustments, usually minor, will need to be made, and these are discussed in the next section.

Nutrition for the Older Adult

The "older American" is portrayed in a report from the President's Council on Aging, which was established in 1962.[2] Figure 22–3 shows the increase in population of older Americans in the twentieth century. He may be between 65 and 70 years but is probably older. He

[2] President's Council on Aging. *The Older American*. Washington, D.C.: Government Printing Office (1963).

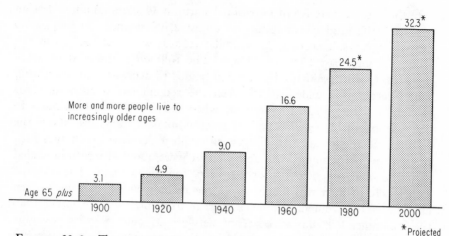

More and more people live to increasingly older ages

Age 65 *plus*

*Projected

FIGURE 22–3. TWENTIETH CENTURY INCREASE IN POPULATION OF OLDER AMERICANS (IN MILLIONS). (*From* The Older American, *President's Council on Aging* [1963].)

may have an adequate income but probably has not. He may be in good health but probably is not. The "older American" comprises 10 per cent of the entire population in the United States. There are more than 10,000 persons over 100 years old in this group, which totals about 18,000,000 people. Millions of older Americans enjoy relatively good health, and many are almost as active as ever. However, more than 12 million have at least one chronic ailment, such as hypertension, arthritis, diabetes, heart disease, or mental disorder. At least 50 per cent have a limiting chronic illness. More than 800,000 are in institutions, while 1,250,000 must have assistance from others to get along. In many instances had preventive and restorative services been promptly used, the disability might have been averted. They did not seek medical services soon enough because they did not appreciate the need or because they were too proud to accept charity. Some treat themselves. Many are not well nourished for various reasons such as poor food habits, lack of interest in eating because they must eat alone, or food fads.

As Dorothy Youland[3] of the U.S. Public Health Service states, public health nutrition has specific and valuable contributions to make in programs for chronic disease and aging through patient education and other services in nutrition and dietary therapy in both the home and the institution. Nutritionists can assist sponsors in setting up programs such as "Meals on Wheels" (services that deliver regular meals to elderly, homebound patients) or give consultation or direct service to organized home-care programs of various types.

[3] Youland, D. "New Dimensions for Public Health Nutrition. The Challenge of Chronic Disease and Aging." *Amer. J. Clin. Nutr.*, 9:211 (1961).

In the extensive study[4] of nutritional status in 39 states conducted from 1947 to 1958, food consumption of almost 2,500 women, 30 to past 80 years of age, was recorded. Also, similar records were obtained from 215 California men past 50 years of age. The following observations were reported. Quantities of food consumed tended to decrease with increasing age. There was a wide gap between the recommended allowance for calcium and the intake for women, whose calcium intake continued to decrease in later years. The average calcium intake of men was above the recommended allowance at all ages, although it decreased with age. Protein intakes for younger men and women were above the recommended allowance but fell below after 65 years for the women. The average iron intake of men was much above the recommended allowance, even above that for women. Women's average iron intakes were lower than the recommended allowance except between 35 and 55 years. Average intakes of men and women were above the recommended allowance for vitamin A, but those of men were higher. Except for the decade 25 to 35 years, the daily riboflavin intake of women was deficient. The average daily ascorbic acid intake of women was marginal or low, but that of men was satisfactory.

As we see from these dietary studies, older folks do not always select food wisely. In general, older men seem to do somewhat better than women perhaps because they tend to eat more food. Drinking an adequate amount of milk obviously needs emphasis because the older women's diet was quite low in calcium and riboflavin.

As Watkin[5] points out, "Basically, ideal nutrition for the elderly person in good health differs insignificantly from that of younger individuals, assuming in both cases that caloric intake is proportional to energy expenditure."

DIETS FOR OLDER FOLKS

The guide rules given in Chapter 21 for the selection of an adequate diet can be followed in planning diets for older folks. In Table A–2 in the Appendix will be found suitable calorie allowances for older men and women of different body weights and ages based on the National Research Council Recommended Allowances (1963). The recommendations for specific nutrients in shares according to calorie requirements are given in Table A–6 in the Appendix. It should be kept in mind that caution must be exercised in order to provide for good appetite and digestion and for ease of mastication. For special suggestions see the references at the end of this chapter.

[4] Morgan, A. F. (ed.). *Nutritional Status U.S.A.* Division of Agricultural Sciences. Berkeley: University of California. Experiment Station Bulletin 769 (1959).
[5] Watkin, D. M. "Nutrition for the Aging and the Aged." Chap. 38 in Wohl, M. G., and Goodhart, R. S. (eds.). *Modern Nutrition in Health and Disease*, 3rd ed. Philadelphia: Lea (1964).

TABLE 22–3. LIFE EXPECTANCY IN YEARS BEYOND AGE 45 FOR SELECTED COUNTRIES*

Country and Period	Male	Female	Country and Period	Male	Female
Austria			Japan		
1960	26.4	30.6	1962	26.8	30.6
1930–33	24.7	27.0	1935–36	22.4	25.9
Canada			Mexico		
1960–62	28.5	32.8	1960	27.3	29.9
1940–42	27.6	29.7	1940	21.9	23.3
Czechoslavakia			Northern Ireland		
1961	27.5	31.4	1960–62	27.1	30.9
1929–32	25.0	26.9	1936–38	25.4	26.4
Denmark			Poland		
1956–60	29.7	32.0	1960–61	27.6	31.5
1936–40	27.9	28.7	1931–32	24.0	26.4
England and Wales			Puerto Rico		
1960–62	27.0	32.0	1960	30.3	33.6
1936–40	25.5	28.8	1939–41	23.5	26.2
Egypt			Scotland		
1960	26.4	30.6	1960–61	25.8	30.4
1936–38	22.7	27.1	1930–32	25.1	27.3
France			Spain		
1962	27.1	32.5	1960	28.4	31.8
1933–38	24.0	28.0	1940	21.8	26.7
Germany			Sweden		
1959–60 (West)	27.5	31.2	1960	29.9	32.5
1932–34	26.6	28.0	1936–40	28.1	29.3
Hungary			United States		
1959–60	27.2	30.2	1962	27.0	32.2
1941	26.1	28.0	1939–41	25.5	28.5
Israel					
1962	30.4	31.5			

* "International Gains in Longevity After Midlife." Metropolitan Life Insurance Co., *Statistical Bulletin*, **45**, 11 (1964). Used with permission.

INTERNATIONAL GAINS IN LIFE EXPECTANCY AFTER MIDDLE LIFE

The expectation of life and mortality rate at single years of age from birth to 67 years in the United States for the year 1963 are given in Table A–21 in the Appendix. The greatest gains in survival have been made in childhood after one year of age and in early adult life, but some progress has been made in increasing the life expectancy beyond the middle years. In Table 22–3 the increases in life expectancy in years beyond age 45 have been tabulated for a selected list of countries providing the most recent data (as given in the *Statistical Bulletin* of the Metropolitan Life Insurance Company, April 1964). Figures on life expectancy beyond the age of 45 years in the original table show a low of 18.1 years for India (1941–50) and the highest life expectancy for Norway (1951–55) averaging 32.1 for men and women combined. As can be seen in Table 22–3, the United States does not have the highest life expectancy for either men or women. However, in every country women can be expected to outlive men on the average. As stated in the March 1965 Metropolitan Life *Statistical Bulletin*, "Longevity in the United States has shown little change in the past decade." This contrasts with the marked progress made earlier.

REFERENCES

A Consumer's Guide to USDA Services. Washington, D.C.: U.S. Department of Agriculture (1964).

Beeuwkes, A. M. "Studying the Food Habits of the Elderly." *J. Amer. Dietet. A.*, 37:215 (1960).

Bymers, G. J., and Murray, J. "Food Marketing Practices of Older Households." *J. Home Econ.*, 52:172 (1960).

Food and Drug Administration. *What Consumers Should Know About Food Additives* (1961); *What Consumers Should Know About Food Standards* (1963). Washington, D.C.: U.S. Department of Health, Education, and Welfare.

Food and Nutrition Council of Greater New York, Inc., in cooperation with the New York State Department of Social Welfare. *Diets for Use in Nursing Homes and Homes for the Aged.* Albany: New York State Department of Social Welfare (1964).

Forget Birthdays, Enjoy Good Eating. Chicago: American Dietetic Association (1961).

Health Committee, The National Council on the Aging, Inc. "Home-Delivered Meals for the Ill, Handicapped, and Elderly." A Project Report. *Amer. J. Pub. Health*, 55:Supplement (May 1965).

Kaufman, M. "The Role of Nutrition in Home Care and Homemaker Programs." *Amer. J. Pub. Health*, 52:55 (1962).

King, C. G., and Britt, G. *Food Hints for Mature People. More Years to Life —More Life to Years.* Public Affairs Pamphlet No. 336. New York: Public Affairs Committee, Inc. (1962).

Leverton, R. M. "Nutritional Trends and the Consumer's Food." *J. Home Econ.,* **56**:317 (1964).

Mirone, L., and Whitehead, E. L. "Milk Drinking by College Students." *J. Amer. Dietet. A.,* **33**:1266 (1957).

Monge, B., and Throssell, D. "Good Nutrition on a Low Income." *Amer. J. Nurs.,* **60**:1290 (1960).

Morgan, A. F. "Programs for the Aging—Nutrition." *J. Home Econ.,* **52**:817 (1960).

Myers, M. L., Sullivan, E. M., and Stare, F. J. "Foods Consumed by University Students." *J. Amer. Dietet. A.,* **43**:336 (1963).

Swanson, P. "Adequacy in Old Age. Part I: Role of Nutrition." *J. Home Econ.,* **56**:651 (1964).

Taylor, C. M. *Food Values in Shares and Weights,* 2nd ed. New York: Macmillan (1959).

Taylor, C. M., and MacLeod, G. *Rose's Laboratory Handbook for Dietetics,* 5th ed. New York: Macmillan (1949).

U.S. Department of Agriculture. *Food Guide for Older Folks.* Home and Garden Bulletin No. 17 (1963).

———. *Food for the Young Couple.* Home and Garden Bulletin No. 85 (1962).

———. *Consumers All.* The Yearbook of Agriculture 1965. Section on Food, pp. 391–480.

U.S. Department of Health, Education, and Welfare. Weight, Height, and Selected Body Dimensions of Adults. PHS Publication No. 1000 (1965).

Watkin, D. M. "New Findings in Nutrition of Older People." *Amer. J. Pub. Health,* **55**:548 (1965).

23

Food in Relation to Weight Control

The normal human body has firm, elastic muscles and a moderate store of fat widely distributed over the body, under the skin, around the visceral organs, among the muscle fibers, and elsewhere. This fat is advantageous as an insulator, saving the combustion of fuel for the production of heat under stimulus of cold. It also serves as padding for the viscera and the muscles, as support for the eyeball and for the kidneys, protecting against jars and blows, and as a storehouse of energy on which the body can draw when for any reason food is not immediately forthcoming.

We burn our fuel foods according to the demand of the muscles for energy, not according to the amount eaten. Whatever is eaten in excess of immediate need is stored for future use. Carbohydrate foods (sugar and starch) are stored as glycogen in the liver and to some extent in the muscles; however, since the body's capacity to store glycogen is limited, when the glycogen storehouses are full, the incoming carbohydrates, if not immediately needed, will be chemically changed and packed away in the more concentrated form of fat. Fat eaten as such is also stored in the body. Protein, in spite of the higher specific dynamic action previously discussed, consumed in excess may also contribute to body fat because up to 58 per cent when metabolized may follow the same pathway as carbohydrate.

An adult can estimate whether he is above or below desirable weight for his age and height by the use of standard height-weight tables (see Appendix, Tables A–12 and A–13). Maximum growth in height is usually attained by age 20 in males and by age 18 in females. Statistics from life insurance companies and other data indicate that the tendency to gain in body weight until 60 years of age is undesirable. This tendency to gain weight is characteristic of the average person in the United States. The most favorable health expectation is associated with the maintenance throughout life of the weight normally attained at age 25. Deviations of

362

10 per cent or more from this in either direction may or may not be significant, but it is advisable to seek the explanation for a deviation of more than 15 per cent, in whichever direction it occurs, and to consider its effect on health and efficiency.

Studies of Body Composition

The nature of the body composition as discussed in Chapter 2 and the proportions of lean body mass and other body compartments such as fat and total body water (TBW) must be considered in judging desirable weight. A number of methods of identifying amount of body fat have been used.

Behnke, Feen, and Welham,[1] of the United States Navy, found that 17 "All American" football players could be classified as unfit for military service because of overweight, and these authors were interested in determining the specific gravity of these and other men. The volume of the subject was determined by weighing him in air as usual and then in water by suspending him below the surface of the water on a line connected with a spring balance which gave his weight. It was found that the specific gravity of healthy men between 20 and 40 years of age ranged from 1.021 to 1.097 and that a value of 1.060 or less indicated excessive fat. Of the 17 men studied, 11 fell into the group with high specific gravity and should have been judged to be in excellent physical condition if absence of excess fat is taken as a criterion of physical fitness.

Another method for estimating body fat is that of measuring, by means of calipers, the thickness of a double layer of the skin at several points on the body surface. Normally the layer of fat under the skin may vary approximately between ¼ and ½ in. thick. Deviations of skinfolds from this range of thickness can be used to estimate the degree of leanness or fatness of the body. See Figure 23–1. Skill and experience in the use of calipers are essential for meaningful interpretation.[2]

Still another method depends on the fact that the water content of the lean, fat-free body mass is very constant. The water content is determined by injecting into the body a water-soluble drug, such as antipyrine. After time is allowed for complete distribution of the drug throughout the water content of the body, a sample of blood is withdrawn and the concentration of the drug in the plasma is determined. From the dilution of the drug it is possible to estimate the total amount of body water and from this the amount of body fat.

[1] Behnke, A. R., Jr., Feen, B. G., and Welham, W. C. "The Specific Gravity of Healthy Men. Body Weight-Volume as an Index of Obesity." *J. Amer. Med. A.*, **118**:495 (1942).

[2] Consolazio, C. F., Johnson, R. E., and Pecora, L. J. *Physiological Measurements of Metabolic Functions in Man*, Chaps. 6 and 7 (Body Composition). New York: McGraw (1963).

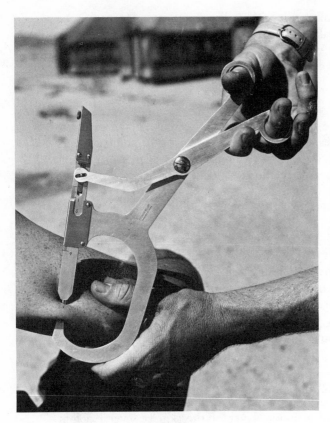

FIGURE 23–1. CALIPERS IN
POSITION FOR MEASURING
THE SKINFOLD THICKNESS.
(*From* Physiological Mea-
surements of Metabolic
Functions in Man *by C. F.
Consolazio, R. E. Johnson,
and L. J. Pecora. Copy-
right 1963 by McGraw-
Hill Book Co., Inc., used
by permission of the Pub-
lishers.*)

Overweight and Obesity

About 25 per cent of the population of the United States is
estimated to be overweight and to such a degree as to cause impairment
in health. The mortality rate for this group is well above average.
Overweight is associated with a high death rate from cardiovascular-renal
disease, diabetes, and liver disease, and in childbirth. In diabetes, the
death rate is three times as high in the obese as in those of average weight
and in liver cirrhosis among men more than twice as high. It is well established that mortality rates for overweight men are 50 per cent greater
than the expected normal and for overweight women 47 per cent greater.
Such figures have resulted in obesity's being called our "Number One
Public Health Problem" and explain why life insurance companies are
reluctant to place standard insurance on people with marked overweight
and, where it is excessive, may refuse insurance altogether. This attitude
of the insurance companies shows that they consider being overweight a
very serious disability. Studies by the Metropolitan Life Insurance
Company show that weight reduction by overweight people apparently

increases the chances for living longer. As a result of this finding, over-weight people who have reduced have been granted standard premium rates after having been charged higher rates because of their excess weight.

It should be pointed out here that the terms "overweight" and "obesity" are used differently by different writers. Some consider them synonymous and use them interchangeably; others use overweight to indicate a body weight 15 to 25 per cent above desirable weight and reserve the term "obesity" for weights 25 per cent or more too high. Another definition of obesity is overweight due to excess fat. Still others would limit the term "obesity" to those cases in which the excess weight is extreme, as in the following example.

An inimitable description of the physical handicap of obesity is found in *The Age of Innocence*.[3]

> The immense accretion of flesh which had descended on her in middle life like a flood of lava on a doomed city had changed her from a plump active little woman with a neatly-turned foot and ankle into something as vast and august as a natural phenomenon. She had accepted this sub-mergence as philosophically as all her other trials, and now, in extreme old age, was rewarded by presenting to her mirror an almost unwrinkled expanse of firm pink and white flesh, in the center of which the traces of a small face survived as if awaiting excavation. A flight of smooth double chins led down to the dizzy depths of a still-snowy bosom veiled in snowy muslins that were held in place by a miniature portrait of the late Mr. Mingott; and around and below, wave after wave of black silk surged away over the edges of a capacious armchair, with two tiny white hands poised like gulls on the surface of the billows.

Many another woman has been forced by the accumulation of body fat so common with advancing years to keep off her feet or suffer because her body has become too heavy for them to carry. We realize the handicap of obesity when it thus impedes locomotion and engenders flatfoot, but we should also realize that the internal organs are working under a handicap not unlike that of the feet. The circulation of the blood is impeded, and this in turn makes the work of the weakening heart more difficult and the strain on the blood vessels greater. Liver, kidneys, and pancreas all are at a disadvantage, and how long they can continue to function properly depends on their native endurance.

CAUSES OF OBESITY

"While a considerable amount of information is available concerning the multiple etiology, mechanisms, and types of obesity in experimental animals, comparable knowledge in man is notably sparse. It all seems so

[3] Wharton, E. *The Age of Innocence*, p. 25. New York: Appleton (1920).

deceptively simple. Food makes fat and obesity results from overeating."[4]
As this editorial comment indicates, the cause of an excessive appetite
leading to an intake of calories greater than expenditure is not well understood. Various theories have been postulated.

Jolliffe stressed that it might be the result of abnormal behavior of an
appetite-regulating center located in the hypothalamus, which is situated
near the pituitary gland in a region of the brain in which are located
also other regulatory centers, such as those governing water balance,
body temperature, and sleep. It is known that damage to the hypothalamus may result from disturbances in other centers located near it and
may cause excessive appetite. Some forms of damage result in loss of
appetite (anorexia). Jolliffe believed that the appetite-regulating center
could be conditioned to demanding a higher intake of food than normal
by simply habitually overeating, and that an "appestat" thus conditioned
might be educated back to normal by reducing food intake, a process
that takes time, patience, and will power.

From his extensive research work in this field, Mayer concludes that
excessive appetite is due to at least three (and probably more) factors,
namely, heredity, environment, and physical or mental injury. As an
example of obesity due to heredity he cites the practice of animal breeders
in producing strains of beef cattle, hogs, and poultry in which fatness is
transmitted from one generation to the next. In human beings, studies
have been reported by various investigators of family occurrence of
obesity. To cite only two of these—Rony, in a study of 250 obese patients,
found that 69 per cent had obese parents (either one or both), and
Angel reported a study in which he found that half the offspring of
parents, one obese and the other normal in weight, were obese, while
two thirds of the children of parents both obese were obese. In these
cases both hereditary and environmental factors are doubtless involved.
The children of overweight parents may be overweight simply because
of family eating habits, for example, too great indulgence in generous
quantities of foods high in calorie value.

Of course, emphasis needs to be placed on the fact that we inherit our
body framework, not our body weight. Mayer and his co-workers[5] have
identified differences in morphological features and physical types between the obese and nonobese and believe that there are constitutional
factors operating in the predisposition to obesity. Recognition of some
of these differences may assist in prevention of overweight in its early
stages.

Examples of environmental obesity are such cases as those due to the
nature of the diet, to immobilization due to convalescence, and to in-

[4] Editorial. "Body Build and Obesity." *J. Amer. Med. A.,* **189**:116 (1964).
[5] Seltzer, C. C., and Mayer, J. "Body Build and Obesity—Who Are the Obese?"
J. Amer. Med. A., **189**:677 (1964).

activity in general. Overeating may also be the result of emotional disturbances or frustrations, the individual resorting to food as compensation for feelings of insecurity or to relieve tensions. Although differences in the metabolism of fat, carbohydrate, and protein have been identified in laboratory animals, for example, in the obese hyperglycemic mouse, they have not been demonstrated unequivocally in man. Current studies suggest that there may be a slight impairment in the ability of the obese to mobilize free fatty acid (FFA). Another area of current research is that of the regulatory mechanisms that control water and electrolyte balance in the obese. All investigators in this field agree that much research remains to be done before the causes of obesity can be fully known and understood.

EXPERIMENTAL APPROACH TO WEIGHT CONTROL

In view of the preceding discussion and the fact that the proportion of older people in our population is increasing markedly, there can be no doubt as to the need for controlling body weight. The best first step would be that of preventing overweight by watching one's weight as one grows older with the object of keeping it within the normal range for age 25. A tendency to increase in weight beyond this range should be checked immediately by making changes in diet and activity. We have seen that the basal metabolism of adults falls slightly year by year, and exercise seldom fails to diminish in duration and intensity. Yet the appetite for food continues or even increases, and more and more is eaten than is needed, the extra fuel being stored as body fat. When riding in automobiles, watching movies, sitting at bridge parties, or looking at television are the most active forms of sport, certainly not many calories in excess of the basal metabolism will be spent.

Fasting as a means to weight reduction should be attempted only under medical guidance. Gordon and co-workers, who have used intermittent fasting as a therapeutic program for certain obese patients, emphasize that it is still in the experimental stage and its validity has not yet been established. Duncan and associates, who have experimented with the fasting program over a two-and-one-half-year period, believe it has merit for some intractably obese patients who are free of certain complicating pathological conditions.[6]

The formula diet, which has gained a degree of popularity, has many disadvantages. As the Council on Foods and Nutrition of the American Medical Association states, "Extensive weight reduction should be carried out only with a physician's guidance, and with diets which are tailored to the individual's needs. . . . Weight reduction must be consi-

[6] Duncan, G. C., Cristofori, F. C., Yue, J. K., and Murthy, M. S. J. "The Control of Obesity by Intermittent Fasts." *Med. Clin. North America*, **48**:1359 (1964).

dered a long-term procedure and education of the individual to the faults of his past eating habits is essential. Only the dietary program which results in permanent weight loss and lifetime control of weight will be a satisfactory one."[7]

The possible influence of meal spacing in human beings on body composition and energy utilization has been suggested by experiments with animals "nibbling" and "gorging." According to Cohn,[8] the quantity of food consumed at one time may noticeably affect the enzyme activity required for its digestion and metabolism. Therefore, he believes that smaller, more frequent meals, if total calories are not increased, might be less likely to produce obesity than the traditional three larger meals.

Pollack[9] recommends a "module plan" for weight reduction, to utilize exercise and energy expenditure, as well as a decrease in food intake, to effect calorie deficits. As Pollack and associates state, "Small increments of excess intake and small decrements in energy expenditure together can be responsible for much adult obesity." The energy value of each pound of body fat is approximately 3,500 calories. Planning in terms of modules of 50 or 100 calories expended in work or exercise, or food removed from the daily diet, makes it possible to adapt patterns of eating and living to achieve weight loss.

Many experimental approaches to the study of obesity and food intake have been tried. Hashim and Van Itallie[10] report their clinical research with the use of an automatic food-dispensing apparatus for monitoring food intake. A single mouthful of a liquid-formula diet is delivered through a mouthpiece when the subject presses a button at will. Some subjects are able voluntarily to keep a constant weight over a period of days using the apparatus, while other obese subjects decrease their intake markedly. One maintained that the machine was keeping track of him, and he increased his intake of formula diet immediately when a pitcher of it was merely left in his room to drink at will.

Sometimes diets developed for experimental purposes under medical management become "popularized" and are used without proper supervision by overweight persons. The diets may be nutritionally unbalanced and can be a health risk if continued too long. For example, Dr. Van Itallie has pointed out that the low carbohydrate diet with increased fat consumption might accelerate atherosclerosis particularly in susceptible persons. Anyone tempted to try one of these special reduction diets should first seek medical advice.

[7] Council on Foods and Nutrition. "Formula Diets and Weight Control." *J. Amer. Med. A.*, **176**:439 (1961).

[8] Cohn, C. "Meals." *Nutr. Rev.*, **20**:321 (1962).

[9] Pollack, H., Consolazio, C. F., and Isaac, G. J. "Metabolic Demands as a Factor in Weight Control." *J. Amer. Med. A.*, **167**:216 (1958).

[10] Hashim, S. A., and Van Itallie, T. B. "Clinical and Physiologic Aspects of Obesity." *J. Amer. Dietet. A.*, **46**:15 (1965).

CONTROL OF APPETITE

Sometimes a craving for food can be assuaged temporarily by drinking water or some other noncalorie beverage. Eating food high in vegetable fiber gives a sense of fullness, which is a part of the normal satisfaction of hunger. Lettuce, cabbage, string beans, celery, Brussels sprouts, asparagus, chard, and other greens can be indulged in freely. Raw fruit, such as apples, oranges, grapefruit, and other fruits in season, may, so far as possible, take the place of other desserts. Some fat in the diet slows up digestion sufficiently to appease hunger. However, the fat should be put where it will count most, on the table where one can see it, and not in the food while cooking.

ADJUSTING ENERGY INTAKE AND ENERGY EXPENDITURE

The scales should be watched week by week. Gain or no gain is the final test of the diet. If one is gaining, there are too many calories. Adjust them until weight remains stationary; or, if overweight, until losing at the desired rate, which should not be over 2 lb a week. Remember that 200 calories a day stored means 21 lb of body fat in one year, and that one insignificant chocolate caramel may yield about 50 calories; one small bar of sweet chocolate, 150 calories; one sundae with whipped cream at the fountain, 500 calories; one large chocolate malted milk with ice cream, 600 to 700 calories.

Loss in weight may not be regular. Fat burned off may be temporarily replaced by water, with little or no change in weight for some time (see Figure 23–2). Then water may be lost rapidly and weight may fall, only to remain stationary again as water accumulates once more. Later, this water will be lost, and then the reduction in fat, which has been going on all the time, becomes evident. If the calories taken are below those

FIGURE 23–2. THE CHANGES IN WEIGHT OF AN OBESE GIRL ON A REDUCING DIET. She retained water for over two weeks and during this time showed no loss in weight, although combustion of body fat was going on all the time. Later the water was excreted and her weight fell. The *broken line* shows the rate at which loss would have occurred had there been no water retention. (*Courtesy of Dr. L. H. Newburgh.*)

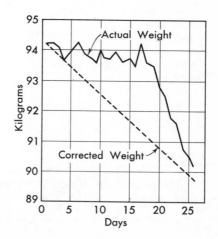

expended, body fat must be used as fuel. There is no escaping this law. If the body persistently retains water, so that after some weeks the weight has not gone down, a physician skilled in the pathology of the endocrine glands should be consulted. The pituitary gland, especially, exercises a control over the water of the body.

In addition to limiting the calories, it may be desirable to increase the energy expenditure by exercise, which should be moderate and regular. If too strenuous exercise is indulged in, the appetite may be stimulated and the object of the low-calorie diet defeated. This must be avoided, but this does not mean a program of no activity, which would also result in putting on weight, as has already been pointed out. A happy medium between these two extremes is that of moderate, regular exercise which does not increase the desire for food but does consume energy. Using such figures as those given in Table 3–1, correcting for the total energy cost of activities, and allowing 3,500 calories for 1 lb of body fat, one can calculate that a man, weighing 194 lb (88.2 kg), who walked one hour each day for 60 days at the moderate rate of 3 mph would expend the energy equivalent of a little less than 5 lb of fat, and this would mean that much loss of body weight.[11] See Table 23–1 for energy equivalents

TABLE 23–1. ENERGY EQUIVALENTS OF FOOD CALORIES EXPRESSED IN MINUTES OF ACTIVITY*

Food	Calo-ries	Activity				
		Walk-ing†	Riding Bicycle‡	Swim-ming**	Run-ning††	Reclin-ing‡‡
		Min	Min	Min	Min	Min
Apple, large	101	19	12	9	5	78
Bacon, 2 strips	96	18	12	9	5	74
Banana, small	88	17	11	8	4	68
Beans, green, 1 cup	27	5	3	2	1	21
Beer, 1 glass	114	22	14	10	6	88
Bread and butter	78	15	10	7	4	60
Cake, $\frac{1}{12}$, 2-layer	356	68	43	32	18	274
Carbonated beverage, 1 glass	106	20	13	9	5	82
Carrot, raw	42	8	5	4	2	32
Cereal, dry, $\frac{1}{2}$ cup, with milk and sugar	200	38	24	18	10	154
Cheese, cottage, 1 tbsp	27	5	3	2	1	21
Cheese, Cheddar, 1 oz	111	21	14	10	6	85
Chicken, fried, $\frac{1}{2}$ breast	232	45	28	21	12	178
Chicken, TV dinner	542	104	66	48	28	417

[11] The total energy expenditure for walking at the rate of 3 miles per hour is 3.1 cal per kilogram per hour. If a person walks 60 hr and weighs 88.2 kg, his total energy expenditure will be 3.1 × 60 × 88.2, or 16,405 cal. Allowing 3,500 cal for each pound of body fat, 16,405 ÷ 3,500 will be 4.7 lb of body fat lost.

TABLE 23-1. ENERGY EQUIVALENTS OF FOOD CALORIES EXPRESSED IN MINUTES OF ACTIVITY* (continued)

Food	Calo-ries	Activity				
		Walk-ing†	Riding Bicycle‡	Swim-ming**	Run-ning††	Reclin-ing‡‡
		Min	Min	Min	Min	Min
Cookie, plain, 148/lb	15	3	2	1	1	12
Cookie, chocolate chip	51	10	6	5	3	39
Doughnut	151	29	18	13	8	116
Egg, fried	110	21	13	10	6	85
Egg, boiled	77	15	9	7	4	59
French dressing, 1 tbsp	59	11	7	5	3	45
Halibut steak, ¼ lb	205	39	25	18	11	158
Ham, 2 slices	167	32	20	15	9	128
Ice cream, ⅙ qt	193	37	24	17	10	148
Ice cream soda	255	49	31	23	13	196
Ice milk, ⅙ qt	144	28	18	13	7	111
Gelatin, with cream	117	23	14	10	6	90
Malted milk shake	502	97	61	45	26	386
Mayonnaise, 1 tbsp	92	18	11	8	5	71
Milk, 1 glass	166	32	20	15	9	128
Milk, skim, 1 glass	81	16	10	7	4	62
Milk shake	421	81	51	38	22	324
Orange, medium	68	13	8	6	4	52
Orange juice, 1 glass	120	23	15	11	6	92
Pancake with syrup	124	24	15	11	6	95
Peach, medium	46	9	6	4	2	35
Peas, green, ½ cup	56	11	7	5	3	43
Pie, apple, ⅙	377	73	46	34	19	290
Pie, raisin, ⅙	437	84	53	39	23	336
Pizza, cheese, ⅛	180	35	22	16	9	138
Pork chop, loin	314	60	38	28	16	242
Potato chips, 1 serving	108	21	13	10	6	83
Sandwiches						
Club	590	113	72	53	30	454
Hamburger	350	67	43	31	18	269
Roast beef with gravy	430	83	52	38	22	331
Tuna fish salad	278	53	34	25	14	214
Sherbet, ⅙ qt.	177	34	22	16	9	136
Shrimp, French-fried	180	35	22	16	9	138
Spaghetti, 1 serving	396	76	48	35	20	305
Steak, T-bone	235	45	29	21	12	181
Strawberry shortcake	400	77	49	36	21	308

* Courtesy of Dr. Frank Konishi, Southern Illinois University, and the *Journal of the American Dietetic Association*, 46: 187 (1965), "Calorie Equivalents of Activities."
† Energy cost of walking for 70-kg individual = 5.2 calories per minute at 3.5 mph.
‡ Energy cost of riding bicycle = 8.2 calories per minute.
** Energy cost of swimming = 11.2 calories per minute.
†† Energy cost of running = 19.4 calories per minute.
‡‡ Energy cost of reclining = 1.3 calories per minute.

of food calories expressed in minutes of activity as calculated by Konishi. In the light of our present-day knowledge of obesity, the best program for reducing weight is the combination of a low-calorie diet adequate in all other respects with regular, moderate exercise.

THE LOW-CALORIE DIET

The tendency to store fat increases as men and women grow older. It varies with individuals and, if hereditary, needs to be carefully watched. It is easier to begin a program of dietary control that is preventive of overweight than to take off extra pounds of fat that should not have been allowed to accumulate. Here an attempt will be made to show how modern knowledge of nutrition makes it possible to adjust one's energy intake to one's energy needs without failing to meet the other dietary needs. In fact, the good reducing diet is unexcelled in quality by any other if rightly chosen.

Although with 1,200 calories or 12 shares, adequate protein, mineral elements, and vitamins can be provided for the reducing diet, if the foods are carefully selected, many people prefer to have a few more calories and reduce more slowly. Therefore, the calories suggested range from 1,200 to 1,500. However, the dietary suggested here is for 1,200 calories. In Table A–6 in the Appendix the following allowances recommended for a woman expressed in shares are as follows: 29 each for calcium, vitamin A, and ascorbic acid; 24 for protein; 44 for iron; 20 for thiamine; and 21 for riboflavin. The recommendations for a man expressed in shares are as follows: 29 for protein, calcium, iron, vitamin A, and ascorbic acid; 20 for thiamine; and 21 for riboflavin.

In planning the low-calorie diet, selections can be made from the four food groups just as in other diets, but it is essential that the foods selected be high in minerals and vitamins in proportion to the calories. Menus such as those suggested below meet these requirements.

A DAY'S MENUS FOR A 1,200-CALORIE DIET

Breakfast	Luncheon	Dinner
Orange, sliced	Minestrone soup	Tomato juice
Toast, enriched	Lettuce, peas, and egg salad	Roast beef
Butter or margarine	with lemon juice dressing	Potato
Coffee, black*	Crackers	Spinach
Milk, skim	Milk, skim	Carrot strips
		Bread, enriched
		Butter or margarine
		Banana, baked
		Coffee, black*

* If desired.

The vegetables chosen are excellent sources of vitamins. If desired, larger quantities of leafy vegetables can be included since they are low in calories. In fact, all green vegetables and all succulent ones such as celery and tomatoes may be used more liberally if no fats are added to season them. Salad dressing of excellent flavor can be made with lemon juice, which yields only a few calories. Also, a number of low-calorie salad dressings are available on the market.

A list of the foods needed for the preparation of these menus is given in Table 23–2. Comparing the totals from the diet with the recommended

TABLE 23–2.   A 1,200-CALORIE DIET

			Shares							
Foods	Measure	Calo-ries	Calo-ries	Pro-tein	Cal-cium	Iron	Vita-min A Value	Thia-mine	Ribo-flavin	Ascor-bic Acid
Milk, nonfat (skim)	1 pt	180	1.80	7.4	21.2	0.6	0.2	5.0	15.2	1.6
Egg, boiled	1	80	0.80	2.5	1.0	3.2	3.4	1.3	2.6	0.0
Beef, sirloin, broiled, lean	3 oz	173	1.73	11.3	0.5	9.8	0.2	2.0	3.6	0.0
Carrot, raw	5 thin strips	4	0.04	0.1	0.1	0.2	6.4	0.2	0.1	0.3
Celery	2 pieces	5	0.05	0.0	0.6	0.3	0.6	0.3	0.2	0.9
Lemon juice	1 tbsp	5	0.05	0.0	0.0	0.0	0.0	0.0	0.0	2.9
Lettuce, Boston	½ head	15	0.15	0.6	1.4	6.5	6.2	1.8	1.1	3.8
Peas, cooked	½ cup	58	0.58	1.9	0.7	4.3	2.5	5.5	1.5	6.9
Potato, boiled	1	105	1.05	1.2	0.4	2.4	0.0	3.3	0.9	9.1
Spinach, cooked	½ cup	20	0.20	1.1	3.0	5.9	42.4	1.7	2.2	10.3
Tomato juice	½ cup	23	0.23	0.4	0.3	3.3	5.7	1.7	0.6	8.1
Banana	1	85	0.85	0.4	0.3	2.1	1.1	1.3	1.0	4.1
Orange	1	75	0.75	0.4	2.4	0.9	1.8	4.0	1.0	29.0
Bread, white enriched	2 slices	120	1.20	1.6	1.2	3.6	0.0	3.0	1.4	0.0
Crackers, Graham	6 small	83	0.83	0.6	0.3	0.9	0.0	0.5	0.8	0.0
Margarine (or butter)	1 tbsp	100	1.00	0.0	0.0	0.0	1.3	0.0	0.0	0.0
Soup, minestrone	¾ cup	79	0.79	1.6	1.0	2.2	10.3	1.4	0.7	0.0
Coffee		0	0.00	0.0	0.0	0.0	0.0	0.0	0.0	0.0
Totals from diet		1,210	12.10	31.1	34.4	46.2	82.1	33.0	32.9	77.0
Recommended Daily Allowances for woman		1,200	12.00	24	29	44	29	20	21	29
Recommended Daily Allowances for man		1,200	12.00	29	29	29	29	20	21	29

allowances, it will be noted that the foods listed for one day provide generous margins of safety for each of the nutrients except calories. In a reducing regime it is necessary, as has already been pointed out, to establish new food habits which can be continued over a period of time in order to maintain the reduced weight.

It is also important to keep in mind the fact that alcoholic beverages furnish calories which must be added to the day's total. See Table A–10 in the Appendix for calorie values.

OBESITY IN THE YOUNG

Obesity is not characteristic of youth. Sometimes overweight, if not extreme, in the period preceding adolescence may actually be an advantage, since often the extra weight is rapidly outgrown in the sudden increase in height that commonly occurs at puberty. However, it is estimated that between 10 to 15 per cent of American children and teenagers are overweight by recognized standards. In a survey of children in Boston it was found that the obese children, on the average, did not eat more than the controls (average-weight children) but were much less active. Mayer and associates[12] utilized motion pictures to compare the activity of 109 obese and 72 nonobese adolescent girls engaged in three sports at a summer camp. It was clear from 27,211 observations that the obese girls were far less active. Obesity, of course, is a handicap to children, because they do not fit well into the regular athletic and play program and are more liable to accidents and strains.

A number of summer camps have been established for overweight youngsters in an effort to develop athletic interest and ability and to establish good dietary habits.

Bruch, Kerley and Lorenze, and Schlutz all report that in their experience as pediatricians they find relatively few cases of obesity due to any glandular disturbance and that, therefore, endocrine treatment is rarely needed.

Ordinarily the basal metabolism of overweight children is within the normal range. Mulier and Topper, of the Pediatric Service of Mount Sinai Hospital, New York City, in a study of 78 boys and girls from 14 to 16 years old, found this to be true in about three fourths of the cases, and in another study of 25 boys and girls between 5 and 14 years of age, they could find no evidence of any endocrine disturbance, though the children were from 20 to 76 per cent overweight. The basal metabolisms were high normals or above. In every case there was a history of overfeeding. Many of the children had voracious appetites, so that the total calorie intake was in some instances twice as much as needed. The diets were rich in carbohydrates and fats, with very little in the way of vegetables or fruits.

Treatment consisted of careful regulation of the total calories, care being taken to select foods that would keep the quantities of protein, the various mineral elements, and the vitamins up to the appropriate amounts

[12] Bullen, B. A., Reed, R. B., and Mayer, J. "Physical Activity of Obese and Non-obese Girls Appraised by Motion Picture Sampling." *Amer. J. Clin. Nutr.*, 14:211 (1964).

for children of their ages. Active physical exercise, such as walking, roller skating, tennis, handball, and swimming, was also prescribed. Under this regimen for about four and a half months the children's weekly average loss was three quarters of a pound and their gain in height above expectation. Furthermore, they acquired a feeling of well-being, an increased capacity for physical activity, an increased interest in all school activities, and greatly improved eating habits, with a loss of their passion for food.[13]

Psychologists call attention to the relation of emotional problems to obesity in children. It is possible that these factors may have a greater role in persistent juvenile obesity than in the case of the adult.

It does not seem wise to reduce the weight of a growing child except under medical supervision, but it may be possible to hold his weight stationary until, by a carefully regulated diet and by suitably planned exercise, he has lowered his excess of fat. As a rule, children do not enjoy being obese and are willing to cooperate in measures to bring their weight to normal, but attention must be given to them over a long period of time.

Prevention is more important than cure, and as Sebrell states, we should include in our health teaching, along with emphasis on good nutrition, the prevention of obesity as a health rule.[14]

Undernutrition

ADULTS

It is possible for the adult to become habituated to living on too low a nutritional level, so that he is unconscious of any disadvantage and will protest that he is "perfectly well," while as a matter of fact he is more liable to both physical and mental fatigue, to nervous tension, and to infections than if he were living on a higher nutritional plane. When the food intake is too limited, the diet is likely to be inadequate in many essential nutrients besides calories. Some years ago investigations were made by Blunt and Bauer at the University of Chicago in regard to the basal metabolism and food habits of 19 underweight college women; 11 of these, although active, were found to be eating less than 500 calories a day in excess of their basal metabolism. They confessed that they became tired very easily and yet they were quite certain they were eating enough and could not possibly eat any more. When one of them was finally induced to increase her food consumption, she admitted that it was astonishing how much more she could eat and how much better she felt. Women even less severely underweight than this suffer from

---

[13] Mulier, H., and Topper, A. "Treatment of Obesity in a Group of Children." *Amer. J. Dis. Child.*, **47**:25 (1934).

[14] Sebrell, W. H., Jr. "Weight Control Through Prevention of Obesity." *J. Amer. Dietet. A.*, **34**:920 (1958).

chronic fatigue to which they have become so accustomed that they are utterly unaware of how much better they might feel. The combination of a long night's sleep and an increased food intake will often increase vitality surprisingly.

A study by Keys and his associates at the University of Minnesota has already been described in Chapter 2. Thirty-two conscientious objectors who maintained their average body weight on an intake of 3,492 calories daily during the pre-experimental period lost 24 per cent in body weight when they were reduced to a level of 1,547 calories daily for a period of six months. The symptoms that developed during the experimental period were characteristic of those of famine victims.

CHILDREN

There is no simple method of determining a child's nutritional status. There must be well-developed muscles with good tone, normally functioning digestive and nervous systems, and evidences of a good blood supply and of skin and mucous membrane in prime condition. Furthermore, there must be assurance that there are ample body reserves of those substances whose storage is known to be favorable to the best development, such as calcium and vitamin A and a certain amount of subcutaneous fat. Growth at a good rate is characteristic of the well-nourished child, but true progress can only be determined by weight and height records over considerable periods of time. And it is not enough that a child carry a certain number of pounds for his height. He may still be flabby and pale, with poor teeth and bad skin, his only nutritional virtue being his subcutaneous fat.

Children's energy needs are so high that it is difficult for some children to accumulate any reserve of fuel in the form of body fat, and when they do, it is usually used up in the next spurt of growth in height. In the process of growth the body must store materials having energy value. A deficiency of calories only will result in stunting, even if all other dietary essentials are adequately supplied. This can be demonstrated by means of laboratory animals. In Figure 23–3 is shown a young male rat and its litter brother. The upper one was allowed just two thirds as many calories as the lower one, but the two diets furnished both animals with adequate amounts of all other dietary essentials. In nine weeks on the restricted diet the one rat made no significant gain in weight although it was very lively and gave every appearance of being in good health, while the other grew steadily. When the stunted animal was changed to the full ration, it doubled its weight in a single week and continued to gain at a rapid rate until it attained the same weight as its brother.

A young child with little adipose tissue is an easy prey to malnutrition; hence it is better for every growing child to have a little surplus rather than to be underweight for his build. Tables and charts to judge desirable

FIGURE 23–3. THE EFFECT OF RESTRICTING CALORIES ONLY IS SHOWN IN THESE TWO ANIMALS. Both are the same age. The upper one had only two thirds as many calories per day as the lower one.

weight of children will be found in the Appendix. The less easily a child fattens, the greater the need to feed him liberally so that sufficient calories may always be available to sustain any spurt of growth. While some underweight children are baffling problems, the majority of them respond to an improvement in their mode of life, including an adequate diet; the others should be under the care of physicians, either privately or at child welfare clinics, so that the fundamental causes of their physical inadequacy may be skillfully investigated and as far as possible removed.

THE CAUSES OF UNDERNUTRITION

In a study of the individual food consumption of a group of healthy and presumably well-fed girls from 10 to 12 years of age,[15] living in the same house and eating at the same table, great variation was found in the amount eaten from day to day. This was especially true in regard to the dinners. By weighing each girl's food for a number of days it was discovered that the greatest single cause of this variation was the presence or absence of milk in the menu. Within a month, 61 dinners weighed on days when milk was not given as a beverage averaged 619 calories, while 23 dinners when milk was supplied averaged 1,038 calories, an increase of 68 per cent. The study also showed that if the main dish and the

[15] Rose, M. S., and Gray, C. E. *Relation of Diet to Health and Growth of Children in Institutions.* Child Development Monograph No. 2. New York: Bureau of Publications, Teachers College, Columbia University (1930).

dessert both happened to be low in calories, when no milk was furnished a dinner might have only half as many calories as the one the next day. The ease with which two people sitting at the same table can vary their food intake is shown by the two breakfasts from the same menu in Table 23–3.

TABLE 23-3. TWO BREAKFASTS FROM THE SAME MENU

Food	Breakfast I		Breakfast II	
	Measure	Calories	Measure	Calories
Orange	$\frac{1}{2}$	38	1	75
Sugar	None	0	4 tsp	60
Corn flakes	$\frac{1}{2}$ cup	41	$\frac{3}{4}$ cup	62
Milk	$\frac{1}{3}$ cup	53	$\frac{1}{2}$ cup	80
Toast	1 slice	60	2 slices	120
Butter	$\frac{1}{2}$ tbsp	50	1 tbsp	100
Coffee	1 cup black	0	With 2 tbsp light cream	60
		242		557

If one trusts solely to inclination, how much one eats depends in part on the attractiveness of the food. Some people on low incomes and without vigorous appetites may find that the monotony of the diet gives little inducement to eat.

Children often suffer from underweight due to unhappiness and nervousness caused by an unfavorable home atmosphere. Emotional excitement may increase the energy expenditure, while at the same time the environment and the character of the diet may tend to decrease appetite. The result is inevitably a discrepancy between energy intake and output, and the child loses weight. Such children improve amazingly in regard to food consumption and body weight when changed to a more favorable environment.

Psychological factors play a large part in determining the food intake of children. This was clearly demonstrated in studies of children observed while eating in their own homes, reported by the University of Chicago.[16] This survey included 50 farm children, 100 city children from comfortable or well-to-do homes, and 100 children from a poor section of Chicago. Everything that happened during at least one meal in each home was recorded—the foods served, the amounts eaten, the time required, the part played in the meal by adults present, etc. In the farm group, only one third showed unwillingness to eat, while of the 100 children in the well-to-do group, two thirds showed varying degrees of

[16] Martin, E. A. *Roberts' Nutrition Work with Children*, 3rd ed., p. 135. Chicago: U. Chicago (1954).

resistance to eating, 40 of them requiring constant coaxing and taking long periods of time to complete the meal. Of the 100 children from the poorer section of the city, only 14 were classified as "nonhungry" and only five of these were described as being extremely so. Psychological factors were noted as the chief cause of the failures in the well-to-do group in view of the fact that their diets were superior as to types of food served and spacing of the meals, medical and dental care was adequate, and sleep and play were well regulated. In the other two groups psychological factors were favorable—the children ate with other hungry members of the family rather than alone. The parents were busy either serving or eating and there was a minimum of coaxing to eat. Although physical factors undoubtedly played some part in creating the eating problems encountered, it was felt that in the great majority of these cases psychological factors played the predominant part.

Another common cause of inadequate appetite and undernutrition is fatigue. In response to a questionnaire several hundred college women gave this as the commonest cause of failure of appetite in their own personal experience. In young children fatigue is undoubtedly very frequently responsible for reduced food intake, and probably affects in other ways the efficient use of food by the body. Children need to be carefully watched as regards the time spent in sleep and rest and to be safeguarded against playing to the point of exhaustion.

Many times loss of appetite is due to some physical defect or disease: enlarged tonsils and adenoids, interfering with full respiration; infected teeth and tonsils, constantly poisoning the body; and latent infectious diseases are among the common causes of undernutrition reported by child health clinics. Still another cause of poor appetite may be too low an intake of thiamine. This vitamin functions as a regulator of both appetite and intestinal motility.

Sometimes attempts to gain weight are discouraging because the person's digestive system is unequal to the new demands abruptly made upon it. Increases should not be too sudden. The girl who learned that peanut butter was high in calories and proceeded to dispose of about half a pound (1,300 calories) a day in addition to her regular diet came quickly to grief because she had given her alimentary tract a task to which it was unaccustomed. It is not enough to know only how much energy is needed; we must also know how to furnish it so as to prevent disturbances of digestion. Since fat is our most concentrated form of fuel, it has to be used with discretion, or digestion may be disturbed and we will defeat our own ends. Carbohydrate in the form of sugar is most attractive, but sugar blunts appetite unless carefully managed. Mrs. Squeers of Dotheboys Hall knew this, for she gave treacle (molasses) to her wretched protégés "partly because it spoils their appetites and comes cheaper than breakfast and dinner."

The exact number of calories that any person will require to induce gain in weight cannot be determined definitely in advance, but must be gauged by watching the scales. Those who do not fatten easily need all the more to learn to live on a high nutritional plane and safeguard themselves against serious undernutrition.

The low-calorie, low-protein diet to which almost 75 per cent of the world's people are subject and the abundant diet to which the majority of people in the United States are accustomed present a contrast which must be kept in mind. Many times family groups seem to adjust to a state of undernutrition and do survive for long periods of time. However, this adaptation may mask a very unstable equilibrium which can be upset by any stress.

REFERENCES

Bullen, B. A., Monello, L. F., Cohen, H., and Mayer, J. "Attitudes Toward Physical Activity, Food and Family in Obese and Nonobese Adolescent Girls." *Amer. J. Clin. Nutr.*, **12**:1 (1963).

Cooper, L. F., Barber, E. M., Mitchell, H. S., Rynbergen, H. J., and Greene, J. *Nutrition in Health and Disease*, 14th ed. Philadelphia: Lippincott (1963).

Egan, M. C. "The Obese Child—A Challenge." *School Lunch J.*, **18**:44 (1964).

Eppright, E. S., Swanson, P., and Iverson, C. A. (eds.). *Weight Control.* Iowa City: Iowa State College P. (1955).

Halpern, S. L. (ed.). "Recent Advances in Applied Nutrition: II. Symposium on Obesity." *Med. Clin. North America*, **48**:1283 (1965).

Irwin, M. H. K. *Overweight a Problem for Millions.* Public Affairs Pamphlet No. 364. New York: Public Affairs Committee, Inc. (1964).

Jolliffe, N. (ed.). *Clinical Nutrition*, Chaps. 4 and 26. New York: Hoeber (1962).

Jolliffe, N. *Reduce and Stay Reduced.* New York: Simon (1963).

Keys, A. "Calorie Undernutrition and Starvation, with Notes on Protein Deficiency." *Handbook of Nutrition*, 2nd ed., Chap. 19. Chicago: American Medical Association (1951).

Martin, E. A. *Roberts' Nutrition Work with Children*, 3rd ed., Chaps. 2–9. Chicago: U. of Chicago (1954).

Shank, R. E. "Weight Reduction and Its Significance." *Nutr. Rev.*, **19**:289 (1961).

U.S. Department of Agriculture. *Food and Your Weight.* Washington, D.C.: Home and Garden Bulletin No. 74 (1960).

Wohl, M. G., and Goodhart, R. S. *Modern Nutrition in Health and Disease*, Chap. 31A. Wohl, M. G. "Obesity"; 31B. Mont, F. G. "Undernutrition." Philadelphia: Lea (1964).

Wyden, P. *The Overweight Society.* New York: Morrow (1965).

Young, C. M. "Comments on the Obesities." *J. Amer. Dietet. A.*, **45**:134 (1964).

≤ **24** ≥

Food Needs of Mothers and Babies

The baby owes nothing at all to his parents. He has no responsibilities, no duties. The parents owe everything to the baby. Their responsibility to him is complete. Their duties are endless. They are most solemnly bound to use every effort to keep him in good health and happy, to build up his constitution to fit him for the world, and to launch him upon the world. In time their responsibility lessens but it never disappears; whatever happens, it cannot end. In other words, we are bound to see that children are given the best opportunity to develop to the limit of their growth capacity.

If we accept this statement by Arnold Bennett as the modern baby's bill of rights, we are solemnly bound to apply all the accumulated knowledge in regard to the nutrition of the growing organism to the problem of feeding the baby.

Good nutrition for the infant begins with the mother. During prenatal life growth goes on at a rate never equaled after birth. The profound effect of diet on the well-being of the fetus has been repeatedly demonstrated in the case of laboratory animals, and observations on human beings reveal similar effects.

The Relation of Nutrition to Reproduction

The earliest convincing evidence we have of the influence of the nutrition of the mother during the prenatal period is that reported by Ebbs, Tisdall, and Scott.[1] They studied during the last three to four months of pregnancy 380 low-income women who had planned on being confined in the Toronto General Hospital. Those who were found to be on a poor diet were divided into two groups, one being continued on the poor diet as a control group and the other receiving supplementary foods to improve the quality of the diet. Those who were

[1] Ebbs, J. H., Tisdall, F. F., and Scott, W. A. "The Influence of Prenatal Diet on the Mother and Child." *J. Nutr.*, **22**:515 (1941).

found to be already on moderately good diets made up the third group, and their diets were improved through education only. The mothers on the good or supplemented diets enjoyed better health, had fewer complications, and proved to be better obstetrical risks. They had fewer miscarriages, stillbirths, and premature births, and a lower incidence of illness in the babies up to six months, as well as fewer deaths resulting from these illnesses.

Several similar studies followed this one of Ebbs and his associates. In 1942, and 1946, a committee of the People's League of Health of England reported the results of investigating the influence of the nutrition of expectant and nursing mothers on maternal and infant mortality and morbidity in a group of about 5,000 English women. Fifty per cent of them received supplements of mineral elements and vitamins, while the other 50 per cent continued on their own diets. The incidence of toxemia was 30 per cent lower in the group receiving the supplements, and premature births were markedly reduced.

In 1943 and 1949 Burke, Stuart, and their associates reported the results of carefully planned studies of 216 women attending the prenatal clinics at the Boston Lying-in Hospital. Detailed studies of the nutritional status of the women were made at intervals during pregnancy, and the physical condition of the infants at birth and within the first two weeks of life was carefully assessed. A significant relationship was found between the physical condition of the infant and the diet during pregnancy. Premature births, stillbirths, and neonatal deaths occurred much less frequently among the women on good diets than among those on poor diets. The infants born to the mothers on poor diets averaged less in weight and were shorter in length, and the majority of the infants born with congenital defects were found in this group. In the paper published in 1949 further studies of the diets of the 216 women were reported. It was found that the women showed little change in food habits in subsequent pregnancies, which probably means that in the majority these were the food habits not only during pregnancy but of long-time duration.

In 1944 Balfour reported a study of 20,000 women in the lowest income groups in England and Wales. It was found that supplements of yeast in one group and of vitamins A and D, calcium, phosphorus, and iron in another resulted in significant advantage to the infants as compared with those born to the women receiving no supplements. Stillbirth and neonatal death rates were significantly lower in the groups receiving the supplements.

Toverud, in 1945, reported from Oslo a study of about 1,000 women who, in a program of prenatal care, were given guidance as to their diet during pregnancy. She found a close correlation between the diet, the course of pregnancy, and also the condition of the newborn infant. The stillbirth rate in this supervised group during the years 1939 to

1944 averaged 16 per thousand live births, while for the city of Oslo it was 30 per thousand, and the neonatal death rate of this group was 11 per thousand compared to 20 per thousand for the city of Oslo.

The effects of severe food restrictions in some of the countries of Europe during World War II have been reported by several investigators. In the rationing program of England special attention was given to the diet of pregnant women in the lower income groups because it was known that previous to the war their diet was poorer than that of the average adult. Additional milk, eggs, and vitamin supplements were allowed for all pregnant women. In 1946 Sutherland reported that a study of stillbirth rates in England and Wales for the years 1928 through 1944 showed a sharp drop after the introduction of rationing and that the drop was most marked in the poorest economic districts. The neonatal death rate also declined but not as much as the stillbirth rate. Baird in Scotland found a similar drop in the stillbirth rate during the wartime rationing.

Smith, working in Holland, where, due to the war, severe famine conditions existed during the winter of 1944 and spring of 1945, found that about 50 per cent of the women suffered from amenorrhea and that this condition disappeared shortly after the return of sufficient food. Birth weight of infants born at full term decreased sharply during the famine months along with a significant drop in birth length. Both birth weight and birth length improved after the end of the starvation period.

Antonov, working in Leningrad during the siege of the city in 1942, found that during the first half of the period the stillbirth rate rose to 5.6 per cent, or double the normal figure, the premature births rose to 41.2 per cent, an unusually high figure, and neonatal deaths to 21.2 per cent, also unusually high.

The normal physiological changes in pregnancy have been followed in the long-range, comprehensive Vanderbilt Cooperative Study of Maternal and Infant Nutrition. Darby and his associates[2] emphasize from their observations on a total obstetrical clinic population that, rather than advising pharmaceutical supplements, in many cases the physician might better give simple dietary instruction to his patients to be sure that they are meeting the dietary allowances recommended by the National Research Council.

Stearns[3] presented a report at a symposium on "Nutrition in Pregnancy" in 1957 in which she expressed concern for the adolescent girl whose ignorance of food values and desire for a slender figure often

[2] McGanity, W. J., Bridgforth, E. B., and Darby, W. J. "Vanderbilt Cooperative Study of Maternal and Infant Nutrition." *J. Amer. Med. A.*, **168**:2138 (1958).

[3] Stearns, G. "Nutritional State of the Mother Prior to Conception." Symposium IV, Council on Foods and Nutrition. Chicago: American Medical Association (1957).

make her refuse nutritious food at home while eating nonnutritious snacks with her peers.

Stearns conducted a metabolic study to determine whether undernourished girls could absorb and store nutrients adequately if a very good diet was followed during pregnancy. The subjects, aged 13 to 30 years, were illegitimately pregnant. Throughout the age range the poorly nourished girls were able to absorb and retain nutrients as well as those who were previously better nourished. Therefore, it would appear that pregnancy increases the ability to utilize and store essential nutrients. The adverse effect of emotional distress was noted. The subject most emotionally disturbed over her situation throughout the study lost calcium continuously. Although less striking, the losses of nitrogen and phosphorus were marked. Stearns states, "If the young pregnant woman remains emotionally stable and ingests a good diet, she is in an excellent position both to improve her own nutritional status and produce a sturdy full-term infant. Obviously, the earlier in pregnancy her nutritional habits can be improved, the better for both her infant and herself."

A number of studies by other workers have shown similar results, leaving no doubt as to the importance of good nutrition during pregnancy. The proper time to begin to improve the diet of the mother is in her own childhood so that she may come to womanhood with her body well developed and at all times in an optimal state of nutrition. Then the diet of pregnancy need differ only in certain details from that to which she has been accustomed.

Controversy over the desirable weight gain during pregnancy has continued over a period of years. In the United States since the 1920's, and in other countries more recently, obstetricians have tended to limit the weight gain of the expectant mother through diet. In this connection recent studies made in Scotland are of interest. Hytten,[4] of the Obstetric Medicine Research Unit at the University of Aberdeen, Scotland, presented data on weight gain of women who were unrestricted in caloric intake during pregnancy. The mean total gain in a "normal" first pregnancy was found to be 27.5 lb (12.5 kg), or about 1 lb per week in the last two trimesters. The components of this average increase in weight are shown in Figure 24–1. In general this mean weight gain was associated with the best reproductive performance of the women observed.

Nutrition Before Birth

Pregnancy is a period of growth and the diet must be relatively rich in all growth-promoting substances. There need be, however, no

[4] Hytten, F. E. "Nutritional Aspects of Foetal Growth," p. 59, *Nutrition*, Proceedings of the 6th International Congress, Edinburgh, 1963. London: Livingstone (1964).

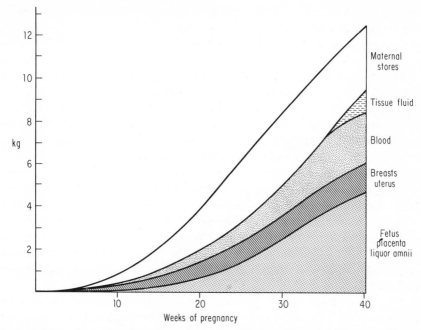

FIGURE 24–1. THE AVERAGE INCREASE OF WEIGHT DURING NORMAL PREG-
NANCY AND ITS COMPONENTS. (*Reproduced by permission of Dr. F. E. Hytten
from "Proceedings of the Sixth International Congress of Nutrition." Edinburgh: Livingston [1964].*)

marked increase in the total energy value of the diet until the second
and third trimesters. The gain in weight of the fetus is at first scarcely
more than 1 gm per day. By the sixth month it is about 10 gm per day,
but about one half of the weight of the newborn is acquired during the
last eight weeks before birth.

Studies of the basal metabolism throughout the gestation period show
that it is only in the last three or four months that the metabolism of the
fetus and the increased weight of the mother (amounting to about 20
to 27 lb) have any noteworthy effect on the total energy requirement of
the mother. Elevation of the basal metabolism at term has been reported
by various workers as amounting to 15 to 30 per cent. See Tables A–1
and A–5 for the Recommended Daily Allowances for pregnant women.

For the construction of new body tissue there must be available all
essential amino acids; hence the quality of the protein of the diet is
important. The storage of mineral elements increases as the fetus develops. The tables of recommended allowances show the increases in
these nutrients that should be made in the second and third trimesters.

The teeth are all under construction before birth. They begin to form
by the third month, and at birth all the 20 teeth of the first set are
inside the jaw and their crowns are almost completely calcified. Their

normal development depends not only on mineral elements (especially calcium and phosphorus), but also on conditions favorable to the utilization of these elements which are ensured by liberal amounts of vitamins A, D, and ascorbic acid.

The thyroid gland is especially active in pregnancy, and if the mother has been living on a narrow margin of safety in regard to iodine, the gland may enlarge in an effort to perform its functions without an adequate supply. In areas where goiter is endemic attention should be given to the iodine supply throughout pregnancy to prevent goiter in the baby as well as in the mother. As pointed out in Chapter 11, the use of iodized table salt is one of the best means of ensuring sufficient iodine.

During pregnancy the mother must eliminate the waste products from the unborn child in addition to those from her own body, and it is important that this be facilitated by a relatively large proportion of liquids. At least 2 qt of fluid may be taken daily. One quart may be milk and, of the remainder, a considerable part may well be the citrus juices. Although fresh whole milk is desirable, milk powder or evaporated milk may take its place.

The diet will also need to be more laxative than usual. Liberal amounts of fresh fruits and green leafy vegetables, with whole-wheat bread and whole-grain breakfast foods, are beneficial at this time, not only for their laxative effect but for the mineral elements and vitamins. Care should be taken in the selection of these foods to secure a liberal supply of vitamin A, thiamine, ascorbic acid, and riboflavin. In addition to a well-regulated diet, the prospective mother may well spend several hours each day out of doors exposed to bright sunshine if possible. The diet of the pregnant woman cannot safely be left to chance. Many women are in a state of undernutrition at the beginning of pregnancy and may require a considerable increase in energy-yielding, body-building, and regulating foods. This is particularly true for the expectant mother between 16 and 19 years of age.

The dietary essentials recommended by the National Research Council (1963) (see Table A–1 in Appendix) will be provided if the following foods are included daily during the second and third trimester:

1 qt of milk (part of this can be evaporated or the equivalent in milk powder).

5 oz of lean cooked meat, fish, poultry, or meat alternate. Use liver or other glandular meat at least once each week.

1 egg daily.

6 to 8 oz of orange juice plus one or more servings of fresh fruit.

1 serving (½ cup) of a dark-green or deep-yellow vegetable.

2 servings of other vegetables such as potato, tomato, cabbage, pepper, broccoli, peas, Brussels sprouts, and green beans.

1 serving of whole-grain, restored, or enriched cereal.

2 to 3 slices of whole-grain or enriched bread.

Other foods, including butter or fortified margarine, salad oil, more vegetables, salad greens, fruits (dried or fresh), bread and cereal, etc., to make up the necessary calories.

A source of vitamin D; vitamin D milk or a fish-liver-oil concentrate according to physician's instructions.

Nutrition of the Nursing Mother

When the baby is born, the demand on the mother for nourishment does not cease; it merely takes another form and continues to increase with the growth of the child. The secretion of the mammary gland is wonderfully adapted to the needs of the baby. With instruction every well-nourished mother should be able to nurse her baby. But it is not to be expected that a mother may entirely overcome bad habits of diet throughout all her previous life in a few days or weeks after lactation has begun. Preparation for lactation begins in pregnancy, and adequate nutrition throughout the gestation period should enable a mother to meet more successfully the strain of lactation. At the Vanderbilt University outpatient clinic it was found that 71 per cent of the mothers were breast-feeding their infants. It was also found that more of the mothers who were taking at least three glasses of milk per day were able to nurse their babies.

Quantitatively, the demands on the mother grow greater day by day. Nutrient needs for milk production must be secured from the food eaten by the mother, or else taken from the reserves of her own body. Often mothers lose weight during the lactating period or fail to produce milk to full capacity because of insufficient food. See Tables A-1 and A-5 (Appendix) for the Recommended Daily Allowances for lactation.

The daily foods for lactation are the same as those for pregnancy (see page 386) except that vegetables and fruits are used more liberally, and larger amounts of bread and other foods of the mother's own choice are recommended to raise the calorie intake to the higher level demanded by lactation. A well-nourished mother must have not only the food required to maintain herself, but in addition the equivalent of the food material given to the baby as milk every day.

The Breast-Fed and Bottle-Fed Baby

In the sixteenth century mothers were advised not to wean their children until they had all their teeth. In many developing countries in different parts of the world it is still desirable for mothers to nurse their babies for long periods. According to Gopalan and Belavady,[5] in the poor communities in South India, 50 per cent of the babies were still breast-fed at 18 months of age. One child in every five was breast-fed beyond two years, and one child in eight was still breast-fed at the age of two and one-half years. Today in the United States it is usual to wean a baby before it is a year old.

The normal child of the well-nourished mother, although requiring constant and intelligent care, should not be a nutritional problem. Nature provides the ideal nourishment in the secretion of the mammary gland, which in response to the sucking of the child yields nutriment proportional to that demand. The vigorous child thus assures his own supply; the delicate child may be the victim of insufficient food because he cannot "work his way" so well. Today such infants are helped along by manual stimulation of the gland.

It is usually best to give the baby the benefit of his mother's milk, if possible, through the first six to nine months of his life. If the supply of mother's milk is not quite sufficient, it may be supplemented in part with bottle feeding. Fortunately, most babies thrive on artificial feeding alone, and mothers do not need to worry if this is necessary.

No matter how strong our convictions as to the importance for the baby of breast feeding through the major portion of the first year, we cannot shut our eyes to the fact that circumstances may arise that make the substitution of some other form of nourishment imperative. We should therefore be prepared to deal intelligently with such emergencies.

One of the special problems of artificial feeding in infancy is that of making the diet sufficiently easy to digest. The selection of foods that will meet all the quantitative requirements, the arrangement of the feeding schedule, the way in which the meals are prepared and fed, in fact the whole daily regime of the baby must have the most careful consideration.

An excellent foundation for the artificially fed baby's diet is pasteurized cow's milk of the best quality or its equivalent of evaporated (unsweetened) milk. Sample formulas are given in Table 24–1.

The milk-carbohydrate-water mixture must be prepared carefully by measure each day and divided among the feeding bottles which represent the number of feedings to be given in 24 hours. As a rule, the interval between meals should not be less than three hours, and after a baby is three months old (if not sooner) may be lengthened to four hours. Cool boiled water should be given between feedings, as the baby's water needs are high. Whatever the schedule decided upon, it should be adhered to as long as it makes for a happy baby.

[5] Gopalan, C., and Belavady, B. "Nutrition and Lactation." *Nutrition in Maternal and Infant Feeding.* Panel IV, p. 14. Washington, D.C.: Fifth International Congress on Nutrition (1960).

TABLE 24–1. SAMPLE FORMULAS*

	First Formula	Later Formulas	
Evaporated milk	6 oz	10 oz	13 oz
Water (boiled)	10 oz	15 oz	19 oz
Sugar or corn syrup	1½ tbsp	2½ tbsp	3 tbsp
		or	
Fresh whole milk (boiled)	12 oz	20 oz	26 oz
Water (boiled)	4 oz	6 oz	6 oz
Sugar or corn syrup	1½ tbsp	2½ tbsp	2 tbsp

* *Infant Care.* Children's Bureau Publication No. 8. Washington, D.C.: U.S. Department of Health, Education, and Welfare, (1963). The directions for preparation of the formula will be found on pages 90 to 98.

There are on the market proprietary infant formulas which have been used widely with success. However, one should consult a pediatrician for advice in the selection of a suitable preparation.

The digestive tract of a baby is delicate and has a great deal of work to do because of the relatively high food needs of this period of very rapid growth. An upset means loss of food that can ill be spared and disturbance of the tract itself, which may lead to irritability, acute indigestion, or, if long continued, chronic malnutrition. When intervals between meals are neither too short nor too long, the intervals of rest for the stomach will aid appetite and digestion. A mother (especially with her first child) will benefit from the advice of a physician. Every day is significant in a little baby's life, and expert supervision makes possible the finest adjustment of the daily program to the needs of the greatest individualist in the world—the baby.

Without adequate rest, growth is impossible. The newborn child sleeps the greater part of the 24-hour day, and by the end of a year may sleep 14 hours or more a day.

Fresh air is the best of tonics, and the necessity for sunshine has been pointed out in the discussion of vitamin D and rickets in Chapter 15. Since babies in the temperate zone, especially if born in the fall, are liable to rickets, they should have a supplementary source of vitamin D within the first two weeks. Cod-liver oil has been satisfactorily used starting with a few drops and gradually increasing the amount to 1 tsp at the end of three months and to 2 tsp by the end of the first year. However, some physicians prefer to recommend a concentrate, and it is desirable to obtain their advice.

Either mother's or bottled milk should also be supplemented by ascorbic acid since liberal amounts of this vitamin are favorable to the development of the teeth and protect against subacute scurvy. For this purpose a teaspoon of strained orange juice (frozen, fresh, or canned) diluted with water, or two of tomato juice is most suitable, and may be introduced in the second week, between two feedings. Vitamin C is also available in the form of ascorbic acid drops and may be given on the advice of a physician.

Introducing Solid Foods

In essence, the problem of planning a diet for a baby is not very different from that of planning a diet for any growing child. There is the same need of an adequate supply of calories; of protein, with growth-sustaining amino acids; of an assortment of mineral elements and vitamins, each suitable in amount for rapid growth; and of a liberal supply of water. The relatively high requirements for mineral elements and vitamins have already been discussed in detail in earlier chapters.

The period of weaning, as discussed in Chapter 8, can be a nutritionally disastrous one for infants in developing countries, if precautions are not taken (see Figure 24–2). In the United States, preparation for weaning starts early, and the baby should be accustomed gradually to the foods that are to be his diet. The first supplements to milk given especially for vitamins C and D have been discussed above, and they should be continued along with the introduction of solid foods. If vitamin D milk is used, a quart will meet the recommended allowance of vitamin D. The milk will also furnish a generous supply of protein of excellent quality, calcium, riboflavin, and preformed vitamin A. However, the iron will be too low and the thiamine will also need supplementation.

The first solid food to be introduced into the diet may well be an iron-and-thiamine-bearing cereal food, especially prepared for infants. This can be started sometime within one to four months. It is recognized that a full-term, well-nourished infant has a reserve supply of iron for the first six months and a requirement from then on of about 8 mg per day for optimal hemoglobin concentration. Since the cereal must be introduced very gradually, it is desirable to begin giving the cereal at least by the third or fourth month. The main object at this time is to establish the habit of eating and enjoying cereals. When the habit is well established, the quantity can easily be increased to 4 or 5 tbsp by the seventh month. The canned cereal foods for infants may be used.

When the cereal food has been well established, strained fruits and vegetables can be added one at a time, starting with not more than a teaspoon and increasing gradually to 1 to 2 tbsp. Sometimes the fruit pulp is given as the first solid food instead of cereal, depending on what seems to agree best with the baby. It is important that the baby enjoys his food and that it agrees with him. Egg yolk can be started between

FIGURE 24–2. DIET SUPPLEMENT. Uganda infant at Mulago hospital is fed supplementary mixture (mashed banana or plantain, with dried skim milk and mashed peanuts or beans) which has been steamed in a plantain leaf. UNICEF encourages and assists governments of the less developed countries in health education programs such as this. (*UNICEF Photo by Peter Larsen.*)

the third and fifth months in very small amounts to be sure that it is well tolerated. Then strained canned meats such as beef and liver can be given, again in small amounts. When several teeth have erupted, a crust of bread, Zwieback, or crackers may be given to start training in mastication.

Many babies are ready for a meal plan such as the one that follows between the sixth and eighth months.

Breakfast: cereal, egg, milk (orange juice).
Midmorning: orange juice if not given at breakfast.
Noon meal: vegetables, meat, milk.
Midafternoon: milk, crusty bread or crackers.
Evening meal: cereal, fruit, milk.

The baby can be offered liquids from a cup about this time.

If there should be a tendency to constipation, a little prune juice can be mixed with the orange juice. The best way to determine whether the total calories are sufficient is by study of the weekly weight record to see whether good progress is made. If a baby does not gain at a steady rate, a pediatrician should be consulted.

In general, one of the best means of checking on the continued health of the young infant is to observe his progress in growth starting with his weight at birth (see Figure 24–3). The growth pattern is an individual one for each infant, the chief criterion being a steady increase in weight and height throughout the first year. Infants vary in these increases. Growth charts showing gains in weight and height from birth to six years of age are found in Figures A–1 and A–2 in the Appendix.

FIGURE 24–3. NURSE-MID-WIFE WEIGHS NEWBORN GHANA BABY IN NET SCALE (part of UNICEF kit). (*UNICEF Photo by Bernheim.*)

Every mother should have at least one handbook on child care. Publication No. 8 of the Children's Bureau entitled *Infant Care*, listed among the references at the end of this chapter, is strongly recommended. Advice from a physician expert in the care of babies or a pediatrician should be secured either privately or at a well-baby clinic or other health center. It pays to take the best possible care to start the baby right and to foster from the beginning those habits which promote health and vigor. The reward will come partly in the present, in a healthy, happy baby who is a delight instead of a worry, but more in the future when to the grown man or woman, the full reward comes in the enjoyment of a vigorous adult life and deferred old age.

REFERENCES

Berry, K., and Wiehl, D. G. "An Experiment in Diet Education During Pregnancy." *Milbank Mem. Fund Quart.*, **30**:119 (1952).

Burke, B. S. "Maternal Nutrition and Other Factors of Importance to the Fetus and Mother as Shown by Dietary Histories." *Currents in Nutrition.* New York: National Vitamin Foundation (1950).

Burke, B. S., and Stuart, H. C. "Nutritional Requirements During Pregnancy and Lactation." *Handbook of Nutrition*, 2nd ed., Chap. 15. Chicago: American Medical Association (1951).

Children's Bureau, Social Security Administration, U.S. Department of Health, Education, and Welfare. *Nutrition and Healthy Growth* (1963).

———. Publication No. 4. *Prenatal Care* (1962); Publication No. 8. *Infant Care* (1963).

Council on Foods and Nutrition. *Infant Nutrition*. Symposium No. 7. Chicago: American Medical Association (1961).

Fleck, H., and Munves, E. *Introduction to Nutrition*, Chap. 25. New York: Macmillan (1962).

Food and Nutrition Section and Maternal and Child Health Section, American Public Health Association. "Some Practical Considerations of Economy and Efficiency in Infant Feeding." *Amer. J. Pub. Health*, **52**:125 (1962).

Food—The Yearbook of Agriculture, 1959. Macy, I. C., and Kelly, H. J. "Food for Expectant and Nursing Mothers," p. 273. Washington, D.C.: U.S. Department of Agriculture.

Harrell, R. F., Woodyard, E., and Gates, A. I. "The Effect of Mothers' Diets on the Intelligence of Offspring." New York: Bureau of Publications, Teachers College, Columbia University (1955).

Holt, L. E., Jr., McIntosh, R., and Barnett, H. *Holt's Pediatrics*, 13th ed. New York: Appleton (1962).

Jeans, P. C. "Feeding of Healthy Infants and Children." *Handbook of Nutrition*, 2nd ed., Chap. 14. Chicago: American Medical Association (1951).

Jeans, P. C., Wright, F., and Blake, F. *Essentials of Pediatrics*, 7th ed. Philadelphia: Lippincott (1963).

Jelliffe, D. B. *Infant Nutrition in the Subtropics and Tropics*. Geneva: World Health Organization (1955).

Jelliffe, D. B., and Bennett, F. J. *Health Education of the Tropical Mother in Feeding Her Young Child*. Washington, D.C.: U.S. Department of Health, Education, and Welfare, Children's Bureau (1964).

Meyer, H. F. "New Ways to Feed the Baby." *Today's Health*, p. 49 (June 1965).

National Research Council. *Recommended Dietary Allowances*. Publication 1146. Washington, D.C. (1964).

Taylor, C. M. *Food Values in Shares and Weights in Common Servings*, 2nd ed. New York: Macmillan (1959).

Toverud, K. U., Stearns, G., and Macy, I. G. *Maternal Nutrition and Child Health*. Washington, D.C.: National Research Council, Bulletin No. 123 (1950).

25

Food Needs of Preschool and Kindergarten Children

No child ever had as good a chance of being well born as one coming into the world in the twentieth century. Down to the nineteenth century babies seemed born to die, for at least a quarter of them failed to survive the perilous first year. But today in the United States the death rate in the first year of life has dropped to only a small fraction of that reported at the beginning of the century. However, in crowded city areas and among certain groups in the United States there is still room for improvement. Recent legislation under Public Law 89–97 provides for additional health services for children about to enter school, as well as school children, particularly in areas with concentrations of low-income families.

Unfortunately, many children in developing countries do not fare so well. Teply, Chief of Applied Nutrition, of UNICEF states that in the one-to-four-year-old age group the mortality rates are up to 40 times as high in developing countries as in the developed countries. He also states that "There are three salient facts about the pre-school child in developing countries: (1) he belongs to the most vulnerable age group with respect to certain physical and social needs; (2) he is in the age group which is being reached least effectively; and (3) for the most part he is not able to understand and articulate his needs."[1] Programs including supplemental meals demonstrate the importance of certain foods for children. An illustration of an experimental meal being given to preschool children in Burma under the direction of Mary Ross, FAO nutritionist, will be observed in Figure 25–1.

Now that sanitary science has conquered many children's diseases in the United States and made the food supply safe, the application of our present knowledge of nutrition is more important than ever, to ensure to these "saved" babies normal growth from birth to maturity and at-

[1] Teply, L. J. "Nutritional Needs of the Pre-School Child." *Nutr. Rev.*, **22**:65 (1964).

FIGURE 25–1. A DAY NURSERY SCHOOL IN RANGOON WHERE THE BENEFICIAL EFFECT OF ADDING FISH FLOUR TO THE NOON MEAL IS BEING TESTED. (*Courtesy of FAO.*)

tainment of such physical vigor as will make their adult years long and fruitful. "Where vitality exists," said Bertrand Russell, "there is pleasure in feeling alive. It makes it easy to take an interest in whatever occurs, and thus promotes objectivity, which is an essential of sanity. Vitality promotes interest in the outside world; it also promotes the power of hard work."

It will, however, take wide adoption of the modern principles of nutrition and carefully controlled observations covering many years to make an impressive demonstration of the improvement in human life that can be achieved by a good diet consistently eaten from birth to old age.

The One-Year-Old Child

A year-old baby of average weight will require from 1,000 to 1,200 or more calories per day, the precise amount varying according to body weight and amount of activity. The large, vigorous, active child will require more total food than the small, delicate, less strenuous one. The energy requirement from day to day cannot be foretold exactly; regular weighing of the child week by week and comparison of his rate of progress with normal growth averages are the best criteria of the adequacy of the food supply. But an approximation of the number of calories required is most useful in planning a good dietary, and such increases or decreases as may be necessary can be readily made. Every calorie must be chosen with regard to the growth-promoting substances it can furnish and the effect on the digestive tract. The best foundation for the diet at this age is milk (three to four glasses), as has been emphasized in Chapter 21. This amount of milk ensures adequate calcium and some other essential mineral elements, a good share of protein, vitamin A, thiamine, and riboflavin for growth, all in a form especially easy to assimilate. For ascorbic acid it is not wise to depend on the variable supply in fluid milk, but always to use some outstanding source such as orange juice or tomato juice, making a small quantity a regular part of the diet. Three to four ounces per day of orange juice is ample as a rule.

Egg and liver are desirable for their value in hemoglobin formation and their many other growth-promoting qualities, including excellent proteins, vitamin A, thiamine, and riboflavin. Lean meat, ground, may be used as an alternate to liver.

Pureed green vegetables should also be included, as a further source of iron and other mineral elements, vitamin A, thiamine, and riboflavin, and for the laxative properties. Spinach, asparagus tips, and peas are suitable, singly or in combination. Many varieties prepared especially for infants and young children are available in small jars. Finger foods such as carrot and celery strips, crackers, and various hard breads help to encourage the toddler's chewing habits.

A cereal food should be given, preferably one of the many varieties especially prepared for toddlers which are generally well reinforced with iron and thiamine. This can be served regularly twice a day if desired, from ¼ to ⅓ cup of the cooked cereal in the morning and another similar portion for supper is usually sufficient. Cooked vegetable or ready-to-eat cereal may be substituted now and then for cooked cereal in the evening meal. A small amount of baked potato is also a desirable selection, reinforcing the diet in regard to ascorbic acid, thiamine, and iron.

A little margarine or butter on the bread is permissible, but the butter fat in the whole milk makes much additional fat at this age undesirable. Generally a little prune pulp or apple pulp, sweetened with the merest trace of sugar, for the sake of palatability, can be used without making the diet too laxative. The prepared canned infant foods are a great help to a busy mother.

Vitamin D, the sunshine vitamin, is readily available in vitamin D milk, a quart furnishing the recommended daily allowance. It is well to consult the pediatrician to get his advice on additional amounts of vitamin D. He may wish to recommend a fish-liver-oil concentrate.

The diet as outlined above may be used with little change throughout the second year. Cereals may be given in larger quantities. The milk to drink should not be too cold. The quantity of bread may be increased and should be dry and hard. The egg may be continued, and vegetables should be increased to meet the child's demand.

Selecting from the foods that are regarded as best suited to a child of this age, menus such as the following can be planned.

A DAY'S MENUS FOR A ONE-YEAR-OLD CHILD

Breakfast
Orange juice, $\frac{1}{2}$ cup
Cereal, $\frac{1}{4}$ cup, with $\frac{1}{4}$ cup milk
Egg
Milk to drink, $\frac{3}{4}$ cup
Bread, $\frac{1}{2}$ slice, toasted, with $\frac{1}{2}$ tsp margarine or butter

Lunch
Liver, canned, strained, 2 tbsp (could be combined with potato)
Potato, baked, $\frac{1}{2}$ medium with 1 tbsp milk to moisten
Peas, strained, 3 to 4 tbsp
Milk to drink, $\frac{3}{4}$ cup
Bread, whole wheat, $\frac{1}{2}$ slice, toasted with $\frac{1}{2}$ tsp margarine or butter

Midafternoon snack
Milk to drink, 1 cup, and bread, $\frac{1}{4}$ slice or graham cracker

Supper
Cereal, $\frac{1}{4}$ cup, with $\frac{1}{4}$ cup milk
Prunes, strained, 2 tbsp
Milk to drink, $\frac{3}{4}$ cup
Bread, white, enriched, $\frac{1}{4}$ slice, toasted, with $\frac{1}{2}$ tsp butter or margarine
Source of vitamin D as recommended by physician

To determine whether or not a diet planned in this way is really adequate one may calculate the contribution of each food item as listed in the menus by referring to Tables A–4 or A–8 in the Appendix. The total of each nutrient in the diet can be compared with the recommended allowances for the one-year-old child found in Tables A–1 or A–5 and A–7 in the Appendix. A representative weight for a one-year-old child is about 10 to 12 kg (22 to 26 lb), and an allowance of 100 calories per kilogram will mean 1,000 to 1,200 calories for the day. A child weighing more than this or one who is very active may need more calories.

The toddler's diet must be administered with scrupulous care. Not only does this ensure immediate needs for growth, but it is also favorably setting eating patterns. Adequate rest is very important. The daily program should include a morning and an afternoon nap and about 12 hours of sleep at night.

Regularity of meals is desirable. This is easy to advise but very difficult to accomplish. Waiting beyond the regular mealtime is likely to bring many undesirable reactions such as irritability, fatigue, loss of appetite, or hurried eating.

The foods should be of the best quality, cautiously seasoned, and carefully prepared. By word and action, respect and enthusiasm for the foods should be subtly imparted. Always the constructive idea that each food is playing its part in building a healthy, happy child should be kept uppermost.

No child should be pitied because of his simple, wholesome diet. No diet is better than that which adequately supports the rapid growth of the early years, and there should be no suggestion of any other possibility than eating it cheerfully at the proper time. Food for the young child is not an amusement but serious business upon which his whole progress in life largely depends. It is not to be expected that all foods will be equally well received at first. New foods are new lessons. They should not be made too difficult. With very small portions at first a ready acceptance of many foods is best built up.

No food between meals should be the usual rule. Nothing is more ruinous to good appetite and good discipline than food at improper times.

Sweets should be withheld since they tend to pervert the appetite. Only the sugar that is necessary to make applesauce, junket, or other very simple milk puddings palatable should be used.

An interesting study of the seven-day food intake of 40 young children, nine months to two years, has been reported by Guthrie.[2] These children were patients of a practicing pediatrician in a college community in Pennsylvania. The daily intake for each child was compared with the Recommended Dietary Allowances for eight nutrients. Ascorbic acid and iron were found to be the nutrients most frequently inadequate. The food groups most often fed in amounts less than that recommended were the citrus fruits and dark-green or yellow vegetables. Twenty children consumed diets that met at least two thirds of all the nutrients calculated.

The Nursery School Child

Imitation plays a large part in the young child's life, and it is much easier for him to eat what is given him when others are doing

[2] Guthrie, H. A. "Nutritional Intake of Infants." *J. Amer. Dietet. A.*, **43**:120 (1963).

the same. Thousands of children have the opportunity of attending nursery schools, day care centers, play schools, or day camps. In the nursery school the usual age range is from two to four or five years.

When the children arrive in the morning they should have a drink of water. If they have breakfast early, they should have 3 to 4 oz of orange, tomato juice, or other fresh fruit or juice between 9:15 and 9:45 A.M., the amount depending on what they have had at home.

At the recommendation of the physician in charge, a desirable source of vitamin A and vitamin D may be given. If this is given regularly at home, it may not be needed at the school. There should be at all times the closest coordination between the home and school programs.

THE MIDDAY MEAL AT THE NURSERY SCHOOL

The noonday meal, taken at the school, affords an unusual opportunity for training in good eating habits. The food should be selected with the greatest care, since the school has considerable responsibility for the well-being of the children. The food must be apportioned as carefully as possible according to the requirements of the individual child, and yet the group spirit must be preserved. A dietitian expert in the training of children as well as in nutrition is essential to the greatest success and should have constant oversight during the meal. The ease with which children two to four years old (and sometimes even younger) can adapt themselves to the food regime of the school is abundant proof of the power of *esprit de corps*. Sitting at their tables with their teachers they eat together in the happiest fashion. Now and then some food seems more of a task than a little child can accomplish, but helped along by an encouraging word, or perhaps a lift with the spoon, the goal is won; or a wise teacher quietly lightens the task if in her judgment it is too great for the moment. It is highly important that anyone who supervises the children's meals have training in nutrition as well as in other phases of child care, so that the child's immediate food needs and his education may be properly related to each other. See Figure 25-2.

Day by day the nursery school menu must exemplify the best that is known in regard to child feeding. It affords education for parents as well as children. A good program for the noon meal will include:

1. *A vegetable.* Children of this age can be educated to a considerable choice of vegetables. While a great variety is not essential to their immediate growth, carrots, spinach, and peas being adequate, it is advisable for the convenience of the home and the future education of the child to widen the selection gradually so that he develops a liking for all wholesome food. A potato each day either at school or at home is desirable along with a raw vegetable such as carrot, tomato, or celery.

FIGURE 25-2. A CORNER OF THE NURSERY SCHOOL AT THE UNIVERSITY OF TENNESSEE SHOWING CHILDREN AT THEIR NOON MEAL. (*Courtesy of Department of Child Development and Family Relationships, University of Tennessee.*)

2. *A protein-rich food such as egg, liver, meat, poultry, or fish.* Liver is by far the best choice in meats and should be included once a week. If the egg is included in the breakfast or supper at home, another protein-rich food should be selected for the noon meal.

3. *A cup or a carton (8 oz) of milk.* This may be managed more easily by the children if a small cup is used and refilled.

4. *Bread.* Half to a whole slice or more of whole-wheat or enriched bread, depending on the child's appetite.

5. *A simple dessert.* This may be a fresh, canned, frozen, or dried fruit, or milk pudding or ice cream, which is always acceptable.

A rather definite pattern for meals helps a child to learn which foods are served together and he will form the habit of eating his vegetables with his egg or meat at the noon meal and his cereal for breakfast. When the appetite is good and there is a desire for more food, starting with small amounts of each food on the plate prevents a child from singling out any one food he likes and thus distorting a well-planned diet.

COOPERATION BETWEEN SCHOOL AND HOME

The nursery school child may remain in school till the middle of the afternoon, in which case the interval between the noon meal and the evening meal may be over five hours. In this case, the school schedule may include a light afternoon feeding, especially for children under three or four. From 6 to 8 oz of milk served with a plain, hard, whole-wheat cracker makes a good afternoon snack, if it does not interfere with the appetite for supper. Here again adjustment between home and nursery school is imperative. If the appetite for supper is interfered with, the afternoon feeding should be omitted or the size of portions decreased until an adjustment is secured.

With the child eating in two places, the best diet cannot be assured unless there is continued cooperation between the school and the home. By frequent conferences with the parents, the dietitian may learn the home situation in detail and they together can arrange a plan that will ensure a unified day's dietary for every child. A weekly plan can be built around the noonday meal at school, which must serve the whole group with only such modification for individual cases as comes from changes in quantities of food served, since it would be impossible to cook a different meal for each child.

The home breakfast should consist of a well-cooked cereal, served with milk, a cup of milk to drink, an egg if not included in another meal, and from one-half to one slice of toast, Zwieback, or dry bread. When orange juice is given at the nursery school, less needs to be given with the breakfast, and an equal amount of fruit pulp may well be substituted. Prunes are valuable sometime in the day if a more laxative diet is needed, and so are cereals made from whole grains.

A good supper may include one or more of these foods: a scalloped or creamed vegetable, cottage cheese, a poached egg on toast, milk toast, or cereal and milk; or sometimes a baked potato with another vegetable, bread spread lightly with margarine or butter, and a cup of milk to drink. For children under nine years of age, two to three 8-oz portions of milk will satisfy the day's needs. Some of the milk may be included in puddings, ice cream, soups, etc.

A small serving of mild stewed fruit such as applesauce, stewed pears, or baked banana may be added. Sometimes a Graham cracker or a plain hard molasses cookie may be given. Menus for one day for a three-year-old child, whether attending nursery school or not, might be as follows:

A DAY'S MENUS FOR A THREE-YEAR-OLD CHILD

Breakfast

Orange juice, $\frac{1}{2}$ cup*
Rolled oats, $\frac{3}{4}$ cup
Milk,† 1 cup (for cereal and to drink)
Toast, whole wheat, 1 slice
Margarine or butter, 1 tsp

2:30 P.M.

Milk, $\frac{1}{2}$ cup
Crackers, Graham, 3 small

Dinner

> Ground beef, 1½ oz
> Potato, baked, mashed, 1 medium
> Green beans, ¼ cup
> Carrots, 5 strips
> Bread, whole wheat, 1 slice
> Margarine or butter, 2 tsp
> Banana, sliced, 1 medium
> Milk, 1 cup

Supper

> Egg, soft cooked, 1
> Spinach, cooked and chopped, ⅓ cup
> Bread, white, enriched, 1 slice
> Margarine or butter, 1 tsp
> Prunes (cooked with 1 tsp sugar), 2 large
> Milk, ½ cup

* If preferred, this can be given as a midmorning feeding.
† Vitamin D milk is assumed.

It is desirable to compare the nutritive value of the foods included in the menu with the suggested recommended allowances of specific nutrients. For these calculations and comparisons expressed in shares, see Table 25–1.

It will be noted that this selection of common food materials provides a good margin of safety above the recommendations for each nutrient.

The Kindergarten Child

The child who does not enter a nursery school at the age of two or three years may begin his school experience at the age of four, five, or six in kindergarten. He may have less feeding at school than the nursery school child, but there will nevertheless be certain adjustments necessary when he starts on his school career. About half of our schools provide kindergartens for five-year-old children. Since school hours may vary in different communities, the actual meal plan will need to be adapted to the school schedule.

Breakfast may have to come earlier and dinner later, and a midmorning or midafternoon school feeding may consist of a carton of milk and a cracker. There is danger of hurrying breakfast and eating an insufficient quantity of food; hence the morning program must be arranged to allow for leisurely eating of the proper amount, no mean achievement for a busy mother and a child sure to be slow when anyone especially wants him to be quick.

The selection of foods is similar to that suggested for the younger child but the size of servings will need to be increased to meet the requirements of the individual child.

Developing Desirable Food Habits

Good eating habits are most easily achieved when children are very young. Healthy, happy children usually have good appetites, but there are times when they do not feel like eating. They may be too tired,

TABLE 25-1. A DAY'S DIETARY FOR
A THREE-YEAR-OLD CHILD

			Shares						
Foods	Measure	Calo-ries	Calo-ries	Pro-tein	Cal-cium	Iron	Vita-min A Value	Thia-mine	Ribo-flavin	Ascor-bic Acid
Milk	3 cups	480	4.80	11.1	30.9	0.9	6.0	6.0	21.6	2.4
Egg, cooked	1	80	0.80	2.5	1.0	3.2	3.4	1.3	2.6	0.0
Beef, lean, ground	1½ oz	93	0.93	4.8	0.2	4.4	0.0	1.0	1.7	0.0
Beans, green, cooked	¼ cup	8	0.08	0.2	0.6	0.6	1.0	0.5	0.5	1.7
Carrot, raw	5 thin strips	4	0.04	0.1	0.1	0.2	6.4	0.2	0.1	0.3
Potato, baked	1 med.	90	0.90	1.2	0.3	2.1	0.0	2.5	0.7	8.3
Spinach, cooked	⅓ cup	13	0.13	0.7	2.0	3.9	28.3	1.1	1.4	6.9
Banana	1	85	0.85	0.4	0.3	2.1	1.1	1.3	1.0	4.1
Prunes, cooked	2 large	54	0.54	0.1	0.4	2.4	2.0	0.4	0.6	0.1
Orange juice	½ cup	55	0.55	0.4	0.4	0.3	1.5	2.7	0.3	23.3
Bread, white, enriched	1 slice	60	0.60	0.8	0.6	1.8	0.0	1.5	0.7	0.0
Bread, whole wheat	2 slices	110	1.10	1.6	1.6	3.0	0.0	3.0	1.0	0.0
Crackers, Graham	3 small	41	0.41	0.3	0.1	0.4	0.0	0.2	0.4	0.0
Oats, rolled, cooked	¾ cup	98	0.98	1.6	0.6	3.1	0.0	3.6	0.7	0.0
Margarine (or butter)	1⅓ tbsp	133	1.33	0.0	0.0	0.0	3.6	0.0	0.0	0.0
Sugar	1 tsp	15	0.15	0.0	0.0	0.0	0.0	0.0	0.0	0.0
Totals from diet		1,419	14.19	25.8	39.1	28.4	53.3	25.3	33.3	47.1
Recommended Daily Allowances		1,400	14.00	15.0	29.0	27.0	14.0	14.0	15.0	18.0

be coming down with a cold, or be out of sorts, and this is not the time to nag or make an issue about cleaning the plate.

When a young child joins the family at the table, he is confronted with many new learning experiences. It is most important at this time that adults set a good example and refrain from discussions of their likes and dislikes which may adversely influence a child's good food habits.

A child should be presented with small servings which can reasonably be consumed. He may become discouraged with a heaped-up plate of food and refuse to eat at all.

In order to fit properly into the family routine every child should be encouraged to taste any food it is important for him to eat, each time it is served, but the quantity should not be too large. Frequent repetition under favorable circumstances is much more likely to be successful than a forced overdose. Other habits are established only by patient repetition, and one should not expect food habits to be any exception.

Minor changes in the food often help the child in such an endeavor. A little difference in appearance, flavor, or texture may mean more than an adult is aware of. Adults make many such adjustments for themselves at the table. "Some like it hot, some like it cold", and which way they have it may be immaterial. It is a wise parent who knows when to insist! Spinach and potato together may be easier to eat than spinach alone. If a child prefers shredded wheat to oatmeal may he not have it, since no work is involved in preparing it and the two foods are nutritionally interchangeable? Eventually, he should learn to eat both, but tastes and ideas change, and if he is eating according to his own nutritional needs, we should not at this time put too much emphasis on variety.

Anyone responsible for feeding a child should be familiar with the effect of food on health and growth, which has been referred to in the preceding chapters. A knowledge of food values will enable one to make wise substitutions when the occasion demands it. The attitude of the parents is often the decisive factor between success and failure. It is important that the parents agree and that the child is not made the victim of arguments.

Helping mother in the kitchen with the simple preparation of food may lead the child to develop a real appetite for tasting and enjoying the final product. There are many constructive tasks for little hands to do in the kitchen, and a wise parent will find them.

A recent study of 104 preschool children, two and one-half to five and one-half years of age, who were enrolled in day care centers or nursery schools in Columbus, Ohio, indicated that iron was the nutrient least well supplied in their diets. This confirms an earlier longitudinal study by Beal in Denver on 58 children under five years of age. Seventy-five per cent of the children studied by Beal had iron intakes below the recommended allowance. Earlier in this chapter we referred to a study by Guthrie of very young children calling attention to the inadequacy of dietary iron. It is obvious that iron-rich foods need to be emphasized in the diet of the preschool child to provide for good hemoglobin production and the prevention of nutritional anemia.

REFERENCES

Beal, V. A. "Nutrition in a Longitudinal Growth Study." *J. Amer. Dietet. A.*, **46**:457 (1965).

Children's Bureau, Social Security Administration, U.S. Department of Health, Education, and Welfare. *Nutrition and Healthy Growth* (1963); *Your Child from One to Six* (1962); Children's Bureau Folder No. 14. *Foods Your Children Need* (1958); *Your Child from One to Three* (1965).

Fleck, H., and Munves, E. *Introduction to Nutrition*, Chap. 19. New York: Macmillan (1962).

Food and Nutrition Board. *Recommended Dietary Allowances,* 6th ed., pp. 8 and 9. Washington, D.C.: National Research Council, Publication 1146 (1964).

Food—The Yearbook of Agriculture, 1959. Stearns, G. "Infants and Toddlers," p. 283. Washington, D.C.: U.S. Department of Agriculture.

Hille, H. *Food for Groups of Young Children Cared for During the Day.* Children's Bureau Publication No. 386. Washington, D.C.: U.S. Department of Health, Education, and Welfare (1960).

Jeans, P. C. "Feeding of Healthy Infants and Children." *Handbook of Nutrition,* 2nd ed., Chap. 14. Chicago: American Medical Association (1951).

Martin, E. A. *Roberts' Nutrition Work with Children,* 3rd ed. Chicago: U. Chicago (1954).

Metheny, N. Y., Hunt, F. E., Patton, M. B., and Heye, H. "The Diets of Preschool Children. I. Nutritional Sufficiency Findings, and Family Marketing Practices." *J. Home Econ.,* **54**:297 (1962).

Sweeny, M. E., and Eichelberger, M. *The Child's Meals Are Family Meals.* Detroit, Mich.: The Merrill Palmer School (1958).

Taylor, C. M. *Food Values in Shares and Weights,* 2nd ed. New York: Macmillan (1959).

Trowell, H., and Jelliffe, D. *Diseases of Children in the Sub-tropics and Tropics.* London: Arnold (1958).

Woodruff, C. W. "Nutrition of Infants and Preschool Children in Ethiopia." *Pub. Health Rep.,* **75**:724 (1960).

26

Food Needs of Boys and Girls of School Age

How much is a child worth? This challenging question is not an easy one to answer. So many factors have to be considered, such as the highly specialized professional services, as well as the many pairs of hands, trained and untrained, that it now takes to maintain a modern home with its variety of mechanized equipment in our complex community life. A mother has always had to assume a "do-it-yourself" philosophy, and the cash value of her varied services is inestimable. Today she must be veritably a "domestic engineer." The success or failure of her efforts is quickly judged on the basis of the child who makes his appearance on the first day of school. Does he look happy? Is he alert and receptive? Does he seem to have that superabundance of health that we often describe as robust? Does he seem to have that all-round physical stamina that every schoolchild must have to carry on successfully?

The greater the attention to the health of the preschool and kindergarten child, the fewer the handicaps among elementary school children. Physical defects should have been as far as possible removed and good health habits already established when the six-year-old enters the elementary school. But he cannot now be safely left to guide himself. He has covered only about one fourth of his period of growth, and good habits are by no means fixed. Furthermore, he is just approaching the years in which inculcation of the reasons for health habits and respect for the laws of hygiene should be a consistent part of his education, both at home and at school.

Elementary School Children

By the time a child is ready to enter the elementary school he should be eating a diet in which milk, eggs, cereals, vegetables in considerable variety, fruits, especially orange juice, and whole-wheat or enriched bread are the chief items. All foods should be cooked as simply as possible. A glass of milk at each meal and some in soup or dessert will take care of the day's quota for children 9 to 12 years of age, while for children under nine years of age, two to three glasses may be adequate. No tea or coffee should be permitted.

GENERAL PLAN OF MEALS

The elementary school child's energy needs are high. Breakfast must be ample but simple and not eaten too hurriedly. No child starts the day well who has not gone to bed early and had a full night's sleep. A good rest should give him a good appetite for breakfast. Fruit, cereal with milk, milk to drink, and toast make an adequate breakfast. An egg may be included if it is not to be served in another meal. The cereal may be cooked or ready to eat. Every day is a growing day for a child, and whatever food program is important today is equally important tomorrow. At this age, if preferred, orange juice can give place to the whole orange, prune pulp to whole stewed prunes, and applesauce to raw apples or pears, provided they are ripe. Other mild fresh fruits in season can also be used for breakfast.

School conditions will now affect the time and character of the midday meal. It may be eaten at home or at the school. A nutritious milk and vegetable soup with an egg or cheese sandwich, or a casserole mixture, milk to drink, and fruit will make a wholesome noonday meal. At other times a potato, another cooked vegetable, an egg, or a little meat, a small portion of some raw vegetable, such as tomatoes, cabbage, or carrots, a glass of milk to drink, and a simple dessert of stewed fruit or a milk pudding make a suitable meal.

The evening meal can be simple for young children, since bedtime is not far away. A creamed vegetable soup with toast or crackers, a cooked vegetable, a soft-cooked egg or chopped meat with a baked potato and one other vegetable, milk toast, and cooked cereal and milk are examples of suitable hot dishes. There should be milk to drink, bread and butter with stewed fruit, or a simple pudding for dessert.

The evening meal for older boys and girls can be more substantial because of their higher calorie needs. To illustrate the selection of food for a ten-and-one-half-year-old boy requiring about 2,400 calories, the following menus have been planned.

A DAY'S MENUS FOR
A TEN-AND-ONE-HALF-YEAR-OLD BOY

Breakfast	**Lunch (at School)**
Orange, 1	Spaghetti, tomato with meat balls, 1 cup
Farina, enriched, 1 cup	Bread, whole wheat, 1 slice

Breakfast (cont.)

Egg, 1
Bread, white, enriched, 1 slice
Bread, whole wheat, 1 slice
Margarine or butter, $\frac{2}{3}$ tbsp
Milk, 1 cup

Snack

Crackers, 3
Peanut butter, 1 tbsp

Lunch (at School) (cont.)

Margarine or butter, $\frac{2}{3}$ tbsp
Banana, 1
Milk, 1 carton

Dinner

Chicken drumstick, 1
Peas, $\frac{3}{4}$ cup
Carrot, raw, $\frac{1}{2}$
Potato, boiled, 1
Bread, white, enriched, 2 slices
Margarine or butter, $1\frac{2}{3}$ tbsp
Ice cream, 1 carton
Fruit cake, 1 slice
Milk, 1 cup

How this plan will meet the needs of the boy is shown by the calculations in Table 26–1.

It is easy to see that requirements for calories, protein, mineral constituents, and vitamins are well met when the foods are selected with regard to these essentials. Also, one may observe how difficult it would be to meet the calcium needs of a rapidly growing child without a liberal amount of milk, since the contributions of the other foods are so insignificant in calcium in comparison. As will be noted, milk also makes a liberal contribution toward the riboflavin allowance.

The value of the orange as a source of ascorbic acid is quite apparent, as it provides enough to meet the recommended allowance without taking account of any other food. The regular use of specific foods for special purposes within the food groups, as in this instance, greatly simplifies the task of providing adequate diets.

In establishing recommended allowances in shares, one may refer to Tables A–5 and A–7 in the Appendix. Children of the same age vary greatly in weight, as will be observed in Figure 26–1, which shows three girls eight years of age, each of whom is normal but quite different in height and weight from the others. Calories for a particular child can be estimated by referring to Figures 4–8 and 4–9 in Chapter 4. If one then refers to Table A–7 in the Appendix, the allowances in shares for the other essential nutrients, corresponding to the estimated calorie allowance, will be found. If the calories correspond to those in the table

TABLE 26–1. A DAY'S DIETARY FOR A
TEN-AND-ONE-HALF-YEAR-OLD BOY

				Shares						
							Vita-			Ascor-
		Calo-	Calo-	Pro-	Cal-		min A	Thia-	Ribo-	bic
Foods	Measure	ries	ries	tein	cium	Iron	Value	mine	flavin	Acid
Milk, whole	3 cups	480	4.80	11.1	30.9	0.9	6.0	6.0	21.6	2.4
Ice cream	1 con-									
	tainer	130	1.30	0.8	2.7	0.3	1.9	0.8	2.1	0.4
Egg, cooked	1	80	0.80	2.7	1.0	3.4	3.5	1.2	2.4	0.0
Chicken, drumstick	1	90	0.90	5.0	0.2	2.6	0.3	0.8	2.6	0.0
Peanut butter	1 tbsp	95	0.95	1.7	0.3	0.9	0.0	0.5	0.3	0.0
Carrot	½ raw	10	0.10	0.2	0.3	0.6	16.0	0.4	0.3	0.9
Peas, cooked	¾ cup	86	0.86	2.8	1.0	6.4	3.8	8.3	2.2	10.3
Potato, boiled	1 med.	105	1.05	1.2	0.4	2.4	0.0	3.3	0.9	9.1
Banana	1 med.	85	0.85	0.4	0.3	2.1	1.1	1.3	1.0	4.1
Orange	1 med.	60	0.60	0.8	1.8	1.5	1.4	3.0	0.9	31.1
Bread, white,										
enriched	3 slices	180	1.80	2.4	1.8	5.4	0.0	4.5	2.1	0.0
Bread, whole wheat	2 slices	110	1.10	1.6	1.6	3.0	0.0	3.0	1.0	0.0
Farina, enriched	1 cup									
	cooked	100	1.00	1.2	0.4	2.1	0.0	2.8	1.2	0.0
Fruit cake	1 slice	115	1.15	0.4	0.8	2.4	0.2	1.0	0.7	0.0
Saltines	3	53	0.53	0.6	0.2	0.5	0.0	0.0	0.0	0.0
Spaghetti, tomato,										
with meat balls	1 cup	335	3.35	7.9	4.5	11.2	9.3	6.5	5.2	9.1
Margarine										
(or butter)	3 tbsp	300	3.00	0.0	0.3	0.0	8.1	0.0	0.0	0.0
Totals from diet		2,414	24.14	40.8	48.5	45.7	51.6	43.4	44.5	67.4
Recommended Daily Allowances		2,400	24.00	25.0	39.0	44.0	26.0	25.0	24.0	29.0

for an older child, one may use the allowances for essential nutrients for the older child just as one would have to get a larger size coat.

Nationwide surveys of diets conducted from 1947 through 1958 on 1,710 children, 5 to 12 years of age, identify some of the dietary problems among this group. Summaries of the data reveal that there are differences in the eating habits of children in different regions of the United States. Eight nutrients in all diets were calculated and compared with the Recommended Dietary Allowances. Almost all the children were found to have diets adequate in protein. More of the diets were deficient in calcium (7 to 20 per cent in all regions had less than two thirds of the recommended allowances). Three to thirteen per cent had less than two thirds of the recommended allowance for iron. Ascorbic acid intake was less than two thirds the recommended amount in 12 to 42 per cent in all regions. These data indicate that the children

FIGURE 26–1. THREE EIGHT-
YEAR-OLD GIRLS SHOWING
HOW CHILDREN OF THE
SAME AGE MAY DIFFER
MARKEDLY IN BODY BUILD.
(*Courtesy of Home Eco-
nomics Research Branch,
Agricultural Research Ser-
vice, U.S. Department of
Agriculture.*)

were eating too little citrus fruits, tomatoes, and other vitamin C-rich
foods.[1]

Secondary School Children

In 1960 there were 19.5 million 13- to 19-year-olds in the United
States, approximately 11 per cent of the population, and at the time of
writing there are about 24 million young people in this age range.

In the survey of the nutritional status of the United States the diets
of about 3,500 adolescents 13 to 20 years of age from 13 states were
studied from 1947 to 1958. These diets were calculated for eight nutrients and compared with the Recommended Dietary Allowances. Intakes of the adolescents, especially girls, were more variable than those
of younger children. In practically all instances except ascorbic acid,
the teen-age girls had more dietary deficiencies than the teen-age boys.
This was particularly notable in respect to calcium, iron, thiamine,
riboflavin, and vitamin A. The protein intake of both girls and boys
tended to be higher than the recommended allowances.

Burke, Stuart, and co-workers made longitudinal studies of growth
and development along with food-intake records of 125 individual boys

[1] Morgan, A. F. (ed.). *Nutritional Status, U.S.A.* Berkeley: University of California Experiment Station Bulletin 769 (1959).

and girls from 1 to 18 years. They found striking variations in the food intake of individuals of the same age and sex.[2]

Teen-age boys and girls face striking changes in physical, mental, and emotional development. These changes are intensified with the acceleration of growth that takes place at different ages and varies with the individual (see Figure 26–2 *A* and *B*). During this period of adolescence lasting about ten years there is a gradual but irregular transition from childhood to maturity. Growth, which has been proceeding with a weight increase averaging between 5 and 6 lb a year, may be accelerated about two years earlier in girls than in boys, as will be observed in Figure 26–2 (*A* and *B*). For comparison one may also be interested in studying the weight-height-age table (Table A–14) for boys and girls of school age and the physical growth charts (Figures A–3 and A–4) given in the Appendix.

For the whole period from 11 to about 15 years in girls and from 12 to 18 years in boys, the food requirements will be much higher than for adults of corresponding size, and emphasis must be put on a diet capable of promoting the best possible growth.

[2] Burke, B. S., Reed, R. B., Van den Berg, A. S., and Stuart, H. C. "Relationships Between Animal Protein, Total Protein and Total Caloric Intakes in the Diets of Children from One to Eighteen Years of Age." *Amer. J. Clin. Nutr.,* 9:729 (1961).

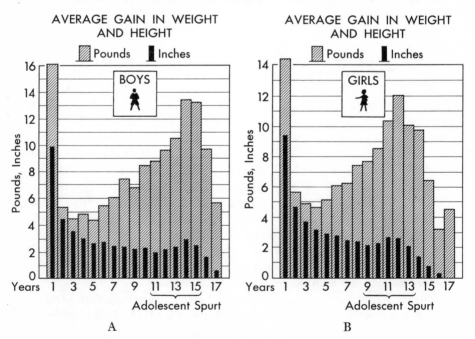

FIGURE 26–2. GROWTH CHARTS FOR BOYS AND GIRLS. (*Courtesy of the Metropolitan Life Insurance Company.*)

FACTORS INFLUENCING THE TEEN-AGER'S CHOICE OF FOOD

Many studies have been conducted in an attempt to get at the root of the problems in the teen-ager's choice of foods. Surveys have shown that the selections of foods are influenced by many factors. The desire for social prestige, "going along with the crowd," reaction against parental restraints, skipping meals to keep slim, and too many activities are just a few of the factors that outweigh the desire for nutritious food in the lives of today's teen-agers.

Boys are more likely than girls to accept without protest a simple regime, provided it really gives them a diet that appeases their chronic hunger. Quantity is the great consideration. Girls, whose urge to eat is not so compelling, pay more attention to the esthetic aspects of their diet. This is also true of girls leading active lives and taking their recreation in the form of outdoor sports.

Many of the dietary problems presented by girls can be solved only as physical perfection can be made to seem worth working for. Not yet do women as a class take pride in physical fitness. A girl must see advantages in health in order to be willing to strive for it. Where thinness is admired, she will work for thinness; if fatness were regarded as a mark of beauty, she would do her best to be fat. Her desire for beauty and praise far outruns her desire for food, and it will only be as higher ideals are developed that she will consciously endeavor to live hygienically. Her diet should be chosen with regard to its appearance and flavor, with emphasis on growth-promoting factors. Snack foods that make a worthwhile contribution to the diet, such as milk beverages, ice cream, nuts, and fruits, can be encouraged for sociability rather than cakes, pies, fancy desserts, and candy.

The foods that should be chosen first are called protective because they are rich in mineral elements and vitamins. It is important for every high school boy and girl to keep in mind the essential foods that should appear in the dietary every day. A review of the four-food-group plan will identify these essential foods, and a list such as the following may be assembled as a daily guide.

1 qt milk.
$\frac{1}{2}$ to $\frac{3}{4}$ cup orange, grapefruit, or tomato juice or the equivalent in fresh fruit.
$\frac{1}{2}$ to $\frac{3}{4}$ cup of green or yellow vegetable.
1 potato.
1 egg daily or at least 3 or 4 per week.
4 to 5 oz of meat, poultry, or fish.
4 to 6 slices of whole-grain or enriched bread or equivalent.
Other foods such as cereals, fats, sweets, and additional vegetables and fruits to meet the calorie requirement.

It will be noted that the only difference between these rules and those given for the adult is in the amount of milk. Every boy and girl of this age should have a full quart of milk each day until they have stopped growing. With these rules in mind, then, a day's menus for a high school boy actively engaged in athletics might be similar to the menus shown below.

The menus allow for three glasses of milk for drinking, part of the fourth glass to be used for cereal and in this menu cheese replaces part of the milk. The breakfast includes fruit juice, eggs, and cereal; and the dinner, green and yellow vegetable, potato, and meat. The bread is distributed throughout the three meals, and the other foods provide the extra calories needed.

A DAY'S MENUS FOR A HIGH SCHOOL BOY

Breakfast

Orange juice
Wheat flakes with dates and milk
Toast, whole wheat, with butter or
   margarine
Jam
Egg
Bacon
Milk to drink

Lunch

Hash, corned beef
Coleslaw
Bread, whole wheat, with butter or
   margarine
Cake
Milk to drink

After School

Cookies
Apple

Dinner

Meat with gravy
Potatoes
Carrots and peas
Rolls with butter or margarine
Apple pie with cheese
Milk to drink

It may be of interest to list the foods included in these menus, decide upon amounts, and calculate the actual contributions of the total dietary to see how well they compare with the recommended allowances and what adjustments need to be made. A high school boy (15 to 18 years of age) engaged in average activity needs about 3,400 calories, but if he participates in football, baseball, or track, he may need 5,000 or more. For the recommended allowances see Tables A–1 and A–7. The allowances for thiamine and riboflavin for energy expenditures above 3,400 are as follows: for each 1,000 calories allow 0.4 mg of thiamine and 0.6 mg of riboflavin. Therefore, for 5,000 calories the allowance for thiamine would be 5×0.4, or 2.0, mg (49 shares); for riboflavin the allowance would be 5×0.6, or 3.0 mg (52 shares).

A girl 12 to 15 years of age may need 2,500 calories per day for growth and average activity, but from 15 to 18 years of age 2,300 calories (on the average) should be adequate. This is in contrast to the boy 12 to 15 years of age engaged in average activity, who needs 3,000 calories, while between 15 and 18 years his needs have increased to 3,400.

The simple rules that were used as a guide for planning menus for the high school boy can be used equally well for the high school girl. The chief difference, of course, is in the total number of calories needed. A day's menus showing how these foods may be combined in simple but attractive meals will be found below.

A DAY'S MENUS FOR A HIGH SCHOOL GIRL

Breakfast	**After School**
Apricot nectar	Peanut cookies
Rice flakes with milk	Milk shake
Muffin with butter or margarine	
Strawberry preserve	
Milk to drink	

Luncheon	**Dinner**
Clam chowder	Grapefruit and orange juice
Egg, lettuce and mayonnaise	Veal cutlet
Bread with butter or margarine	Sweet potato, baked
Carton of milk	Stewed tomatoes
Ice cream	Hard roll with butter or margarine
	Blancmange

To see how well the foods in these menus provide the recommended allowances for the high school girl, they should be listed and calculated. Some adjustment in the size of the servings will be needed depending on individual requirements.

Weight Control for the Teen-Ager

As already discussed in Chapter 23, the teen-ager faces the same problems as the adult in this land of abundant food supply. Estimates show that between 10 and 44 per cent of American children may be overweight, the percentage varying in different regions of the country. More teen-age girls tend to be overweight than teen-age boys; the percentage of overweight girls studied in three states (Maine, Iowa, and Oregon) shows a range of 39 to 44 per cent compared with 10 to 29 per cent of the boys in these states. The tendency to overweight seems to parallel the periods of greatest growth and development when excess food is required for these normal processes. The danger is in establishing a food pattern of overeating following this period of rapid growth. High-calorie foods and snacks are an integral part of the social life of the teen-ager. These foods often contribute nothing but calories and not only replace those foods furnishing essential nutrients but add excess calories which would be needed only by a very active teen-ager.

The overweight adolescent naturally tends to spend more time in sitting activities, such as looking at television rather than engaging in active sports or dancing. A very active teen-ager may fail to eat enough to meet these high caloric requirements and will tend to lose weight.

Studies reported in West Virginia show that nearly 30 per cent of the boys and nearly 60 per cent of the girls between 13 and 15 years of age were underweight. These are unusual figures when compared with those from other states, for example Maine, where only about 30 per cent of the boys and girls were underweight. In New York State more girls than boys were underweight.

The School Lunch Program

The earliest records of feeding groups of children in the United States date back to the middle of the nineteenth century when such programs were started in our large cities by voluntary societies. The Children's Aid Society of New York served some meals at its vocational school in 1853. Programs of this nature increased rapidly, and by the turn of the century many were under way, but it was not until June 4, 1946, that the National School Lunch Act was made effective, thus making the school lunch available to all children. This is the most important practical step ever taken by our government to improve the health of all children through improvement in their nutrition.

The educational opportunities that a well-organized school lunch program provides for the establishment of good food habits are unlimited. The school lunch program is a community affair and has brought many a mother to the school because she is interested in participating in the program. Space does not permit an extended discussion of the many advantages of the program.

During the fifteen years from 1947 through 1961, the number of schools participating in the National School Lunch Program almost doubled. Lunches are now available in schools representing two thirds of the nation's school population. In 1947, less than one of every six students received lunch under the program. During 1961 almost one of every three students had a type "A" lunch. For growth of the program see Figure 26–3.

Number of schools participating*

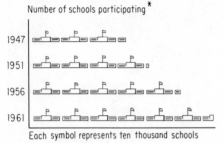

1947

1951

1956

1961

Each symbol represents ten thousand schools

*Includes both public and private schools

• The number of schools participating in the national school lunch program has almost *doubled* over the past 15 years.

• Lunches are now available in schools having two-thirds of the nation's total enrollment.

Number of children participating*

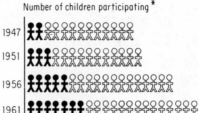

1947

1951

1956

1961

Each figure represents two million children

Children participating in national school lunch program.

Total enrollment in U.S. schools

*Represents a daily average for the peak month of participation

• In 1947, less than one of every six students received lunch under the program.

• During 1961, nearly one of every three students ate a type "A" lunch.

FIGURE 26–3. GROWTH OF THE SCHOOL LUNCH PROGRAM FROM 1947–61. (*Courtesy of U.S. Department of Agriculture.*)

Lunches served in schools under the National School Lunch Program, in order to be eligible for reimbursement, must contain the following foods to meet the requirements for a type "A" lunch:

1. Whole milk—½ pt (8 oz) of fluid whole milk served as a beverage.

2. Protein-rich foods—2 oz of cooked or canned lean meat, poultry, or fish; or 2 oz of cheese; or 1 egg; or ½ cup cooked dry beans or peas; or 4 tbsp of peanut butter; or an equivalent combination of these foods.

3. Vegetables and fruits—a ¾-cup serving consisting of two or more vegetables or fruits, or both, in raw or cooked form. It is important to include a vitamin C-rich food every day, and a vitamin A-rich food twice a week, since studies show that these foods are frequently short in children's diets.

4. Bread—1 slice (or equivalent) of whole-grain or enriched bread.

5. Butter or fortified margarine—2 tsp.

Since 1954, the Department of Agriculture has operated a Special Milk Program to increase fluid milk consumption among children attending schools of high school grades and under. Later, nonprofit child-care institutions such as settlement houses, summer camps, child-care centers, and similar institutions became eligible for participation. The program has proved to be an effective means of encouraging more children to drink more milk. See Figure 26–4 for illustration of boys enjoying type "A" lunch.

Figure 26–4. Fourth Graders Enjoy a "Type A" Lunch in a Georgia School. (*Courtesy of U.S. Department of Agriculture.*)

A clear-cut statement on confections and carbonated beverages in schools was made by the Council on Foods and Nutrition of the American Medical Association.

> One of the functions of a school lunch program is to provide training in sound food habits. The sale of foods, confections, and beverages in lunchrooms, recreation rooms, and other school facilities influences directly the food habits of the students. Every effort should be extended to encourage students to adopt and enjoy good food habits. The availability of confections and carbonated beverages on school premises may tempt children to spend lunch money for them and lead to poor food habits. Their high energy value and continual availability are likely to affect children's appetites for regular meals. Expenditures for carbonated beverages and most confections yield a nutritional return greatly inferior to that from milk, fruit, and other foods included in the basic food groups. When given a choice between carbonated beverages and milk or between candy and fruit, a child may choose the less nutritious. In view of these considerations, the Council on Foods and Nutrition is particularly opposed to the sale and distribution of confections and carbonated beverages in school lunchrooms.[3]

[3] Council on Foods and Nutrition. "Confections and Carbonated Beverages in Schools." *J. Amer. Med. A.*, **180**:92 (1962).

In recent years, school feeding has been extended in a number of developing nations. A group of children showed a significant improvement in nutrition when given one third of their daily food needs in an experimental school lunch program in India. Nutrients that are low in the regular diet can be added to the lunch in amounts approaching the daily requirement.[4] As this report from India indicates, school feeding programs offer an excellent opportunity for improving the nutrition of millions of children in all parts of the world.

REFERENCES

Aldrich, R. A. "Nutrition and Human Development. *J. Amer. Dietet. A.,* **46**:453 (1965).

Children's Bureau, Social Security Administration, U.S. Department of Health, Education, and Welfare. *Nutrition and Healthy Growth* (reprinted 1963); *Your Child from Six to Twelve,* Publication 324 (reprinted 1963).

Edwards, C. H., Hogan, G., Spahr, S., and Guilford County Nutrition Committee. "Nutrition Survey of 6200 Teen-Age Youth." *J. Amer. Dietet. A.,* **45**:543 (1964).

Egan, M. "The Obese School Child—A Challenge." *School Lunch J.,* **18**:44 (1964).

Everson, G. J. "Bases for Concern About Teenagers' Diets." *J. Amer. Dietet. A.,* **36**:17 (1960).

Food and Agriculture Organization of the United Nations. Scott, M. *School Feeding. Its Contribution to Child Nutrition* (1953).

Food—The Yearbook of Agriculture, 1959. Storvick, C. A., and Fincke, M. L. "Adolescents and Young Adults," p. 303. Washington, D.C.: U.S. Department of Agriculture.

Hinton, M. A., Eppright, E. S., Chadderdon, H., and Wolins, L. "Eating Behavior and Dietary Intake of Girls, 12 to 14 Years Old." *J. Amer. Dietet. A.,* **43**:223 (1963).

King, C. G., and Lam, G. *Personality "Plus" Through Diet.* Public Affairs Pamphlet No. 299. New York: Public Affairs Committee, Inc. (1960).

Martin, E. A. *Roberts' Nutrition Work with Children,* 3rd ed. Chicago: U. Chicago (1954).

Taylor, C. M. *Food Values in Shares and Weights,* 2nd ed. New York: Macmillan (1959).

U.S. Department of Agriculture. Agricultural Marketing Service. *The National School Lunch Program. Fifteen Years of Progress 1947–1961.* (1962); *Selected References on Nutrition and School Lunch* (1963).

[4] Review. "The Effects of a Balanced Lunch Program on the Growth and Nutritional Status of School Children." *Nutr. Rev.,* **23**:35 (1965).

U.S. Department of Agriculture. Federal Extension Service. *Improving Teenage Nutrition* (1963).

U.S. Department of Health, Education, and Welfare, Office of Education, Nutrition Education Series, Pamphlet No. 6. *The School Lunch—Its Educational Contribution* (1954).

White House Conference on Children and Youth, 1960. *Proceedings; The Nation's Children; Children in a Changing World*. Washington, D.C.: U.S. Government Printing Office.

ᴗ **27** ᴗ

Adequate Diets for the Family

In a single family we expect to find (1) differences of age, infants, children, parents, and sometimes grandparents, (2) differences of activity, ranging from active children to sedentary parents, and (3) differences of taste, e.g., the boy whose sole criterion of a good meal is "enough" and his finicky teen-age sister who cannot even peck at a meal unless the whole setting of the table appeals to her soul. Each member of the family group has his own particular food requirements which are matters of fact not fancy, and yet each claims a seat at the family table, for this is not merely the place where sustenance is furnished for the body, but it is also a center of the social life of the group. It offers important training in the graces of human intercourse and in the development of those esthetic standards of choice, preparation, and service of food that are an expression of the culture and refinement of the household.

In the majority of homes, the cost of food is a matter that requires much attention, but spending or saving should be done without impairing the nutritive value of the diet. A distinction must be made between food expenditures for nutriment and those for social purposes. Plain bread and milk make a nutritious meal at a very low cost, but it is considered too simple and monotonous to be served daily. Each family needs to determine for itself the relationship between the expenditure for actual nourishment and the additional sum to be allowed for enjoyment and entertainment and maintenance of social prestige. The influence of the education of the homemaker on the adequacy of the family diet is shown in Figure 27–1.

We are living in an age when it is possible to get an abundance of all kinds of food the year around. Supermarkets are found throughout the country, and with modern transportation, regional foods are available to all.

The budget-minded housewife can take advantage of information via radio, television, newspapers, and special flyers calling attention to foods in plentiful supply and bargains. Depending on storage facilities, perishable foods can be purchased when in top quality.

Whether the fresh, dry, frozen, or canned foods are the best buy at a given time requires cost comparison. The homemaker's time is always a consideration. If she is employed outside the home, or if she has a large family and no help, her time is valuable. A study was made by the U.S. Department of Agriculture on the comparative cost of convenience foods and of their fresh or homemade counterparts. They studied 158 convenience foods in different cities in 1959–60, and of these, only 42 were less expensive than their home-prepared counterparts. The greatest savings of convenience foods at that time included frozen orange concentrate, frozen Lima beans, chicken chow mein, and devil's food cake mix. However, even where the convenience food was more expensive than preparing the same food at home, in terms of the value of the homemaker's time, the saving was small. Thus, a decision has to be made by the individual homemaker in terms of her pleasure in cooking, the acceptability to the family of the finished product, and her available time.

There is little difference in nutritive value between fresh, frozen, and canned foods, but by current methods of processing some of the dehydrated products lose considerable ascorbic acid. If another excellent source of ascorbic acid such as orange juice is included in the diet, it makes little practical difference if, for example, instant dehydrated

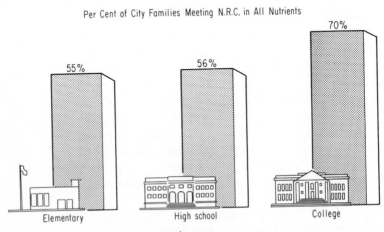

Per Cent of City Families Meeting N.R.C. in All Nutrients

Wife's education
Families with $4,000- $6,000 income; spring 1955

FIGURE 27–1. WIVES WITH HIGHER EDUCATION PROVIDE BETTER FAMILY DIETS. (*Courtesy of U.S. Department of Agriculture.*)

potatoes retain only 25 per cent of their original ascorbic acid. With the modern advances in food technology new methods of processing may obviate these losses. We are fortunate indeed to be able to enjoy this high level of living and the fact that modern farm production and marketing make possible a basic foundation for good health.

As it is outside the scope of this book to consider in detail the social aspects of the food problem, this discussion will be confined to the food requirements of representative family groups and plans for meeting them successfully so far as nutrition is concerned.

While the requirements of the individual members may seem to differ considerably, the divergences are more in quantity and mode of service than in kind of food. With minor adjustments, it is possible to keep those who are 6, 16, 36, and 66 well and happy on meals composed of practically the same kinds of food, if suitably prepared and apportioned with discretion. Infants and children young enough to require specially prepared food are best cared for by themselves. In this way they are not only likely to have a more carefully selected diet, but the children can also be more effectively guided in good eating habits.

The Dietary for a Budget-Minded Family

Before selecting foods for a given family we must consider first the make-up of the family, that is, the number in the family, their ages, their activities, and the percentage of the income available for food. Figure 27–2 shows graphically the percentage of family diets in the United States not meeting the recommended allowances.

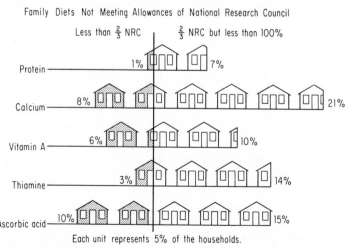

Family Diets Not Meeting Allowances of National Research Council

Less than ⅔ NRC | ⅔ NRC but less than 100%

Protein — 1% — 7%

Calcium — 8% — 21%

Vitamin A — 6% — 10%

Thiamine — 3% — 14%

Ascorbic acid — 10% — 15%

Each unit represents 5% of the households.

FIGURE 27–2. NEED FOR IMPROVED DIETS. (*Courtesy of U.S. Department of Agriculture.*)

The requirements of the family group will, of course, be the sum of those of the individuals composing it. Suppose, for example, we consider a family consisting of a father, mother, and three children. Of the three children, two are in the elementary school, a boy ten and one-half years of age and a girl of seven and one-half years, and one is a preschool child, a boy of four years. According to the recommended daily calorie allowances for the "reference" man and woman under 35 years in age and weighing approximately 70 and 58 kg, respectively, it will be noted, in Table A–1 in the Appendix, that the father of this family needs 2,900 calories and the mother 2,100 calories per day. The allowances for other nutrients expressed in shares corresponding to these calorie requirements for adults are shown in Table A–5. The recommended daily allowances for children are found in Table A–7 in the Appendix. The requirements for each member of the family can now be summarized (see Table 27–1).

TABLE 27–1. RECOMMENDED DAILY ALLOWANCES FOR A BUDGET-MINDED FAMILY

| | | | | | | Shares | | | |
| | | | | Cal- | | Vita-min A | Thia- | Ribo- | Ascor-bic |
	Calories	Calories	Protein	cium	Iron	Value	mine	flavin	Acid
Father	2,900	29.00	29	29	29	29	29	29	29
Mother	2,100	21.00	24	29	44	29	20	22	29
Boy, 10½	2,400	24.00	25	39	44	26	25	24	29
Girl, 7½	2,100	21.00	22	29	35	20	20	22	25
Boy, 4	1,500	15.00	16	29	28	15	15	16	20
Total	11,000	110.00	116	155	180	119	109	113	132

The 2,900 calories allotted to the father of this family would meet the energy expenditure of a clerk or salesman who has to do some walking but no heavy manual labor. The mother's energy allowance would take care of the daily tasks about the home but would not be high enough to allow for heavy cleaning. The energy allowances for the children are average allowances for healthy children of the ages stated.

Since we have already demonstrated that the simple rules, as described in the Four Food Groups, for the choice of foods serve as a satisfactory guide in the selection of adequate diets for individual adults and children, we may safely use them for the family group.

In the choice of food for this family, then, we should provide daily for the seven-and-one-half- and four-year-old children two to three 8-oz portions of milk and for the ten-and-one-half-year-old boy, 1 qt daily. The parents should have 1 pt each daily. This means 3½ qt each day for the family.

If we allow ½ cup of citrus fruit juice per person per day, for a family of five we would need 2½ cups. Tomato juice can be used part of the time for variety since it also is a fairly good source of ascorbic acid. Fresh oranges or other vitamin C-rich fruits may be used in season. Figure 27–3 shows the changes in the consumption of citrus and potatoes in the United States.

An allowance of ½ cup or more of a dark-green or deep-yellow vegetable should be included at least four times a week for each member of the family. The four-year-old may have a smaller portion. This would mean a minimum of 2½ cups of green or yellow vegetables (cooked measure) for a family of five, and in the case of spinach, would amount to about 1½ lb as purchased. If generous amounts of dark-green leaves are included in a salad, the cooked greens can be omitted. One potato per person each day would mean at least five for the family, including a small one for the four-year-old. This would amount to 1⅔ to 2 lb each day. At least one additional fruit or vegetable is desirable depending on the calorie needs.

With a recommendation of one egg daily or at least three a week for each member of the family, the weekly order for eggs would be between 1¼ and 3 dozen. The number used daily would depend, of course, on the menus. Eggs are especially significant in the diet of young children.

The meat allowance is about 4 or 5 oz (as purchased depending on the cuts, the amount of bone, and fat) per day for adults and less than this for children, with probably not more than 2 oz for a child of four. This would mean that 1 to 1¼ lb of lean meat (cooked weight) would be enough for one day for this particular family. Meat is almost invariably one of the expensive items, and its cost is out of proportion to its nutritive value. Meat or one of its alternates should be included in the main course each day. Liver, which is richer in iron and vitamin A, thiamine, and riboflavin, gives a better return in nutritive value than muscle meats.

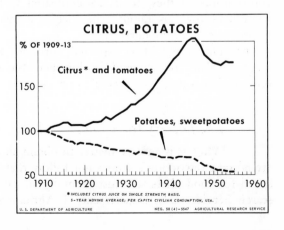

FIGURE 27–3. TRENDS IN CONSUMPTION OF CITRUS AND POTATOES. (*Courtesy of U.S. Department of Agriculture.*)

Fish (fresh, canned, or frozen), eggs, poultry of all kinds, and dried legumes are desirable alternatives for meat.

The bread allowance of four or more slices per person per day would amount to 1 lb or more per day for a family of five. The bread used should be whole grain or enriched, and if hot breads are included in the menu, they should be made with enriched flour. Cereal in some other form is desirable and is usually included in the breakfast. Either the cooked or ready-to-eat cereal may be used, and here again it is desirable to use the whole-grain cereals or enriched or restored products.

Menus for one day for a budget-minded family planned with the preceding suggestions for the choice of food will be found below and the contributions of the foods needed for their preparation in Table 27–2 on page 427.

MENUS FOR ONE DAY FOR A BUDGET-MINDED FAMILY*

Breakfast	Luncheon	Dinner
Grapefruit juice	Bouillon with	Baked Virginia ham
Rolled wheat, milk and	whole-wheat crackers	Browned potatoes
sugar	Spinach ring with	Winter squash
Toast, enriched bread,	creamed eggs	Lettuce with French
with margarine	Muffins with margarine	dressing
Milk for children	Orange and banana	Whole-wheat bread with
Coffee with milk and	salad	margarine
sugar, for adults†	Milk to drink	Chocolate blancmange
		Milk for children

* The dinner salad either can be omitted entirely for the four-year-old since there are other vegetables or a small portion can be given without the dressing.

† Coffee and tea are not essential but may be served in moderate amounts to adults at any meal as desired.

An examination of the day's dietary reveals that when the total contributions of these foods are compared with the recommended daily allowances for this family, the diet is exceedingly well protected in respect to each of the nutrients.

The milk, as would be expected, furnishes almost enough calcium to meet the daily recommended allowance, the other foods contributing only small amounts which help to provide a safe surplus.

The Dietary for a Family of Liberal Income

While it is an easy matter to obtain an adequate diet when there are no cost restrictions, it does not follow that with plenty of money to spend for food, diets will just naturally be good. The Agricultural Research Service, U.S. Department of Agriculture, found this to be the

TABLE 27–2. A DAY'S DIETARY FOR A BUDGET-MINDED FAMILY

Foods	Measure	Calories	Shares							
			Calories	Protein	Calcium	Iron	Vitamin A Value	Thiamine	Ribo-flavin	Ascorbic Acid
Milk, whole	3 qt.	1,920	19.20	44.4	123.6	3.6	24.0	24.0	86.4	9.6
Milk (nonfat), skim	1 pt	180	1.80	7.4	21.2	0.6	0.2	5.0	15.2	1.6
Eggs, cooked	5	400	4.00	12.5	5.0	16.0	17.0	6.5	13.0	0.0
Ham, light cure, lean and fat, roasted	1 lb	1,306	13.06	40.0	1.6	34.7	0.0	53.3	14.9	0.0
Lettuce	1 head	30	0.30	1.2	2.8	12.9	12.4	3.5	2.2	7.5
Potatoes, boiled	6	630	6.30	7.2	2.4	14.4	0.0	19.8	5.4	54.6
Spinach, cooked	3 cups	120	1.20	6.3	18.0	35.4	254.4	9.9	12.9	62.1
Squash (winter), cooked	2½ cups	325	3.25	4.3	5.0	11.8	125.3	6.3	11.8	28.0
Bananas	2	170	1.70	0.8	0.6	4.2	2.2	2.6	2.0	8.2
Grapefruit juice, frozen, sweetened, diluted	2½ cups	288	2.88	1.0	1.8	1.5	0.3	5.0	1.3	85.0
Oranges	4	300	3.00	1.6	9.6	3.6	7.2	16.0	4.0	116.0
Bread, white, enriched	10 slices	600	6.00	8.0	7.0	18.0	0.0	15.0	9.0	0.0
Bread, whole wheat	10 slices	550	5.50	8.0	8.0	15.0	0.0	15.0	5.0	0.0
Crackers, Graham	12 small	165	1.65	1.2	0.6	1.8	0.0	0.9	1.5	0.0
Flour, enriched, all-purpose	2⅛ cups	850	8.50	10.6	1.3	19.9	0.0	25.4	10.6	0.0
Wheat, rolled, cooked	3½ cups	613	6.13	7.4	2.5	17.5	0.0	15.1	3.5	0.0
Margarine	10 tbsp	1,000	10.00	0.0	1.0	0.0	27.0	0.0	0.0	0.0
Salad oil, corn	5 tbsp	625	6.25	0.0	0.0	0.0	0.0	0.0	0.0	0.0
Fats, cooking, vegetable	1½ tbsp	165	1.65	0.0	0.0	0.0	0.0	0.0	0.0	0.0
Sugar	⅔ cup	514	5.14	0.0	0.0	0.0	0.0	0.0	0.0	0.0
Bouillon, beef, broth, 4 cubes	4 cups	20	0.20	1.6	0.0	0.0	0.0	0.0	0.0	0.0
Chocolate, baking	1 oz	145	1.45	1.2	0.8	5.6	0.1	0.3	1.2	0.0
Cornstarch	¼ cup	116	1.16	0.0	0.0	0.0	0.0	0.0	0.0	0.0
Vinegar	2 tbsp	4	0.04	0.0	0.0	0.0	0.0	0.0	0.0	0.0
Coffee		0	0.00	0.0	0.0	0.0	0.0	0.0	0.0	0.0
Totals from diet		11,036	110.36	164.7	212.8	216.5	470.1	223.6	199.9	372.6
Recommended Daily Allowances		11,000	110.00	116.0	155.0	180.0	119.0	109.0	113.0	132.0

427

case in a nationwide study of family diets. When the quality of the diets of city families in the United States was compared with the amounts spent for food per person per week, it was found that although the percentage of the families having good diets was greater where the money for food was generous, there were, nevertheless, some families in the high-income group whose diets were classified as poor. That there should be any poor diets on a liberal food expenditure is shocking since for the most part this is due to factors that can be controlled, such as bad food habits, food notions, poorly prepared food, or too much dependence on appetite as a guide in food selection.

When the diets were compared on the basis of the abundance of protective foods, it was observed that where more money was available for food, the quantities of protective foods were greater. The possibility of having more protective foods makes the thought of planning diets without cost restriction a real delight. There is no end to the pleasing combinations that an unlimited food budget makes possible. It is fun indeed just to pause long enough to think of the great variety of gourmet delicacies and deluxe convenience foods available in American supermarkets. No place in the world offers such a choice of foods, and they may be found at all seasons of the year and irrespective of transportation difficulties. Under normal conditions almost any whim can be satisfied for the asking if one can pay the price. Many of these more expensive foods have much to offer the epicure nutritionally as well as from the standpoints of flavor, texture, and esthetic appeal. A few of these delicacies are listed in Table 27–3 along with the nutritive values of portions commonly served.

In glancing through the foods listed, it will be observed, for example, that the Gruyère and Parmesan cheeses and the clams make rather significant contributions of calcium.

The filet mignon and clams are the best sources of iron in the list, while artichokes, frog's legs, shad roe, squab, paté de foie gras, and sweetbreads also make outstanding contributions of iron.

Many of these foods are good sources of the vitamins. The mango heads the list for vitamin A value, while persimmons and paté de foie gras make significant contributions toward the recommended daily allowance of vitamin A.

None of these foods would be selected primarily for their thiamine content, although it will be noted that many of them carry more than their share of thiamine when compared with their respective calorie shares.

As a source of riboflavin shad roe and sweetbreads top the list. Among the other foods making significant contributions we find Camembert cheese, filet mignon, and frog's legs.

TABLE 27–3. NUTRITIVE VALUES OF SOME MORE EXPENSIVE FOODS*

			Shares							
Foods	Measure	Calo-ries	Calo-ries	Pro-tein	Cal-cium	Iron	Vita-min A Value	Thia-mine	Ribo-flavin	Ascor-bic Acid
Anchovies	4 small filets	28	0.28	1.3	1.0	0.3	—	—	0.5	—
Artichokes, French cooked	1 med.	43	0.43	1.4	2.2	3.8	1.0	2.0	0.9	4.1
Avocado	½ pear	171	1.71	0.9	0.4	1.7	1.7	2.8	3.4	5.8
Brownies	1 square frozen, iced	126	1.26	0.6	0.4	1.5	0.4	0.8	0.3	0.0
Caviar	1 tbsp	16	0.16	0.7	0.6	2.1	—	—	—	—
Celery	1 heart	11	0.11	0.2	0.9	0.6	0.9	0.5	0.3	2.5
Cheese, Camembert	Sector	126	1.26.	3.1	1.6	0.6	2.5	0.5	5.5	(0)
Cheese, Gruyère	Sector	95	0.95	2.9	8.9	0.9	2.3	0.0	1.9	(0)
Cheese, Parmesan, grated	¼ cup	83	0.83	3.2	8.5	0.0	1.3	0.0	2.6	(0)
Cheese, Roquefort	Sector	129	1.29	3.1	3.9	0.6	2.5	0.3	3.6	(0)
Clams, long (soft shell)	12	104	1.04	7.4	4.7	12.9	0.2	0.8	0.5	3.3
Filet mignon	5 oz	233	2.33	12.5	0.6	13.2	0.2	3.3	4.7	—
Frog's legs	4 oz	82	0.82	7.7	0.7	5.0	0.0	4.0	4.8	—
Honeydew melon	Wedge 2″ X 7″	49	0.49	0.5	0.8	1.8	0.3	1.5	0.9	14.5
Lobster meat	½ cup	62	0.62	5.1	1.5	1.5	—	1.8	0.9	—
Mango	1 med.	90	0.90	0.4	0.5	1.5	38.2	1.8	1.2	19.9
Paté de foie gras	1 tbsp	65	0.65	0.7	0.0	(2.4)	(5.2)	0.3	0.7	—
Persimmons	1 med.	95	0.95	0.4	0.3	1.2	19.7	1.0	0.5	5.8
Shad roe	½ pair	186	1.86	14.5	—	2.6	—	3.5	18.8	8.3
Squab	½ small	155	1.55	4.3	0.4	(3.6)	—	—	—	—
Sweetbreads, beef	½ pair	362	3.62	12.2	0.6	5.3	—	4.3	10.7	—

* In the above tabulation (compiled from various sources), — is used to represent a lack of information. 0.0 indicates an amount too small to record. ( ) indicates that the value given is imputed.

The mango stands out as a source of ascorbic acid. Persimmons, shad roe, and the avocado carry several times their share of ascorbic acid, while the honeydew melon carries many times its quota.

Thus the art of good eating need not be sacrificed to meet the requirements of an adequate diet. The gastronomist does not need to cramp his style but rather needs to extend his knowledge of food values so that he will be better equipped to select foods from the standpoints of both their psychological appeal and their nutritive value. A clever epicure will not be baffled by this challenge and will find the planning of his menus more fun than ever before.

Following the same procedures used to establish the recommended allowances for the budget-minded family, it will be easy to set up the recommended allowances for a specific family with a liberal income. Probably the father of this family holds an executive position which entails only a small expenditure of energy, since the activity involved is chiefly sitting. Consequently, the calorie allowance need not be more than 2,500 calories. The mother, probably doing little of her housework, would undoubtedly need no more than 1,800 calories. The children, of course, need calorie allowances in accordance with their ages. See Figures 4–8 and 4–9 in Chapter 4. Allowances for the other nutrients will be found in Tables A–1 and A–7 in the Appendix.

Assuming that there are two children, a boy of 12 years and a girl of eight years, and that they are of average weight and are moderately active—according to Table A–7 in the Appendix, the boy will need approximately 2,700 calories and his sister 2,100 calories. The daily recommended allowances for the family may be summarized as in Table 27–4.

In planning the menus for this family of liberal income, one should refer to the four-food-group plan and make a list of the essential foods needed. However, the choices may be made from a greater variety of foods since the selection is not curtailed by the cost.

Menus have been planned keeping these facts in mind as a guide and they are given below. In studying the menus it is easy to check them against the simple rules of nutrition.

MENUS FOR ONE DAY FOR A FAMILY OF LIBERAL INCOME

Breakfast	Luncheon	Dinner
Melon	Creamed oysters in	Grapefruit salad on
Wheat flakes with milk	toast cups	endive
and sugar	Toast fingers	Lamb chops
Shirred eggs	Salad bowl (mixed greens)	Buttered peas and
Toast, whole wheat, with	Fresh blueberries	mushrooms
butter or margarine	Milk to drink	Parsley potatoes
Milk for children		Grilled tomatoes
Coffee for adults*		Dinner rolls with butter
		or margarine
		Pineapple sherbet
		Milk for children
		Coffee for adults*

* Coffee and tea are not essential but may be served in moderate amounts to adults at any meal as desired with or without cream and sugar.

Instead of fruit juice for ascorbic acid, fresh fruit has been selected for this particular day, and the salad greens have been included for vitamin

TABLE 27–4. RECOMMENDED DAILY ALLOWANCES FOR A FAMILY OF LIBERAL INCOME

| | Calo-ries | Shares | | | | | | | |
		Calo-ries	Pro-tein	Cal-cium	Iron	Vita-min A Value	Thia-mine	Ribo-flavin	Ascor-bic Acid
Father	2,500	25	29	29	29	29	25	26	29
Mother	1,800	18	24	29	44	29	20	21	29
Boy, 12 years	2,700	27	27	45	44	27	27	27	31
Girl, 8 years	2,100	21	22	29	35	20	21	22	25
Total	9,100	91	102	132	152	105	93	96	114

A value instead of a cooked green-leaf vegetable. Shirred eggs have been included in the breakfast menu, one egg being allotted for each member of the family. Lamb chops have been selected for dinner, each member of the family having a large chop, except possibly the eight-year-old girl.

The quantities of other foods needed to meet the allowances recommended for the family can be estimated by referring to Table A–15 in the Appendix, which gives the approximate servings per person on a weekly basis. The daily amounts can be calculated for each member of the family. When the lists of foods and amounts are completed, the nutritive values of the day's dietary can be calculated using Table A–8 in the Appendix and compared with the recommended daily allowances for this family of four given in Table 27–4.

The Economical Dietary for a Family with Limited Income

Among people of very limited means the largest item in the budget is food; however, while some years ago 50 per cent of the total income was spent for food, today a family of low income may spend 30 per cent for food. The average American family in the United States spends less than 20 per cent for food, although urban families may spend more than this.

Food economies can be effected in a variety of ways without sacrifice of nutritive value. The first change should generally be to increase the amount of food from cereal grains and decrease the amount from meat.

Milk, whole fluid, evaporated, or dried nonfat, gives the best nutritive return for the money invested. The vitamin D fresh milk and the reconstituted evaporated milk with vitamin D added are practically equivalent in nutritive value. The nonfat dry milk under current practices needs to be safeguarded for vitamin A value. Because of its low calorie content it is more suitable for adults. A glass of whole fluid milk may cost several times as much as a glass of reconstituted nonfat dry milk.

Among vegetables and fruits economies must be sought in use of foods at the height of their abundance and not when scarce and therefore expensive. Purchasing should be done with regard to nutritive value rather than size or color, but every effort should be made in buying fresh vegetables to have them as fresh as possible, since both flavor and nutritive value depend on this. Vegetables should be cooked with regard to conserving mineral elements and vitamins.

Meat is usually the most expensive food. Even cheap cuts are not so very cheap, or else they consist largely of waste. Meat is appetizing and a good source of protein; therefore, a certain amount is desirable, but the quantity consumed at a meal need not be large, and should be used in such a way as to extend its flavor with cereal, bread, and other bland food. Glandular meats such as liver (beef, lamb, or pork) and kidney will fortify the low-income diet with iron, vitamin A, thiamine, and riboflavin. One of these may well be included at least once a week.

Since the quantity of meat must be limited if the cost is to be kept low, it might be well at this point to compare the nutritive values of servings of other foods that may be used to replace meat. Poultry and fish are often very economical buys and are very good sources of protein. Foods such as beans (various kinds), lentils, eggs, cheese, and peanut butter may be used as alternates. See the comparative values in the Appendix (Tables A–4 or A–8). It should be noted that in a number of cases these foods surpass meat for their contributions of iron, thiamine, and riboflavin; and soybeans, salmon, and cheese are superior as sources of calcium.

A considerable saving in food expenditures can be made by using margarine in place of butter. Sugar and syrups often tend to be used too freely in economical diets, displacing foods that are more important. Pure cane molasses is significant for calcium and iron and, in a family where there are growing children, may be used to replace some cane sugar. Jams and jellies, unless made at home with fruits obtained at the height of the season at a reasonable price or home grown, are too expensive a source of calories to be included very often in the low-income diet. The fruit obtained in this way is far too insignificant in quantity to play any important role in the dietary.

We might suggest planning a day's dietary for a family of limited income following the procedures worked out for the budget-minded family and the family of liberal income discussed earlier in this chapter.

In setting up the allowances for an average family with little money to spend for food, the energy allowances should be generous since the father of this family may be doing heavier work and the mother probably does her own housework. If in a particular case this is not true and the father is not doing heavy work, the calorie allowance needs to be adjusted to fit his requirements. Allowances for children according to age are given in Table A–7 in the Appendix.

Again taking the simple rules of nutrition as a guide, and making selections from foods of lower cost but of high nutritive quality, typical menus for one day can be planned such as those found below. Suggestions for cutting food costs are given in Table A–19.

MENUS FOR ONE DAY FOR A FAMILY OF LIMITED INCOME

Breakfast	Luncheon	Dinner
Prunes	Spaghetti with tomato	Tomato juice cocktail
Oatmeal, milk and sugar	and cheese	Chicken potpie
Toast, enriched bread,	Carrot and cabbage	Kale
with margarine	slaw, French dressing	Potatoes, boiled in jackets
Milk for children	Peanut-butter-and-raisin	Bread, whole wheat, with
Coffee for adults*	sandwiches	margarine
	(whole-wheat bread)	Custard
	Milk to drink	Milk for children
		Coffee for adults*

* Coffee and tea are not essential but may be served in moderate amounts to adults at any meal if the budget permits with or without milk and sugar.

With these menus in mind and using the tables in the Appendix, a list of foods and quantities for the day may be compiled and the nutritive value calculated. Comparison with the recommended allowances should show a generous margin of safety for each of the essential nutrients (with the exception of calories). Indeed, if the totals of each of the three family diets (after calculation) are compared, it will be noted that regardless of the cost, each day's dietary provides generous surpluses of all the specific nutrients. The smallest surpluses are found in the calorie column. This is as it should be since there is no virtue in storing up calories. The surpluses of the other nutrients show no particular trends that can be lined up with the cost. This demonstrates that it is the choice of foods that determines the nutritive quality of the diet rather than the expenditure for food. However, since the choices are more limited when the income level is low, it is highly desirable that educational programs be sponsored in all communities where large proportions of the population have to live on restricted incomes. This can best be accomplished by engaging the services of a trained nutritionist who appreciates the many problems concerned with the choice of foods, including the economic aspects of marketing as well as the nutritive value and preparation of the food in the home.

One of the programs where nutrition education is especially needed is that concerned with donated foods. The foods are made available to needy families through the Food Distribution Program. The foods available vary depending on the surpluses of federal foods and the area, but include dried eggs, dried skim milk, cornmeal, wheat, rice, oatmeal, canned meat, peanut butter, butter, beans, and cheese.

The fact that in June 1963 approximately 6½ million people in needy family units were receiving donated foods is of interest. The food distribution is in the hands of the state and local welfare agencies. It is important that an educational program on the better use and care of donated foods by recipient families be carried on along with the distribution of the food. Many times families cannot make use of unfamiliar foods without help.

The Food Stamp Program[1] administered under the U.S. Department of Agriculture is another program to get more food to low-income families. Eligible families may exchange the amount of money they could normally be expected to spend on food for federal food-stamp coupons worth more at retail stores. How much more depends on the size and income of the family. Figure 27–4 shows a family that has taken advantage of this program.

[1] *Expanding the Food Stamp Program.* Washington, D.C.: U.S. Department of Agriculture, Picture Story No. 177 (March 1965).

FIGURE 27–4. FAMILY OF SIX ARE BETTER FED AS A RESULT OF THE FOOD STAMP PLAN. (*Courtesy of U.S. Department of Agriculture.*)

Plans for family diets at different cost levels proposed by the U.S. Department of Agriculture are given in the Appendix (Tables A–16, A–17, and A–18). These plans suggest quantities of food needed by the various members of the family on a weekly basis. The cost of these food plans for families of different size at December 1964 retail food prices (United States average) is given in Table 27–5.

TABLE 27–5. ESTIMATED COST OF ONE WEEK'S FOOD* COMPUTED FROM QUANTITIES IN U.S. DEPARTMENT OF AGRICULTURE FOOD PLANS AS OF DECEMBER 1964—UNITED STATES AVERAGE

Families	Economy Plan	Low-Cost Plan	Moderate-Cost Plan
Family of 2, 20–35 years	$11.10	$14.70	$19.80
Family of 2, 55–75 years	9.40	12.30	16.70
Family of 4, preschoolchildren	16.70	21.60	28.80
Family of 4, schoolchildren	19.20	24.80	33.20

*Family Economics Review, ARS 62–5, p. 21. Washington, D.C.: U.S. Department of Agriculture (March 1965).

That it will pay to master the art of selecting an adequate diet at any cost level has been the lesson taught by the most careful investigations in the field of nutrition. As Sherman said, "With heredity and all the conditions of environment except food the same, those enjoying the better diet are bound to inherit the earth."

REFERENCES

Community Council of Greater New York. *A Family Budget Standard*. New York: Budget Standard Service (1963).

Delgado, G., Brumback, C. L., and Deaver, M. B. "Eating Patterns Among Migrant Families." *Pub. Health Rep.*, **76**:349 (1961).

Farmer's World—The Yearbook of Agriculture (1964). Steven, R. D. "Population, Income, and Food," p. 53; Hoecker, R. W. "Supermarkets Around the World," p. 279. Washington, D.C.: U.S. Department of Agriculture.

Fleck, H., and Munves, E. *Introduction to Nutrition*, Chaps. 27 and 28. New York: Macmillan (1962).

Food—The Yearbook of Agriculture, 1959. Murray, J., and Blake, E. *What Do We Eat?* p. 609; Le Bovit, C., and Clark, F. *Are We Well Fed?* p. 620.

Leverton, R. M. *Food Becomes You*, Chap. 16. Iowa City: Iowa State U. P. (1961).

Reh, E. *Manual on Household Food Consumption Surveys*. FAO Nutritional Study No. 18. Rome: Food and Agriculture Organization (1962).

Riley, M. A., and Dodds, M. L. "Use of Government-Donated Foods by Married Students." *J. Amer. Dietet. A.*, **47**:110 (1965).

Rose, M. S. *Feeding the Family*, 4th ed., Chaps. 3, 4, and 14. New York: Macmillan (1940).

U.S. Department of Agriculture. *Convenience Foods in the Grocery Basket*. Marketing Bulletin No. 22 (1962); *The Food We Eat*, Miscellaneous Publication No. 870 (1961); *Using Donated Foods*. Cooperative Extension Service (1963); *Money-Saving Main Dishes*. Home and Garden Bulletin No. 43 (1962); *Family Food Plans and Food Costs* (for nutritionists and other leaders who develop or use food plans). Home Economics Research Report No. 20 (1962); *Family Fare—Food Management and Recipes*. Home and Garden Bulletin No. 1 (1961); *Food for the Family with Young Children*. Home and Garden Bulletin No. 5 (1962); *Food for Families with School Children*. Home and Garden Bulletin No. 13 (1963); *Food for the Young Couple*. Home and Garden Bulletin No. 85 (1962); *Family Food Budgeting*. Home and Garden Bulletin No. 94 (1964); *Conserving the Nutritive Values in Foods*. Home and Garden Bulletin No. 90 (1963); *Family Meals at Low Cost*. PA 472 (1965); *Household Food Consumption Survey, 1955*. No. 16, *Dietary Evaluation of Foods Used in Households in the United States* (1963); *A Guide to Budgeting for the Young Couple*. Home and Garden Bulletin No. 98 (1964); *U.S. Food Consumption, 1909–63*. Statistical Bulletin No. 364 (1965).

৺ 28 ৺

International Nutrition and Nutrition Education Programs

International Nutrition

THE CHALLENGE OF HUNGER

The challenges of our age are well known to us all. We hear about them, read about them, discuss them. No challenge is greater or more vitally important than that of adequate food for the world's peoples.

Dr. Sen, Director-General of the Food and Agriculture Organization (FAO) of the United Nations, reminds us that three major revolutions have taken place thus far in the twentieth century and impart a greater sense of urgency in attempts to cope with problems of hunger and malnutrition. One revolution is political, establishing self-government for almost a third of the world's population and alerting world attention to their hopes and desires for a better life. The second revolution, in communications, has caused our world to shrink, breaking down barriers of distance and language. The third revolution Dr. Sen cites is the demographic, or the population explosion. In 1965, Dr. Sen warns that the next 35 years, till the end of the century, will be a most critical period in man's history because of food shortage.

In 1964 Dr. Stiebeling,[1] for many years in charge of nutrition and food economic activities in the U.S. Department of Agriculture and advisor to FAO, commented on the implications of the current rapid increase in world population. In 1600 the world had 400 million people to feed; by 1800 this number had doubled; by 1900 it had again almost doubled; now in the 1960's it has again doubled. Today there are 3,000 million people on our planet. It is predicted that there may be 6,000 million by the year 2000. This accelerating increase in numbers to be fed, clothed, housed, and educated is almost overwhelming in its impact. The developed countries can produce, most of them reasonably well, by the application of science and technology, the quantities of additional food their popula-

[1] Stiebeling, H. K. "Our Share in Better World Nutrition." *J. Amer. Dietet. A.*, **45**:315 (1964).

tions will require. But in the developing lands population gains are greater, and these countries are less able to produce the extra food needed. Table 28–1, taken from the Third World Food Survey of FAO, summarizes data on the average per capita supply of calories and proteins in different regions. Because the more technically advanced lands cannot produce sufficient abundance to cover the needs of these developing countries, it is urgent that they be helped to help themselves. An old saying quoted by FAO refers to the advantage of teaching a man to fish, which will feed him for a lifetime, rather than just giving him a fish, which will last but a day.

In 1963, at the World Food Congress, it was estimated that up to half of the world's current population (representing 1,000 to 1,500 million people) were underfed or malnourished or both. Some are at the starvation level, while others are borderline. As discussed in earlier chapters, people adjust in some degree to meager or nutritionally inadequate food supplies but often at a severe cost in stunted growth, reduced work output, and lower resistance. Recent reports make us aware of the related, more subtle effects of undernutrition on the function of the brain and central nervous system. Mental ability may be reduced irreversibly by food shortages in the first few years of life. These facts emphasize the loss of potential for both the individual and his nation.[2]

When we remember that food in human existence has meanings over and above biochemical nutrition and physical survival in terms of the social aspects of life, we can understand the grave nature of this problem of food scarcity.

Calder[3] points out the political dangers of hunger. As he states, "Democracy is a word which rumbles meaninglessly in empty bellies." Sir John Boyd Orr, the first Director-General of FAO, argued as early as 1946 that failure to carry out measures to eliminate hunger and poverty could lead to the spread of communism in many areas of the world.

It is apparent from discussion in earlier chapters that each country around the world has its unique nutrition problems, some of scarcity, some of abundance, some of specific nutritional deficiencies. Many agencies are working on these multiple problems.

THE INTERNATIONAL AGENCIES CONCERNED WITH NUTRITION PROBLEMS IN DEVELOPING COUNTRIES

In an earlier chapter reference was made to the nutrition activities of the League of Nations and the setting of dietary standards. Although politically the League of Nations was unsuccessful, in the area of nutrition the Mixed Committee of the League of Nations surveyed world

[2] Coursin, D. B. "Effects of Undernutrition on Central Nervous System Function." *Nutr. Rev.*, **23**:65 (1965).
[3] Calder, R. *A Starving World*. New York: Macmillan (1962).

TABLE 28-1. AVERAGE DAILY PER CAPUT SUPPLIES OF CALORIES, TOTAL PROTEINS, AND ANIMAL PROTEINS AT THE RETAIL LEVEL, BY REGIONS*

| Regions | Period | Calories | | Total Protein | Animal Protein |
		Number	% Derived from Cereals, Starchy Roots, and Sugar	Grams	
Far East					
(incl. China, Mainland)	Prewar	2,090	78	61	7
	Postwar	1,890	79	54	6
	Recent	2,060	81	56	8
Near East	Prewar	2,295	78	72	12
	Postwar	2,220	78	69	12
	Recent	2,470	71	76	14
Africa	Prewar	—	—	—	—
	Postwar	—	—	—	—
	Recent	2,360	74	61	11
Latin America	Prewar	2,160	63	64	28
	Postwar	2,315	66	62	22
	Recent	2,510	63	67	24
Europe (incl. U.S.S.R.)	Prewar	2,870	67	85	28
	Postwar	2,760	68	82	29
	Recent	3,040	63	88	36
North America	Prewar	3,260	48	86	51
	Postwar	3,170	43	91	61
	Recent	3,110	40	93	66
Oceania	Prewar	3,290	50	103	67
	Postwar	3,250	50	98	66
	Recent	3,250	48	94	62
Low-calorie countries†	Prewar	2,110	77	62	10
	Postwar	1,960	78	56	8
	Recent	2,150	78	58	9
High-calorie countries	Prewar	2,950	62	85	34
	Postwar	2,860	62	85	37
	Recent	3,050	57	90	44
World†	Prewar	2,380	71	69	18
	Postwar	2,240	71	64	18
	Recent	2,420	70	68	20

* From Third World Food Survey, Table 13, p. 34. Rome: FAO (1963).
† Includes estimates for Africa for prewar and postwar.

problems and established guidelines for nutrition activities.[4] This made possible the establishment of the Food and Agriculture Organization as the first of the United Nations agencies in 1945.

The Food and Agriculture Organization took as its motto "Fiat Panis," which means "Let There Be Bread." This is on the FAO seal. The primary mission of FAO is to improve nutritional levels in its member countries (107 full members, two associate members), through improvement of the production and distribution, conservation, and consumer use of food. In 1951, its program of technical assistance was expanded, and over 2,000 assignments have been carried out in about 100 countries. These have included such activities as advisement on agricultural policies in government and projects in food technology and nutrition education. Seminars, workshops, and conferences on nutrition and home economics in various regions of the world have been held, often cooperatively with other interested agencies. Many fellowships have been awarded to individuals for technical study abroad. Thus staff is prepared for the less-developed countries to carry on nutrition programs. In 1960 the intensive "Freedom from Hunger" campaign was initiated. FAO and two other United Nations Agencies concerned with nutrition problems, the World Health Organization (WHO) and the United Nations Children's Emergency Fund (UNICEF), work cooperatively on a number of projects. One such project is involved with the development of protein-rich foods and their promotion in child-feeding programs in countries where animal protein foods are in short supply. In the chapter on protein and amino acids, some of this work has been discussed, for example, the development of Incaparina. Another means of increasing the protein supply is fish culture in ponds and rivers. See Figure 28–1.

The United States has been making a contribution to the hunger problem. Senator McGovern,[5] in his discussion of America's Food for Peace Program, points out that 40 million schoolchildren receive lunches through this program in 80 countries. The United States also has several programs designed to assist the developing countries to help themselves. The American International Development Agency (AID) has sent at the request of governments experienced personnel to assist officials in evaluating their food and agricultural policies and to organize educational and action programs. Another United States agency is the Interdepartmental Committee on Nutrition for National Development (ICNND), which conducts nutrition surveys referred to in earlier chapters. This agency sends interdisciplinary teams consisting of biochemists, nutritionists, nurses, clinicians, agricultural experts, home economists, food technologists, anthropologists, and other disciplines, mostly from the United

[4] League of Nations. Final Report. *The Relation of Nutrition to Health, Agriculture and Economic Policy*. Mixed Committee. Geneva (1937).

[5] McGovern, G. S. *War Against Want*. New York: Walker (1964).

FIGURE 28–1. FISH CULTURE IN THAILAND. This photograph shows experimental fishing with a seine net in a river. (*Courtesy of FAO.*)

States, to the country to be surveyed. These teams work with counterpart personnel from that country, which provides an opportunity for training local leaders. This also stimulates interest and activity in nutrition within the country. Many countries have established centers or institutes of nutrition. The nutritional survey provides invaluable information on the food and nutrition situation that can be used in program development focused directly at the specific needs and potentials of the particular country. Surveys have been conducted in a number of countries including Lebanon, Ethiopia, Pakistan, Turkey, Spain, Peru, Ecuador, Chile, Colombia, Taiwan, Thailand, Korea, Vietnam, and the Philippines. Each country has characteristic problems, and programs are being developed to achieve a higher level of nutrition. Some representative examples are discussed in the following sections.

THE PHILIPPINES AND OTHER FAR EASTERN COUNTRIES

The Institute of Nutrition established in 1948 in the Philippines was reorganized under the National Science Development Board as the Food and Nutrition Center. The ICNND conducted a nutrition survey in the Philippines in 1957, and the nutrition program was again reviewed to implement the recommendations of this survey. In 1959, the Philippine Government requested the ICNND to supply a nutritionist and food technologist to give additional help in promoting better nutrition.

The Food and Nutrition Research Center in the Philippines (as in many other countries—see Appendix Table A–9) has worked out specific recommended dietary allowances or standards appropriate for the population in terms of body size, activity, climate, and other special conditions. In the Philippines allowances are designed for men and women, for women during pregnancy and lactation, and for children during the growing period. For example, calorie allowances suggested for men and women are lower than those in the United States because of the smaller size of the people and the warmer climate. See discussion of food groups and menu plans, Chapter 21.

The classical nutritional problem in the Far East is, of course, beriberi, always a threat in rice-eating countries if the rice is polished and makes up a large proportion of the diet. Throughout Burma, Thailand, and Vietnam, beriberi has been relatively uncommon because the grain has been dehulled by pounding it at home. Paradoxically, in some rice-eating countries, periods of prosperity result in an increase in beriberi because the "socially superior" highly polished white rice is then on sale in the markets and the people have money to buy it.

In Japan, because of the increasing variety of the diet, beriberi has largely disappeared. Indeed the nutritional problems of Japan today are less acute even though the country is small in proportion to population. The stature of the Japanese is increasing, in part, no doubt, due to dietary improvement. Japan has become quite nutrition conscious, has a school lunch program and has taken other measures to improve nutritional status.

In 1964 Mitchell[6] discussed the changing heights of Japanese children, 6 to 18 years of age, as shown in Figure 28–2 (*A* and *B*) for the years 1900–60. These data show a slow but continuous increase in height for each age group from 1900 to 1939, when measurement was interrupted by World War II. In 1948, when records were again taken, the stature at each age level was less than it had been in 1939, with the greatest decrease in the 14-year-old groups. Wartime food restrictions are probably responsible, according to the Japanese nutritionists. Since 1948 there has been a steady and rapid increase in both height and weight at each age level.

[6] Mitchell, H. "Protein Limitation and Human Growth." *J. Amer. Dietet. A.,* **44**:165 (1964).

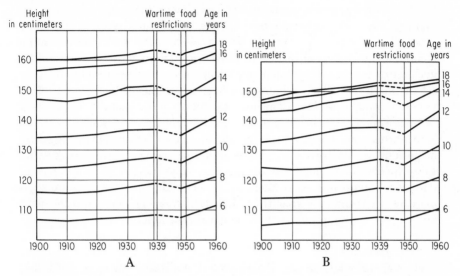

FIGURE 28–2. GROWTH RATES OF JAPANESE SCHOOLCHILDREN. Note the changes in height for boys (*A*) and girls (*B*) over a period of 60 years. (*Courtesy of Helen S. Mitchell and the* J. Amer. Dietet. A., **44**:*168* [*1964*].)

INDIA

There are some 564,000 separate villages in India, and farm workers make up about 70 per cent of the population. This is now the highest percentage of an agricultural population in the world except for Pakistan. Millions of Indian farmers live chiefly on cereals and vegetables that they themselves grow. For centuries the farmer has gone his own way silent and unchanging. An enormous proportion of the population still dies young. Malnutrition for many Indians begins with weaning and lasts until death comes, prematurely.

Despite the many early deaths, the present population explosion in India is very extensive, and the population is expected to reach 492 million by 1966. Each year the country adds more than the approximate equivalent of the population of New York City to its numbers. There are over 9,000 government-maintained "family planning centers" scattered around the vast country. While these are successful within their areas, they are not able to reach the majority of the people.

Indian food plans call for an increase in grain production from 78 million tons a year (1960) to 100 million tons in 1966. There was a bad growing season in 1962–63, and production is still far from the goal (1965).

India has conducted an impressive series of land reforms, and considerable efforts are being made to help the farmer and improve the health of the villagers. The Community Development Program was launched in 1952. The program now covers almost all of rural India. Villages are grouped into "development blocks" of about 100 each. New farming techniques, irrigation projects, improved sanitation practices, and other health practices are suggested and demonstrated. The development of school meals in village schools has been encouraged. See Figure 28–3. Another program is that of promoting school gardens. See Figure 28–4.

After training of village leaders, the villagers are encouraged to try to help themselves. Despite the apathy of centuries, and the staggering magnitude of the problem, the program has been notably successful. Life expectancy has increased from 32 to 42 years, and agricultural production has increased more than 40 per cent. But because of population increases, it is unlikely that there has been much, if any, improvement in the food consumption of the average Indian family.

LATIN AMERICA

Harrar,[7] president of the Rockefeller Foundation, stated in 1963 that ". . . interplanetary exchange is apparently just around a cosmic corner. Modern technology is dazzling in what it can do, not only in space but here on earth in the creation of new sources of energy, new methods of production, and new products for those who can buy and use them. But in the meantime the melancholy fact is that half the people in the world go to bed hungry every night." The Rockefeller Foundation has been a

FIGURE 28–3. CHILDREN IN ORISSA, INDIA, ENJOY A LOW-COST SCHOOL LUNCH. (*Courtesy of FAO.*)

[7] Harrar, J. G. *Strategy for the Conquest of Hunger.* New York: Rockefeller Foundation (1963).

philanthropic force for good in the fulfillment of mankind's ideals for world health and well-being.

One example of the work of the Rockefeller Foundation is in Mexico. The Mexican Revolution, which originally started in 1910, later had as its battle cry "Paz y Pan" ("Peace and Bread"). Day by day the population was outdistancing its food production. In 1943 the improvement of maize and wheat, the principal food crops of Mexico, was emphasized. The pattern established by the Rockefeller Foundation was later followed by improving other crops. An American and Mexican agricultural expert working together were aided by many staff specialists in corn, wheat, soil science, etc. Each of these specialists became the leader of small

FIGURE 28–4. CHILDREN TENDING PAPAYA TREES IN THEIR SCHOOL GARDEN IN INDIA. (*Courtesy of WHO and FAO.*)

groups of young Mexican agronomists (experts in applied phases of soil and plant science) selected by the Ministry of Agriculture for training. Natively adapted varieties of maize (or other crops) were collected and tested and the best were released to farmers for planting. Promising materials from other countries were also brought in. Higher-yielding, disease-resistant varieties were adapted to appropriate Mexican areas. In a cooperatively sponsored effort of the Mexican government and the Rockefeller Foundation, both crops and personnel were "cultivated." Promising young men were given grants for study abroad, returning to jobs in Mexico.

The farmers responded nobly to the strategy of improved seeds and methods of farming, and in 20 years, Mexico's population of 21 million rose to 37 million, but per person the more varied average diet increased from 1,700 to 2,700 calories. Similar programs have been started in other Latin American countries as well as elsewhere in the world.

The work of the Institute of Nutrition of Central America and Panama (INCAP) has already been referred to in the discussion in earlier chapters of kwashiorkor and protein supplementation. This institute was developed under the guidance of Dr. Scrimshaw, who served as director for many years. The institute was established with the assistance of the Pan American Sanitary Bureau, WHO, and has played a major role in coping with the tremendous nutrition problems encountered in the area, which include food scarcity, an inadequate supply of good quality protein, anemia, and goiter.

Many other nutrition activities have been carried out in South and Central America adapted to the nutrition problems characteristic of the different countries and communities.

AFRICA

A number of agencies are at work in Africa in an attempt to raise the nutritional level of the natives in the many fast-developing African countries. Since many of the nutrition problems have been discussed in earlier chapters, it is not necessary to discuss them in detail in this chapter. The work at Mulago Hospital, Kampala, Uganda, has been referred to in connection with the problem of protein-calorie malnutrition. Dr. Jelliffe heads the Department of Pediatrics and Child Health. The small African house known as the Mulago Parents Club is situated near the wards and is used for health education of the mothers who accompany their sick children to the hospital. See Figure 28–5.

NUTRITION IN THE DEVELOPED COUNTRIES

A problem in the northern countries of Europe, including Great Britain, has been to obtain an adequate supply of ascorbic acid. They, of course, cannot grow the citrus fruits that we depend on in the United

FIGURE 28–5. PARENTS OBSERVING A FOOD DEMONSTRATION IN FRONT OF THE MULAGO PARENTS CLUB IN KAMPALA, UGANDA, AFRICA. (*Courtesy of D. B. Jelliffe.*)

States, and it is usually expensive to import much of these foods from southern countries. In both Great Britain and Scandinavia sources of ascorbic acid unfamiliar to us are used, such as rose hips and lingonberries. The potato has always been a dependable antiscorbutic in these countries, and during the Nazi occupation of Norway, home-grown potatoes kept many families free from scurvy.

Proja,[8] of the Nutrition Section of the Italian Ministry of Public Health in Rome, summarizes the food and nutrition situation in Italy in 1962 as "rather satisfactory" owing in large part to the economic progress of the last 15 years. As he points out, the passage from the deficiency level to the level of excess in nutrition can be easily reached, and this level in high-calorie foods may be equally dangerous. Western Europe, like the United States in a prosperous era, is beginning to face the problems of overabundance of the food supply and its effect on the public health.

Interest in nutrition in Russia is keen, and a great deal of research is conducted in institutes of nutrition under the universities in several cities. Like ourselves, the Russians are actively studying the intricacies of atherosclerosis, fat, and cholesterol metabolism. On the other hand, emphasis is given to the effects of starvation and famine. Even during

[8] Proja, M. "Nutrition Problems and Activities in Italy." *Nutr. Rev.,* **20:**129 (1962).

World War II studies were carried out at the siege of Leningrad to investigate the effects of hunger.

Nutrition Education

Education in nutrition has a special role to play and is or should be an integral part of programs designed to promote better health of all population groups. Earlier discussions in this chapter direct attention to the special nutrition problems in particular areas in different parts of the world. These problems have been clarified through the many nutrition surveys conducted by various agencies, and attempts have been made to find ways of promoting effective educational programs.

What are some of the factors, other than those concerned with the availability of foods and their cost, that must be considered before making any recommendations? Most dietary patterns that have been continued over the years have certain desirable features that need to be appreciated even though they differ greatly from our own. The use of soybeans with rice in the basic diet of Orientals makes a nutritionally acceptable combination but may be improved by supplementation. In most instances it is not necessary to change long-accustomed food habits but rather to encourage the use of available supplementary foods that will help to raise the level of nutrition and provide an adequate diet.

The prestige value given to foods is often an important consideration. Sometimes certain vegetables are thought to be the foods of the poor and others will not eat them. Refined cereals have been preferred to the whole grains in areas throughout the world.

In many situations religious and social customs influence not only food habits but food production. In some countries it may be more difficult to promote egg production or to expand the fishing industry than in others. For example, in India many Hindus do not eat eggs because of religious beliefs but can be persuaded to use them if candling indicates nonfertility.

Unfortunate experiences in the use of certain foods may have established fear, and this is handed down from mother to daughter—for example, the concept that milk causes diarrhea when given to small children without the realization that it was probably the bacterial contamination that made the milk harmful. It is always difficult to separate magic and scientific facts.

In Indonesia the most favored women are slim and, even as adolescent girls, are not allowed to eat watery fruit such as melon (a good source of vitamins). Even when a mother is nursing her baby, she commonly takes less food than required. It is no wonder that a mother having had uninterrupted pregnancies may look old for her age, be anemic, lose her hair, and have unhealthy skin.

The idea that men are superior sometimes means that their likes and dislikes in regard to food as well as other customs are given cognizance at the expense of the woman. It is difficult for one to understand and be wholly objective in dealing with the culture of another. Human behavior in a particular society depends on the long-established acceptable customs and varies in different situations. Our world today, because of our advances in technology, communication, and transportation, has become a mixture of the cultures of many groups, and consequently population groups are far more complex than they were even 25 years ago.

However, the great challenge is that of motivating the people to do something about their food habits, and we continue to search for the "know-how." The old saying "You can lead a horse to water but you can't make him drink" still holds. Cultural patterns that have continued for generations are not easy to change. It is a wise nutrition educator who takes time to explore the possible reasons for "resistance to change" before making suggestions, and the current diet of any population group certainly needs to be given a "hard look" before new and unfamiliar foods are introduced. Unless the people themselves develop a self-awareness and appreciate the need for change, little progress will be possible.

To bring about desirable changes in the lives of people, programs must be closely linked to the well-established habits and customs. It has been said that a good educator must be a "people watcher" with a seeing eye, listening ear, inquiring mind, understanding heart, welcoming tongue, sharing hand, unending patience, true humility, and a long view. These ideas and others have been incorporated into the approaches successfully used in the Peace Corps Program.[9]

Nutrition Education Programs

Many effective nutrition education programs have been conducted in practically every state in the United States, Canada, and other areas around the world. A few of these programs which have been continued over a period of years are described in more detail in the following pages as representative of types of programs adapted to specific locations. It takes time and continued effort to establish an "on-going" program in nutrition education.

Under the direction of the late Mary Swartz Rose, professor of nutrition at Teachers College, Columbia University, and a pioneer in the development of nutrition education, programs were under way in the schools and community surrounding the university by the early 1920's. Students were given an opportunity to participate in these programs, and

[9] Shriver, S. "Ambassadors of Good Will, the Peace Corps." *Nat. Geographic,* **126:**297 (1964).

basic techniques and methods of teaching nutrition were established some of which are still applicable today. Under the inspiring leadership of Mary Swartz Rose, the program was expanded, reaching out to many communities and other parts of the world. These programs at Teachers College started so many years ago have been continued and now cover a period of almost half a century.

One of the outstanding programs was that conducted at the Speyer School covering a period of five years under the direction of Dr. Rose with the able assistance of Dr. Bertlyn Bosley. This program was established jointly by the Board of Education of New York City and Teachers College, Columbia University, for the purpose of developing suitable curricula for exceptional children. A number of noteworthy publications by Mary Swartz Rose and Bertlyn Bosley followed this extensive nutrition education research. These publications were particularly designed to help teachers in the elementary school.

A CITY PROGRAM

Taylor directed a comprehensive nutrition research project in a New York City public elementary school which covered a period of eight years. This served as a demonstration center in nutrition education for a number of schools in the neighborhood and in other areas. Graduate students participated in the program and in this way gained first-hand experience in working with teachers, parents, and children. The school was located in the heart of a crowded low-income area, the children coming from families representing 43 different national backgrounds with a preponderance of children from Spanish-speaking countries. About 75 per cent of the teachers in this school cooperated on the program. The cooperation of the principal was most helpful in making nutrition a part of the entire school program.

The nutrition program was planned with the teachers working at different grade levels to meet the needs indicated in initial surveys. Units on nutrition were easily integrated into the regular classroom programs in science, health, social studies, language arts, etc.

In the kindergarten and first and second grades, activities promoting good food habits, such as simple experiences in food preparation, trips to markets, indoor gardening, and tasting parties, were carried out. Guinea pigs, albino rats, chickens, and rabbits were kept in the classrooms as pets and helped to teach the younger children the importance of cleanliness, good care, and good foods for health and growth. Each of these activities directed attention to the foods that are nutritionally desirable for growing boys and girls.

In the third and fourth grades emphasis was placed on breakfasts and lunches. Simple meals were prepared in the classrooms and became a part of other units, such as a colonial breakfast in a social studies unit. A classroom luncheon at minimum cost created an interest in the bargain lunch served at school. Studies of vegetables, fruits, and grains, their source, and how they grow were of special interest to the city children, whose experience centered around foods as they appear in city markets. The importance of the pasteurization of milk and the preservation of other foods worked in well with science and health units.

Fourth-, fifth-, and sixth-grade boys and girls were thrilled to have an animal experiment and to watch the effect of a good in contrast to a poor breakfast on the growth of animals—a most rewarding and convincing experience which could readily be integrated with their study of science (see Figure 28–6).

More detailed studies of the individual nutrients, their food sources, and their function in maintaining health were planned for the upper grades. Slides, film strips, and motion pictures helped to enrich the program. These are just a few of the many activities that the teachers and children found both stimulating and enjoyable.

The parents were invited to participate whenever possible. Special meetings with food demonstrations were planned, the mothers and fathers both being urged to attend. These meetings for parents were con-

FIGURE 28–6. FOURTH-GRADE CHILDREN IN A NEW YORK CITY SCHOOL CONDUCT A BREAKFAST EXPERIMENT IN THE SCIENCE CORNER OF THEIR CLASSROOM.

tinued throughout the eight years of the demonstration and are still being held by request.

To learn more about the actual accomplishments of the program, Sostman[10] (now associate professor of home economics at Douglass College, Rutgers University) made an evaluation covering a period of six of the eight years of the demonstration as a doctoral project. She found that 36 per cent of the children in the classrooms where nutrition was a regular part of the classroom program and only 11 per cent of those in classrooms where nutrition was not taught had fully adequate breakfasts. The survey also showed that the number of children preparing their own breakfasts at home had increased by 17 per cent as a result of the satisfying experience of preparing simple breakfasts as a classroom activity. Some of these boys and girls were also able to prepare breakfasts for younger brothers and sisters. The number participating in the school lunch program increased from 25 to 42 per cent. The lunches eaten at home showed an improvement in nutritional adequacy. Records kept of the heights and weights favored the children who had had continued nutrition education experience in the classroom.

Other projects patterned in somewhat the same manner but planned to meet a particular situation have been carried out in other schools. Graduate students with this type of experience have been able to adapt their nutrition education programs to meet the needs of situations in many parts of the world.

THE CAPE SABLE ISLAND PROJECT

Archibald[11] (now Dr. Juanita A. Eagles) a staff member of the Teachers College, Columbia University Nutrition Education project and later director of the Nutrition Division, Department of Public Health, Nova Scotia, conducted a convincing nutrition education program on Cape Sable Island, a small island off the coast of Nova Scotia, from 1949 to 1954 using part of this as her Doctorate of Education project. The people on this island were typical of those in fishing communities.

A carefully detailed survey was made of the schools and schoolchildren, the families (their size, age, sex, where they lived, their occupations, and their living conditions), and the nutritional status of the population. A random sample including one fifth of the families of the island was chosen, visited, and asked to cooperate in the program. Then followed five years of nutrition education programs in the schools, the homes, and the communities.

---

[10] Sostman, E. R., "An Evaluation of the Methods, Techniques, and Findings Used During a Six-Year Nutrition Education Program in a City School." Doctor of Education Project in Nutrition, Teachers College, Columbia University (1957).

[11] Archibald, J. H., "A Nutrition Education Program in Cape Sable Island." Doctor of Education Project in Nutrition, Teachers College, Columbia University (1952).

A resurvey was conducted at the end of the five years using the same methods as in the original survey. It was found that dietary inadequacy had been reduced from 18.5 per cent to 8.4, obesity from 3 per cent to 2.4, underweight from 6.6 per cent to 4.9, a low hemoglobin level from 36.5 per cent to 15.4, and the incidence of gingivitis from 45.4 per cent to 38.9. In this program the nutritionist had the full cooperation of medical health officers, the assistant superintendent of education, the inspector of schools, physicians, and public health nurses as well as that of the teachers.

THE DONA ELENA PROJECT

Lydia Roberts, a pioneer in nutrition education working from the University of Chicago, started some interesting community nutrition education programs in the Middle West in the early 1920's and continued her interest in nutrition education throughout her lifetime. In 1963, she made a five-year report of a project of outstanding merit that she directed in Puerto Rico entitled "The Dona Elena Project."[12]

This project, still continuing, is located in an isolated mountain community in Puerto Rico. It was planned to help the families in the community to improve their nutrition and other conditions of home and family living. With the help of the governor, funds were provided, and the Puerto Rico Nutrition Committee, including representatives of all agencies and organizations concerned with the nutrition of the people, sponsored the project. A subcommittee consisting of representatives of the Division of Nutrition of the Department of Health, the School Lunch Program of the Department of Public Instruction, the Food Distribution Division of the U.S. Department of Agriculture, and the Department of Home Economics of the University of Puerto Rico took over the responsibility for the direction and operation of the project. A medical nutrition consultant carried out a parasite control program and, working with a nutritionist, organized a clinic for infants and preschool-children. The Bureau of Sanitation cooperated on sanitary aspects, and the Division of Dental Hygiene made the dental examinations. Dr. Roberts served as over-all director of the project. One of the staff members of the university served full time as the home economist to live in the area and be locally in charge. The department's agronomist served as one of the major sponsors and also lived in the area.

The mountain community was isolated and living conditions were very primitive, but the constant encouragement of committee members helped to promote a happy atmosphere. As with other mountain communities, the roads were miserable, best traveled only by foot, jeep, or horseback. The families were large, with low incomes, inadequate diets, bad housing,

[12] Roberts, L. J. *The Dona Elena Project—A Better-Living Program in an Isolated Rural Community.* Río Piedras: Department of Home Economics, U. of Puerto Rico (1963).

and lack of water, lights, sanitary facilities, and health services. Government agencies provided a school. Local persons chosen by the people of five different sections served as a local council.

The school served as the center for the nutrition program. Three meals a day were provided to the children on school days. Weekly weight records were taken and heights were recorded monthly. These were matched with the records in a control community. The nutrition education program was carried out with the children in the school and through meetings with the parents. Attempts were made to improve the family food supply by planting vegetable gardens, cultivating fruit trees, and raising animals for milk and meat. The living conditions were also improved.

The attendance of children at school increased from 37 per cent in the first year to 88 per cent by the third year and ceased to be a problem thereafter. The proportion of children eating all the food served them increased from 11 per cent in the first year to 90 per cent or more by the fourth year. The height and weight records showed clearly that the program had helped to improve the nutrition and growth of children. The family diets also improved, showing a small but significant trend toward a more adequate diet.

It is concluded that more important than the tangible things reported is the change in the attitude of the community from one of hopelessness to an uplift in spirit and optimism. How fortunate this community has been to be the one selected for a demonstration of this kind.

THE HAZARDS OF FOOD FADS AND FRAUDS

One of the most baffling problems in nutrition education has been that of finding ways to combat the work of the ever-present charlatan who twists the meaning of scientific facts and interprets them with his pseudomagic touch to deceive his audience and line his pockets from the sale of useless wares. It is puzzling indeed that many intelligent people are willing to pay big money for frauds when we are living in an era when great advances in medical science are producing true miracles. Can it be that P. T. Barnum, the great showman, was right when he said that his success was based on the fact that people like to be fooled? Surely, when it comes to nutrition, a science linked so closely with the health and well-being of man, it should be easy to separate facts from myths and folklore.

It has been reported that 500 million dollars are spent each year on quack diets, fake pills, and false cures recommended by these self-styled nutritionists. What a scandalous waste of money this is! But what may be even more serious is that the person thus victimized may be suffering from a chronic illness and may fail to seek reliable medical treatment until it is too late to be effective.

The food quacks appear to be gifted in the psychology of salesmanship and use such clever devices in appealing to the public that even the intelligent layman is misled. The glamorous approach and promises of easy and quick cures with special health foods identified as the very elixir of life have an appeal beyond that of the sound, factual advice given by a well-informed scientist. References are given at the end of this chapter that direct attention to some of the fallacies promulgated by these distorters of the truth.

Many government and voluntary agencies sponsor educational programs of various kinds that are instrumental in combating misinformation. State, county, and city departments of health also have excellent programs over the radio, on television, and in the local newspapers. It is important to know the agencies that can be depended on for reliable information and to seek their guidance in answering special questions.

AGENCIES IN THE UNITED STATES CONCERNED WITH NUTRITION EDUCATION PROGRAMS

Outstanding programs in nutrition education sponsored by agencies in the United States have been conducted for years. Each decade has introduced new problems in our constantly changing and complex society. Thus policies and approaches in education and motivation must also undergo continuous re-examination and appraisal. New advances in the science of nutrition must be interpreted to meet the needs and concerns of a more sophisticated population. These agencies, with their background of experience and highly trained staffs, are well prepared to direct their energies to the new problems as they arise and to work with new agencies as they are created.

Interesting new nutrition programs are developing in connection with the Office of Economic Opportunity, under the Executive Office of the President (initiated under Public Law 88–452, 1964). For example, Project Head-Start, part of the program to combat poverty, is designed to give children a chance to get ready for school. As stated, "A well nourished child has the best chance, so feeding is important." Project Head-Start began to operate during the summer of 1965 to help youngsters entering school in the fall. Children attending the Project Head-Start center may have breakfast in some instances, always lunch—and a snack. The goal is to provide one third to one half the child's daily food needs. These centers are eligible for the U.S. Department of Agriculture Special Milk Program and surplus foods.

The government agencies can be depended on for publications on nutrition research, pamphlets, and bulletins dealing with the numerous practical nutrition problems of concern to individuals of all ages and to family groups. The Office of Information of the U.S. Department of Agriculture is prepared to direct requests to the division best prepared to take care of the question. Single copies of pamphlets may sometimes be obtained free, or for a nominal sum, by writing to the Superintendent of Documents.

Government agencies concerned with nutrition education include those listed below. A comprehensive report of the food and nutrition services performed by federal agencies is given in the Agricultural Research Service Booklet 62–9.[13]

U.S. Department of Agriculture (USDA)
  Agricultural Research Service: Consumer and Food Economics Research Division
  Extension Service
  Experiment Stations
  Agricultural Marketing Service
Department of Health, Education, and Welfare (HEW)
  Children's Bureau
  Public Health Service
  Office of Education
The Interagency Committee on Nutrition Education (ICNE)

Government agencies concerned with the protection of the public against fraudulent and misleading claims include the following:

Food and Drug Administration, U.S. Department of Health, Education, and Welfare. This agency protects the public against violations of federal labeling laws (false and misleading statements on containers or material accompanying them).

Federal Trade Commission. This agency has authority to deal with false and misleading matter such as that of commodity advertising related to food quacks.

The U.S. Post Office, Washington, D.C., protects against fraudulent or false advertising and soliciting money by mail.

Federal Communications Commission reviews radio and television broadcasts with regard to program and advertising material. It has the function of granting licenses to operate.

State, county, and city departments of public health (nutrition divisions or bureaus) conduct nutrition programs and publish educational materials designed to meet the state, county, and local needs.

NATIONAL ORGANIZATIONS

Better Business Bureau (BBB), with offices in most cities, is a national association sponsored by responsible businessmen that protects against unorthodox or illegal trade practices.

---

[13] Stiebeling, H. K. *Food and Nutrition Services of Federal and Quasi-Official Agencies of the United States.* ARS Publication No. 62–9. Washington, D.C.: U.S. Department of Agriculture (1960).

Food and Nutrition Board of the National Research Council (NRC) —National Academy of Sciences. This serves as an advisory body in the field of food and nutrition. It promotes needed research in this broad field and helps interpret nutritional science in the interests of public welfare.

The Nutrition Foundation, Inc. (NF). Organized as a nonprofit foundation by a group of food and related manufacturers interested in scientific progress and human health, the foundation promotes fundamental research and assists in making the science of nutrition effective in the lives of present and future generations. It publishes *Nutrition Reviews*.

PROFESSIONAL ORGANIZATIONS INTERESTED IN NUTRITION AND RELATED FIELDS

The American Institute of Nutrition (AIN) is one of the Federated Societies of Experimental Biology. The *Journal of Nutrition* is the official organ. The *American Journal of Clinical Nutrition* is the official organ of the American Society for Clinical Nutrition, an affiliated society of the American Institute of Nutrition.

The American Dietetic Association (ADA). The *Journal of the American Dietetic Association* is the official organ of the Association.

American Medical Association (AMA). The *Journal of the American Medical Association* is the official organ. The special council known as the Foods and Nutrition Council works with advertisers in stating claims suitably and correctly. The Bureau of Investigation exposes quacks, their programs, publications, and products sold. *Today's Health*, directed to the lay public, is also published by the AMA.

The Food and Nutrition Section of the American Public Health Association, Inc. (APHA). The *American Journal of Public Health* is the official organ of the association.

The American Home Economics Association (AHEA). The *Journal of Home Economics* is the official organ.

The American School Food Service Association. The *School Lunch Journal* is the official organ.

American Association for Advancement of Science (AAAS). *Science* is the official organ.

The Institute of Food Technologists (IFT). The *Journal of Food Science* is the official organ.

OTHER GROUPS INTERESTED IN NUTRITION

Food and nutrition departments of colleges and universities.

Visiting nurse services (VNS).

State, county, and city nutrition committees and councils.

While America continues to be the land of opportunity and food supplies are abundant, other problems are still unsolved. The nutritional status of our schoolchildren, as national surveys show, is not ideal, and our draft and selective-service records have revealed a low state of vigor in many of our young men. Also, as has been cited in earlier chapters, we have a high percentage of the population suffering from an over-indulgence in food. These problems emphasize the great significance of more effective nutrition education programs for all ages. Disraeli, the great British statesman, said "The health of the people is really the foundation upon which all our happiness and all our powers as a state depends."

In spite of cultural differences between nations, the recognition of certain universal human needs and motives gives us hope in facing the future. If some of our food and health problems can be solved on a world-wide basis, the possibility of a peaceful universe will be brought closer. The great historian, Hendrik Van Loon, observed, "The history of the world is the record of man in quest of his daily bread and butter."

REFERENCES

Agency for International Development. *Food for Peace Around the World.* A Manual for Leaders in Community Feeding Programs. Washington, D.C.: Department of State (1962).

Archibald, J. H., Eagles, E. L., and Pett, L. B. "Recent Nutrition Surveys and Nutrition Education Programme in Cape Sable, Nova Scotia." *Canad. Bull. Nutr.,* 4:1 (1956).

Berry, F. B., and Schaefer, A. "Nutrition Surveys in the Near and Far East. Report of the ICNND." *Amer. J. Clin. Nutr.,* 6:342 (1958).

Bosley, B. "Public Health Nutritionist." *Amer. J. Pub. Health,* 55:246 (1965).

Bourne, G. H. (ed.). *World Review of Nutrition and Dietetics,* Vol. 5. Beeuwkes, A. M. "Nutrition Education," p. 1; McKenzie, J. C., and Mumford, P. "The Evaluation of Nutrition Education Programmes: A Review of the Present Situation," p. 21. New York: Hafner (1965).

———. *World Review of Nutrition and Dietetics,* Vol. 4. Ferber, E. "Nutritional Conditions in Yugoslavia and Their Reflection on Health," p. 25; Verzar, F. "The Nutritional Status of Mountain Populations in Switzerland," p. 36. New York: Hafner (1963).

Brock, J. F. *Recent Advances in Human Nutrition.* Chap. 31, Tremolières, J. "Trends in Nutrition in the French-Speaking Countries"; Chap. 33, "Human Nutrition and the United Nations Agencies." Boston: Little (1961).

Burgess, A. "Nutrition Education in Public Health Programs—What We Have Learned." *Amer. J. Pub. Health,* 51:1715 (1961).

Burgess, A., and Dean, R. F. A. *Malnutrition and Food Habits.* London: Tavistock (1962).

Clarkson, M. R. "Health and Agriculture—A Vital Partnership." *Nutr. Rev.,* 22:129 (1964).

Darby, W. J. "Research Developments in International Nutrition." *Amer. J. Pub. Health,* 53:1789 (1963).

Deutsch, R. M. *The Nuts Among the Berries*. New York: Ballantine (1961).

Eppright, E., Pattison, M., and Barbour, H. *Teaching Nutrition*, 2nd ed. Iowa City: Iowa State U. P. (1963).

Farmer's World—The Yearbook of Agriculture, 1964. Phipard, E., and Kirby, R. H. "Nutritional Status of the World," p. 37; Phillips, R. W., and Haines, K. A., "FAO of the United Nations," p. 434; Stiebeling, H. K., and Leverton, R. M. "Problems in Human Nutrition," p. 558. Washington, D.C.: U.S. Department of Agriculture.

Food and Agriculture Organization. (Freedom from Hunger Campaign.) *Development Through Food—A Strategy for Surplus Utilization*. Basic Study No. 2 (1961); *Education and Training in Nutrition*. Basic Study No. 6 (1962); *Population and Food Supplies*. Basic Study No. 7 (1962); *Increasing Food Production Through Education, Research, and Extension*, Basic Study No. 9 (1963).

Food—The Yearbook of Agriculture, 1959. Stiebeling, H. K., and Dreis, T. A. "Habits—and More," p. 631; Mitchell, H. S. "Don't Be Fooled by Fads," p. 660. Washington, D.C.: U.S. Department of Agriculture.

Hampton, M. C., Shapiro, L. R., and Huenemann, R. "Helping Teen-Age Girls Improve Their Diets." *J. Home Econ.*, 53:835 (1961).

Hill, M. M. "Nutrition Committees and Their Role in Community Action Programs." *Nutr. Program News*. Washington, D.C.: U.S. Department of Agriculture (January–February 1964).

Interdepartmental Committee on Nutrition for National Defense. *Manual for Nutrition Surveys*. Washington, D.C.: U.S. Government Printing Office (1965).

Larrick, G. P. "The Nutritive Adequacy of Our Food Supply." *Amer. J. Pub. Health*, 39:117 (1961).

Leverton, R. M. *Food Becomes You*, rev. ed. Iowa City: Iowa State U. P. (1960).

McHenry, E. W. *Foods Without Fads*. Philadelphia: Lippincott (1960).

Martin, E. A. *Nutrition in Action; Nutrition Education in Action*. New York: Holt (1963).

May, J. M. *The Ecology of Malnutrition in the Far and Near East*, Vol. 3. New York: Hafner (1961).

Mayer, J. "Food and Population: A Different View." *Nutr. Rev.*, 22:353 (1964).

———. "The Nutritional Status of American Negroes." *Nutr. Rev.*, 23:161 (1965).

Mead, M. *Food Habits Research: Problems of the 1960's*. Washington, D.C.: National Academy of Sciences, National Research Council Publication 1225 (1964).

Mott, M. A. "Better Business Bureaus Fight Food Faddism." *J. Amer. Dietet. A.*, 39:122 (1961).

National Research Council. *The Problem of Changing Food Habits*. Bulletin

108 (1943); *Manual for the Study of Food Habits.* Bulletin 111 (1945). (Reprinted 1964).

Orr, J. B. *The Wonderful World of Food.* Garden City, N.Y.: Doubleday (1958).

Ritchie, J. A. S. *Teaching Better Nutrition. A Study of Approaches and Techniques.* Rome: FAO (1950). (6th printing, 1963.)

Ross, M. A. "Nutrition and Home Economics Program in Egyptian Villages." *Proc. Nutr. Soc.,* **15**:30 (1956).

Schaefer, A. E., and Berry, F. B. "U.S. Interest in World Nutrition," *Pub. Health Rep.,* **75**:677 (1960).

Scrimshaw, N. S. "Progress in Solving World Nutrition Problems." *J. Amer. Dietet. A.,* **35**:441 (1959).

Symposium. *Hunger; Disease of Millions.* New Orleans Council for UNESCO. New Orleans: Tulane U. Center (1963).

Taylor, C. M. "Nutrition Education Demonstrations." *Nutr. Committee News* (May–June 1960). Washington, D.C.: Interagency Committee on Nutrition Education and School Lunch, U.S. Department of Agriculture.

Taylor, C. M. (ed.). "Food and Nutrition—A Special Section"; Pye, O. F. "Foods Eaten Around the World," p. 109. *Grade Teacher,* **82**:99 (1964).

The Nutrition Foundation. "The Role of Nutrition Education in Combatting Food Fads." New York (1959).

U.S. Department of Agriculture. *Nutrition Education Conference, Proceedings.* Washington, D.C. (1962).

Woodruff, C. "Growth and Nutrition of Lebanese Children." *Nutr. Rev.,* **23**:97 (1965).

Appendix

TABLE A-1. RECOMMENDED DAILY DIETARY ALLOWANCES[1], Revised 1963**

Food and Nutrition Board, National Academy of Sciences—National Research Council

Designed for the Maintenance of Good Nutrition of Practically All Healthy Persons in the U.S.A.
(Allowances are intended for persons normally active in a temperate climate)

	Age[2] Years from to	Weight kg (lb.)	Height cm (in.)	Calories[3]	Protein, gm	Calcium, gm	Iron, mg	Vitamin A Value, I U	Thiamine, mg	Riboflavin, mg	Niacin, Equiv.[4] mg	Ascorbic Acid, mg	Vitamin D I U
Men	18 35	70 (154)	175 (69)	2,900	70	0.8	10	5,000*	1.2	1.7	19	70	
	35 55	70 (154)	175 (69)	2,600	70	0.8	10	5,000	1.0	1.6	17	70	
	55 75	70 (154)	175 (69)	2,200	70	0.8	10	5,000	0.9	1.3	15	70	
Women	18 35	58 (128)	163 (64)	2,100	58	0.8	15	5,000	0.8	1.3	14	70	
	35 55	58 (128)	163 (64)	1,900	58	0.8	15	5,000	0.8	1.2	13	70	
	55 75	58 (128)	163 (64)	1,600	58	0.8	10	5,000	0.8	1.2	13	70	
	Pregnant (2nd and 3rd trimester)			+ 200	+20	+0.5	+ 5	+1,000	+0.2	+0.3	+ 3	+30	400
	Lactating			+1,000	+40	+0.5	+ 5	+3,000	+0.4	+0.6	+ 7	+30	400
Infants[5]	0 1	8 (18)		kg x 115 ±15	kg x 2.5 ±0.5	0.7	kg x 1.0	1,500	0.4	0.6	6	30	400
Children	1 3	13 (29)	87 (34)	1,300	32	0.8	8	2,000	0.5	0.8	9	40	400
	3 6	18 (40)	107 (42)	1,600	40	0.8	10	2,500	0.6	1.0	11	50	400
	6 9	24 (53)	124 (49)	2,100	52	0.8	12	3,500	0.8	1.3	14	60	400
Boys	9 12	33 (72)	140 (55)	2,400	60	1.1	15	4,500	1.0	1.4	16	70	400
	12 15	45 (98)	156 (61)	3,000	75	1.4	15	5,000	1.2	1.8	20	80	400
	15 18	61 (134)	172 (68)	3,400	85	1.4	15	5,000	1.4	2.0	22	80	400
Girls	9 12	33 (72)	140 (55)	2,200	55	1.1	15	4,500	0.9	1.3	15	80	400
	12 15	47 (103)	158 (62)	2,500	62	1.3	15	5,000	1.0	1.5	17	80	400
	15 18	53 (117)	163 (64)	2,300	58	1.3	15	5,000	0.9	1.3	15	70	400

[1] The allowance levels are intended to cover individual variations among most persons as they live in the United States under usual environmental stresses. The recommended allowances can be attained with a variety of common foods, providing other nutrients for which human requirements have been less well defined. See Publication No. 1146 text for more detailed discussion of allowances and nutrients not tabulated.

[2] Entries on lines for age range 18-35 years represent the 25-year age. All other entries represent allowances for the midpoint of the specified age periods, i.e., line for children 1-3 is for age 2 years (24 months); 3-6 is for age 4-1/2 years (54 months), etc.

[3] Table A-2 and figures 4-8 and 4-9 in text show calorie adjustments for weight and age.

[4] Niacin equivalents include dietary sources of the preformed vitamin and the precursor, tryptophan. 60 mg tryptophan represents 1 mg niacin.

[5] The calorie and protein allowances per kg for infants are considered to decrease progressively from birth. Allowances for calcium, thiamine, riboflavin, and niacin increase proportionately with calories to the maximum values shown.

* 1,000 I U from preformed Vitamin A and 4,000 I U from beta-carotene.

** See Recommended Dietary Allowances, Publication No. 1146, Washington, D.C.: National Research Council (1964).

TABLE A-2. ADJUSTMENT OF CALORIE ALLOWANCES FOR ADULT INDIVIDUALS
OF VARIOUS BODY WEIGHTS AND AGES*

(At a mean environmental temperature of 20°C. (68°F.) assuming average physical activity)

Desirable Weight		Calorie Allowance[1]		
kg	lb	25 years	45 years	65 years
		Men		
50	110	2,300	2,050	1,750
55	121	2,450	2,200	1,850
60	132	2,600	2,350	1,950
65	143	2,750	2,500	2,100
70	154	2,900	2,600	2,200
75	165	3,050	2,750	2,300
80	176	3,200	2,900	2,450
85	187	3,350	3,050	2,550
		Women		
40	88	1,600	1,450	1,200
45	99	1,750	1,600	1,300
50	110	1,900	1,700	1,450
55	121	2,000	1,800	1,550
58	128	2,100	1,900	1,600
60	132	2,150	1,950	1,650
65	143	2,300	2,050	1,750
70	154	2,400	2,200	1,850

* From Recommended Dietary Allowances, 6th rev. ed., 1964. Washington, D.C.: National
Research Council Publication No. 1146, p. 5.

[1] Values have been rounded to nearest 50 calories.

TABLE A-3. SOME USEFUL EQUIVALENTS *

1 meter (m)	=	1000 millimeters (mm)
1 meter	=	100 centimeters
1 meter	=	39.37 inches
1 centimeter (cm)	=	0.394 inch
1 inch (in.)	=	2.54 centimeters
1 microgram** (mcgm)	=	0.001 milligram
1 milligram (mg)	=	1000 micrograms
1 gram (gm)	=	1000 milligrams
1 gram	=	0.035 ounce
1 grain	=	0.065 gram
1 ounce (oz)	=	28.35 grams
1 pound (lb)	=	453.6 grams
1 pound	=	16 ounces
1 kilogram (kg)	=	2.2 pounds
1 teaspoon (tsp)	=	5 milliliters (ml)
1 tablespoon (tbsp)	=	15 milliliters
1 tablespoon	=	3 teaspoons
2 tablespoons	=	1 fluid ounce
1 dessertspoon	=	2 teaspoons
1 cup	=	16 tablespoons (level)
1 cup	=	8 fluid ounces
1 pint (pt)	=	2 cups (4 gills)
1 quart (qt)	=	4 cups
1 gallon (gal)	=	4 quarts
1 liter (l)	=	1.06 quarts (1,000 milliliters)
1 peck (pk)	=	8 quarts
1 bushel (bu)	=	4 pecks
1 pound butter or margarine	=	4 sticks
	=	2 cups
	=	64 pats or squares
1 stick butter or margarine	=	1/2 cup (approximately)
	=	16 pats or squares

Common can sizes:

No. 2, 1 lb 4 oz	=	2-1/2 cups
No. 2-1/2, 1 lb 13 oz	=	3-1/2 cups
No. 10, 6 lb 2 oz		
to 7 lb 5 oz	=	12 to 13 cups
No. 300, 14 oz to 16 oz	=	1-3/4 cups
No. 303, 16 oz to 17 oz	=	2 cups

* For additional information on practical container measures, see Handbook of Food Preparation, American Home Economics Association (1964).

** Also called gamma ug.

Explanation of the Table

Foods are grouped under the following main headings: milk; eggs; meat, poultry, and fish; dry beans and peas, nuts; vegetables; fruits; grain products; fats; sugars; and miscellaneous items.

Most of the foods listed are in ready-to-eat form. Some are basic products widely used in food preparation, such as flour, fat, and cornmeal.

Weight in grams is shown for an approximate measure of each food as it is described; if inedible parts are included in the description, both measure and weight include these parts.

The approximate measure shown for each food is in cups, ounces, pounds, a piece of a certain size, or some other well-known unit. The measure shown can be calculated readily to larger or smaller amounts by multiplying or dividing. However, because the measures are approximate (some are rounded for convenient use), calculated nutritive values for very large quantities of some food items may be less representative than those for smaller quantities.

The cup measure refers to the standard measuring cup of 8 fluid ounces or 1/2 liquid pint. The ounce refers to 1/16 of a pound avoirdupois, unless fluid ounce is indicated. The weight of a fluid ounce varies according to the food measured.

Values are shown for protein; fat; fatty acids; total carbohydrate; two minerals – calcium and iron; and five vitamins – vitamin A, thiamine, riboflavin, niacin, and ascorbic acid (vitamin C). Calories are shown also, in the column headed "Food Energy."

These values can be used as the basis for comparing kinds and amounts of nutrients in different foods.

Water content is also shown in the table because the percentage of moisture present is needed for identification and comparison of many food items.

Nutritive values are shown for only the parts of food customarily eaten - corn without the cob, meat without bone, potatoes without the skin, American-type grapes without seeds and skin, European-type grapes without seeds. If additional parts are eaten – the skin of the potato, for example – amounts of some nutrients obtained will be somewhat greater than those shown.

For many of the prepared items, values have been calculated from the ingredients in typical recipes. Examples of such items are: biscuits, corn muffins, oyster stew, macaroni and cheese, and custard and a number of other dessert-type items.

For vegetables and for toast, values are without fat added, either during preparation or at the table. Some destruction of vitamins, especially of ascorbic acid, may occur when foods are cut or shredded. Such losses are variable, and no deduction for these losses has been made.

For meat, values are for meat as cooked and drained and without drippings. For many cuts, values are shown for the meat both with and without the fat that can be trimmed off in the kitchen or on the plate.

The niacin values given do not include niacin equivalent and as given cannot be compared with the recommended allowance for niacin equivalent.

TABLE A-4. NUTRITIVE VALUES OF THE EDIBLE PART OF FOODS

(Dashes show that no basis could be found for imputing a value although there was some reason to believe that a measurable amount of the constituent might be present)

| | Food, Approximate Measure, and Weight (in grams) | | Water | Food Energy | Protein | Fat (Total Lipid) | Fatty Acids | | | Carbohydrate | Calcium | Iron | Vitamin A Value | Thiamine | Riboflavin | Niacin | Ascorbic Acid |
| | | | | | | | Saturated (Total) | Unsaturated Oleic | Unsaturated Linoleic | | | | | | | | |
		Grams	Percent	Calories	Grams	Grams	Grams	Grams	Grams	Grams	Milligrams	Milligrams	International Units	Milligrams	Milligrams	Milligrams	Milligrams
	Milk, Cream, Cheese; Related Products																
	Milk, cow's:																
1	Fluid, whole (3.5% fat) 1 cup	244	87	160	9	9	5	3	Trace	12	288	0.1	350	0.08	0.42	0.1	2
2	Fluid, nonfat (skim) 1 cup	246	90	90	9	Trace	---	---	---	13	298	0.1	10	0.10	0.44	0.2	2
3	Buttermilk, cultured, from skim milk 1 cup	246	90	90	9	Trace	---	---	---	13	298	0.1	10	0.09	0.44	0.2	2
4	Evaporated, unsweetened, undiluted 1 cup	252	74	345	18	20	11	7	1	24	635	0.3	820	0.10	0.84	0.5	3
5	Condensed, sweetened, undiluted 1 cup	306	27	980	25	27	15	9	1	166	802	0.3	1,090	0.23	1.17	0.5	3
6	Dry, whole 1 cup	103	2	515	27	28	16	9	1	39	936	0.5	1,160	0.30	1.50	0.7	6
7	Dry, nonfat, instant 1 cup	70	3	250	25	Trace	---	---	---	36	905	0.4	20	0.24	1.25	0.6	5
	Milk, goat's:																
8	Fluid, whole 1 cup	244	88	165	8	10	6	2	Trace	11	315	0.2	390	0.10	0.27	0.7	2
	Cream:																
9	Half-and-half (cream and milk) 1 cup	242	80	325	8	28	16	9	1	11	261	0.1	1,160	0.08	0.38	0.1	2
10	1 tablespoon	15	80	20	Trace	2	1	1	Trace	1	16	Trace	70	Trace	0.02	Trace	Trace
11	Light, coffee or table 1 cup	240	72	505	7	49	27	16	1	10	245	0.1	2,030	0.07	0.36	0.1	2
12	1 tablespoon	15	72	30	Trace	3	2	1	Trace	1	15	Trace	130	Trace	0.02	Trace	Trace
	Whipping, unwhipped (volume about double when whipped):																
13	Light 1 cup	239	62	715	6	75	41	25	2	9	203	0.1	3,070	0.06	0.30	0.1	2
14	1 tablespoon	15	62	45	Trace	5	3	2	Trace	1	13	Trace	190	Trace	0.02	Trace	Trace
15	Heavy 1 cup	238	57	840	5	89	49	29	3	7	178	0.1	3,670	0.05	0.26	0.1	2
16	1 tablespoon	15	57	55	Trace	6	3	2	Trace	Trace	11	Trace	230	Trace	0.02	Trace	Trace
	Cheese:																
17	Blue or Roquefort type 1 ounce	28	40	105	6	9	5	3	Trace	1	89	0.1	350	0.01	0.17	0.1	0
	Cheddar or American:																
18	Ungrated 1 inch cube	17	37	70	4	5	3	2	Trace	Trace	128	0.2	220	Trace	0.08	Trace	0
19	Grated 1 cup	112	37	445	28	36	20	12	1	Trace	840	1.1	1,470	0.03	0.51	0.1	0
20	1 tablespoon	7	37	30	2	2	1	1	Trace	Trace	52	0.1	90	Trace	0.03	Trace	0
21	Cheddar, process 1 ounce	28	40	105	7	9	5	3	Trace	1	219	0.3	350	Trace	0.12	Trace	0
22	Cheese foods, Cheddar 1 ounce	28	43	90	6	7	4	3	Trace	2	162	0.2	280	0.01	0.16	Trace	0
	Cottage cheese, from skim milk:																
23	Creamed 1 cup	225	78	240	31	9	5	3	Trace	7	212	0.7	380	0.07	0.56	0.2	0
24	1 ounce	28	78	30	4	1	1	Trace	Trace	1	27	0.1	50	0.01	0.07	Trace	0

467

Table A-4. Nutritive Values of the Edible Part of Foods (Continued)

(Dashes show that no basis could be found for imputing a value although there was some reason to believe that a measurable amount of the constituent might be present)

	Food, Approximate Measure, and Weight (in grams)		Water	Food Energy	Protein	Fat (Total Lipid)	Fatty Acids Saturated (Total)	Fatty Acids Unsaturated Oleic	Fatty Acids Unsaturated Linoleic	Carbohydrate	Calcium	Iron	Vitamin A Value	Thiamine	Riboflavin	Niacin	Ascorbic Acid
		Grams	Percent	Calories	Grams	Grams	Grams	Grams	Grams	Grams	Milligrams	Milligrams	International Units	Milligrams	Milligrams	Milligrams	Milligrams
	Milk, Cream, Cheese; Related Products (Continued)																
	Cheese—Continued																
	Cottage cheese, from skim milk (Continued)																
25	Uncreamed	1 cup	225	79	195	38	1	Trace	Trace	Trace	6	202	0.9	20	0.07	0.63	0.2	0
26		1 ounce	28	79	25	5	Trace				1	26	0.1	Trace	0.01	0.08	Trace	0
27	Cream cheese	1 ounce	28	51	105	2	11	6	4	Trace	1	18	0.1	440	Trace	0.07	Trace	0
28		1 tablespoon	15	51	55	1	6	3	2	Trace	Trace	9	Trace	230	Trace	0.04	Trace	0
29	Swiss (domestic)	1 ounce	28	39	105	8	8	4	3	Trace	1	262	0.3	320	Trace	0.11	Trace	0
	Milk beverages:																
30	Cocoa	1 cup	242	79	235	9	11	6	4	Trace	26	286	0.9	390	0.09	0.45	0.4	2
31	Chocolate-flavored milk drink (made with skim milk)	1 cup	250	83	190	8	6	3	2	Trace	27	270	0.4	210	0.09	0.41	0.2	2
32	Malted milk	1 cup	270	78	280	13	12				32	364	0.8	670	0.17	0.56	0.2	2
	Milk desserts:																
33	Cornstarch pudding, plain (blanc mange)	1 cup	248	76	275	9	10	5	3	Trace	39	290	0.1	390	0.07	0.40	0.1	2
34	Custard, baked	1 cup	248	77	285	13	14	6	5	1	28	278	1.0	870	0.10	0.47	0.2	1
	Ice cream, plain, factory packed:																
35	Slice or cut brick, 1/8 of quart brick	1 slice or cut brick	71	62	145	3	9	5	3	Trace	15	87	0.1	370	0.03	0.13	0.1	1
36	Container	3-1/2 fluid ounces	62	62	130	2	8	4	3	Trace	13	76	0.1	320	0.03	0.12	0.1	1
37	Container	8 fluid ounces	142	62	295	6	18	10	6	1	29	175	0.1	740	0.06	0.27	0.1	1
38	Ice milk	1 cup	187	67	285	9	10	6	3	Trace	42	292	0.2	390	0.09	0.41	0.2	2
39	Yoghurt, from partially skimmed milk	1 cup	246	89	120	8	4	2	1	Trace	13	295	0.1	170	0.09	0.43	0.2	2
	Eggs																
	Eggs, large, 24 ounces per dozen:																
	Raw:																
40	Whole, without shell	1 egg	50	74	80	6	6	2	3	Trace	Trace	27	1.1	590	0.05	0.15	Trace	0
41	White of egg	1 white	33	88	15	4	Trace				Trace	3	Trace	0	Trace	0.09	Trace	0
42	Yolk of egg	1 yolk	17	51	60	3	5	2	2	Trace	Trace	24	0.9	580	0.04	0.07	Trace	0

Table A-4. Nutritive Values of the Edible Part of Foods (Continued)

(Dashes show that no basis could be found for imputing a value although there was some reason to believe that a measurable amount of the constituent might be present)

	Food, Approximate Measure, and Weight (in grams)	Water	Food Energy	Protein	Fat (Total Lipid)	Fatty Acids Saturated (Total)	Fatty Acids Unsaturated Oleic	Fatty Acids Unsaturated Linoleic	Carbohydrate	Calcium	Iron	Vitamin A Value	Thiamine	Riboflavin	Niacin	Ascorbic Acid
		Per-cent	Calories	Grams	Grams	Grams	Grams	Grams	Grams	Milligrams	Milligrams	International Units	Milligrams	Milligrams	Milligrams	Milligrams
	Eggs (Continued)															
	Eggs, large, 24 ounces per dozen–Continued	Grams														
	Cooked:															
43	Boiled, shell removed 2 eggs 100	74	160	13	12	4	5	1	1	54	2.3	1,180	0.09	0.28	0.1	0
44	Scrambled, with 1 egg 64	72	110	7	8	3	3	Trace	1	51	1.1	690	0.05	0.18	Trace	0
	milk and fat															
	Meat, Poultry, Fish, Shellfish; Related Products															
45	Bacon, broiled or fried, 2 slices crisp 16	8	100	5	8	3	4	1	1	2	0.5	0	0.08	0.05	0.8	----
	Beef, trimmed to retail basis,[1] cooked:															
	Cuts braised, simmered, or pot-roasted:															
46	Lean and fat 3 ounces 85	53	245	23	16	8	7	Trace	0	10	2.9	30	0.04	0.18	3.5	----
47	Lean only 2.5 ounces 72	62	140	22	5	2	2	Trace	0	10	2.7	10	0.04	0.16	3.3	----
	Hamburger (ground beef), broiled:															
48	Lean 3 ounces 85	60	185	23	10	5	4	Trace	0	10	3.0	20	0.08	0.20	5.1	----
49	Regular 3 ounces 85	54	245	21	17	8	8	Trace	0	9	2.7	30	0.07	0.18	4.6	----
	Roast, oven-cooked, no liquid added:															
	Relatively fat, such as rib:															
50	Lean and fat 3 ounces 85	40	375	17	34	16	15	1	0	8	2.2	70	0.05	0.13	3.1	----
51	Lean only 1.8 ounces 51	57	125	14	7	3	3	Trace	0	6	1.8	10	0.04	0.11	2.6	----
	Relatively lean, such as heel of round:															
52	Lean and fat 3 ounces 85	62	165	25	7	3	3	Trace	0	11	3.2	10	0.06	0.19	4.5	----
53	Lean only 2.7 ounces 78	65	125	24	3	1	1	Trace	0	10	3.0	Trace	0.06	0.18	4.3	----
	Steak, broiled:															
	Relatively fat, such as sirloin:															
54	Lean and fat 3 ounces 85	44	330	20	27	13	12	1	0	9	2.5	50	0.05	0.16	4.0	----
55	Lean only 2.0 ounces 56	59	115	18	4	2	2	Trace	0	7	2.2	10	0.05	0.14	3.6	----
	Relatively lean, such as round:															
56	Lean and fat 3 ounces 85	55	220	24	13	6	6	Trace	0	10	3.0	20	0.07	0.19	4.8	----
57	Lean only 2.4 ounces 68	61	130	21	4	2	2	Trace	0	9	2.5	10	0.06	0.16	4.1	----

1 Outer layer of fat on the cut was removed to within approximately 1/2 in. of the lean. Deposits of fat within the cut were not removed.

Table A-4. Nutritive Values of the Edible Part of Foods (Continued)

(Dashes show that no basis could be found for imputing a value although there was some reason to believe that a measurable amount of the constituent might be present)

	Food, Approximate Measure, and Weight (in grams)	Weight	Water	Food Energy	Protein	Fat (Total Lipid)	Fatty Acids Saturated (Total)	Unsaturated Oleic	Unsaturated Linoleic	Carbohydrate	Calcium	Iron	Vitamin A Value	Thiamine	Riboflavin	Niacin	Ascorbic Acid
		Grams	Per-cent	Calories	Grams	Grams	Grams	Grams	Grams	Grams	Milli-grams	Milli-grams	Inter-national Units	Milli-grams	Milli-grams	Milli-grams	Milli-grams
	Meat, Poultry, Fish, Shellfish; Related Products (Continued)																
	Beef, canned:																
58	Corned beef, 3 ounces	85	59	185	22	10	5	4	Trace	0	17	3.7	20	0.01	0.20	2.9	---
59	Corned beef hash, 3 ounces	85	67	155	7	10	5	4	Trace	9	11	1.7	---	0.01	0.08	1.8	---
60	Beef, dried or chipped, 2 ounces	57	48	115	19	4	2	2	Trace	0	11	2.9	---	0.04	0.18	2.2	---
61	Beef and vegetable stew, 1 cup	235	82	210	15	10	5	4	Trace	15	28	2.8	2,310	0.13	0.17	4.4	15
62	Beef potpie, baked: 1 pie	227	55	560	23	33	9	20	2	43	32	4.1	1,860	0.25	0.27	4.5	7
	Individual pie, 4-1/4-inch diameter, weight before baking about 8 ounces																
	Chicken, cooked:																
63	Flesh only, broiled, 3 ounces	85	71	115	20	3	1	1	1	0	8	1.4	80	0.05	0.16	7.4	---
	Breast, fried, 1/2 breast:																
64	With bone, 3.3 ounces	94	58	155	25	5	1	2	1	1	9	1.3	70	0.04	0.17	11.2	---
65	Flesh and skin only, 2.7 ounces	76	58	155	25	5	1	2	1	1	9	1.3	70	0.04	0.17	11.2	---
	Drumstick, fried:																
66	With bone, 2.1 ounces	59	55	90	12	4	1	2	1	Trace	6	0.9	50	0.03	0.15	2.7	---
67	Flesh and skin only, 1.3 ounces	38	55	90	12	4	1	2	1	Trace	6	0.9	50	0.03	0.15	2.7	---
68	Chicken, canned, boneless, 3 ounces	85	65	170	18	10	3	4	2	0	18	1.3	200	0.03	0.11	3.7	3
	Chicken potpie. See Poultry potpie.																
	Chile con carne, canned:																
69	With beans, 1 cup	250	72	335	19	15	7	7	Trace	30	80	4.2	150	0.08	0.18	3.2	---
70	Without beans, 1 cup	255	67	510	26	38	18	17	1	15	97	3.6	380	0.05	0.31	5.6	---
71	Heart, beef, lean, braised, 3 ounces	85	61	160	27	5				1	5	5.0	20	0.21	1.04	6.5	1
	Lamb, trimmed to retail basis,[1] cooked:																
72	Chop, thick, with bone, 1 chop, 4.8 ounces broiled	137	47	400	25	33	18	12	1	0	10	1.5	---	0.14	0.25	5.6	---
73	Lean and fat, 4.0 ounces	112	47	400	25	33	18	12	1	0	10	1.5	---	0.14	0.25	5.6	---
74	Lean only, 2.6 ounces	74	62	140	21	6	3	2	Trace	0	9	1.5	---	0.11	0.20	4.5	---
	Leg, roasted:																
75	Lean and fat, 3 ounces	85	54	235	22	16	9	6	Trace	0	9	1.4	---	0.13	0.23	4.7	---
76	Lean only, 2.5 ounces	71	62	130	20	5	3	2	Trace	0	9	1.4	---	0.12	0.21	4.4	---

[1] Outer layer of fat on the cut was removed to within approximately 1/2 in. of the lean. Deposits of fat within the cut were not removed.

Table A-4. Nutritive Values of the Edible Part of Foods (Continued)

(Dashes show that no basis could be found for imputing a value although there was some reason to believe that a measurable amount of the constituent might be present)

Food, Approximate Measure, and Weight (in grams)		Grams	Water Per-cent	Food Energy Calories	Protein Grams	Fat (Total Lipid) Grams	Fatty Acids Saturated (Total) Grams	Fatty Acids Unsaturated Oleic Grams	Fatty Acids Unsaturated Linoleic Grams	Carbo-hy-drate Grams	Cal-cium Milli-grams	Iron Milli-grams	Vita-min A Value Inter-national Units	Thia-mine Milli-grams	Ribo-flavin Milli-grams	Niacin Milli-grams	Ascor-bic Acid Milli-grams
Meat, Poultry, Fish, Shellfish; Related Products (Continued)																	
Lamb, trimmed to retail basis,[1] cooked (Continued)																	
Shoulder, roasted:																	
77 Lean and fat	3 ounces	85	50	285	18	23	13	8	1	0	9	1.0	-----	0.11	0.20	4.0	-----
78 Lean only	2.3 ounces	64	61	130	17	6	3	2	Trace	0	8	1.0	-----	0.10	0.18	3.7	-----
79 Liver, beef, fried	2 ounces	57	57	130	15	6	6			3	6	5.0	30,280	0.15	2.37	9.4	15
Pork, cured, cooked:																	
80 Ham, light cure, lean and fat, roasted	3 ounces	85	54	245	18	19	7	8	2	0	8	2.2	0	0.40	0.16	3.1	-----
Luncheon meat:																	
81 Boiled ham, sliced	2 ounces	57	59	135	11	10	4	4	1	0	6	1.6	0	0.25	0.09	1.5	-----
82 Canned, spiced or unspiced	2 ounces	57	55	165	8	14	5	6	1	1	5	1.2	0	0.18	0.12	1.6	-----
Pork, fresh, trimmed to retail basis,[1] cooked:																	
83 Chop, thick, with bone	1 chop, 3.5 ounces	98	42	260	16	21	8	9	2	0	8	2.2	0	0.63	0.18	3.8	-----
84 Lean and fat	2.3 ounces	66	42	260	16	21	8	9	2	0	8	2.2	0	0.63	0.18	3.8	-----
85 Lean only	1.7 ounces	48	53	130	15	7	2	3	1	0	7	1.9	0	0.54	0.16	3.3	-----
Roast, oven-cooked, no liquid added:																	
86 Lean and fat	3 ounces	85	46	310	21	24	9	10	2	0	9	2.7	0	0.78	0.22	4.7	-----
87 Lean only	2.4 ounces	68	55	175	20	10	3	4	1	0	9	2.6	0	0.73	0.21	4.4	-----
Cuts, simmered:																	
88 Lean and fat	3 ounces	85	46	320	20	26	9	11	2	0	8	2.5	0	0.46	0.21	4.1	-----
89 Lean only	2.2 ounces	63	60	135	18	6	2	3	1	0	8	2.3	0	0.42	0.19	3.7	-----
90 Poultry potpie (based on chicken potpie). Individual pie, 4-1/4-inch diam.	1 pie	227	57	535	23	31	10	15	3	42	68	3.0	3,020	0.25	0.26	4.1	5
Sausage:																	
91 Bologna, slice, 4.1 by 0.1 inch	8 slices	227	56	690	27	62				2	16	4.1	-----	0.36	0.49	6.0	-----
92 Frankfurter, cooked	1 frankfurter	51	58	155	6	14				1	3	0.8	-----	0.08	0.10	1.3	-----
93 Pork, links or patty, cooked	4 ounces	113	35	540	21	50	18	21	5	Trace	8	2.7	0	0.89	0.39	4.2	-----

[1] Outer layer of fat on the cut was removed to within approximately 1/2 in. of the lean. Deposits of fat within the cut were not removed.

Table A-4. Nutritive Values of the Edible Part of Foods (Continued)

(Dashes show that no basis could be found for imputing a value although there was some reason to believe that a measurable amount of the constituent might be present)

	Food, Approximate Measure, and Weight (in grams)	Weight Grams	Water Per-cent	Food Energy Calories	Protein Grams	Fat (Total Lipid) Grams	Fatty Acids Saturated (Total) Grams	Fatty Acids Unsaturated Oleic Grams	Fatty Acids Unsaturated Linoleic Grams	Carbo-hydrate Grams	Calcium Milligrams	Iron Milligrams	Vitamin A Value International Units	Thiamine Milligrams	Ribo-flavin Milligrams	Niacin Milligrams	Ascorbic Acid Milligrams
	Meat, Poultry, Fish, Shellfish; Related Products (Continued)																
94	Tongue, beef, braised, 3 ounces	85	61	210	18	14	---	---	---	Trace	6	1.9	---	0.04	0.25	3.0	---
	Turkey potpie. See Poultry potpie																
	Veal, cooked:																
95	Cutlet, without bone, broiled, 3 ounces	85	60	185	23	9	5	4	Trace	---	9	2.7	---	0.06	0.21	4.6	---
96	Roast, medium fat, medium done; lean and fat, 3 ounces	85	55	230	23	14	7	6	Trace	0	10	2.9	---	0.11	0.26	6.6	---
	Fish and shellfish:																
97	Bluefish, baked or broiled, 3 ounces	85	68	135	22	4	---	---	---	0	25	0.6	40	0.09	0.08	1.6	---
	Clams:																
98	Raw, meat only, 3 ounces	85	82	65	11	1	---	---	---	2	59	5.2	90	0.08	0.15	1.1	8
99	Canned, solids and liquid, 3 ounces	85	86	45	7	1	---	---	---	2	47	3.5	---	0.01	0.09	0.9	---
100	Crabmeat, canned, 3 ounces	85	77	85	15	2	---	---	---	1	38	0.7	---	0.07	0.07	1.6	---
101	Fish sticks, breaded, cooked, frozen; stick, 3.8 by 1.0 by 0.5 inch, 10 sticks or 8-ounce package	227	66	400	38	20	5	4	10	15	25	0.9	---	0.09	0.16	3.6	---
102	Haddock, fried, 3 ounces	85	66	140	17	5	1	3	Trace	5	34	1.0	---	0.03	0.06	2.7	---
	Mackerel:																
103	Broiled, Atlantic, 3 ounces	85	62	200	19	13	---	---	---	0	5	1.0	450	0.13	0.23	6.5	---
104	Canned, Pacific, solids and liquid[2], 3 ounces	85	66	155	18	9	---	---	---	0	221	1.9	20	0.02	0.28	7.4	---
105	Ocean perch, breaded (egg and bread-crumbs), fried, 3 ounces	85	59	195	16	11	---	---	---	6	28	1.1	---	0.08	0.09	1.5	---
	Oysters, meat only:																
106	Raw, 13-19 medium selects, 1 cup	240	85	160	20	4	---	---	---	8	226	13.2	740	0.33	0.43	6.0	---
107	Oyster stew, 1 part oysters to 3 parts milk by volume, 3-4 oysters, 1 cup	230	84	200	11	12	---	---	---	11	269	3.3	640	0.13	0.41	1.6	2

2 Vitamin values based on drained solids.

Table A-4. Nutritive Values of the Edible Part of Foods (Continued)

(Dashes show that no basis could be found for imputing a value although there was some reason to believe that a measurable amount of the constituent might be present)

Food, Approximate Measure, and Weight (in grams)	Water Per-cent	Food Energy Calories	Protein Grams	Fat (Total Lipid) Grams	Fatty Acids Saturated (Total) Grams	Unsaturated Oleic Grams	Unsaturated Linoleic Grams	Carbohydrate Grams	Calcium Milligrams	Iron Milligrams	Vitamin A Value International Units	Thiamine Milligrams	Riboflavin Milligrams	Niacin Milligrams	Ascorbic Acid Milligrams
Meat, Poultry, Fish, Shellfish; Related Products (Continued)															
Weight: Grams															
Fish and shellfish (Continued)															
108 Salmon, pink, canned 3 ounces 85	71	120	17	5	1	1	Trace	0	167[3]	0.7	60	0.03	0.16	6.8	----
109 Sardines, Atlantic, canned in oil, drained solids 3 ounces 85	62	175	20	9	----	----	----	0	372	2.5	190	0.02	0.17	4.6	----
110 Shad, baked 3 ounces 85	64	170	20	10	----	----	----	0	20	0.5	20	0.11	0.22	7.3	----
111 Shrimp, canned, meat only 3 ounces 85	70	100	21	1	----	----	----	1	98	2.6	50	0.01	0.03	1.5	----
112 Swordfish, broiled with butter or margarine 3 ounces 85	65	150	24	5	----	----	----	0	23	1.1	1,750	0.03	0.04	9.3	----
113 Tuna, canned in oil, drained solids 3 ounces 85	61	170	24	7	----	----	----	0	7	1.6	70	0.04	0.10	10.1	----
Mature Dry Beans and Peas, Nuts, Peanuts; Related Products															
114 Almonds, shelled 1 cup 142	5	850	26	77	6	52	15	28	332	6.7	0	0.34	1.31	5.0	Trace
Beans, dry: Common varieties, such as Great Northern, navy, and others, canned:															
115 Red 1 cup 256	76	230	15	1	----	----	----	42	74	4.6	Trace	0.13	0.10	1.5	----
White, with tomato sauce:															
116 With pork 1 cup 261	71	320	16	7	3	3	1	50	141	4.7	340	0.20	0.08	1.5	5
117 Without pork 1 cup 261	68	310	16	1	----	----	----	60	177	5.2	160	0.18	0.09	1.5	5
118 Lima, cooked 1 cup 192	64	260	16	1	----	----	----	48	56	5.6	Trace	0.26	0.12	1.3	Trace
119 Brazil nuts 1 cup 140	5	915	20	94	19	45	24	15	260	4.8	Trace	1.34	0.17	2.2	----
120 Cashew nuts, roasted 1 cup 135	5	760	23	62	10	43	4	40	51	5.1	140	0.58	0.33	2.4	----
Coconut:															
121 Fresh, shredded 1 cup 97	51	335	3	34	29	2	Trace	9	13	1.6	0	0.05	0.02	0.5	3
122 Dried, shredded, sweetened 1 cup 62	3	340	2	24	21	2	Trace	33	10	1.2	0	0.02	0.02	0.2	0
123 Cowpeas or blackeye peas, dry, cooked 1 cup 248	80	190	13	1	----	----	----	34	42	3.2	20	0.41	0.11	1.1	Trace

[3] Based on total contents of can. If bones are discarded, value will be greatly reduced.

473

Table A-4. Nutritive Values of the Edible Part of Foods (Continued)

(Dashes show that no basis could be found for imputing a value although there was some reason to believe that a measurable amount of the constituent might be present)

	Food, Approximate Measure, and Weight (in grams)	Water	Food Energy	Protein	Fat (Total Lipid)	Fatty Acids			Carbohydrate	Calcium	Iron	Vitamin A Value	Thiamine	Riboflavin	Niacin	Ascorbic Acid
						Saturated (Total)	Unsaturated Oleic	Linoleic								
		Percent	Calories	Grams	Grams	Grams	Grams	Grams	Grams	Milligrams	Milligrams	International Units	Milligrams	Milligrams	Milligrams	Milligrams
	Mature Dry Beans and Peas, Nuts, Peanuts; Related Products (Continued)															
		Grams														
	Peanuts, roasted, salted:															
124	Halves 1 cup 144	2	840	37	72	16	31	21	27	107	3.0	-----	0.46	0.19	24.7	0
125	Chopped 1 tablespoon 9	2	55	2	4	1	2	1	2	7	0.2	-----	0.03	0.01	1.5	0
126	Peanut butter 1 tablespoon 16	2	95	4	8	2	4	2	3	9	0.3	-----	0.02	0.02	2.4	0
127	Peas, split, dry, cooked 1 cup 250	70	290	20	1	-----		2	52	28	4.2	100	0.37	0.22	2.2	-----
	Pecans:															
128	Halves 1 cup 108	3	740	10	77	5	48	15	16	79	2.6	140	0.93	0.14	1.0	2
129	Chopped 1 tablespoon 7.5	3	50	1	5	Trace	3	1	1	5	0.2	10	0.06	0.01	0.1	Trace
	Walnuts, shelled:															
130	Black or native, chopped 1 cup 126	3	790	26	75	4	26	36	19	Trace	7.6	380	0.28	0.14	0.9	-----
	English or Persian:															
131	Halves 1 cup 100	4	650	15	64	4	10	40	16	99	3.1	30	0.33	0.13	0.9	3
132	Chopped 1 tablespoon 8	4	50	1	5	Trace	1	3	1	8	0.2	Trace	0.03	0.01	0.1	Trace
	Vegetables and Vegetable Products															
	Asparagus:															
133	Cooked, cut spears 1 cup 175	94	35	4	Trace	-----			6	37	1.0	1,580	0.27	0.32	2.4	46
	Canned spears, medium:															
134	Green 6 spears 96	92	20	2	Trace	-----			3	18	1.8	770	0.06	0.10	0.8	14
135	Bleached 6 spears 96	92	20	2	Trace	-----			4	15	1.0	80	0.05	0.06	0.7	14
	Beans:															
136	Lima, immature, cooked 1 cup 160	71	180	12	1	-----			32	75	4.0	450	0.29	0.16	2.0	28
	Snap, green:															
	Cooked:															
137	In small amount of water, short time 1 cup 125	92	30	2	Trace	-----			7	62	0.8	680	0.08	0.11	0.6	16
138	In large amount of water, long time 1 cup 125	92	30	2	Trace	-----			7	62	0.8	680	0.07	0.10	0.4	13
	Canned:															
139	Solids and liquid 1 cup 239	94	45	2	Trace	-----			10	81	2.9	690	0.08	0.10	0.7	9
140	Strained or chopped 1 ounce 28 (baby food)	92	5	Trace	Trace	-----			1	9	0.3	110	0.01	0.02	0.1	Trace

Table A-4. Nutritive Values of the Edible Part of Foods (Continued)

(Dashes show that no basis could be found for imputing a value although there was some reason to believe that a measurable amount of the constituent might be present)

Food, Approximate Measure, and Weight (in grams)		Water Per-cent	Food Energy Calories	Protein Grams	Fat (Total Lipid) Grams	Fatty Acids Saturated (Total) Grams	Unsaturated Oleic Grams	Linoleic Grams	Carbohydrate Grams	Calcium Milligrams	Iron Milligrams	Vitamin A Value International Units	Thiamine Milligrams	Riboflavin Milligrams	Niacin Milligrams	Ascorbic Acid Milligrams
Vegetables and Vegetable Products (Continued)	Grams															
141 Beets, cooked, diced	1 cup 165	91	50	2	Trace	—			12	23	0.8	40	0.04	0.07	0.5	11
142 Broccoli spears, cooked	1 cup 150	91	40	5	Trace	—			7	132	1.2	3,750	0.14	0.29	1.2	135
143 Brussels sprouts, cooked	1 cup 130	88	45	5	1	—			8	42	1.4	680	0.10	0.18	1.1	113
Cabbage:																
Raw:																
144 Finely shredded	1 cup 100	92	25	1	Trace	—			5	49	0.4	130	0.05	0.05	0.3	47
145 Coleslaw	1 cup 120	83	120	1	9	2	2	5	9	52	0.5	180	0.06	0.06	0.3	35
Cooked:																
146 In small amount of water, short time	1 cup 170	94	35	2	Trace	—			7	75	0.5	220	0.07	0.07	0.5	56
147 In large amount of water, long time	1 cup 170	94	30	2	Trace	—			7	71	0.5	200	0.04	0.04	0.2	40
Cabbage, celery or Chinese:																
148 Raw, leaves and stalk, 1-inch pieces	1 cup 100	95	15	1	Trace	—			3	43	0.6	150	0.05	0.04	0.6	25
149 Cabbage, spoon (or pakchoy), cooked	1 cup 150	95	20	2	Trace	—			4	222	0.9	4,650	0.07	0.12	1.1	23
Carrots:																
Raw:																
150 Whole, 5-1/2 by 1 inch, (25 thin strips)	1 carrot 50	88	20	1	Trace	—			5	18	0.4	5,500	0.03	0.03	0.3	4
151 Grated	1 cup 110	88	45	1	Trace	—			11	41	0.8	12,100	0.06	0.06	0.7	9
152 Cooked, diced	1 cup 145	91	45	1	Trace	—			10	48	0.9	15,220	0.08	0.07	0.7	9
153 Canned, strained or chopped (baby food)	1 ounce 28	92	10	Trace	Trace	—			2	7	0.1	3,690	0.01	0.01	0.1	1
154 Cauliflower, cooked, flowerbuds	1 cup 120	93	25	3	Trace	—			5	25	0.8	70	0.11	0.10	0.7	66
Celery, raw:																
155 Stalk, large outer, 8 by about 1-1/2 inches, at root end	1 stalk 40	94	5	Trace	Trace	—			2	16	0.1	100	0.01	0.01	0.1	4
156 Pieces, diced	1 cup 100	94	15	1	Trace	—			4	39	0.3	240	0.03	0.03	0.3	9

Table A-4. Nutritive Values of the Edible Part of Foods (Continued)

(Dashes show that no basis could be found for imputing a value although there was some reason to believe that a measurable amount of the constituent might be present)

| | Food, Approximate Measure, and Weight (in grams) | Water | Food Energy | Protein | Fat (Total Lipid) | Fatty Acids | | | Carbohydrate | Calcium | Iron | Vitamin A Value | Thiamine | Riboflavin | Niacin | Ascorbic Acid |
| | | | | | | Saturated (Total) | Unsaturated Oleic | Linoleic | | | | | | | | |
		Percent	Calories	Grams	Grams	Grams	Grams	Grams	Grams	Milligrams	Milligrams	International Units	Milligrams	Milligrams	Milligrams	Milligrams
	Vegetables and Vegetable Products (Continued)															
157	Collards, cooked, 1 cup, 190 Grams	91	55	5	1	---	---	---	9	289	1.1	10,260	0.27	0.37	2.4	87
158	Corn, sweet: Cooked, ear 5 by 1-3/4 inches[4], 140	74	70	3	1	---	---	---	16	2	0.5	310[5]	0.09	0.08	1.0	7
159	Canned, solids and liquid, 1 cup, 256	81	170	5	2	---	---	---	40	10	1.0	690[5]	0.07	0.12	2.3	13
160	Cowpeas, cooked, immature seeds, 1 cup, 160	72	175	13	1	---	---	---	29	38	3.4	560	0.49	0.18	2.3	28
	Cucumbers, 10-ounce; 7-1/2 by about 2 inches:															
161	Raw, pared, 1 cucumber, 207	96	30	1	Trace	---	---	---	7	35	0.6	Trace	0.07	0.09	0.4	23
162	Raw, pared, center slice 1/8-inch thick, 6 slices, 50	96	5	Trace	Trace	---	---	---	2	8	0.2	Trace	0.02	0.02	0.1	6
163	Dandelion greens, cooked, 1 cup, 180	90	60	4	1	---	---	---	12	252	3.2	21,060	0.24	0.29	----	32
164	Endive, curly (including escarole), 2 ounces, 57	93	10	1	Trace	---	---	---	2	46	1.0	1,870	0.04	0.08	0.3	6
165	Kale, leaves including stems, cooked, 1 cup, 110	91	30	4	1	---	---	---	4	147	1.3	8,140	----	----	----	68
	Lettuce, raw:															
166	Butterhead, as Boston types; head, 4-inch diameter, 1 head, 220	95	30	3	Trace	---	---	---	6	77	4.4	2,130	0.14	0.13	0.6	18
167	Crisphead, as Iceberg; head, 4-3/4-inch diameter, 1 head, 454	96	60	4	Trace	---	---	---	13	91	2.3	1,500	0.29	0.27	1.3	29
168	Looseleaf, or bunching varieties, leaves, 2 large, 50	94	10	1	Trace	---	---	---	2	34	0.7	950	0.03	0.04	0.2	9
169	Mushrooms, canned, solids and liquid, 1 cup, 244	93	40	5	Trace	---	---	---	6	15	1.2	Trace	0.04	0.60	4.8	4
170	Mustard greens, cooked, 1 cup, 140	93	35	3	1	---	---	---	6	193	2.5	8,120	0.11	0.19	0.9	68
171	Okra, cooked, pod 3 by 5/8 inch, 8 pods, 85	91	25	2	Trace	---	---	---	5	78	0.4	420	0.11	0.15	0.8	17

4 Measure and weight apply to entire vegetable or fruit including parts not usually eaten.

5 Based on yellow varieties; white varieties contain only a trace of cryptoxanthin and carotenes, the pigments in corn that have biological activity.

Table A-4. Nutritive Values of the Edible Part of Foods (Continued)

(Dashes show that no basis could be found for imputing a value although there was some reason to believe that a measurable amount of the constituent might be present)

	Food, Approximate Measure, and Weight (in grams)		Water	Food Energy	Protein	Fat (Total Lipid)	Fatty Acids			Carbohydrate	Calcium	Iron	Vitamin A Value	Thiamine	Riboflavin	Niacin	Ascorbic Acid
							Saturated (Total)	Unsaturated Oleic	Unsaturated Linoleic								
		Grams	Per-cent	Calories	Grams	Grams	Grams	Grams	Grams	Grams	Milligrams	Milligrams	International Units	Milligrams	Milligrams	Milligrams	Milligrams
	Vegetables and Vegetable Products (Continued)																
	Onions:																
	Mature:																
172	Raw, onion 2-1/2-inch diameter 1 onion	110	89	40	2	Trace	------	------	------	10	30	0.6	40	0.04	0.04	0.2	11
173	Cooked 1 cup	210	92	60	3	Trace	------	------	------	14	50	0.8	80	0.06	0.06	0.4	14
174	Young green, small, without tops 6 onions	50	88	20	1	Trace	------	------	------	5	20	0.3	Trace	0.02	0.02	0.2	12
175	Parsley, raw, chopped 1 tablespoon	3.5	85	1	Trace	Trace	------	------	------	Trace	7	0.2	300	Trace	0.01	Trace	6
176	Parsnips, cooked 1 cup	155	82	100	2	1	------	------	------	23	70	0.9	50	0.11	0.13	0.2	16
	Peas, green:																
177	Cooked 1 cup	160	82	115	9	1	------	------	------	19	37	2.9	860	0.44	0.17	3.7	33
178	Canned, solids and liquid 1 cup	249	83	165	9	1	------	------	------	31	50	4.2	1,120	0.23	0.13	2.2	22
179	Canned, strained (baby food) 1 ounce	28	86	15	1	Trace	------	------	------	3	3	0.4	140	0.02	0.02	0.4	3
180	Peppers, hot, red, without seeds, dried (ground chili powder, added seasonings) 1 tablespoon	15	8	50	2	2	------	------	------	8	40	2.3	9,750	0.03	0.17	1.3	2
	Peppers, sweet:																
	Raw, medium, about 6 per pound:																
181	Green pod without stem and seeds 1 pod	62	93	15	1	Trace	------	------	------	3	6	0.4	260	0.05	0.05	0.3	79
182	Red pod without stem and seeds 1 pod	60	91	20	1	Trace	------	------	------	4	8	0.4	2,670	0.05	0.05	0.3	122
183	Canned, pimientos, medium 1 pod	38	92	10	Trace	Trace	------	------	------	2	3	0.6	870	0.01	0.02	0.1	36
	Potatoes, medium (about 3 per pound raw):																
184	Baked, peeled after baking 1 potato	99	75	90	3	Trace	------	------	------	21	9	0.7	Trace	0.10	0.04	1.7	20
	Boiled:																
185	Peeled after boiling 1 potato	136	80	105	3	Trace	------	------	------	23	10	0.8	Trace	0.13	0.05	2.0	22
186	Peeled before boiling 1 potato	122	83	80	2	Trace	------	------	------	18	7	0.6	Trace	0.11	0.04	1.4	20

Table A-4. Nutritive Values of the Edible Part of Foods (Continued)

(Dashes show that no basis could be found for imputing a value although there was some reason to believe that a measurable amount of the constituent might be present)

	Food, Approximate Measure, and Weight (in grams)		Water	Food Energy	Protein	Fat (Total Lipid)	Fatty Acids Saturated (Total)	Unsaturated Oleic	Unsaturated Linoleic	Carbohydrate	Calcium	Iron	Vitamin A Value	Thiamine	Riboflavin	Niacin	Ascorbic Acid
		Grams	Percent	Calories	Grams	Grams	Grams	Grams	Grams	Grams	Milligrams	Milligrams	International Units	Milligrams	Milligrams	Milligrams	Milligrams
	Vegetables and Vegetable Products (Continued)																
	Potatoes, medium (about 3 per pound raw): (Continued)																
	French-fried, piece 2 by 1/2 by 1/2 inch:																
187	Cooked in deep fat 10 pieces	57	45	155	2	7	2	2	4	20	9	0.7	Trace	0.07	0.04	1.8	12
188	Frozen, heated 10 pieces	57	53	125	2	5	1	1	2	19	5	1.0	Trace	0.08	0.01	1.5	12
	Mashed:																
189	Milk added 1 cup	195	83	125	4	1	---	---	---	25	47	0.8	50	0.16	0.10	2.0	19
190	Milk and butter added 1 cup	195	80	185	4	8	4	3	Trace	24	47	0.8	330	0.16	0.10	1.9	18
191	Potato chips, medium, 2-inch diameter 10 chips	20	2	115	1	8	2	2	4	10	8	0.4	Trace	0.04	0.01	1.0	3
192	Pumpkin, canned 1 cup	228	90	75	2	1	---	---	---	18	57	0.9	14,590	0.07	0.12	1.3	12
193	Radishes, raw, small, without tops 4 radishes	40	94	5	Trace	Trace	---	---	---	1	12	0.4	Trace	0.01	0.01	0.1	10
194	Sauerkraut, canned, solids and liquid 1 cup	235	93	45	2	Trace	---	---	---	9	85	1.2	120	0.07	0.09	0.4	33
	Spinach:																
195	Cooked 1 cup	180	92	40	5	1	---	---	---	6	167	4.0	14,580	0.13	0.25	1.0	50
196	Canned, drained solids 1 cup	180	91	45	5	1	---	---	---	6	212	4.7	14,400	0.03	0.21	0.6	24
197	Canned, strained or chopped (baby food) 1 ounce	28	88	10	1	Trace	---	---	---	2	18	0.2	1,420	0.01	0.04	0.1	2
	Sprouts, raw:																
198	Mung bean 1 cup	90	89	30	3	Trace	---	---	---	6	17	1.2	20	0.12	0.12	0.7	17
199	Soybean 1 cup	107	89	40	6	2	---	---	---	4	46	0.7	90	0.17	0.16	0.8	4
	Squash:																
	Cooked:																
200	Summer, diced 1 cup	210	96	30	2	Trace	---	---	---	7	52	0.8	820	0.10	0.16	1.6	21
201	Winter, baked, mashed 1 cup	205	81	130	4	1	---	---	---	32	57	1.6	8,610	0.10	0.27	1.4	27
202	Canned, winter, strained and chopped (baby food) 1 ounce	28	92	10	Trace	Trace	---	---	---	2	7	0.1	510	0.01	0.01	0.1	1

Table A-4. Nutritive Values of the Edible Part of Foods (Continued)

(Dashes show that no basis could be found for imputing a value although there was some reason to believe that a measurable amount of the constituent might be present)

Food, Approximate Measure, and Weight (in grams)	Grams	Water Per-cent	Food Energy Calories	Pro-tein Grams	Fat (Total Lipid) Grams	Fatty Acids Satu-rated (Total) Grams	Unsaturated Oleic Grams	Unsaturated Lino-leic Grams	Carbo-hy-drate Grams	Cal-cium Milli-grams	Iron Milli-grams	Vita-min A Value Inter-national Units	Thia-mine Milli-grams	Ribo-flavin Milli-grams	Niacin Milli-grams	Ascor-bic Acid Milli-grams
Vegetables and Vegetable Products (Continued)																
Sweetpotatoes:																
Cooked, medium, 5 by 2 inches, weight raw about 6 ounces:																
203 Baked, peeled after baking · 1 sweetpotato	110	64	155	2	1				36	44	1.0	8,910	0.10	0.07	0.7	24
204 Boiled, peeled after boiling · 1 sweetpotato	147	71	170	2	1				39	47	1.0	11,610	0.13	0.09	0.9	25
205 Candied, 3-1/2 by 2-1/4 inches · 1 sweetpotato	175	60	295	2	6	2	3	1	60	65	1.6	11,030	0.10	0.08	0.8	17
206 Canned, vacuum or solid pack · 1 cup	218	72	235	4	Trace				54	54	1.7	17,000	0.10	0.10	1.4	30
Tomatoes:																
207 Raw, medium, 2 by 2-1/2 inches, about 3 per pound · 1 tomato	150	94	35	2	Trace				7	20	0.8	1,350	0.10	0.06	1.0	34[6]
208 Canned · 1 cup	242	94	50	2	Trace				10	15	1.2	2,180	0.13	0.07	1.7	40
209 Tomato juice, canned · 1 cup	242	94	45	2	Trace				10	17	2.2	1,940	0.13	0.07	1.8	39
210 Tomato catsup · 1 tablespoon	17	69	15	Trace	Trace				4	4	0.1	240	0.02	0.01	0.3	3
211 Turnips, cooked, diced · 1 cup	155	94	35	1	Trace				8	54	0.6	Trace	0.06	0.08	0.5	33
Turnip greens:																
Cooked:																
212 In small amount of water, short time · 1 cup	145	93	30	3	Trace				5	267	1.6	9,140	0.21	0.36	0.8	100
213 In large amount of water, long time · 1 cup	145	94	25	3	Trace				5	252	1.4	8,260	0.14	0.33	0.8	68
214 Canned, solids and liquid · 1 cup	232	94	40	3	1				7	232	3.7	10,900	0.04	0.21	1.4	44
Fruits and Fruit Products																
215 Apples, raw, medium, 2-1/2-inch diameter, about 3 per pound[4] · 1 apple	150	85	70	Trace	Trace				18	8	0.4	50	0.04	0.02	0.1	3
216 Apple brown betty · 1 cup	230	64	345	4	8	4	3	Trace	68	41	1.4	230	0.13	0.10	0.9	3

[4] Measure and weight apply to entire vegetable or fruit including parts not usually eaten.

[6] Year-round average. Samples marketed from November through May average around 15 mg per 150-gm tomato; from June through October, around 39 mg.

Table A-4. Nutritive Values of the Edible Part of Foods (Continued)

(Dashes show that no basis could be found for imputing a value although there was some reason to believe that a measurable amount of the constituent might be present)

	Food, Approximate Measure, and Weight (in grams)		Water	Food Energy	Pro-tein	Fat (Total Lipid)	Fatty Acids			Carbo-hy-drate	Cal-cium	Iron	Vita-min A Value	Thia-mine	Ribo-flavin	Niacin	Ascor-bic Acid
							Satu-rated (Total)	Unsaturated Oleic	Lino-leic								
		Grams	Per-cent	Calo-ries	Grams	Grams	Grams	Grams	Grams	Grams	Milli-grams	Milli-grams	Inter-national Units	Milli-grams	Milli-grams	Milli-grams	Milli-grams
	Fruits and Fruit Products (Continued)																
217	Apple juice, bottled or canned 1 cup	249	88	120	Trace	Trace	----			30	15	1.5	----	0.01	0.04	0.2	2
	Applesauce, canned:																
218	Sweetened 1 cup	254	76	230	1	Trace	----			60	10	1.3	100	0.05	0.03	0.1	3
219	Unsweetened or artificially sweetened 1 cup	239	88	100	Trace	Trace	----			26	10	1.2	100	0.04	0.02	0.1	2
220	Applesauce and apricots, canned, strained or junior (baby food) 1 ounce	28	77	25	Trace	Trace	----			6	1	0.1	170	Trace	Trace	Trace	1
	Apricots:																
221	Raw, about 12 per pound[4] 3 apricots	114	85	55	1	Trace	----			14	18	0.5	2,890	0.03	0.04	0.7	10
	Canned in heavy sirup:																
222	Halves and sirup 1 cup	259	77	220	2	Trace	----			57	28	0.8	4,510	0.05	0.06	0.9	10
223	Halves (medium) and sirup 4 halves; 2 tablespoons sirup	122	77	105	1	Trace	----			27	13	0.4	2,120	0.02	0.03	0.4	5
	Dried:																
224	Uncooked, 40 halves, small 1 cup	150	25	390	8	1	----			100	100	8.2	16,350	0.02	0.23	4.9	19
225	Cooked, unsweetened, fruit and liquid 1 cup	285	76	240	5	1	----			62	63	5.1	8,550	0.01	0.13	2.8	8
226	Apricot nectar, canned 1 cup	250	85	140	1	Trace	----			36	22	0.5	2,380	0.02	0.02	0.5	7
	Avocados, raw:																
	California varieties, mainly Fuerte:																
227	10-ounce avocado about 3-1/3 by 4-1/4 inches, peeled, pitted 1/2 avocado	108	74	185	2	18	4	8	2	6	11	0.6	310	0.12	0.21	1.7	15
228	1/2-inch cubes 1 cup	152	74	260	3	26	5	12	3	9	15	0.9	440	0.16	0.30	2.4	21
	Florida varieties:																
229	13-ounce avocado, about 4 by 3 inches peeled, pitted 1/2 avocado	123	78	160	2	14	3	6	2	11,	12	0.7	360	0.13	0.24	2.0	17
230	1/2-inch cubes 1 cup	152	78	195	2	17	3	8	2	13	15	0.9	440	0.16	0.30	2.4	21

[4] Measure and weight apply to entire vegetable or fruit including parts not usually eaten.

480

(Dashes show that no basis could be found for imputing a value although there was some reason to believe that a measurable amount of the constituent might be present)

| | Food, Approximate Measure, and Weight (in grams) | Weight | Water | Food Energy | Protein | Fat (Total Lipid) | Fatty Acids | | | Carbohydrate | Calcium | Iron | Vitamin A Value | Thiamine | Riboflavin | Niacin | Ascorbic Acid |
							Saturated (Total)	Unsaturated Oleic	Unsaturated Linoleic								
		Grams	Percent	Calories	Grams	Grams	Grams	Grams	Grams	Grams	Milligrams	Milligrams	International Units	Milligrams	Milligrams	Milligrams	Milligrams
	Fruits and Fruit Products (Continued)																
231	Bananas, raw, 6 by 1-1/2 inches, about 3 per pound[4]	150	76	85	1	Trace	---	---	---	23	8	0.7	190	0.05	0.06	0.7	10
232	Blackberries, raw — 1 cup	144	84	85	2	1	---	---	---	19	46	1.3	290	0.05	0.06	0.5	30
233	Blueberries, raw — 1 cup	140	83	85	1	1	---	---	---	21	21	1.4	140	0.04	0.08	0.6	20
234	Cantaloupes, raw; medium, 5-inch diameter, about 1-2/3 pounds[4] — 1/2 melon	385	91	60	1	Trace	---	---	---	14	27	0.8	6,540[7]	0.08	0.06	1.2	63
	Cherries:																
235	Raw, sweet, with stems[4] — 1 cup	130	80	80	2	Trace	---	---	---	20	26	0.5	130	0.06	0.07	0.5	12
236	Canned, red, sour, pitted, heavy sirup — 1 cup	260	76	230	2	1	---	---	---	59	36	0.8	1,680	0.07	0.06	0.4	13
237	Cranberry juice cocktail, canned — 1 cup	250	83	160	Trace	Trace	---	---	---	41	12	0.8	Trace	0.02	0.02	0.1	8
238	Cranberry sauce, sweetened, canned, strained — 1 cup	277	62	405	Trace	1	---	---	---	104	17	0.6	40	0.03	0.03	0.1	5
239	Dates, domestic, natural, and dry, pitted, cut — 1 cup	178	22	490	4	1	---	---	---	130	105	5.3	90	0.16	0.17	3.9	0
	Figs:																
240	Raw, small, 1-1/2-inch diameter, about 12 per pound — 3 figs	114	78	90	1	Trace	---	---	---	23	40	0.7	90	0.07	0.06	0.5	2
241	Dried, large, 2 by 1 inch — 1 fig	21	23	60	1	Trace	---	---	---	15	26	0.6	20	0.02	0.02	0.1	0
242	Fruit cocktail, canned in heavy sirup, solids and liquid — 1 cup	256	80	195	1	1	---	---	---	50	23	1.0	360	0.04	0.03	1.1	5
	Grapefruit: Raw, medium, 4-1/4-inch diameter, size 64:																
243	White[4] — 1/2 grapefruit	285	89	55	1	Trace	---	---	---	14	22	0.6	10	0.05	0.02	0.2	52
244	Pink or red[4] — 1/2 grapefruit	285	89	60	1	Trace	---	---	---	15	23	0.6	640	0.05	0.02	0.3	52

[4] Measure and weight apply to entire vegetable or fruit including parts not usually eaten.
[7] Value based on varieties with orange-colored flesh; for green-fleshed varieties value is about 540 IU per 1/2 melon.
[8] About 5 mg per 8 fl oz is from cranberries. Ascorbic acid is usually added to approximately 100 mg per 8 fl oz.

481

Table A-4. Nutritive Values of the Edible Part of Foods (Continued)

(Dashes show that no basis could be found for imputing a value although there was some reason to believe that a measurable amount of the constituent might be present)

	Food, Approximate Measure, and Weight (in grams)			Water	Food Energy	Protein	Fat (Total Lipid)	Fatty Acids			Carbohydrate	Calcium	Iron	Vitamin A Value	Thiamine	Riboflavin	Niacin	Ascorbic Acid
								Saturated (Total)	Unsaturated									
									Oleic	Linoleic								
			Grams	Per-cent	Calo-ries	Grams	Grams	Grams	Grams	Grams	Grams	Milli-grams	Milli-grams	Inter-national Units	Milli-grams	Milli-grams	Milli-grams	Milli-grams
	Fruits and Fruit Products (Continued)																	
	Grapefruit (Continued)																	
245	Raw sections, white	1 cup	194	89	75	1	Trace	------	------	------	20	31	0.8	20	0.07	0.03	0.3	72
	Canned, white:																	
246	Sirup pack, solids and liquid	1 cup	249	81	175	1	Trace	------	------	------	44	32	0.7	20	0.07	0.04	0.5	75
247	Water pack, solids and liquid	1 cup	240	91	70	1	Trace	------	------	------	18	31	0.7	20	0.07	0.04	0.5	72
	Grapefruit juice:																	
248	Fresh	1 cup	246	90	95	1	Trace	------	------	------	23	22	0.5	9	0.09	0.04	0.4	92
	Canned, white:																	
249	Unsweetened	1 cup	247	89	100	1	Trace	------	------	------	24	20	1.0	20	0.07	0.04	0.4	84
250	Sweetened	1 cup	250	86	130	1	Trace	------	------	------	32	20	1.0	20	0.07	0.04	0.4	78
	Frozen, concentrate, unsweetened:																	
251	Undiluted, can, 6 fluid ounces	1 can	207	62	300	4	1	------	------	------	72	70	0.8	60	0.29	0.12	1.4	286
252	Diluted with 3 parts water, by volume	1 cup	247	89	100	1	Trace	------	------	------	24	25	0.2	20	0.10	0.04	0.5	96
	Frozen, concentrate, sweetened:																	
253	Undiluted, can, 6 fluid ounces	1 can	211	57	350	3	1	------	------	------	85	59	0.6	50	0.24	0.11	1.2	245
254	Diluted with 3 parts water, by volume	1 cup	249	88	115	1	Trace	------	------	------	28	20	0.2	20	0.08	0.03	0.4	82
	Dehydrated:																	
255	Crystals, can, net weight 4 ounces	1 can	114	1	430	5	1	------	------	------	103	99	1.1	90	0.41	0.18	2.0	399
256	Prepared with water (1 pound yields about 1 gallon)	1 cup	247	90	100	1	Trace	------	------	------	24	22	0.2	20	0.10	0.05	0.5	92
	Grapes, raw:																	
257	American type (slip skin), such as Concord, Delaware, Niagara, Catawba, and Scuppernong[4]	1 cup	153	82	65	1	1	------	------	------	15	15	0.4	100	0.05	0.03	0.2	3

[4] Measure and weight apply to entire vegetable or fruit including parts not usually eaten.
[9] For white-fleshed varieties value is about 20 IU per cup; for red-fleshed varieties, 1,080 IU per cup.

Table A-4. Nutritive Values of the Edible Part of Foods (Continued)

(Dashes show that no basis could be found for imputing a value although there was some reason to believe that a measurable amount of the constituent might be present)

	Food, Approximate Measure, and Weight (in grams)	Weight	Water	Food Energy	Protein	Fat (Total Lipid)	Fatty Acids Saturated (Total)	Unsaturated Oleic	Unsaturated Linoleic	Carbohydrate	Calcium	Iron	Vitamin A Value	Thiamine	Riboflavin	Niacin	Ascorbic Acid
		Grams	Per cent	Calories	Grams	Grams	Grams	Grams	Grams	Grams	Milligrams	Milligrams	International Units	Milligrams	Milligrams	Milligrams	Milligrams
	Fruits and Fruit Products (Continued)																
	Grapes, raw (Continued)																
258	European type (adherent skin), such as Malaga, Muscat, Thompson Seedless, Emperor, and Flame Tokay[4] 1 cup	160	81	95	1	Trace	-----	-----	-----	25	17	0.6	140	0.07	0.04	0.4	6
259	Grape juice, bottled or canned 1 cup	254	83	165	1	Trace	-----	-----	-----	42	28	0.8	-----	0.10	0.05	0.6	Trace
260	Lemons, raw, medium, 2-1/5-inch diameter, size 150[4] 1 lemon	106	90	20	1	Trace	-----	-----	-----	6	18	0.4	10	0.03	0.01	0.1	38
	Lemon juice:																
261	Fresh 1 cup	246	91	60	1	Trace	-----	-----	-----	20	17	0.5	40	0.08	0.03	0.2	113
262	1 tablespoon	15	91	5	Trace	Trace	-----	-----	-----	1	1	Trace	Trace	Trace	Trace	Trace	7
263	Canned, unsweetened 1 cup	245	92	55	1	Trace	-----	-----	-----	19	17	0.5	40	0.07	0.03	0.2	102
	Lemonade concentrate, frozen, sweetened:																
264	Undiluted, can, 6 fluid ounces 1 can	220	48	430	Trace	Trace	-----	-----	-----	112	9	0.4	40	0.05	0.06	0.7	66
265	Diluted with 4-1/3 parts water, by volume 1 cup	248	88	110	Trace	Trace	-----	-----	-----	28	2	0.1	10	0.01	0.01	0.2	17
	Lime juice:																
266	Fresh 1 cup	246	90	65	1	Trace	-----	-----	-----	22	22	0.5	30	0.05	0.03	0.3	80
267	Canned 1 cup	246	90	65	1	Trace	-----	-----	-----	22	22	0.5	30	0.05	0.03	0.3	52
	Limeade concentrate, frozen, sweetened:																
268	Undiluted, can, 6 fluid ounces 1 can	218	50	410	Trace	Trace	-----	-----	-----	108	11	0.2	Trace	0.02	0.02	0.2	26
269	Diluted with 4-1/3 parts water, by volume 1 cup	248	90	105	Trace	Trace	-----	-----	-----	27	2	Trace	Trace	Trace	Trace	Trace	6
	Oranges, raw:																
270	California, Navel (winter), 2-4/5-inch diameter, size 88[4] 1 orange	180	85	60	2	Trace	-----	-----	-----	16	49	0.5	240	0.12	0.05	0.5	75

[4] Measure and weight apply to entire vegetable or fruit including parts not usually eaten.

483

Table A-4. Nutritive Values of the Edible Part of Foods (Continued)

(Dashes show that no basis could be found for imputing a value although there was some reason to believe that a measurable amount of the constituent might be present)

	Food, Approximate Measure, and Weight (in grams)	Water	Food Energy	Protein	Fat (Total Lipid)	Fatty Acids			Carbohydrate	Calcium	Iron	Vitamin A Value	Thiamine	Riboflavin	Niacin	Ascorbic Acid
						Saturated (Total)	Unsaturated									
							Oleic	Linoleic								
		Per-cent	Calo-ries	Grams	Grams	Grams	Grams	Grams	Grams	Milli-grams	Milli-grams	Inter-national Units	Milli-grams	Milli-grams	Milli-grams	Milli-grams
				Grams												
	Fruits and Fruit Products (Continued) Grams															
	Oranges, raw (Continued)															
271	Florida, all varieties, 1 orange 3-inch diameter[4] — 210	86	75	1	Trace	----			19	67	0.3	310	0.16	0.06	0.6	70
	Orange juice:															
	Fresh:															
272	California, Valencia (summer) 1 cup — 249	88	115	2	1	----			26	27	0.7	500	0.22	0.06	0.9	122
	Florida varieties:															
273	Early and mid-season 1 cup — 247	90	100	1	Trace	----			23	25	0.5	490	0.22	0.06	0.9	127
274	Late season, Valencia 1 cup — 248	88	110	1	Trace	----			26	25	0.5	500	0.22	0.06	0.9	92
275	Canned, unsweetened 1 cup — 249	87	120	2	Trace	----			28	25	1.0	500	0.17	0.05	0.6	100
	Frozen concentrate:															
276	Undiluted, can, 6 fluid ounces — 210	58	330	5	Trace	----			80	69	0.8	1,490	0.63	0.10	2.4	332
277	Diluted with 3 parts water, by volume 1 cup — 248	88	110	2	Trace	----			27	22	0.2	500	0.21	0.03	0.8	112
	Dehydrated:															
278	Crystals, can, net weight 4 ounces 1 can — 113	1	430	6	2	----			100	95	1.9	1,900	0.76	0.24	3.3	406
279	Prepared with water, 1 pound yields about 1 gallon 1 cup — 248	88	115	1	Trace	----			27	25	0.5	500	0.20	0.06	0.9	108
	Orange and grapefruit juice:															
	Frozen concentrate:															
280	Undiluted, can, 6 fluid ounces 1 can — 209	59	325	4	1	----			78	61	0.8	790	0.47	0.06	2.3	301
281	Diluted with 3 parts water, by volume 1 cup — 248	88	110	1	Trace	----			26	20	0.2	270	0.16	0.02	0.8	102
282	Papayas, raw, 1/2-inch cubes 1 cup — 182	89	70	1	Trace	----			18	36	0.5	3,190	0.07	0.08	0.5	102

4 Measure and weight apply to entire vegetable or fruit including parts not usually eaten.

Table A-4. Nutritive Values of the Edible Part of Foods (Continued)

(Dashes show that no basis could be found for imputing a value although there was some reason to believe that a measurable amount of the constituent might be present)

	Food, Approximate Measure, and Weight (in grams)		Water	Food Energy	Protein	Fat (Total Lipid)	Fatty Acids			Carbohydrate	Calcium	Iron	Vitamin A Value	Thiamine	Riboflavin	Niacin	Ascorbic Acid
							Saturated (Total)	Unsaturated Oleic	Unsaturated Linoleic								
		Grams	Percent	Calories	Grams	Grams	Grams	Grams	Grams	Grams	Milligrams	Milligrams	International Units	Milligrams	Milligrams	Milligrams	Milligrams
	Fruits and Fruit Products (Continued)																
	Peaches:																
	Raw:																
283	Whole, medium, 2-inch diameter, about 4 per pound[4] — 1 peach	114	89	35	1	Trace	-------	-------	-------	10	9	0.5	1,320[10]	0.02	0.05	1.0	7
284	Sliced — 1 cup	168	89	65	1	Trace	-------	-------	-------	16	15	0.8	2,230[10]	0.03	0.08	1.6	12
	Canned, yellow-fleshed, solids and liquid:																
	Sirup pack, heavy:																
285	Halves or slices — 1 cup	257	79	200	1	Trace	-------	-------	-------	52	10	0.8	1,100	0.02	0.06	1.4	7
286	Halves (medium) and 2 tablespoons sirup — 2 halves and 2 tablespoons sirup	117	79	90	Trace	Trace	-------	-------	-------	24	5	0.4	500	0.01	0.03	0.7	3
287	Water pack — 1 cup	245	91	75	1	Trace	-------	-------	-------	20	10	0.7	1,100	0.02	0.06	1.4	7
288	Strained or chopped (baby food) — 1 ounce	28	78	25	Trace	Trace	-------	-------	-------	6	2	0.1	140	Trace	0.01	0.2	1
	Dried:																
289	Uncooked — 1 cup	160	25	420	5	1	-------	-------	-------	109	77	9.6	6,240	0.02	0.31	8.5	28
290	Cooked, unsweetened, 10-12 halves and 6 tablespoons liquid — 1 cup	270	77	220	3	1	-------	-------	-------	58	41	5.1	3,290	0.01	0.15	4.2	6
	Frozen:																
291	Carton, 12 ounces, not thawed — 1 carton	340	76	300	1	Trace	-------	-------	-------	77	14	1.7	2,210	0.03	0.14	2.4	135[11]
292	Can, 16 ounces, not thawed — 1 can	454	76	400	2	Trace	-------	-------	-------	103	18	2.3	2,950	0.05	0.18	3.2	181[11]
293	Peach nectar, canned — 1 cup	250	87	120	Trace	Trace	-------	-------	-------	31	10	0.5	1,080	0.02	0.05	1.0	1
	Pears:																
294	Raw, 3 by 2-1/2-inch diameter[4] — 1 pear	182	83	100	1	1	-------	-------	-------	25	13	0.5	30	0.04	0.07	0.2	7
	Canned, solids and liquid:[4]																
	Sirup pack, heavy:																
295	Halves or slices — 1 cup	255	80	195	1	1	-------	-------	-------	50	13	0.5	Trace	0.03	0.05	0.3	4
296	Halves (medium) and 2 tablespoons sirup — 2 halves and 2 tablespoons sirup	117	80	90	Trace	Trace	-------	-------	-------	23	6	0.2	Trace	0.01	0.02	0.2	2

[4] Measure and weight apply to entire vegetable or fruit including parts not usually eaten.
[10] Based on yellow-fleshed varieties; for white-fleshed varieties value is about 50 IU per 114-gm peach and 80 IU per cup of sliced peaches.
[11] Average weighted in accordance with commercial freezing practices. For products without added ascorbic acid, value is about 37 mg per 12-oz carton and 50 mg per 16-oz can; for those with added ascorbic acid, 139 mg per 12 and 186 mg per 16 oz.

Table A-4. Nutritive Values of the Edible Part of Foods (Continued)

(Dashes show that no basis could be found for imputing a value although there was some reason to believe that a measurable amount of the constituent might be present)

	Food, Approximate Measure, and Weight (in grams)	Water	Food Energy	Pro-tein	Fat (Total Lipid)	Fatty Acids Saturated (Total)	Unsaturated Oleic	Lino-leic	Carbo-hy-drate	Cal-cium	Iron	Vita-min A Value	Thia-mine	Ribo-flavin	Niacin	Ascor-bic Acid
	Grams	Per-cent	Calo-ries	Grams	Grams	Grams	Grams	Grams	Grams	Milli-grams	Milli-grams	Inter-national Units	Milli-grams	Milli-grams	Milli-grams	Milli-grams
	Fruits and Fruit Products (Continued)															
	Pears (Continued)															
	Canned, solids and liquid (Continued)															
297	Water pack 1 cup 243	91	80	Trace	Trace				20	12	0.5	Trace	0.02	0.05	0.3	4
298	Strained or chopped 1 ounce 28	82	20	Trace	Trace				5	2	0.1	10	0.01	0.01	0.1	1
	(baby food)															
299	Pear nectar, canned 1 cup 250	86	130	1	Trace				33	8	0.2	Trace	0.01	0.05	Trace	1
300	Persimmons, Japanese 1 persimmon 125	79	75	1	Trace				20	6	0.4	2,740	0.03	0.02	0.1	11
	or kaki, raw, seedless, 2-1/2-inch diameter[4]															
	Pineapple:															
301	Raw, diced 1 cup 140	85	75	1	Trace				19	24	0.7	100	0.12	0.04	0.3	24
	Canned, heavy sirup pack, solids and liquid:															
302	Crushed 1 cup 260	80	195	1	Trace				50	29	0.8	120	0.20	0.06	0.5	17
303	Sliced, slices and 2 small or 122	80	90	Trace	Trace				24	13	0.4	50	0.09	0.03	0.2	8
	juice 1 large and 2 tablespoons juice															
304	Pineapple juice, canned 1 cup 249	86	135	1	Trace				34	37	0.7	120	0.12	0.04	0.5	22
	Plums, all except prunes:															
305	Raw, 2-inch diameter, 1 plum 60	87	25	Trace	Trace				7	7	0.3	140	0.02	0.02	0.3	3
	about 2 ounces[4]															
	Canned, sirup pack (Italian prunes):															
306	Plums (with pits) 1 cup 256	77	205	1	Trace				53	22	2.2	2,970	0.05	0.05	0.9	4
	and juice[4]															
307	Plums (without pits) 3 plums and 122	77	100	Trace	Trace				26	11	1.1	1,470	0.03	0.02	0.5	2
	and juice 2 tablespoons juice															
	Prunes, dried, "softenized", medium:															
308	Uncooked[4] 4 prunes 32	28	70	1	Trace				18	14	1.1	440	0.02	0.04	0.4	1
309	Cooked, unsweetened, 1 cup 270	66	295	2	1				78	60	4.5	1,860	0.08	0.18	1.7	2
	17-18 prunes and 1/3 cup liquid[4]															
310	Prunes with tapioca, 1 ounce 28	77	25	Trace	Trace				6	2	0.3	110	0.01	0.02	0.1	1
	canned, strained or junior (baby food)															

[4] Measure and weight apply to entire vegetable or fruit including parts not usually eaten.

Table A-4. Nutritive Values of the Edible Part of Foods (Continued)

(Dashes show that no basis could be found for imputing a value although there was some reason to believe that a measurable amount of the constituent might be present)

	Food, Approximate Measure, and Weight (in grams)		Water	Food Energy	Protein	Fat (Total Lipid)	Fatty Acids Saturated (Total)	Unsaturated Oleic	Unsaturated Linoleic	Carbohydrate	Calcium	Iron	Vitamin A Value	Thiamine	Riboflavin	Niacin	Ascorbic Acid
		Grams	Per cent	Calories	Grams	Grams	Grams	Grams	Grams	Grams	Milligrams	Milligrams	International Units	Milligrams	Milligrams	Milligrams	Milligrams
	Fruits and Fruit Products (Continued)																
311	Prune juice, canned, 1 cup	256	80	200	1	Trace	----	----	----	49	36	10.5	----	0.02	0.03	1.1	4
312	Raisins, dried, 1 cup	160	18	460	4	Trace	----	----	----	124	99	5.6	30	0.18	0.13	0.9	2
	Raspberries, red:																
313	Raw, 1 cup	123	84	70	1	1	----	----	----	17	27	1.1	160	0.04	0.11	1.1	31
314	Frozen, 10-ounce carton, not thawed, 1 carton	284	74	275	2	1	----	----	----	70	37	1.7	200	0.06	0.17	1.7	59
315	Rhubarb, cooked, sugar added, 1 cup	272	63	385	1	Trace	----	----	----	98	212	1.6	220	0.06	0.15	0.7	17
	Strawberries:																
316	Raw, capped, 1 cup	149	90	55	1	1	----	----	----	13	31	1.5	90	0.04	0.10	1.0	88
317	Frozen, 10-ounce, 1 carton	284	71	310	1	1	----	----	----	79	40	2.0	90	0.06	0.17	1.5	150
318	Frozen, 16-ounce can, not thawed, 1 can	454	71	495	2	1	----	----	----	126	64	3.2	150	0.09	0.27	2.4	240
319	Tangerines, raw, medium, 2-1/2-inch diameter, about 4 per pound[4], 1 tangerine	114	87	40	1	Trace	----	----	----	10	34	0.3	350	0.05	0.02	0.1	26
	Tangerine juice:																
320	Canned, unsweetened, 1 cup	248	89	105	1	Trace	----	----	----	25	45	0.5	1,040	0.14	0.04	0.3	56
321	Frozen concentrate: Undiluted, can, 6 fluid ounces, 1 can	210	58	340	4	1	----	----	----	80	130	1.5	3,070	0.43	0.12	0.9	202
322	Diluted with 3 parts water, by volume, 1 cup	248	88	115	1	Trace	----	----	----	27	45	0.5	1,020	0.14	0.04	0.3	67
323	Watermelon, raw, wedge, 4 by 8 inches (1/16 of 10 by 16-inch melon, about 2 pounds with rind)[4], 1 wedge	925	93	115	2	1	----	----	----	27	30	2.1	2,510	0.13	0.13	0.7	30
	Grain Products																
324	Barley, pearled, light, uncooked, 1 cup	203	11	710	17	2	Trace	1	1	160	32	4.1	0	0.25	0.17	6.3	0
325	Biscuits, baking powder with enriched flour, 2-1/2 inch diameter, 1 biscuit	38	27	140	3	6	2	3	1	17	46	0.6	Trace	0.08	0.08	0.7	Trace

[4] Measure and weight apply to entire vegetable or fruit including parts not usually eaten.

Table A-4. Nutritive Values of the Edible Part of Foods (Continued)

(Dashes show that no basis could be found for imputing a value although there was some reason to believe that a measurable amount of the constituent might be present)

	Food, Approximate Measure, and Weight (in grams)		Water	Food Energy	Protein	Fat (Total Lipid)	Fatty Acids			Carbo-hy-drate	Cal-cium	Iron	Vita-min A Value	Thia-mine	Ribo-flavin	Niacin	Ascor-bic Acid
							Satu-rated (Total)	Unsaturated Oleic	Unsaturated Lino-leic								
		Grams	Per-cent	Calo-ries	Grams	Grams	Grams	Grams	Grams	Grams	Milli-grams	Milli-grams	Inter-national Units	Milli-grams	Milli-grams	Milli-grams	Milli-grams
	Grain Products (Continued)																
326	Bran flakes (40 per cent bran) added thiamine, 1 ounce	28	3	85	3	1	---	---	---	23	20	1.2	0	0.11	0.05	1.7	0
	Breads:																
327	Boston brown bread, slice, 3 by 3/4 inch, 1 slice	48	45	100	3	1	---	---	---	22	43	0.9	0	0.05	0.03	0.6	0
	Cracked-wheat bread:																
328	Loaf, 1-pound, 20 slices, 1 loaf	454	35	1,190	39	10	2	5	2	236	399	5.0	Trace	0.53	0.42	5.8	Trace
329	Slice, 1 slice	23	35	60	2	1	---	---	---	12	20	0.3	Trace	0.03	0.02	0.3	Trace
	French or vienna bread:																
330	Enriched, 1-pound loaf, 1 loaf	454	31	1,315	41	14	3	8	2	251	195	10.0	Trace	1.26	0.98	11.3	Trace
331	Unenriched, 1-pound loaf, 1 loaf	454	31	1,315	41	14	3	8	2	251	195	3.2	Trace	0.39	0.39	3.6	Trace
	Italian bread:																
332	Enriched, 1-pound loaf, 1 loaf	454	32	1,250	41	4	Trace	1	2	256	77	10.0	0	1.31	0.93	11.7	0
333	Unenriched, 1-pound loaf, 1 loaf	454	32	1,250	41	4	Trace	1	2	256	77	3.2	0	0.39	0.27	3.6	0
	Raisin bread:																
334	Loaf, 1-pound, 20 slices, 1 loaf	454	35	1,190	30	13	3	8	2	243	322	5.9	Trace	0.24	0.42	3.0	Trace
335	Slice, 1 slice	23	35	60	2	1	---	---	---	12	16	0.3	Trace	0.01	0.02	0.2	Trace
	Rye bread:																
	American, light (1/3 rye, 2/3 wheat):																
336	Loaf, 1-pound, 20 slices, 1 loaf	454	36	1,100	41	5	---	---	---	236	340	7.3	0	0.81	0.33	6.4	0
337	Slice, 1 slice	23	36	55	2	Trace	---	---	---	12	17	0.4	0	0.04	0.02	0.3	0
338	Pumpernickel, loaf, 1 pound, 1 loaf	454	34	1,115	41	5	---	---	---	241	381	10.9	0	1.05	0.63	5.4	0
	White bread, enriched:																
	1 to 2 percent nonfat dry milk:																
339	Loaf, 1-pound, 20 slices, 1 loaf	454	36	1,225	39	15	3	8	2	229	318	10.9	Trace	1.13	0.77	10.4	Trace
340	Slice, 1 slice	23	36	60	2	1	Trace	Trace	Trace	12	16	0.6	Trace	0.06	0.04	0.5	Trace

Table A-4. Nutritive Values of the Edible Part of Foods (Continued)

(Dashes show that no basis could be found for imputing a value although there was some reason to believe that a measurable amount of the constituent might be present)

	Food, Approximate Measure, and Weight (in grams)	Water	Food Energy	Pro-tein	Fat (Total Lipid)	Fatty Acids			Carbo-hy-drate	Cal-cium	Iron	Vita-min A Value	Thia-mine	Ribo-flavin	Niacin	Ascor-bic Acid
						Satu-rated (Total)	Unsaturated Oleic	Lino-leic								
		Per-cent	Calo-ries	Grams	Grams	Grams	Grams	Grams	Grams	Milli-grams	Milli-grams	Inter-national Units	Milli-grams	Milli-grams	Milli-grams	Milli-grams
		Grams															
	Grain Products (Continued)																
	Breads (Continued)																
	White bread, enriched (Continued)																
	3 to 4 percent nonfat dry milk:[12]																
341	Loaf, 1-pound 454	36	1,225	39	15	3	8	2	229	381	11.3	Trace	1.13	0.95	10.8	Trace
342	Slice, 20 per loaf 23	36	60	2	1	Trace	Trace	Trace	12	19	0.6	Trace	0.06	0.05	0.6	Trace
343	Slice, toasted 20	25	60	2	1	Trace	Trace	Trace	12	19	0.6	Trace	0.05	0.05	0.6	Trace
344	Slice, 26 per loaf 17	36	45	1	1	Trace	Trace	Trace	9	14	0.4	Trace	0.04	0.04	0.4	Trace
	5 to 6 percent nonfat dry milk:																
345	Loaf, 1-pound, 20 slices 454	35	1,245	41	17	4	10	2	228	435	11.3	Trace	1.22	0.91	11.0	Trace
346	Slice 23	35	65	2	1	Trace	Trace	Trace	12	22	0.6	Trace	0.06	0.05	0.6	Trace
	White bread, unenriched:																
	1 to 2 percent nonfat dry milk:																
347	Loaf, 1-pound, 20 slices 454	36	1,225	39	15	3	8	2	229	318	3.2	Trace	0.40	0.36	5.6	Trace
348	Slice 23	36	60	2	1	Trace	Trace	Trace	12	16	0.2	Trace	0.02	0.02	0.3	Trace
	3 to 4 percent nonfat dry milk:[12]																
349	Loaf, 1-pound 454	36	1,225	39	15	3	8	2	229	381	3.2	Trace	0.31	0.39	5.0	Trace
350	Slice, 20 per loaf 23	36	60	2	1	Trace	Trace	Trace	12	19	0.2	Trace	0.02	0.02	0.3	Trace
351	Slice, toasted 20	25	60	2	1	Trace	Trace	Trace	12	19	0.2	Trace	0.01	0.02	0.3	Trace
352	Slice, 26 per loaf 17	36	45	1	1	Trace	Trace	Trace	9	14	0.1	Trace	0.01	0.01	0.2	Trace
	5 to 6 percent nonfat dry milk:																
353	Loaf, 1 pound, 20 slices 454	35	1,245	41	17	4	10	2	228	435	3.2	Trace	0.32	0.59	4.1	Trace
354	Slice 23	35	65	2	1	Trace	Trace	Trace	12	22	0.2	Trace	0.02	0.03	0.2	Trace
	Whole-wheat bread, made with 2 percent nonfat dry milk:																
355	Loaf, 1-pound, 20 slices 454	36	1,105	48	14	3	3	6	216	449	10.4	Trace	1.17	0.56	12.9	Trace
356	Slice 23	36	55	2	1	Trace	Trace	Trace	11	23	0.5	Trace	0.06	0.03	0.7	Trace
357	Slice, toasted 19	24	55	2	1	Trace	Trace	Trace	11	22	0.5	Trace	0.05	0.03	0.6	Trace
358	Breadcrumbs, dry, grated 88	6	345	11	4	1	3	1	65	107	3.2	Trace	0.19	0.26	3.1	Trace

12 When the amount of nonfat dry milk in commercial white bread is unknown, values for bread with 3 to 4 percent nonfat dry milk are suggested.

Table A-4. Nutritive Values of the Edible Part of Foods (Continued)

(Dashes show that no basis could be found for imputing a value although there was some reason to believe that a measurable amount of the constituent might be present)

	Food, Approximate Measure, and Weight (in grams)	Weight Grams	Water Per-cent	Food Energy Calo-ries	Pro-tein Grams	Fat (Total Lipid) Grams	Fatty Acids Satu-rated (Total) Grams	Fatty Acids Unsaturated Oleic Grams	Fatty Acids Unsaturated Lino-leic Grams	Carbo-hy-drate Grams	Cal-cium Milli-grams	Iron Milli-grams	Vita-min A Value Inter-national Units	Thia-mine Milli-grams	Ribo-flavin Milli-grams	Niacin Milli-grams	Ascor-bic Acid Milli-grams
	Grain Products (Continued)																
	Cakes:[13]																
359	Angelfood cake; 1 sector, 2-inch (1/12 of 8-inch-diameter cake)	40	32	110	3	Trace	------			24	4	0.1	0	Trace	0.06	0.1	0
360	Chocolate cake, chocolate icing; sector, 2-inch (1/16 of 10-inch-diameter layer cake)	120	22	445	5	20	8	10	1	67	84	1.2	190[14]	0.03	0.12	0.3	Trace
361	Fruitcake, dark (made with enriched flour); piece, 2 by 2 by 1/2 inch	30	18	115	1	5	1	3	1	18	22	0.8	40[14]	0.04	0.04	0.2	Trace
362	Gingerbread (made with enriched flour); piece, 2 by 2 by 2 inches	55	31	175	2	6	1	4	Trace	29	37	1.3	50	0.06	0.06	0.5	0
	Plain cake and cupcakes, without icing:																
363	Piece, 3 by 2 by 1-1/2 inches	55	24	200	2	8	2	5	1	31	35	0.2	90[14]	0.01	0.05	0.1	Trace
364	Cupcake, 2-3/4-inch diameter	1 cupcake 40	24	145	2	6	1	3	Trace	22	26	0.2	70[14]	0.01	0.03	0.1	Trace
	Plain cake and cupcakes, with chocolate icing:																
365	Sector, 2-inch (1/16 of 10-inch-layer cake)	100	21	370	4	14	5	7	1	59	63	0.6	180[14]	0.02	0.09	0.2	Trace
366	Cupcake, 2-3/4-inch diameter	1 cupcake 50	21	185	2	7	2	4	Trace	30	32	0.3	90[14]	0.01	0.04	0.1	Trace
367	Poundcake, old-fashioned (equal weights flour, sugar, fat, eggs); slice 2-3/4 by 3 by 5/8 inch	1 slice 30	17	140	2	9	2	5	1	14	6	0.2	80[14]	0.01	0.03	0.1	0
368	Sponge cake; sector, 2-inch (1/12 of 8-inch-diameter cake)	1 sector 40	32	120	3	2	1	1	Trace	22	12	0.5	180	0.02	0.06	0.1	Trace

13 Unenriched cake flour and vegetable cooking fat used unless otherwise specified.

14 If the fat used in the recipe is butter or fortified margarine, the vitamin A value for chocolate cake with chocolate icing will be 490 IU per 2-in. sector, item 360; 100 IU for fruitcake, item 361; for plain cake without icing, item 363; 220 IU per cupcake, item 364; for plain cake with icing, 440 IU per 2-in. sector, item 365; 220 IU per cupcake, item 366; and 300 IU for poundcake, item 367.

Table A-4. Nutritive Values of the Edible Part of Foods (Continued)

(Dashes show that no basis could be found for imputing a value although there was some reason to believe that a measurable amount of the constituent might be present)

	Food, Approximate Measure, and Weight (in grams)		Water	Food Energy	Protein	Fat (Total Lipid)	Fatty Acids			Carbohydrate	Calcium	Iron	Vitamin A Value	Thiamine	Riboflavin	Niacin	Ascorbic Acid
							Saturated (Total)	Unsaturated									
								Oleic	Linoleic								
		Grams	Per-cent	Calories	Grams	Grams	Grams	Grams	Grams	Grams	Milli-grams	Milli-grams	Inter-national Units	Milli-grams	Milli-grams	Milli-grams	Milli-grams
	Grain Products (Continued)																
	Cookies:																
369	Plain and assorted, 3-inch diameter	25	3	120	1	5	-----			18	9	0.2	20	0.01	0.01	0.1	Trace
370	Fig bars, small	16	14	55	1	1	-----			12	12	0.2	20	0.01	0.01	0.1	Trace
371	Corn, rice and wheat flakes, mixed, added nutrients	28	3	110	2	Trace	-----			24	11	0.5	0	0.11	----	0.9	0
	Corn flakes, added nutrients:																
372	Plain	28	4	110	2	Trace				24	5	0.4	0	0.12	0.02	0.6	0
373	Sugar-covered	28	2	110	1	Trace				26	3	0.3	0	0.12	0.01	0.5	0
	Corn grits, degermed, cooked:																
374	Enriched	242	87	120	3	Trace				27	2	0.7[15]	150[16]	0.10[15]	0.07[15]	1.0[15]	0
375	Unenriched	242	87	120	3	Trace				27	2	0.2	150[16]	0.05	0.02	0.5	0
	Cornmeal, white or yellow, dry:																
376	Whole ground, unbolted	118	12	420	11	5	1	2	2	87	24	2.8[15]	600[16]	0.45[15]	0.13[15]	2.4[15]	0
377	Degermed, enriched	145	12	525	11	2	Trace	1	1	114	9	4.2[15]	640[16]	0.64[15]	0.38[15]	5.1[15]	0
378	Corn muffins, made with enriched degermed cornmeal and enriched flour; muffin, 2-3/4-inch diameter 1 muffin	48	33	150	3	5	2	2	Trace	23	50	0.8	80[17]	0.09	0.11	0.8	Trace
379	Corn, puffed, pre-sweetened, added nutrients	28	5	110	1	Trace	-----			26	3	0.5	0	0.12	0.05	0.6	0
380	Corn, shredded, added nutrients	28	3	110	2	Trace	-----			25	1	0.7	0	0.12	0.05	0.6	0
	Crackers:																
381	Graham, plain	14	6	55	1	1				10	6	0.2	0	0.01	0.03	0.2	0
382	Saltines, 2 inches square	8	4	35	1	1				6	2	0.1	0	Trace	Trace	0.1	0
	Soda:																
383	Cracker, 2-1/2 inches square	11	4	50	1	1	Trace	1	Trace	8	2	0.2	0	Trace	Trace	0.1	0
384	Oyster crackers	10	4	45	1	1	Trace	1	Trace	7	2	0.2	0	Trace	Trace	0.1	0
385	Cracker meal	10	6	45	1	1	Trace	1	Trace	7	2	0.1	0	0.01	Trace	0.1	0

(Measure column entries: 369 – 1 cookie; 370 – 1 fig bar; 371 – 1 ounce; 372 – 1 ounce; 373 – 1 ounce; 374 – 1 cup; 375 – 1 cup; 376 – 1 cup; 377 – 1 cup; 379 – 1 ounce; 380 – 1 ounce; 381 – 4 small or 2 medium; 382 – 2 crackers; 383 – 2 crackers; 384 – 10 crackers; 385 – 1 tablespoon)

15 Iron, thiamine, riboflavin, and niacin are based on the minimum levels of enrichment specified in standards of identity promulgated under the Federal Food, Drug, and Cosmetic Act.

16 Vitamin A values based on yellow product. White product contains only a trace.

17 Based on recipe using white cornmeal; if yellow cornmeal is used, the vitamin A value is 140 IU per muffin.

Table A-4. Nutritive Values of the Edible Part of Foods (Continued)

(Dashes show that no basis could be found for imputing a value although there was some reason to believe that a measurable amount of the constituent might be present)

	Food, Approximate Measure, and Weight (in grams)		Water	Food Energy	Protein	Fat (Total Lipid)	Fatty Acids Saturated (Total)	Fatty Acids Unsaturated Oleic	Fatty Acids Unsaturated Linoleic	Carbohydrate	Calcium	Iron	Vitamin A Value	Thiamine	Riboflavin	Niacin	Ascorbic Acid
		Grams	Percent	Calories	Grams	Grams	Grams	Grams	Grams	Grams	Milligrams	Milligrams	International Units	Milligrams	Milligrams	Milligrams	Milligrams
	Grain Products (Continued)																
386	Doughnuts, cake type, enriched	1 doughnut / 32	24	125	1	6	1	4	Trace	16	13	0.4[18]	30	0.05[18]	0.05[18]	0.4[18]	Trace
387	Farina, regular, cooked	1 cup / 238	90	100	3	Trace	---	---	---	21	10	0.7[15]	0	0.11[15]	0.07[15]	1.0[15]	0
388	Macaroni, cooked: Enriched: Cooked, firm stage (8 to 10 minutes; undergoes additional cooking in a food mixture)	1 cup / 130	64	190	6	1	---	---	---	39	14	1.4[15]	0	0.23[15]	0.14[15]	1.9[15]	0
389	Cooked until tender	1 cup / 140	72	155	5	1	---	---	---	32	11	1.3[15]	0	0.19[15]	0.11[15]	1.5[15]	0
390	Unenriched: Cooked, firm stage (8 to 10 minutes; undergoes additional cooking in a food mixture)	1 cup / 130	64	190	6	1	---	---	---	39	14	0.6	0	0.02	0.02	0.5	0
391	Cooked until tender	1 cup / 140	72	155	5	1	---	---	---	32	11	0.6	0	0.02	0.02	0.4	0
392	Macaroni (enriched) and cheese, baked	1 cup / 220	58	470	18	24	11	10	1	44	398	2.0	950	0.22	0.44	2.0	Trace
393	Muffins, with enriched white flour; muffin, 2-3/4-inch diameter	1 muffin / 48	38	140	4	5	1	3	Trace	20	50	0.8	50	0.08	0.11	0.7	Trace
	Noodles (egg noodles), cooked:																
394	Enriched	1 cup / 160	70	200	7	2	1	1	Trace	37	16	1.4[15]	110	0.23[15]	0.14[15]	1.8[15]	0
395	Unenriched	1 cup / 160	70	200	7	2	1	1	Trace	37	16	1.0	110	0.04	0.03	0.7	0
396	Oats (with or without corn) puffed, added nutrients	1 ounce / 28	3	115	3	2	Trace	1	1	21	50	1.3	0	0.28	0.05	0.5	0
397	Oatmeal or rolled oats, regular or quick-cooking, cooked	1 cup / 236	86	130	5	2	Trace	1	1	23	21	1.4	0	0.19	0.05	0.3	0
398	Pancakes (griddlecakes), 4-inch diameter: Wheat, enriched flour (home recipe)	1 cake / 27	50	60	2	2	Trace	1	Trace	9	27	0.4	30	0.05	0.06	0.3	Trace

15 Iron, thiamine, riboflavin, and niacin are based on the minimum levels of enrichment specified in standards of identity promulgated under the Federal Food, Drug, and Cosmetic Act.

18 Based on product made with enriched flour, approximate values with unenriched flour. With enriched flour, approximate values per doughnut are: iron, 0.2 mg; thiamine, 0.01 mg; riboflavin, 0.03 mg; niacin, 0.2 mg.

Table A-4. Nutritive Values of the Edible Part of Foods (Continued)

(Dashes show that no basis could be found for imputing a value although there was some reason to believe that a measurable amount of the constituent might be present)

	Food, Approximate Measure, and Weight (in grams)		Water	Food Energy	Protein	Fat (Total Lipid)	Fatty Acids			Carbohydrate	Calcium	Iron	Vitamin A Value	Thiamine	Riboflavin	Niacin	Ascorbic Acid
							Saturated (Total)	Unsaturated Oleic	Unsaturated Linoleic								
		Grams	Percent	Calories	Grams	Grams	Grams	Grams	Grams	Grams	Milligrams	Milligrams	International Units	Milligrams	Milligrams	Milligrams	Milligrams
	Grain Products (Continued)																
399	Pancakes (griddlecakes), 4-inch diameter (Continued) Buckwheat (buckwheat pancake mix, made with egg and milk) 1 cake	27	58	55	2	2	1	1	Trace	6	59	0.4	60	0.03	0.04	0.2	Trace
	Piecrust, plain, baked: Enriched flour:																
400	Lower crust, 9-inch shell 1 crust	135	15	675	8	45	10	29	3	59	19	2.3	0	0.27	0.19	2.4	0
401	Double crust, 9-inch pie 1 double crust	270	15	1,350	16	90	21	58	7	118	38	4.6	0	0.55	0.39	4.9	0
	Unenriched flour:																
402	Lower crust, 9-inch shell 1 crust	135	15	675	8	45	10	29	3	59	19	0.7	0	0.04	0.04	0.6	0
403	Double crust, 9-inch pie 1 double crust	270	15	1,350	16	90	21	58	7	118	38	1.4	0	0.08	0.07	1.3	0
	Pies (piecrust made with unenriched flour); sector, 4-inch, 1/7 of 9-inch-diameter pie:																
404	Apple 1 sector	135	48	345	3	15	4	9	1	51	11	0.4	40	0.03	0.02	0.5	1
405	Cherry 1 sector	135	47	355	4	15	4	10	1	52	19	0.4	590	0.03	0.03	0.6	1
406	Custard 1 sector	130	58	280	8	14	5	8	1	30	125	0.8	300	0.07	0.21	0.4	0
407	Lemon meringue 1 sector	120	47	305	4	12	4	7	1	45	17	0.6	200	0.04	0.10	0.2	4
408	Mince 1 sector	135	43	365	3	16	4	10	1	56	38	1.4	Trace	0.09	0.05	0.5	1
409	Pumpkin 1 sector	130	59	275	5	15	5	7	1	32	66	0.6	3,210	0.04	0.13	0.6	Trace
410	Pizza (cheese); 5-1/2-inch sector; 1/8 of 14-inch-diameter pie 1 sector	75	45	185	7	6	2	3	Trace	27	107	0.7	290	0.04	0.12	0.7	4
411	Popcorn, popped, with added oil and salt 1 cup	14	3	65	1	3	2	Trace	Trace	8	1	0.3	------	------	0.01	0.2	0
412	Pretzels, small stick 5 sticks	5	8	20	Trace	Trace	------	------	------	4	1	0	0	Trace	Trace	Trace	0
	Rice, white (fully milled or polished), enriched, cooked:																
413	Common commercial varieties, all types 1 cup	168	73	185	3	Trace	------	------	------	41	17	1.5[19]	0	0.19[19]	0.01[19]	1.6[19]	0
414	Long grain, parboiled 1 cup	176	73	185	4	Trace	------	------	------	41	33	1.4[19]	0	0.19[19]	0.02[19]	2.0[19]	0

19 Iron, thiamine, and niacin are based on the minimum levels of enrichment specified in standards of identity promulgated under the Federal Food, Drug, and Cosmetic Act. Riboflavin is based on unenriched rice. When the minimum level of enrichment for riboflavin specified in the standards of identity becomes effective, the value will be 0.12 mg per cup of parboiled rice and of white rice.

493

Table A-4. Nutritive Values of the Edible Part of Foods (Continued)

(Dashes show that no basis could be found for imputing a value although there was some reason to believe that a measurable amount of the constituent might be present)

	Food, Approximate Measure, and Weight (in grams)	Weight	Water	Food Energy	Protein	Fat (Total Lipid)	Fatty Acids			Carbohydrate	Calcium	Iron	Vitamin A Value	Thiamine	Riboflavin	Niacin	Ascorbic Acid
							Saturated (Total)	Unsaturated Oleic	Unsaturated Linoleic								
		Grams	Per cent	Calories	Grams	Grams	Grams	Grams	Grams	Grams	Milligrams	Milligrams	International Units	Milligrams	Milligrams	Milligrams	Milligrams
	Grain Products (Continued)																
415	Rice, puffed, added nutrients (without salt) 1 cup	14	4	55	1	Trace	---			13	3	0.3	0	0.06	0.01	0.6	0
416	Rice flakes, added nutrients 1 cup	30	3	115	2	2	---			26	9	0.5	0	0.10	0.02	1.6	0
	Rolls: Plain, pan; 12 per 16 ounces:																
417	Enriched 1 roll	38	31	115	3	2	Trace	1	Trace	20	28	0.7	Trace	0.11	0.07	0.8	Trace
418	Unenriched 1 roll	38	31	115	3	2	Trace	1	Trace	20	28	0.3	Trace	0.02	0.03	0.3	Trace
419	Hard, round; 12 per 22 ounces 1 roll	52	25	160	5	2	Trace	1	Trace	31	24	0.4	Trace	0.03	0.05	0.4	Trace
420	Sweet, pan; 12 per 18 ounces 1 roll	43	32	135	4	4	1	2	Trace	21	37	0.3	30	0.03	0.06	0.4	Trace
421	Rye wafers, whole-grain, 1-7/8 by 3-1/2 inches 2 wafers	13	6	45	2	Trace	---			10	7	0.5	0	0.04	0.03	0.2	0
	Spaghetti: Cooked, tender stage (14 to 20 minutes):																
422	Enriched 1 cup	140	72	155	5	1	---			32	11	1.3[15]	0	0.19[15]	0.11[15]	1.5[15]	0
423	Unenriched 1 cup	140	72	155	5	1	---			32	11	0.6	0	0.02	0.02	0.4	0
424	Spaghetti with meat balls in tomato sauce (home recipe) 1 cup	250	70	335	19	12	4	6	1	39	125	3.8	1,600	0.26	0.30	4.0	22
425	Spaghetti in tomato sauce with cheese (home recipe) 1 cup	250	77	260	9	9	2	5	1	37	80	2.2	1,080	0.24	0.18	2.4	14
426	Waffles, with enriched flour, 1/2 by 4-1/2 by 5-1/2 inches 1 waffle	75	41	210	7	7	2	4	1	28	85	1.3	250	0.13	0.19	1.0	Trace
	Wheat, puffed:																
427	With added nutrients (without salt) 1 ounce	28	3	105	4	Trace	---			22	8	1.2	0	0.15	0.07	2.2	0
428	With added nutrients, with sugar and honey 1 ounce	28	3	105	2	1	---			25	7	0.9	0	0.14	0.05	1.8	0

15 Iron, thiamine, riboflavin, and niacin are based on the minimum levels of enrichment specified in standards of identity promulgated under the Federal Food, Drug, and Cosmetic Act.

Table A-4. Nutritive Values of the Edible Part of Foods (Continued)

(Dashes show that no basis could be found for imputing a value although there was some reason to believe that a measurable amount of the constituent might be present)

	Food, Approximate Measure, and Weight (in grams)	Weight Grams	Water Percent	Food Energy Calories	Protein Grams	Fat (Total Lipid) Grams	Fatty Acids Saturated (Total) Grams	Unsaturated Oleic Grams	Unsaturated Linoleic Grams	Carbohydrate Grams	Calcium Milligrams	Iron Milligrams	Vitamin A Value International Units	Thiamine Milligrams	Riboflavin Milligrams	Niacin Milligrams	Ascorbic Acid Milligrams
	Grain Products (Continued)																
429	Wheat, rolled; cooked	1 cup — 236	80	175	5	1	---			40	19	1.7	0	0.17	0.06	2.1	0
430	Wheat, shredded, plain (long, round, or bite-size)	1 ounce — 28	7	100	3	1	---			23	12	1.0	0	0.06	0.03	1.2	0
431	Wheat and malted barley flakes, with added nutrients	1 ounce — 28	3	110	2	Trace	---			24	14	0.7	0	0.13	0.03	1.1	0
432	Wheat flakes, with added nutrients	1 ounce — 28	4	100	3	Trace	---			23	12	1.2	0	0.18	0.04	1.4	0
	Wheat flours:																
433	Whole-wheat, from hard wheats, stirred	1 cup — 120	12	400	16	2	Trace	1	1	85	49	4.0	0	0.66	0.14	5.2	0
	All-purpose or family flour:																
434	Enriched, sifted	1 cup — 110	12	400	12	1	Trace	Trace	Trace	84	18	3.2[15]	0	0.48[15]	0.29[15]	3.8[15]	0
435	Unenriched, sifted	1 cup — 110	12	400	12	1	Trace	Trace	Trace	84	18	0.9[15]	0	0.07	0.05[15]	1.0[15]	0
436	Self-rising, enriched	1 cup — 110	11	385	10	1	Trace	Trace	Trace	82	292	3.2[15]	0	0.49[15]	0.29[15]	3.9[15]	0
437	Cake or pastry flour, sifted	1 cup — 100	12	365	8	1	Trace	Trace	Trace	79	17	0.5	0	0.03	0.03	0.7	0
438	Wheat germ, crude, commercially milled	1 cup — 68	11	245	18	7	1	2	4	32	49	6.4	0	1.36	0.46	2.9	0
	Fats, Oils																
	Butter, 4 sticks per pound:																
439	Sticks, 2	1 cup — 227	16	1,625	1	184	101	61	6	1	45	0	7,500[20]	---	---	---	0
440	Stick, 1/8	1 tablespoon — 14	16	100	Trace	11	6	4	Trace	Trace	3	0	460[20]	---	---	---	0
441	Pat or square (64 per pound)	1 pat — 7	16	50	Trace	6	3	2	Trace	Trace	1	0	230[20]	---	---	---	0
	Fats, cooking:																
442	Lard	1 cup — 220	0	1,985	0	220	84	101	22	0	0	0	0	0	0	0	0
443	Lard	1 tablespoon — 14	0	125	0	14	5	6	1	0	0	0	0	0	0	0	0
444	Vegetable fats	1 cup — 200	0	1,770	0	200	46	130	14	0	0	0	---	0	0	0	0
445	Vegetable fats	1 tablespoon — 12.5	0	110	0	12	3	8	1	0	0	0	---	0	0	0	0

[15] Iron, thiamine, riboflavin, and niacin are based on the minimum levels of enrichment specified in standards of identity promulgated under the Federal Food, Drug, and Cosmetic Act.

[20] Year-round average.

495

Table A-4. Nutritive Values of the Edible Part of Foods (Continued)

(Dashes show that no basis could be found for imputing a value although there was some reason to believe that a measurable amount of the constituent might be present)

	Food, Approximate Measure, and Weight (in grams)	Weight (Grams)	Water (Per-cent)	Food Energy (Calories)	Protein (Grams)	Fat (Total Lipid) (Grams)	Fatty Acids Saturated (Total) (Grams)	Fatty Acids Unsaturated Oleic (Grams)	Fatty Acids Unsaturated Linoleic (Grams)	Carbohydrate (Grams)	Calcium (Milligrams)	Iron (Milligrams)	Vitamin A Value (International Units)	Thiamine (Milligrams)	Riboflavin (Milligrams)	Niacin (Milligrams)	Ascorbic Acid (Milligrams)
	Fats, Oils (Continued)																
	Margarine, 4 sticks per pound:																
446	Sticks, 2 — 1 cup	227	16	1,635	1	184	37	105	33	1	45	0	7,500[21]	---	---	---	0
447	Stick, 1/8 — 1 tablespoon	14	16	100	Trace	11	2	6	2	Trace	3	0	460[21]	---	---	---	0
448	Pat or square (64 per pound) — 1 pat	7	16	50	Trace	6	1	3	1	Trace	1	0	230[21]	---	---	---	0
	Oils, salad or cooking:																
449	Corn — 1 tablespoon	14	0	125	0	14	1	4	7	0	0	0	---	0	0	0	0
450	Cottonseed — 1 tablespoon	14	0	125	0	14	4	3	7	0	0	0	---	0	0	0	0
451	Olive — 1 tablespoon	14	0	125	0	14	2	11	1	0	0	0	---	0	0	0	0
452	Soybean — 1 tablespoon	14	0	125	0	14	2	3	7	0	0	0	---	0	0	0	0
	Salad dressings:																
453	Blue cheese — 1 tablespoon	16	32	80	1	8	2	2	4	1	13	Trace	30	Trace	0.02	Trace	Trace
454	Commercial, mayonnaise type — 1 tablespoon	15	41	65	Trace	6	1	1	3	2	2	Trace	30	Trace	Trace	Trace	---
455	French — 1 tablespoon	15	39	60	Trace	6	1	1	3	3	2	0.1	---	---	---	---	---
456	Home cooked, boiled — 1 tablespoon	17	69	30	1	2	1	1	Trace	3	15	0.1	80	0.01	0.03	Trace	Trace
457	Mayonnaise — 1 tablespoon	15	15	110	Trace	12	2	3	6	Trace	3	0.1	40	Trace	0.01	Trace	---
458	Thousand island — 1 tablespoon	15	32	75	Trace	8	1	2	4	2	2	0.1	50	Trace	Trace	Trace	Trace
	Sugars, Sweets																
	Candy:																
459	Caramels — 1 ounce	28	8	115	1	3	2	1	Trace	22	42	0.4	Trace	0.01	0.05	Trace	Trace
460	Chocolate, milk, plain — 1 ounce	28	1	150	2	9	5	3	Trace	16	65	0.3	80	0.02	0.09	0.1	Trace
461	Fudge, plain — 1 ounce	28	8	115	1	3	2	1	Trace	21	22	0.3	Trace	0.01	0.03	0.1	Trace
462	Hard candy — 1 ounce	28	1	110	0	Trace	---	---	---	28	6	0.5	0	0	Trace	0	0
463	Marshmallows — 1 ounce	28	17	90	1	Trace	---	---	---	23	5	0.5	0	0	Trace	0.1	0
464	Chocolate sirup, thin type — 1 tablespoon	20	32	50	Trace	Trace	Trace	Trace	Trace	13	3	0.3	---	Trace	0.01	0.1	Trace
465	Honey, strained or extracted — 1 tablespoon	21	17	65	Trace	0	---	---	---	17	1	0.1	0	Trace	0.01	0.1	Trace
466	Jams and preserves — 1 tablespoon	20	29	55	Trace	Trace	---	---	---	14	4	0.2	Trace	Trace	0.01	Trace	Trace
467	Jellies — 1 tablespoon	20	29	55	Trace	Trace	---	---	---	14	4	0.3	Trace	Trace	0.01	Trace	1
	Molasses, cane:																
468	Light (first extraction) — 1 tablespoon	20	24	50	---					13	33	0.9	---	0.01	0.01	Trace	---

21 Based on the average vitamin A content of fortified margarine. Federal specifications for fortified margarine require a minimum of 15,000 IU of vitamin A per pound,

Table A-4. Nutritive Values of the Edible Part of Foods (Continued)

(Dashes show that no basis could be found for imputing a value although there was some reason to believe that a measurable amount of the constituent might be present)

	Food, Approximate Measure, and Weight (in grams)	Water	Food Energy	Protein	Fat (Total Lipid)	Fatty Acids Saturated (Total)	Unsaturated Oleic	Linoleic	Carbohydrate	Calcium	Iron	Vitamin A Value	Thiamine	Riboflavin	Niacin	Ascorbic Acid
		Percent	Calories	Grams	Grams	Grams	Grams	Grams	Grams	Milligrams	Milligrams	International Units	Milligrams	Milligrams	Milligrams	Milligrams
	Sugars, Sweets (Continued)															
	Molasses, cane (Continued)															
469	Blackstrap (third extraction) 1 tablespoon 20	24	45	-----	-----	-----			11	137	3.2	-----	0.02	0.04	0.4	-----
470	Sirup, table blends (chiefly corn, light and dark) 1 tablespoon 20	24	60	0	0	-----			15	9	0.8	0	0	0	0	0
	Sugars (cane or beet):															
471	Granulated 1 cup 200	Trace	770	0	0	-----			199	0	0.2	0	0	0	0	0
472	1 tablespoon 12	Trace	45	0	0	-----			12	0	Trace	0	0	0	0	0
473	1 lump, 1-1/8 by 3/4 by 3/8 6	Trace	25	0	0	-----			6	0	Trace	0	0	0	0	0
474	Powdered, stirred before measuring 1 cup 128	Trace	495	0	0	-----			127	0	0.1	0	0	0	0	0
475	Brown, firm-packed 1 tablespoon 8	Trace	30	0	0	-----			8	0	Trace	0	0	0	0	0
476	1 cup 220	2	820	0	0	-----			212	187	7.5	0	0.02	0.07	0.4	0
477	1 tablespoon 14	2	50	0	0	-----			13	12	0.5	0	Trace	Trace	Trace	0
	Miscellaneous Items															
478	Beer (average 3.6 percent alcohol by weight) 1 cup 240	92	100	1	0	-----			9	12	Trace	-----	0.01	0.07	1.6	-----
	Beverages, carbonated:															
479	Cola type 1 cup 240	90	95	0	0	-----			24	-----	-----	0	0	0	0	0
480	Ginger ale 1 cup 230	92	70	0	0	-----			18	-----	-----	0	0	0	0	0
481	Bouillon cube, 5/8 inch 1 cube 4	4	5	1	Trace	-----			Trace	-----	-----					-----
	Chili powder. See Vegetables, peppers															
482	Chili sauce (mainly tomatoes) 1 tablespoon 17	68	20	Trace	Trace	-----			4	3	0.1	240	0.02	0.01	0.3	3
	Chocolate:															
483	Bitter or baking 1 ounce 28	2	145	3	15	8	6	Trace	8	22	1.9	20	0.01	0.07	0.4	0
484	Sweet 1 ounce 28	1	150	1	10	6	4	Trace	16	27	0.4	Trace	0.01	0.04	0.1	Trace
	Cider, See Fruits, apple juice															

Table A-4. Nutritive Values of the Edible Part of Foods (Continued)

(Dashes show that no basis could be found for imputing a value although there was some reason to believe that a measurable amount of the constituent might be present)

	Food, Approximate Measure, and Weight (in grams)	Grams	Water Per-cent	Food Energy Calo-ries	Pro-tein Grams	Fat (Total Lipid) Grams	Fatty Acids Satu-rated (Total) Grams	Unsaturated Oleic Grams	Unsaturated Lino-leic Grams	Carbo-hy-drate Grams	Cal-cium Milli-grams	Iron Milli-grams	Vita-min A Value Inter-national Units	Thia-mine Milli-grams	Ribo-flavin Milli-grams	Niacin Milli-grams	Ascor-bic Acid Milli-grams
	Miscellaneous Items (Continued)																
	Gelatin, dry:																
485	Plain, 1 tablespoon	10	13	35	9	Trace											
486	Dessert powder, 3-ounce package, 1/2 cup	85	2	315	8	0				75							
	Gelatin dessert, ready-to-eat:																
487	Plain, 1 cup	239	84	140	4	0				34							
488	With fruit, 1 cup	241	82	160	3	Trace				40							
	Olives, pickled:																
489	Green, 4 medium or 3 extra large or 2 giant	16	78	15	Trace	2	Trace	2	Trace	Trace	8	0.2	40		Trace		
490	Ripe: Mission, 3 small or 2 large	10	73	15	Trace	2	Trace	2	Trace	Trace	9	0.1	10	Trace	Trace		
	Pickles, cucumber:																
491	Dill, large, 4 by 1-3/4 inches, 1 pickle	135	93	15	1	Trace				3	35	1.4	140	Trace	0.03	Trace	8
492	Sweet, 2-3/4 by 3/4 inches, 1 pickle	20	61	30	Trace	Trace				7	2	0.2	Trace	Trace	Trace	Trace	1
	Popcorn. See Grain products																
493	Sherbet, orange, 1 cup	193	67	260	2	2				59	31	Trace	110	0.02	0.06	Trace	4
	Soups, canned; ready-to-serve (prepared with equal volume of water):																
494	Bean with pork, 1 cup	250	84	170	8	6	1	2	2	22	62	2.2	650	0.14	0.07	1.0	2
495	Beef noodle, 1 cup	250	93	70	4	3	1	1	1	7	8	1.0	50	0.05	0.06	1.1	Trace
496	Beef bouillon, broth, consomme, 1 cup	240	96	30	5	0	0	0	0	3	Trace	0.5	Trace	Trace	0.02	1.2	
497	Chicken noodle, 1 cup	250	93	65	4	2	Trace	1	1	8	10	0.5	50	0.02	0.02	0.8	Trace
498	Clam chowder, 1 cup	255	92	85	2	3		3	5	13	36	1.0	920	0.03	0.03	1.0	
499	Cream soup (mushroom), 1 cup	240	90	135	2	10	1	3	5	10	41	0.5	70	0.02	0.12	0.7	Trace
500	Minestrone, 1 cup	245	90	105	5	3		1	1	14	37	1.0	2,350	0.07	0.05	1.0	
501	Pea, green, 1 cup	245	86	130	6	2		1		23	44	1.0	340	0.05	0.05	1.0	7
502	Tomato, 1 cup	245	90	90	2	2	Trace	1	Trace	16	15	0.7	1,000	0.06	0.05	1.1	12
503	Vegetable with beef broth, 1 cup	250	92	80	3	2		1	1	14	20	0.8	3,250	0.05	0.02	1.2	

Table A-4. Nutritive Values of the Edible Part of Foods (Continued)

(Dashes show that no basis could be found for imputing a value although there was some reason to believe that a measurable amount of the constituent might be present)

	Food, Approximate Measure, and Weight (in grams)		Water Per-cent	Food Energy Calories	Protein Grams	Fat (Total Lipid) Grams	Fatty Acids Saturated (Total) Grams	Unsaturated Oleic Grams	Linoleic Grams	Carbohydrate Grams	Calcium Milligrams	Iron Milligrams	Vitamin A Value International Units	Thiamine Milligrams	Riboflavin Milligrams	Niacin Milligrams	Ascorbic Acid Milligrams
	Miscellaneous Items (Continued)	Grams															
504	Starch (cornstarch)	1 cup 128	12	465	Trace	Trace	---	---	---	112	0	0	0	0	0	0	0
505		1 tablespoon 8	12	30	Trace	Trace	---	---	---	7	0	0	0	0	0	0	0
506	Tapioca, quick-cooking granulated, dry, stirred before measuring	1 cup 152	13	535	1	Trace	---	---	---	131	15	0.6	0	0	0	0	0
507	Vinegar	1 tablespoon 10	13	35	Trace	Trace	---	---	---	9	1	Trace	0	0	0	0	0
508		1 tablespoon 15	--	2	0	---	---	11	1	1	1	0.1	---	---	---	---	---
509	White sauce, medium	1 cup 265	73	430	10	33	18	11	1	23	305	0.5	1,220	0.12	0.44	0.6	Trace
	Yeast: Baker's:																
510	Compressed	1 ounce 28	71	25	3	Trace	---	---	---	3	4	1.4	Trace	0.20	0.47	3.2	Trace
511	Dry active	1 ounce 28	5	80	10	Trace	---	---	---	11	12	4.6	Trace	0.66	1.53	10.4	Trace
512	Brewer's, dry, debittered	1 tablespoon 8	5	25	3	Trace	---	---	---	3	17	1.4	Trace	1.25	0.34	3.0	Trace
	Yoghurt. See Milk, cream, cheese; related products																

TABLE A-5. RECOMMENDED DAILY DIETARY ALLOWANCES (Revised 1963)* Expressed in Shares**

	Age, Years	Calories	Protein	Calcium	Iron	Vitamin A Value	Thiamine	Riboflavin	Ascorbic Acid
Men	18-35	29.00	29	29	29	29	29	29	29
	35-55	26.00	29	29	29	29	25	28	29
	55-75	22.00	29	29	29	29	23	22	29
Women	18-35	21.00	24	29	44	29	20	22	29
	35-55	19.00	24	29	44	29	20	20	29
	55-75	16.00	24	29	29	29	20	20	29
Pregnant (2nd & 3rd trimester)		23.00	32	46	59	35	25	28	41
Lactating		31.00	40	46	59	47	30	33	41
Infants	0-1	9.20***	8***	25	24***	9	10	10	12
Children	1-3	13.00	13	29	24	12	13	14	17
	3-6	16.00	17	29	29	15	15	17	21
	6-9	21.00	22	29	35	20	20	22	25
Boys	9-12	24.00	25	39	44	26	25	24	29
	12-15	30.00	31	50	44	29	29	31	33
	15-18	34.00	35	50	44	29	35	34	33
Girls	9-12	22.00	23	39	44	26	23	22	33
	12-15	25.00	26	46	44	29	25	26	33
	15-18	23.00	24	46	44	29	23	22	29

* These allowances have been calculated from the Recommended Daily Dietary Allowances suggested by the Food and Nutrition Board, Revised 1963, Publication No. 1146. Washington, D.C.: National Research Council, National Academy of Sciences.

** For share values see Chap. 20 and introduction to Table A-8.

*** Based on average weight of infant, 8 kg. A variation in calorie, protein, and iron allowances is suggested according to weight. See Table A-1.

TABLE A-6. RECOMMENDED DAILY DIETARY ALLOWANCES* for Adults
According to Calorie Requirements Expressed in Shares

Calories	Protein		Calcium	Iron		Vitamin A Value	Thiamine	Riboflavin	Ascorbic Acid
	Men	Women		Men	Women				
14.00 - 20.00	29	24	29	29	44	29	20	21	29
21.00 - 22.00	29	24	29	29	44	29	23	22	29
23.00 - 24.00	29	24	29	29	44	29	23	24	29
25.00 - 26.00	29	24	29	29	44	29	25	26	29
27.00 - 28.00	29	24	29	29	44	29	28	28	29
29.00 - 31.00	29	24	29	29	44	29	30	31	29
32.00 - 37.00	29	24	29	29	44	29	32-37	33-38	29
38.00 - 42.00	29	24	29	29	44	29	38-42	38-42	29
43.00 - 45.00	29	24	29	29	44	29	43-45	43-45	29
12.00 - 15.00 (reducing)	29	24	29	29	44	29	20	21	29

* Based on 1963 recommendations of the Food and Nutrition Board of the National Research Council.
For share values see Chap. 20 and introduction to Table A-8.

TABLE A-7. RECOMMENDED DAILY DIETARY ALLOWANCES for Children Expressed in Shares *

Years of Age	Calories	Protein	Calcium	Iron	Vitamin A Value	Thiamine	Riboflavin	Ascorbic Acid
1	12.00	12	29	24	12	13	14	17
2	13.00	13	29	24	12	13	14	17
3	14.00	15	29	27	14	14	15	18
4	15.00	16	29	28	15	15	16	20
4-1/2	16.00	17	29	29	15	15	17	21
5	17.00	18	29	29	16	17	17	21
6	18.00	19	29	31	17	18	18	25
7	20.00	21	29	33	19	20	20	25
7-1/2	21.00	22	29	35	20	20	22	25
8	21.00	22	29	35	20	21	22	25
9	22.00	23	29	35	24	22	22	27

Boys

Years of Age	Calories	Protein	Calcium	Iron	Vitamin A Value	Thiamine	Riboflavin	Ascorbic Acid
10	23.00	24	39	44	26	23	23	29
10-1/2	24.00	25	39	44	26	25	24	29
11	25.00	25	42	44	26	25	25	30
12	27.00	27	45	44	27	27	27	31
13	28.50	29	48	44	28	28	29	32
13-1/2	30.00	31	50	44	29	29	31	33
14	30.50	31	50	44	29	31	31	33
15	31.50	32	50	44	29	32	32	33
16	33.00	33	50	44	29	33	33	33
16-1/2	34.00	35	50	44	29	35	34	33
17	34.00	35	50	44	29	35	34	33
18	34.00	35	50	44	29	35	34	33

Girls

Years of Age	Calories	Protein	Calcium	Iron	Vitamin A Value	Thiamine	Riboflavin	Ascorbic Acid
10	22.00	22	39	44	26	22	22	33
10-1/2	22.00	23	39	44	26	23	22	33
11	22.50	23	39	44	26	23	23	33
12	23.00	24	39	44	27	23	23	33
13	24.00	25	46	44	28	24	25	33
13-1/2	25.00	26	46	44	29	25	26	33
14	24.00	25	46	44	29	24	25	33
15	24.00	24	46	44	29	24	24	33
16	23.00	24	46	44	29	23	23	29
16-1/2	23.00	24	46	44	29	23	22	29
17	23.00	24	46	44	29	23	22	29
18	23.00	24	46	44	29	23	22	29

* These allowances have been obtained by interpolation after calculating share values for the Recommended Daily Dietary Allowances (1963) of the Food and Nutrition Board, National Research Council.

For share values see Chap. 20 and introduction to Table A-8.

TABLE A-8. NUTRITIVE VALUES OF THE EDIBLE PART OF FOODS IN SHARES

Explanation of Table

See introduction to Table A-4, "Explanation of Table," for information on approximate measures, parts of food included in items given, and details on food preparation.

For explanation of share values see Chap. 20.

Values For One Share of Each Nutrient

One share of energy	=	100 calories
One share of protein	=	2.41 grams protein
One share of calcium	=	0.028 gram or 28 milligrams of calcium
One share of iron	=	0.34 milligram iron
One share of vitamin A	=	172 International Units vitamin A
One share of thiamine	=	0.041 milligram thiamine
One share of riboflavin	=	0.058 milligram riboflavin
One share of ascorbic acid	=	2.41 milligrams ascorbic acid

"0.0" is used to indicate a trace or less than 0.05 share

TABLE A-8. NUTRITIVE VALUES OF THE EDIBLE PART OF FOODS IN SHARES

| | Food and Approximate Measure | Weight, Grams | Calories | Shares | | | | | | | |
				Calories	Protein	Calcium	Iron	Vitamin A Value	Thiamine	Riboflavin	Ascorbic Acid
	Milk, Cream, Cheese; Related Products										
	Milk, cow's:										
1	Fluid, whole (3.5% fat) 1 cup	244	160	1.60	3.7	10.3	0.3	2.0	2.0	7.2	0.8
2	Fluid, nonfat (skim) 1 cup	246	90	0.90	3.7	10.6	0.3	0.1	2.5	7.6	0.8
3	Buttermilk, cultured, from skim milk 1 cup	246	90	0.90	3.7	10.6	0.3	0.1	2.3	7.6	0.8
4	Evaporated, unsweetened, undiluted 1 cup	252	345	3.45	7.5	22.7	0.9	4.8	2.5	14.5	1.2
5	Condensed, sweetened, undiluted 1 cup	306	980	9.80	10.4	28.6	0.9	6.3	5.8	20.2	1.2
6	Dry, whole 1 cup	103	515	5.15	11.2	33.4	1.5	6.7	7.5	25.9	2.5
7	Dry, nonfat, instant 1 cup	70	250	2.50	10.4	32.3	1.2	0.1	6.0	21.6	2.1
	Milk, goat's:										
8	Fluid, whole 1 cup	244	165	1.65	3.3	11.3	0.6	2.3	2.5	4.7	0.8
	Cream:										
9	Half-and-half (cream and milk) 1 cup	242	325	3.25	3.3	9.3	0.3	6.7	2.0	6.6	0.8
10	1 tablespoon	15	20	0.20	0.0	0.6	0.0	0.4	0.0	0.3	0.0
11	Light, coffee or table 1 cup	240	505	5.05	2.9	8.8	0.3	11.8	1.8	6.2	0.0
12	1 tablespoon	15	30	0.30	0.0	0.5	0.0	0.8	0.0	0.3	0.0
	Whipping, unwhipped (volume about double when whipped):										
13	Light 1 cup	239	715	7.15	2.5	7.3	0.3	17.8	1.5	5.2	0.8
14	1 tablespoon	15	45	0.45	0.0	0.5	0.0	1.1	0.0	0.3	0.0
15	Heavy 1 cup	238	840	8.40	2.1	6.4	0.3	21.3	1.3	4.5	0.8
16	1 tablespoon	15	55	0.55	0.0	0.4	0.0	1.3	0.0	0.3	0.0
	Cheese:										
17	Blue or Roquefort type 1 ounce	28	105	1.05	2.5	3.2	0.3	2.0	0.3	2.9	0.0
	Cheddar or American:										
18	Ungrated 1 inch cube	17	70	0.70	1.7	4.6	0.6	1.3	0.0	1.4	0.0
19	Grated 1 cup	112	445	4.45	11.6	30.0	3.2	8.5	0.8	8.8	0.0
20	1 tablespoon	7	30	0.30	0.8	1.9	0.3	0.5	0.0	0.5	0.0
21	Cheddar, process 1 ounce	28	105	1.05	2.9	7.8	0.9	2.0	0.0	2.1	0.0
22	Cheese foods, Cheddar 1 ounce	28	90	0.90	2.5	5.8	0.6	1.6	0.3	2.8	0.0
	Cottage cheese, from skim milk:										
23	Creamed 1 cup	225	240	2.40	12.9	7.6	2.1	2.2	1.8	9.7	0.0
24	1 ounce	28	30	0.30	1.7	1.0	0.3	0.3	0.3	1.2	0.0
25	Uncreamed 1 cup	225	195	1.95	15.8	7.2	2.6	0.1	1.8	10.9	0.0
26	1 ounce	28	25	0.25	2.1	0.9	0.3	0.0	0.3	1.4	0.0
27	Cream cheese 1 ounce	28	105	1.05	0.8	0.6	0.3	2.6	0.0	1.2	0.0
28	1 tablespoon	15	55	0.55	0.4	0.3	0.0	1.3	0.0	0.7	0.0
29	Swiss (domestic) 1 ounce	28	105	1.05	3.3	9.4	0.9	1.9	0.0	1.9	0.0
	Milk beverages:										
30	Cocoa 1 cup	242	235	2.35	3.7	10.2	2.6	2.3	2.3	7.8	0.8
31	Chocolate-flavored milk drink (made with skim milk) 1 cup	250	190	1.90	3.3	9.6	1.2	1.2	2.3	7.1	0.8
32	Malted milk 1 cup	270	280	2.80	5.4	13.0	2.4	3.9	4.3	9.7	0.8

Table A-8. Nutritive Values of the Edible Part of Foods in Shares (Continued)

		Weight, Grams	Calories	Shares							
	Food and Approximate Measure			Calories	Protein	Calcium	Iron	Vitamin A Value	Thiamine	Riboflavin	Ascorbic Acid
	Milk, Cream, Cheese; Related Products (Continued)										
	Milk desserts:										
33	Cornstarch pudding, plain (blanc mange) 1 cup	248	275	2.75	3.7	10.4	0.3	2.3	1.8	6.9	0.8
34	Custard, baked 1 cup	248	285	2.85	5.4	9.9	2.9	5.1	2.5	8.1	0.4
	Ice cream, plain, factory packed:										
35	Slice or cut brick, 1/8 of quart brick 1 slice or cut brick	71	145	1.45	1.2	3.1	0.3	2.2	0.8	2.2	0.4
36	Container 3-1/2 fluid ounces	62	130	1.30	0.8	2.7	0.3	1.9	0.8	2.1	0.4
37	Container 8 fluid ounces	142	295	2.95	2.5	6.3	0.3	4.3	1.5	4.7	0.4
38	Ice milk 1 cup	187	285	2.85	3.7	10.4	0.6	2.3	2.3	7.1	0.8
39	Yoghurt, from partially skimmed milk 1 cup	246	120	1.20	3.3	10.5	0.3	1.0	2.3	7.4	0.8
	Eggs										
	Eggs, large, 24 ounces per dozen:										
	Raw:										
40	Whole, without shell 1 egg	50	80	0.80	2.5	1.0	3.2	3.4	1.3	2.6	0.0
41	White of egg 1 white	33	15	0.15	1.7	0.1	0.0	0.0	0.0	1.6	0.0
42	Yolk of egg 1 yolk	17	60	0.60	1.2	0.9	2.6	3.4	1.0	1.2	0.0
	Cooked:										
43	Boiled, shell removed 2 eggs	100	160	1.60	5.4	1.9	6.8	6.9	2.3	4.8	0.0
44	Scrambled, with milk and fat 1 egg	64	110	1.10	2.9	1.8	3.2	4.0	1.3	3.1	0.0
	Meat, Poultry, Fish, Shellfish; Related Products										
45	Bacon, broiled or fried, crisp 2 slices	16	100	1.00	2.1	0.1	1.5	0.0	2.0	0.9	0.0
	Beef, trimmed to retail[1] basis, cooked:										
	Cuts braised, simmered, or pot-roasted:										
46	Lean and fat 3 ounces	85	245	2.45	9.5	0.4	8.5	0.2	1.0	3.1	0.0
47	Lean only 2.5 ounces	72	140	1.40	9.1	0.4	7.9	0.1	1.0	2.8	0.0
	Hamburger (ground beef), broiled:										
48	Lean 3 ounces	85	185	1.85	9.5	0.4	8.8	0.1	2.0	3.4	0.0
49	Regular 3 ounces	85	245	2.45	8.7	0.3	7.9	0.2	1.8	3.1	0.0
	Roast, oven-cooked, no liquid added:										
	Relatively fat, such as rib:										
50	Lean and fat 3 ounces	85	375	3.75	7.1	0.3	6.5	0.4	1.3	2.2	0.0
51	Lean only 1.8 ounces	51	125	1.25	5.8	0.2	5.3	0.1	1.0	1.9	0.0
	Relatively lean, such as heel of round:										
52	Lean and fat 3 ounces	85	165	1.65	10.4	0.4	9.4	0.1	1.5	3.3	0.0
53	Lean only 2.7 ounces	78	125	1.25	10.0	0.4	8.8	0.0	1.5	3.1	0.0

[1] 1/2 inch fat left on cut, fat within cut retained.

Table A–8. Nutritive Values of the Edible Part of Foods in Shares (Continued)

	Food and Approximate Measure	Weight, Grams	Calories	Shares							
				Calories	Protein	Calcium	Iron	Vitamin A Value	Thiamine	Riboflavin	Ascorbic Acid
	Meat, Poultry, Fish, Shellfish; Related Products (Continued)										
	Beef, trimmed to retail basis, cooked (Continued)										
	Steak, broiled:										
	Relatively fat, such as sirloin:										
54	Lean and fat — 3 ounces	85	330	3.30	8.3	0.3	7.4	0.3	1.3	2.8	0.0
55	Lean only — 2.0 ounces	56	115	1.15	7.5	0.3	6.5	0.1	1.3	2.4	0.0
	Relatively lean, such as round:										
56	Lean and fat — 3 ounces	85	220	2.20	10.0	0.4	8.8	0.1	1.8	3.3	0.0
57	Lean only — 2.4 ounces	68	130	1.30	8.7	0.3	7.4	0.1	1.5	2.8	0.0
	Beef, canned:										
58	Corned beef — 3 ounces	85	185	1.85	9.1	0.6	10.9	0.1	0.3	3.4	0.0
59	Corned beef hash — 3 ounces	85	155	1.55	2.9	0.4	5.0	0.0	0.3	1.4	0.0
60	Beef, dried or chipped — 2 ounces	57	115	1.15	7.9	0.4	8.5	0.0	1.0	3.1	0.0
61	Beef and vegetable stew — 1 cup	235	210	2.10	6.2	1.0	8.2	13.4	3.3	2.9	6.2
62	Beef potpie, baked: Individual pie, 4-1/4-inch diameter, weight before baking about 8 ounces — 1 pie	227	560	5.60	9.5	1.1	12.1	10.8	6.3	4.7	2.9
	Chicken, cooked:										
63	Flesh only, broiled — 3 ounces	85	115	1.15	8.3	0.3	4.1	0.5	1.3	2.8	0.0
	Breast, fried, 1/2 breast:										
64	With bone — 3.3 ounces	94	155	1.55	10.4	0.3	3.8	0.4	1.0	2.9	0.0
65	Flesh and skin only — 2.7 ounces	76	155	1.55	10.4	0.3	3.8	0.4	1.0	2.9	0.0
	Drumstick, fried:										
66	With bone — 2.1 ounces	59	90	0.90	5.0	0.2	2.6	0.3	0.8	2.6	0.0
67	Flesh and skin only — 1.3 ounces	38	90	0.90	5.0	0.2	2.6	0.3	0.8	2.6	0.0
68	Chicken, canned, boneless — 3 ounces	85	170	1.70	7.5	0.6	3.8	1.2	0.8	1.9	1.2
	Chicken potpie, See Poultry potpie, Item 90										
	Chili con carne, canned:										
69	With beans — 1 cup	250	335	3.35	7.9	2.9	12.4	0.9	2.0	3.1	0.0
70	Without beans — 1 cup	255	510	5.10	10.8	3.5	10.6	2.2	1.3	5.3	0.0
71	Heart, beef, lean, braised — 3 ounces	85	160	1.60	11.2	0.2	14.7	0.1	5.3	17.9	0.4
	Lamb trimmed for retail,[1] cooked:										
	Chop, thick, with bone, broiled:										
72	Lean and fat — 4.8 ounces	137	400	4.00	10.4	0.4	4.4	0.0	3.5	4.3	0.0
73	Lean and fat — 4.0 ounces	112	400	4.00	10.4	0.4	4.4	0.0	3.5	4.3	0.0
74	Lean only — 2.6 ounces	74	140	1.40	8.7	0.3	4.4	0.0	2.8	3.4	0.0
	Leg, roasted:										
75	Lean and fat — 3 ounces	85	235	2.35	9.1	0.3	4.1	0.0	3.3	4.0	0.0
76	Lean only — 2.5 ounces	71	130	1.30	8.3	0.3	4.1	0.0	3.0	3.6	0.0
	Shoulder, roasted:										
77	Lean and fat — 3 ounces	85	285	2.85	7.5	0.3	2.9	0.0	2.8	3.4	0.0
78	Lean only — 2.3 ounces	64	130	1.30	7.1	0.3	2.9	0.0	2.5	3.1	0.0

1 1/2 inch fat left on cut, fat within cut retained.

Table A-8. Nutritive Values of the Edible Part of Foods in Shares (Continued)

	Food and Approximate Measure	Weight, Grams	Calories	Shares							
				Calories	Protein	Calcium	Iron	Vitamin A Value	Thiamine	Riboflavin	Ascorbic Acid
	Meat, Poultry, Fish, Shellfish; Related Products (Continued)										
79	Liver, beef, fried	2 ounces	130	1.30	6.2	0.2	14.7	176.0	3.8	40.9	6.2
	Pork, cured, cooked:										
80	Ham, light cure, lean and fat, roasted	3 ounces	245	2.45	7.5	0.3	6.5	0.0	10.0	2.8	0.0
	Luncheon meat:										
81	Boiled ham, sliced	2 ounces	135	1.35	4.6	0.2	4.7	0.0	6.3	1.6	0.0
82	Canned, spiced or unspiced	2 ounces	165	1.65	3.3	0.2	3.5	0.0	4.5	2.1	0.0
	Pork, fresh, trimmed to retail[1] basis, cooked:										
83	Chop, thick, with bone	1 chop, 3.5 ounces	260	2.60	6.6	0.3	6.5	0.0	15.8	3.1	0.0
84	Lean and fat	2.3 ounces	260	2.60	6.6	0.3	6.5	0.0	15.8	3.1	0.0
85	Lean only	1.7 ounces	130	1.30	6.2	0.3	5.6	0.0	13.5	2.8	0.0
	Roast, oven-cooked, no liquid added:										
86	Lean and fat	3 ounces	310	3.10	8.7	0.3	7.9	0.0	19.5	3.8	0.0
87	Lean only	2.4 ounces	175	1.75	8.3	0.3	7.6	0.0	18.3	3.6	0.0
	Cuts, simmered:										
88	Lean and fat	3 ounces	320	3.20	8.3	0.3	7.4	0.0	11.5	3.6	0.0
89	Lean only	2.2 ounces	135	1.35	7.5	0.3	6.8	0.0	10.5	3.3	0.0
90	Poultry potpie (based on chicken potpie). Individual pie, 4-1/4-inch diam.	1 pie	535	5.35	9.5	2.4	8.8	17.6	6.3	4.5	2.1
	Sausage:										
91	Bologna, slice, 4.1 by 0.1 inch	8 slices	690	6.90	11.2	0.6	12.1	0.0	9.0	8.4	0.0
92	Frankfurter, cooked	1 frankfurter	155	1.55	2.5	0.1	2.4	0.0	2.0	1.7	0.0
93	Pork, links or patty, cooked	4 ounces	540	5.40	8.7	0.3	7.9	0.0	22.3	6.7	0.0
94	Tongue, beef, braised	3 ounces	210	2.10	7.5	0.2	5.6	0.0	1.0	4.3	0.0
	Turkey potpie. See Poultry potpie, Item 90.										
	Veal, cooked:										
95	Cutlet, without bone, broiled	3 ounces	185	1.85	9.5	0.3	7.9	0.0	1.5	3.6	0.0
96	Roast, medium fat, medium done; lean and fat	3 ounces	230	2.30	9.5	0.4	8.5	0.0	2.8	4.5	0.0
	Fish and shellfish:										
97	Bluefish, baked or broiled	3 ounces	135	1.35	9.1	0.9	1.8	0.2	2.3	1.4	0.0
	Clams:										
98	Raw, meat only	3 ounces	65	0.65	4.6	2.1	15.3	0.5	2.0	2.6	3.3
99	Canned, solids and liquid	3 ounces	45	0.45	2.9	1.7	10.3	0.0	0.3	1.6	0.0
100	Crabmeat, canned	3 ounces	85	0.85	6.2	1.4	2.1	0.0	1.8	1.2	0.0
101	Fish sticks, breaded, cooked, frozen; stick, 3.8 by 1.0 by 0.5 inch	10 sticks or 8-ounce package	400	4.00	15.8	0.9	2.6	0.0	2.3	2.8	0.0
102	Haddock, fried	3 ounces	140	1.40	7.1	1.2	2.9	0.0	0.8	1.0	0.8

1 1/2 inch fat left on cut, fat within cut retained.

Table A-8. Nutritive Values of the Edible Part of Foods in Shares (Continued)

	Food and Approximate Measure	Weight, Grams	Calories	Shares Calories	Protein	Calcium	Iron	Vitamin A Value	Thiamine	Riboflavin	Ascorbic Acid
	Meat, Poultry, Fish, Shellfish; Related Products (Continued)										
	Fish and shellfish (Continued)										
	Mackerel:										
103	Broiled, Atlantic	3 ounces	85	200	2.00	7.9	0.2	2.9	2.6	3.3	4.0	0.0
104	Canned, Pacific, solids and liquid[2]	3 ounces	85	155	1.55	7.5	7.9	5.6	0.1	0.5	4.8	0.0
105	Ocean perch, breaded (egg and bread-crumbs), fried	3 ounces	85	195	1.95	6.6	1.0	3.2	0.0	2.0	1.6	0.0
106	Oysters, meat only: Raw, 13–19 medium selects	1 cup	240	160	1.60	8.3	8.1	38.8	4.3	8.3	7.4	0.0
107	Oyster stew, 1 part oysters to 3 parts milk by volume, 3–4 oysters	1 cup	230	200	2.00	4.6	9.6	9.7	3.7	3.3	7.1	0.0
108	Salmon, pink, canned	3 ounces	85	120	1.20	7.1	6.0[3]	2.1	0.3	0.8	2.8	0.0
109	Sardines, Atlantic, canned in oil, drained solids	3 ounces	85	175	1.75	8.3	13.3	7.4	1.1	0.5	2.9	0.0
110	Shad, baked	3 ounces	85	170	1.70	8.3	0.7	1.5	0.1	2.8	3.8	0.0
111	Shrimp, canned, meat only	3 ounces	85	100	1.00	8.7	3.5	7.6	0.3	0.3	0.5	0.0
112	Swordfish, broiled with butter or margarine	3 ounces	85	150	1.50	10.0	0.8	3.2	10.2	0.8	0.7	0.0
113	Tuna, canned in oil, drained solids	3 ounces	85	170	1.70	10.0	0.3	4.7	0.4	1.0	1.7	0.0
	Mature Dry Beans and Peas, Nuts, Peanuts; Related Products										
114	Almonds, shelled	1 cup	142	850	8.50	10.8	11.9	19.7	0.0	8.5	22.6	0.0
	Beans, dry:										
	Common varieties, such as Great Northern, navy, and others, canned:										
115	Red	1 cup	256	230	2.30	6.2	2.6	13.5	0.0	3.3	1.7	0.0
	White, with tomato sauce:										
116	With pork	1 cup	261	320	3.20	6.6	5.0	13.8	2.0	5.0	1.4	2.1
117	Without pork	1 cup	261	310	3.10	6.6	6.3	15.3	0.9	4.5	1.6	2.1
118	Lima, cooked	1 cup	192	260	2.60	6.6	2.0	16.5	0.0	6.5	2.1	0.0
119	Brazil nuts	1 cup	140	915	9.15	8.3	9.3	14.1	0.0	33.5	2.9	0.0
120	Cashew nuts, roasted	1 cup	135	760	7.60	9.5	1.8	15.0	0.8	14.5	5.7	0.0
	Coconut:										
121	Fresh, shredded	1 cup	97	335	3.35	1.2	0.5	4.7	0.0	1.3	0.3	1.2
122	Dried, shredded, sweetened	1 cup	62	340	3.40	0.8	0.4	3.5	0.0	0.5	0.3	0.0
123	Cowpeas or blackeye peas, dry, cooked	1 cup	248	190	1.90	5.4	1.5	9.4	0.1	10.3	1.9	0.0

[2] Vitamin values based on drained solids.

[3] Based on total contents of can, including bones.

Table A-8. Nutritive Values of the Edible Part of Foods in Shares (Continued)

	Food and Approximate Measure		Weight, Grams	Calories	Shares							
					Calories	Protein	Calcium	Iron	Vitamin A Value	Thiamine	Riboflavin	Ascorbic Acid
	Mature Dry Beans and Peas, Nuts, Peanuts; Related Products (Continued)											
	Peanuts, roasted, salted:											
124	Halves	1 cup	144	840	8.40	15.4	3.8	8.8	0.0	11.5	3.3	0.0
125	Chopped	1 tablespoon	9	55	0.55	0.8	0.3	0.6	0.0	0.8	0.2	0.0
126	Peanut butter	1 tablespoon	16	95	0.95	1.7	0.3	0.9	0.0	0.5	0.3	0.0
127	Peas, split, dry, cooked	1 cup	250	250	2.50	8.3	1.0	12.4	0.6	9.3	3.8	0.0
	Pecans:											
128	Halves	1 cup	108	740	7.40	4.1	2.8	7.6	0.8	23.3	2.4	0.8
129	Chopped	1 tablespoon	8	50	0.50	0.4	0.2	0.6	0.1	1.5	0.2	0.0
	Walnuts, shelled:											
130	Black or native, chopped	1 cup	126	790	7.90	10.8	0.0	22.4	2.2	7.0	2.4	0.0
	English or Persian:											
131	Halves	1 cup	100	650	6.50	6.2	3.5	9.1	0.2	8.3	2.2	1.2
132	Chopped	1 tablespoon	8	50	0.50	0.4	0.3	0.6	0.0	0.8	0.2	0.0
	Vegetables and Vegetable Products											
	Asparagus:											
133	Cooked, cut spears	1 cup	175	35	0.35	1.7	1.3	2.9	9.2	6.8	5.5	19.1
	Canned spears, medium:											
134	Green	6 spears	96	20	0.20	0.8	0.6	5.3	4.5	1.5	1.7	5.8
135	Bleached	6 spears	96	20	0.20	0.8	0.5	2.9	0.5	1.3	1.0	5.8
	Beans:											
136	Lima, immature, cooked	1 cup	160	180	1.80	5.0	2.7	11.8	2.6	7.3	2.8	11.6
	Snap, green:											
	Cooked:											
137	In small amount of water, short time	1 cup	125	30	0.30	0.8	2.2	2.4	4.0	2.0	1.9	6.6
138	In large amount of water, long time	1 cup	125	30	0.30	0.8	2.2	2.4	4.0	1.8	1.7	5.4
	Canned:											
139	Solids and liquid	1 cup	239	45	0.45	0.8	2.9	8.5	4.0	2.0	1.7	3.7
140	Strained or chopped (baby food)	1 ounce	28	5	0.05	0.0	0.3	0.9	0.6	0.3	0.3	0.0
	Bean sprouts. See Sprouts, Items 198 & 199.											
141	Beets, cooked, diced	1 cup	165	50	0.50	0.8	0.8	2.4	0.2	1.0	1.2	4.6
142	Broccoli spears, cooked	1 cup	150	40	0.40	2.1	4.7	3.5	21.8	3.5	5.0	56.0
143	Brussels sprouts, cooked	1 cup	130	45	0.45	2.1	1.5	4.1	4.0	2.5	3.1	46.9

Table A-8. Nutritive Values of the Edible Part of Foods in Shares (Continued)

	Food and Approximate Measure		Weight, Grams	Calories	Shares							
					Calories	Protein	Calcium	Iron	Vitamin A Value	Thiamine	Riboflavin	Ascorbic Acid
	Vegetables and Vegetable Products (Continued)											
	Cabbage:											
	Raw:											
144	Finely shredded	1 cup	100	25	0.25	0.4	1.8	1.2	0.8	1.3	0.9	19.5
145	Coleslaw	1 cup	120	120	1.20	0.4	1.9	1.5	1.0	1.5	1.0	14.5
	Cooked:											
146	In small amount of water, short time	1 cup	170	35	0.35	0.8	2.7	1.5	1.3	1.8	1.2	23.2
147	In large amount of water, long time	1 cup	170	30	0.30	0.8	2.5	1.5	1.2	1.0	0.7	16.6
	Cabbage, celery or Chinese:											
148	Raw, leaves and stalk, 1-inch pieces	1 cup	100	15	0.15	0.4	1.5	1.8	0.9	1.3	0.7	10.4
149	Cabbage, spoon (or pakchoy), cooked	1 cup	150	20	0.20	0.8	7.9	2.6	27.0	1.8	2.1	9.5
	Carrots:											
	Raw:											
150	Whole, 5-1/2 by 1 inch, (25 thin strips)	1 carrot	50	20	0.20	0.4	0.6	1.2	32.0	0.8	0.5	1.7
151	Grated	1 cup	110	45	0.45	0.4	1.5	2.4	70.3	1.5	1.0	3.7
152	Cooked, diced	1 cup	145	45	0.45	0.4	1.7	2.6	88.5	2.0	1.2	3.7
153	Canned, strained or chopped (baby food)	1 ounce	28	10	0.10	0.0	0.3	0.3	21.5	0.3	0.2	0.4
154	Cauliflower, cooked, flowerbuds	1 cup	120	25	0.25	1.2	0.9	2.4	0.4	2.8	1.7	27.4
	Celery, raw:											
155	Stalk, large outer, 8 by about 1-1/2 inches, at root end	1 stalk	40	5	0.05	0.0	0.6	0.3	0.6	0.3	0.2	1.7
156	Pieces, diced	1 cup	100	15	0.15	0.4	1.4	0.9	1.4	0.8	0.5	3.7
157	Collards, cooked	1 cup	190	55	0.55	2.1	10.3	3.2	59.7	6.8	6.4	36.1
	Corn, sweet:											
158	Cooked, ear 5 by 1-3/4 inches	1 ear[4]	140[4]	70	0.70	1.2	0.1	1.5	1.8[5]	2.3	1.4	2.9
159	Canned, solids and liquid	1 cup	256	170	1.70	2.1	0.4	2.9	4.0[5]	1.8	2.1	5.4
160	Cowpeas, cooked, immature seeds	1 cup	160	175	1.75	5.4	1.4	10.0	3.3	12.3	3.1	11.6
	Cucumbers, 10-ounce; 7-1/2 by about 2 inches:											
161	Raw, pared	1 cucumber	207	30	0.30	0.4	1.3	1.8	0.0	1.8	1.6	9.5
162	Raw, pared, center slice 1/8-inch thick	6 slices	50	5	0.05	0.0	0.3	0.6	0.0	0.5	0.3	2.5
163	Dandelion greens, cooked	1 cup	180	60	0.60	1.7	9.0	9.4	122.4	6.0	5.0	13.3
164	Endive, curly (including escarole)	2 ounces	57	10	0.10	0.4	1.6	2.9	10.9	1.0	1.4	2.5
165	Kale, leaves including stems, cooked	1 cup	110	30	0.30	1.7	5.3	3.8	47.3	0.0	0.0	28.2

[4] Includes parts not usually eaten.

[5] Vitamin A values based on yellow varieties; white, trace only.

Table A-8. Nutritive Values of the Edible Part of Foods in Shares (Continued)

| | Food and Approximate Measure | | Weight, Grams | Calories | Shares | | | | | | | | |
					Calories	Protein	Calcium	Iron	Vitamin A Value	Thiamine	Riboflavin	Ascorbic Acid
	Vegetables and Vegetable Products (Continued)												
	Lettuce, raw:												
166	Butterhead, as Boston types; head, 4-inch diameter	1 head	220	30	0.30	1.2	2.8	12.9	12.4	3.5	2.2	7.5
167	Crisphead, as Iceberg; head, 4-3/4-inch diameter	1 head	454	60	0.60	1.7	3.3	6.8	8.7	7.3	4.7	12.0
168	Looseleaf, or bunching varieties, leaves	2 large	50	10	0.10	0.4	1.2	2.1	5.5	0.8	0.7	3.7
169	Mushrooms, canned, solids and liquid	1 cup	244	40	0.40	2.1	0.5	3.5	0.0	1.0	10.3	1.7
170	Mustard greens, cooked	1 cup	140	35	0.35	1.2	6.9	7.4	47.2	2.8	3.3	28.2
171	Okra, cooked, pod 3 by 5/8 inch	8 pods	85	25	0.25	0.8	2.8	1.2	2.4	2.8	2.6	7.1
	Onions:												
	Mature:												
172	Raw, onion 2-1/2-inch diameter	1 onion	110	40	0.40	0.8	1.1	1.8	0.2	1.0	0.7	4.6
173	Cooked	1 cup	210	60	0.60	1.2	1.8	2.4	0.5	1.5	1.0	5.8
174	Young green, small, without tops	6 onions	50	20	0.20	0.4	0.7	0.9	0.0	0.0	0.3	5.0
175	Parsley, raw, chopped	1 tablespoon	4	1	0.01	0.0	0.3	0.6	1.7	0.0	0.2	2.5
176	Parsnips, cooked	1 cup	155	100	1.00	0.8	2.5	2.6	0.3	2.8	2.2	6.6
	Peas, green:												
177	Cooked	1 cup	160	115	1.15	3.7	1.3	8.5	5.0	11.0	2.9	13.7
178	Canned, solids and liquid	1 cup	249	165	1.65	3.7	1.8	12.4	6.5	5.8	2.2	9.1
179	Canned, strained (baby food)		28	15	0.15	0.4	0.1	1.2	0.8	0.5	0.3	1.2
180	Peppers, hot, red, without seeds, dried (ground chili powder, added seasonings)	1 tablespoon	15	50	0.50	0.8	1.4	6.8	56.7	0.8	2.9	0.8
	Peppers, sweet:												
	Raw, medium, about 6 per pound:												
181	Green pod without stem, no seeds	1 pod	62	15	0.15	0.4	0.2	1.2	1.5	1.3	0.9	32.8
182	Red pod without stem, no seeds	1 pod	60	20	0.20	0.4	0.3	1.2	15.5	1.3	0.9	50.6
183	Canned, pimientos, medium	1 pod	38	10	0.10	0.0	0.1	1.8	5.1	0.3	0.3	14.9
184	Potatoes, medium (about 3 per pound raw): Baked, peeled after baking	1 potato	99	90	0.90	1.2	0.3	2.1	0.0	2.5	0.7	8.3
	Boiled:												
185	Peeled after boiling	1 potato	136	105	1.05	1.2	0.4	2.4	0.0	3.3	0.9	9.1
186	Peeled before boiling	1 potato	122	80	0.80	0.8	0.3	1.8	0.0	2.8	0.7	8.3
187	French-fried, piece 2 by 1/2 by 1/2 inch: Cooked in deep fat	10 pieces	57	155	1.55	0.8	0.3	2.1	0.0	1.8	0.7	5.0
188	Frozen, heated	10 pieces	57	125	1.25	0.8	0.2	2.9	0.0	2.0	0.2	5.0
	Mashed:												
189	Milk added	1 cup	195	125	1.25	1.7	1.7	2.4	0.3	4.0	1.7	7.9
190	Milk and butter added	1 cup	195	185	1.85	1.7	1.7	2.4	1.9	4.0	1.7	7.5

511

Table A-8. Nutritive Values of the Edible Part of Foods in Shares (Continued)

| | Food and Approximate Measure | Weight, Grams | Calories | Shares | | | | | | | |
				Calories	Protein	Calcium	Iron	Vitamin A Value	Thiamine	Riboflavin	Ascorbic Acid
	Vegetables and Vegetable Products (Continued)										
191	Potato chips, medium, 2-inch diameter	10 chips	20	115	1.15	0.4	0.3	1.2	0.0	1.0	0.2	1.2
192	Pumpkin, canned	1 cup	228	75	0.75	0.8	2.0	2.6	84.8	1.8	2.1	5.0
193	Radishes, raw, small, without tops	4 radishes	40	5	0.05	0.0	0.4	1.2	0.0	1.8	0.2	4.1
194	Sauerkraut, canned, solids and liquid	1 cup	235	45	0.45	0.8	3.0	3.5	0.7	1.8	1.6	13.7
	Spinach:											
195	Cooked	1 cup	180	40	0.40	2.1	6.0	11.8	84.8	3.3	4.3	20.7
196	Canned, drained solids	1 cup	180	45	0.45	2.1	7.6	13.8	83.7	0.8	3.6	10.0
197	Canned, strained or chopped (baby food)	1 ounce	28	10	0.10	0.4	0.6	0.6	8.3	0.3	0.7	0.8
	Sprouts, raw:											
198	Mung bean	1 cup	90	30	0.30	1.2	0.6	3.5	0.1	3.0	2.1	7.1
199	Soybean	1 cup	107	40	0.40	2.5	1.6	2.1	0.5	4.3	2.8	1.7
	Squash:											
	Cooked:											
200	Summer, diced	1 cup	210	30	0.30	0.8	1.9	2.4	4.8	2.5	2.8	8.7
201	Winter, baked, mashed	1 cup	205	130	1.30	1.7	2.0	4.7	50.1	2.5	4.7	11.2
202	Canned, winter, strained and chopped (baby food)	1 ounce	28	10	0.10	0.0	0.3	3.0	0.3	0.3	0.2	0.4
	Sweetpotatoes:											
	Cooked, medium, 5 by 2 inches, weight raw about 6 ounces:											
203	Baked, peeled after baking	1 sweetpotato	110	155	1.55	0.8	1.6	2.9	51.8	2.5	1.2	10.0
204	Boiled, peeled after boiling	1 sweetpotato	147	170	1.70	0.8	1.7	2.9	67.5	3.3	1.6	10.4
205	Candied, 3-1/2 by 2-1/4 inches	1 sweetpotato	175	295	2.95	0.8	2.3	4.7	64.1	2.5	1.4	7.1
206	Canned, vacuum or solid pack	1 cup	218	235	2.35	1.7	1.9	5.0	98.8	2.5	1.7	12.4
	Tomatoes:											
207	Raw, medium, 2 by 2-1/2 inches, about 3 per pound	1 tomato	150	35	0.35	0.8	0.7	2.4	7.8	2.5	1.0	14.1[6]
208	Canned	1 cup	242	50	0.50	0.8	0.5	3.5	12.7	3.3	1.2	16.6
209	Tomato juice, canned	1 cup	242	45	0.45	0.8	0.6	6.5	11.3	3.3	1.2	16.2
210	Tomato catsup	1 tablespoon	17	15	0.15	0.0	0.1	0.3	1.4	0.5	0.2	1.2
211	Turnips, cooked, diced	1 cup	155	35	0.35	0.4	1.9	1.8	0.0	1.5	1.4	13.7
	Turnip greens:											
	Cooked:											
212	In small amount of water, short time	1 cup	145	30	0.30	1.2	9.5	4.7	53.1	5.3	6.2	41.5
213	In large amount of water, long time	1 cup	145	25	0.25	1.2	9.0	4.1	48.0	3.5	5.7	28.2
214	Canned, solids and liquid	1 cup	232	40	0.40	1.2	8.3	10.9	63.4	1.0	3.6	18.3

6 Year-round average. Nov.-May average around 6.3 shares, June-Oct., 16.3 shares.

	Food and Approximate Measure	Weight, Grams	Calories	Shares							
				Calories	Protein	Calcium	Iron	Vitamin A Value	Thiamine	Riboflavin	Ascorbic Acid
	Fruits and Fruit Products										
215	Apples, raw, medium, 2-1/2-inch diameter, about 3 per pound	150[4]	70	0.70	0.0	0.3	1.2	0.3	1.0	0.3	1.2
	1 apple[4]										
216	Apple brown betty	230	345	3.45	1.7	1.5	4.1	1.3	3.3	1.7	1.2
217	Apple juice, bottle or canned	249	120	1.20	0.0	0.5	4.4	0.0	0.3	0.7	0.8
	Applesauce, canned:										
218	Sweetened	254	230	2.30	0.4	0.4	3.8	0.6	1.3	0.5	1.2
219	Unsweetened or artificially sweetened	239	100	1.00	0.4	0.4	3.5	0.6	1.0	0.3	0.8
220	Applesauce and apricots, canned, strained or junior (baby food)	28	25	0.25	0.0	0.0	0.3	1.0	0.0	0.0	0.4
	Apricots:										
221	Raw, about 12 per pound	114[4]	55	0.55	0.4	0.6	1.5	16.8	0.8	0.7	4.1
	Canned in heavy sirup:										
222	Halves and sirup	259	220	2.20	0.8	1.0	2.4	26.2	1.3	1.0	4.1
223	Halves (medium) and sirup	122	105	1.05	0.4	0.5	1.2	12.3	0.5	0.5	2.1
	Dried:										
224	Uncooked, 40 halves, small	150	390	3.90	3.3	3.6	24.1	95.1	0.5	4.0	7.9
225	Cooked, unsweetened, fruit and liquid	285	240	2.40	2.1	2.3	15.0	49.7	0.3	2.2	3.3
226	Apricot nectar, canned	250	140	1.40	0.4	0.8	1.5	13.8	0.5	0.3	2.9
	Avocados, raw:										
	California varieties, mainly Fuerte:										
227	10-ounce avocado about 3-1/3 by 4-1/4 inches, peeled, pitted	108	185	1.85	0.8	0.4	1.8	1.8	3.0	3.6	6.2
228	1/2-inch cubes	152	260	2.60	1.2	0.5	2.6	2.6	4.0	5.2	8.7
	Florida varieties:										
229	13-ounce avocado, about 4 by 3 inches peeled, pitted	123	160	1.60	0.8	0.4	2.1	2.1	3.3	4.1	7.1
230	1/2-inch cubes	152[4]	195	1.95	0.8	0.5	2.6	2.6	4.0	5.2	8.7
231	Bananas, raw, 6 by 1-1/2 inches, about 3 per pound	150[4]	85	0.85	0.4	0.3	2.1	1.1	1.3	1.0	4.1
232	Blackberries, raw	144	85	0.85	0.8	1.6	3.8	1.7	1.3	1.0	12.4
233	Blueberries, raw	140	85	0.85	0.4	0.8	4.1	0.8[7]	1.0	1.4	8.3
234	Cantaloupes, raw, medium, 5-inch diameter, about 1-2/3 pounds	385[4]	60	0.60	0.4	1.0	2.4	38.0[7]	2.0	1.0	26.1
	Cherries:										
235	Raw, sweet, with stems	130[4]	80	0.80	0.8	0.9	1.5	0.8	1.5	1.2	5.0
236	Canned, red, sour, pitted, heavy sirup	260	230	2.30	0.8	1.3	2.4	9.8	1.8	1.0	5.4

[4] Includes parts not usually eaten.

[7] Values based on varieties with orange flesh; green-fleshed, 3.1 shares.

Table A-8. Nutritive Values of the Edible Part of Foods in Shares (Continued)

	Food and Approximate Measure	Weight, Grams	Calories	Shares							
				Calories	Protein	Calcium	Iron	Vitamin A Value	Thiamine	Riboflavin	Ascorbic Acid
	Fruits and Fruit Products (Continued)										
237	Cranberry juice cocktail, canned 1 cup	250	160	1.60	0.0	0.4	2.4	0.0	0.5	0.3	[8]
238	Cranberry sauce, sweetened, canned, strained 1 cup	277	405	4.05	0.0	0.6	1.8	0.2	0.8	0.5	2.1
239	Dates, domestic, natural, and dry, pitted, cut 1 cup	178	490	4.90	1.7	3.8	15.6	0.5	4.0	2.9	0.0
	Figs:										
240	Raw, small, 1-1/2-inch diameter, about 12 per pound 3 figs	114	90	0.90	0.4	1.4	2.1	0.5	1.8	1.0	0.8
241	Dried, large, 2 by 1 inch 1 fig	21	60	0.60	0.4	0.9	1.8	0.1	0.5	0.3	0.0
242	Fruit cocktail, canned in heavy sirup, solids and liquid 1 cup	256	195	1.95	0.4	0.8	2.9	2.1	1.0	0.5	2.1
	Grapefruit:										
	Raw, medium, 4-1/4-inch diameter, size 64:										
243	White 1/2 grapefruit[4]	285[4]	55	0.55	0.4	0.8	1.8	0.1	1.3	0.3	21.6
244	Pink or red 1/2 grapefruit[4]	285[4]	60	0.60	0.4	0.8	1.8	3.7	1.3	0.3	21.6
245	Raw sections, white 1 cup	194	75	0.75	0.4	1.1	2.4	0.1	1.8	0.5	29.9
	Canned, white:										
246	Sirup pack, solids and liquid 1 cup	249	175	1.75	0.4	1.1	2.1	0.1	1.8	0.7	31.1
247	Water pack, solids and liquid 1 cup	240	70	0.70	0.4	1.1	2.1	0.1	1.8	0.7	29.9
	Grapefruit juice:										
248	Fresh 1 cup	246	95	0.95	0.4	0.8	1.5	0.0[9]	2.3	0.7	38.2
	Canned, white:										
249	Unsweetened 1 cup	247	100	1.00	0.4	0.7	2.9	0.1	1.8	0.7	34.9
250	Sweetened 1 cup	250	130	1.30	0.4	0.7	2.9	0.1	1.8	0.7	32.4
	Frozen, concentrate, unsweetened:										
251	Undiluted, can, 6 fluid ounces 1 can	207	300	3.00	1.7	2.5	2.4	0.3	7.3	2.1	118.7
252	Diluted with 3 parts water, by volume 1 cup	247	100	1.00	0.4	0.9	0.6	0.1	2.5	0.7	39.8
	Frozen, concentrate, sweetened:										
253	Undiluted, can, 6 fluid ounces 1 can	211	350	3.50	1.2	2.1	1.8	0.3	6.0	1.9	101.7
254	Diluted with 3 parts water, by volume 1 cup	249	115	1.15	0.4	0.7	0.6	0.1	2.0	0.5	34.0
	Dehydrated:										
255	Crystals, can, net weight 4 ounces 1 can	114	430	4.30	2.1	3.5	3.2	0.5	10.3	3.1	165.6
256	Prepared with water (1 pound yields about 1 gallon) 1 cup	247	100	1.00	0.4	0.8	0.6	0.1	2.5	0.9	38.2
	Grapes, raw:										
257	American type (slip skin), such as Concord, Delaware, Niagara, Catawba, and Scuppernong 1 cup[4]	153[4]	65	0.65	0.4	0.5	1.2	0.6	1.3	0.5	1.2

4 Includes parts not usually eaten.
8 About 2.1 shares per 8 fl oz from cranberries; ascorbic acid usually added to about 41.7 shares.
9 White-flesh, varieties about 0.1 share per cup; red-flesh, 6.3 shares per cup.

Table A-8. Nutritive Values of the Edible Part of Foods in Shares (Continued)

	Food and Approximate Measure	Weight, Grams	Calories	Shares							
				Calories	Protein	Calcium	Iron	Vitamin A Value	Thiamine	Riboflavin	Ascorbic Acid
	Fruits and Fruit Products (Continued)										
	Grapes, raw (Continued)										
258	European type (adherent skin), such as Malaga, Muscat, Thompson Seedless, Emperor, and Flame Tokay — 1 cup[4]	160[4]	95	0.95	0.4	0.6	1.8	0.8	1.8	0.7	2.5
259	Grape juice, bottled or canned — 1 cup	254[4]	165	1.65	0.4	1.0	2.4	0.0	2.5	0.9	0.0
260	Lemons, raw, medium, 2-1/5-inch diameter, size 150 — 1 lemon[4]	106[4]	20	0.20	0.4	0.6	1.2	0.1	0.8	0.2	15.8
	Lemon juice										
261	Fresh — 1 cup	246	60	0.60	0.4	0.6	1.5	0.2	2.0	0.5	46.9
262	1 tablespoon	15	5	0.05	0.0	0.0	0.0	0.0	0.0	0.0	2.9
263	Canned, unsweetened — 1 cup	245	55	0.55	0.4	0.6	1.5	0.2	1.8	0.5	42.3
	Lemonade concentrate, frozen, sweetened:										
264	Undiluted, can, 6 fluid ounces — 1 can	220	430	4.30	0.0	0.3	1.2	0.2	1.3	1.0	27.4
265	Diluted with 4-1/3 parts water, by volume — 1 cup	248	110	1.10	0.0	0.1	0.3	0.1	0.3	0.2	7.1
	Lime juice										
266	Fresh — 1 cup	246	65	0.65	0.4	0.8	1.5	0.2	1.3	0.5	33.2
267	Canned — 1 cup	246	65	0.65	0.4	0.8	1.5	0.2	1.3	0.5	21.6
	Limeade concentrate, frozen, sweetened:										
268	Undiluted, can, 6 fluid ounces — 1 can	218	410	4.10	0.0	0.4	0.6	0.0	0.5	0.3	10.8
269	Diluted with 4-1/3 parts water, by volume — 1 cup	248	105	1.05	0.0	0.1	0.0	0.0	0.0	0.0	2.5
	Oranges, raw:										
270	California, Navel (winter), 2-4/5-inch diameter, size 88 — 1 orange[4]	180[4]	60	0.60	0.8	1.8	1.5	1.4	3.0	0.9	31.1
271	Florida, all varieties, 3-inch diameter — 1 orange[4]	210[4]	75	0.75	0.4	2.4	0.9	1.8	4.0	1.0	29.0
	Orange juice:										
	Fresh:										
272	California, Valencia (summer) — 1 cup	249	115	1.15	0.8	1.0	2.1	2.9	5.5	1.0	50.6
	Florida varieties:										
273	Early and mid-season — 1 cup	247	100	1.00	0.4	0.9	1.5	2.8	5.5	1.0	52.7
274	Late season, Valencia — 1 cup	248	110	1.10	0.4	0.9	1.5	2.9	5.5	1.0	38.2
275	Canned, unsweetened — 1 cup	249	120	1.20	0.8	0.9	2.9	2.9	4.3	0.9	41.5
	Frozen concentrate:										
276	Undiluted, can, 6 fluid ounces — 1 can	210	330	3.30	2.1	2.5	2.4	8.7	15.8	1.7	137.8
277	Diluted with 3 parts water, by volume — 1 cup	248	110	1.10	0.8	0.8	0.6	2.9	5.3	0.5	46.5
	Dehydrated:										
278	Crystals, can, net weight 4 ounces — 1 can	113	430	4.30	2.5	3.4	5.6	11.0	19.0	4.1	168.5
279	Prepared with water, 1 pound yields about 1 gallon — 1 cup	248	115	1.15	0.4	0.9	1.5	2.9	5.0	1.0	44.8

4 Includes parts not usually eaten.

Table A-8. Nutritive Values of the Edible Part of Foods in Shares (Continued)

	Food and Approximate Measure		Weight, Grams	Calories	Shares							
					Calories	Protein	Calcium	Iron	Vitamin A Value	Thiamine	Riboflavin	Ascorbic Acid
	Fruits and Fruit Products (Continued)											
	Orange and grapefruit juice:											
	Frozen concentrate:											
280	Undiluted, can, 6 fluid ounces	1 can	209	325	3.25	1.7	2.2	2.4	4.6	11.8	1.0	124.9
281	Diluted with 3 parts water, by volume	1 cup	248	110	1.10	0.4	0.7	0.6	1.6	4.0	0.3	42.3
282	Papayas, raw, 1/2-inch cubes	1 cup	182	70	0.70	0.4	1.3	1.5	18.5	1.8	1.4	42.3
	Peaches:											
	Raw:											
283	Whole, medium, 2-inch diameter, about 4 per pound	1 peach[4]	114[4]	35	0.35	0.4	0.3	1.5	7.7[10]	0.5	0.9	2.9
284	Sliced	1 cup	168	65	0.65	0.4	0.5	2.4	13.0[11]	0.8	1.4	5.0
	Canned, yellow-fleshed, solids and liquid:											
	Sirup pack, heavy:											
285	Halves or slices	1 cup	257	200	2.00	0.4	0.4	2.4	6.4	0.5	1.0	2.9
286	Halves (medium) and sirup	2 halves and 2 tablespoons sirup	117	90	0.90	0.0	0.2	1.2	2.9	0.3	0.5	1.2
287	Water pack	1 cup	245	75	0.75	0.4	0.4	2.1	6.4	0.5	1.0	2.9
288	Strained or chopped (baby food)	1 ounce	28	25	0.25	0.0	0.1	0.3	0.8	0.0	0.2	0.4
	Dried:											
289	Uncooked	1 cup	160	420	4.20	2.1	2.8	28.2	36.3	0.5	5.3	11.6
290	Cooked, unsweetened, 10-12 halves and 6 tablespoons liquid	1 cup	270	220	2.20	1.2	1.5	15.0	19.1	0.3	2.6	2.5
	Frozen:											
291	Carton, 12 ounces, not thawed	1 carton	340	300	3.00	0.4	0.5	5.0	12.8	0.8	2.4	56.0[12]
292	Can, 16 ounces, not thawed	1 can	454	400	4.00	0.8	0.6	6.8	17.2	1.3	3.1	75.1[12]
293	Peach nectar, canned	1 cup	250	120	1.20	0.0	0.4	1.5	6.3	0.5	0.9	0.4
	Pears:											
294	Raw, 3 by 2-1/2-inch diameter	1 pear[4]	182[4]	100	1.00	0.4	0.5	1.5	0.2	1.0	1.2	2.9
	Canned, solids and liquid:											
	Sirup pack, heavy:											
295	Halves or slices	1 cup	255	195	1.95	0.4	0.5	1.5	0.0	0.8	0.9	1.7
296	Halves (medium) and sirup	2 halves and 2 tablespoons sirup	117	90	0.90	0.0	0.2	0.6	0.0	0.3	0.3	0.8
297	Water pack	1 cup	243	80	0.80	0.0	0.4	1.5	0.0	0.5	0.9	1.7
298	Strained or chopped (baby food)	1 ounce	28	20	0.20	0.0	0.1	0.3	0.1	0.0	0.2	0.4
299	Pear nectar, canned	1 cup	250[4]	130	1.30	0.4	0.3	0.6	0.0	0.3	0.9	0.4
300	Persimmons, Japanese or kaki, raw, seedless, 2-1/2-inch diameter	1 persimmon[4]	125[4]	75	0.75	0.4	0.2	1.2	15.9	0.8	0.3	4.6

[4] Includes parts not usually eaten.
[10] Yellow-fleshed varieties; white-fleshed, 0.3 share.
[11] Yellow-fleshed varieties; white-fleshed, 0.5 share.
[12] Average weighted in accordance with commercial freezing practices; if ascorbic acid is not added, Item 291 equals 15.4 shares and Item 292 equals 20.8 shares.

Table A-8. Nutritive Values of the Edible Part of Foods in Shares (Continued)

	Food and Approximate Measure	Weight, Grams	Calories	Shares Calories	Protein	Calcium	Iron	Vitamin A Value	Thiamine	Riboflavin	Ascorbic Acid
	Fruits and Fruit Products (Continued)										
	Pineapple:										
301	Raw, diced — 1 cup	140	75	0.75	0.4	0.9	2.1	0.6	3.0	0.7	10.0
	Canned, heavy sirup pack, solids and liquid:										
302	Crushed — 1 cup	260	195	1.95	0.4	1.0	2.4	0.7	5.0	1.0	7.1
303	Sliced, slices and juice — 2 small or 1 large and 2 tablespoons juice	122	90	0.90	0.0	0.5	1.2	0.3	2.3	0.5	3.3
304	Pineapple juice, canned — 1 cup	249	135	1.35	0.4	1.3	2.1	0.7	3.0	0.7	9.1
	Plums, all except prunes:										
305	Raw, 2-inch diameter, about 2 ounces — 1 plum [4]	60 [4]	25	0.25	0.0	0.3	0.9	0.8	0.5	0.3	1.2
	Canned, sirup pack (Italian prunes):										
306	Plums (with pits) and juice — 1 cup [4]	256 [4]	205	2.05	0.4	0.8	6.5	17.3	1.3	0.9	1.7
307	Plums (without pits) and juice — 3 plums and 2 tablespoons juice	122	100	1.00	0.0	0.4	3.2	8.5	0.8	0.3	0.8
	Prunes, dried, "softenized," medium:										
308	Uncooked — 4 prunes [4]	32 [4]	70	0.70	0.4	0.5	3.2	2.6	0.5	0.7	0.4
309	Cooked, unsweetened, 17–18 prunes and 1/3 cup liquid — 1 cup [4]	270 [4]	295	2.95	0.8	2.1	13.2	10.8	2.0	3.1	0.8
310	Prunes with tapioca, canned, strained or junior (baby food) — 1 ounce	28	25	0.25	0.0	0.1	0.9	0.6	0.3	0.3	0.4
311	Prune juice, canned — 1 cup	256	200	2.00	0.4	1.3	30.9	0.0	0.5	0.5	1.7
312	Raisins, dried — 1 cup	160	460	4.60	1.7	3.5	16.5	0.2	4.5	2.2	0.8
	Raspberries, red:										
313	Raw — 1 cup	123	70	0.70	0.4	1.0	3.2	0.9	1.0	1.9	12.9
314	Frozen, 10-ounce carton, not thawed — 1 carton	284	275	2.75	0.8	1.3	5.0	1.2	1.5	2.9	24.5
315	Rhubarb, cooked, sugar added — 1 cup	272	385	3.85	0.4	7.6	4.7	1.3	1.5	2.6	7.1
	Strawberries:										
316	Raw, capped — 1 cup	149	55	0.55	0.4	1.1	4.4	0.5	1.0	1.7	36.5
317	Frozen, 10-ounce carton — 1 carton	284	310	3.10	0.4	1.4	5.9	0.5	1.5	2.9	62.2
318	Frozen, 16-ounce can, not thawed — 1 can	454	495	4.95	0.8	2.3	9.4	0.9	2.3	4.7	99.6
319	Tangerines, raw, medium, 2-1/2-inch diameter, about 4 per pound — 1 tangerine [4]	114 [4]	40	0.40	0.4	1.2	0.9	2.0	1.3	0.3	10.8
	Tangerine juice:										
320	Canned, unsweetened — 1 cup	248	105	1.05	0.4	1.6	1.5	6.0	3.5	0.7	23.2
	Frozen concentrate:										
321	Undiluted, can, 6 fluid ounces — 1 can	210	340	3.40	1.7	4.6	4.4	17.8	10.8	2.1	83.8
322	Diluted with 3 parts water, by volume — 1 cup	248	115	1.15	0.4	1.6	1.5	5.9	3.5	0.7	27.8

[4] Includes parts not usually eaten.

Table A-8. Nutritive Values of the Edible Part of Foods in Shares (Continued)

	Food and Approximate Measure	Weight, Grams	Calories	Shares							
				Calories	Protein	Calcium	Iron	Vitamin A Value	Thiamine	Riboflavin	Ascorbic Acid
	Fruits and Fruit Products (Continued)										
323	Watermelon, raw, wedge, 4 by 8 inches (1/16 of 10 by 16-inch melon, about 2 pounds with rind)	925[4]	115	1.15	0.8	1.1	6.2	14.6	3.3	2.2	12.4
	Grain Products										
324	Barley, pearled, light, uncooked	203	710	7.10	7.1	1.1	12.1	0.0	6.3	2.9	0.0
325	Biscuits, baking powder with enriched flour, 2-1/2 inch diameter	38	140	1.40	1.2	1.6	1.8	0.0	2.0	1.4	0.0
326	Bran flakes (40 percent bran) added thiamine	28	100	1.00	1.2	0.7	3.5	0.0	2.8	0.9	0.0
	Breads:										
327	Boston brown bread, slice, 3 by 3/4 inch	48	100	1.00	1.2	1.5	2.6	0.0	1.3	0.5	0.0
	Cracked-wheat bread:										
328	Loaf, 1-pound, 20 slices	454	1190	11.90	16.2	14.3	14.7	0.0	13.3	7.2	0.0
329	Slice	23	60	0.60	0.8	0.7	0.9	0.0	0.8	0.3	0.0
	French or vienna bread:										
330	Enriched, 1-pound loaf	454	1315	13.15	17.0	7.0	29.4	0.0	31.5	16.9	0.0
331	Unenriched, 1-pound loaf	454	1315	13.15	17.0	7.0	9.4	0.0	9.8	6.7	0.0
	Italian bread:										
332	Enriched, 1-pound loaf	454	1250	12.50	17.0	2.8	29.4	0.0	32.8	16.0	0.0
333	Unenriched, 1-pound loaf	454	1250	12.50	17.0	2.8	9.4	0.0	9.8	4.7	0.0
	Raisin bread:										
334	Loaf, 1-pound, 20 slices	454	1190	11.90	12.4	11.5	17.4	0.0	6.0	7.2	0.0
335	Slice	23	60	0.60	0.8	0.6	0.9	0.0	0.3	0.3	0.0
	Rye bread:										
	American, light (1/3 rye, 2/3 wheat):										
336	Loaf, 1-pound, 20 slices	454	1100	11.00	17.0	12.1	21.5	0.0	20.3	5.7	0.0
337	Slice	23	55	0.55	0.8	0.6	1.2	0.0	1.0	0.3	0.0
338	Pumpernickel, loaf, 1 pound	454	1115	11.15	17.0	13.6	32.1	0.0	26.3	10.9	0.0
	White bread, enriched:										
	1 to 2 percent nonfat dry milk:										
339	Loaf, 1-pound, 20 slices	454	1225	12.25	16.2	11.4	32.1	0.0	28.3	13.3	0.0
340	Slice	23	60	0.60	0.8	0.6	1.8	0.0	1.5	0.7	0.0
	3 to 4 percent nonfat dry milk:[13]										
341	Loaf, 1-pound	454	1225	12.25	16.2	13.6	33.2	0.0	28.3	16.4	0.0
342	Slice, 20 per loaf	23	60	0.60	0.8	0.7	1.8	0.0	1.5	0.9	0.0
343	Slice, toasted	20	60	0.60	0.8	0.7	1.8	0.0	1.3	0.9	0.0
344	Slice, 26 per loaf	17	45	0.45	0.4	0.5	1.2	0.0	1.0	0.7	0.0

4 Includes parts not usually eaten.

13 Values given also apply when amount of nonfat dry milk in commercial white bread is unknown.

Table A–8. Nutritive Values of the Edible Part of Foods in Shares (Continued)

Food and Approximate Measure		Weight, Grams	Calories	Shares							
				Calories	Protein	Calcium	Iron	Vitamin A Value	Thiamine	Riboflavin	Ascorbic Acid
Grain Products (Continued)											
Breads (Continued)											
White bread, enriched (Continued)											
5 to 6 percent nonfat dry milk:											
345 Loaf, 1-pound, 20 slices	1 loaf	454	1245	12.45	17.0	15.5	33.2	0.0	30.5	15.7	0.0
346 Slice	1 slice	23	65	0.65	0.8	0.8	1.8	0.0	1.5	0.9	0.0
White bread, unenriched:											
1 to 2 percent nonfat dry milk:											
347 Loaf, 1-pound, 20 slices	1 loaf	454	1225	12.25	16.2	11.4	9.4	0.0	10.0	6.2	0.0
348 Slice	1 slice	23	60	0.60	0.8	0.6	0.6	0.0	0.5	0.3	0.0
3 to 4 percent nonfat dry milk:[13]											
349 Loaf, 1-pound	1 loaf	454	1225	12.25	16.2	13.6	9.4	0.0	7.8	6.7	0.0
350 Slice, 20 per loaf	1 slice	23	60	0.60	0.8	0.7	0.6	0.0	0.5	0.3	0.0
351 Slice, toasted	1 slice	20	60	0.60	0.8	0.7	0.6	0.0	0.3	0.3	0.0
352 Slice, 26 per loaf	1 slice	17	45	0.45	0.4	0.5	0.3	0.0	0.3	0.2	0.0
5 to 6 percent nonfat dry milk:											
353 Loaf, 1-pound, 20 slices	1 loaf	454	1245	12.45	17.0	15.5	9.4	0.0	8.0	10.2	0.0
354 Slice	1 slice	23	65	0.65	0.8	0.8	0.6	0.0	0.5	0.5	0.0
Whole-wheat bread, made with 2 percent nonfat dry milk:											
355 Loaf, 1-pound, 20 slices	1 loaf	454	1105	11.05	19.9	16.0	30.6	0.0	29.3	9.7	0.0
356 Slice	1 slice	23	55	0.55	0.8	0.8	1.5	0.0	1.5	0.5	0.0
357 Slice, toasted	1 slice	19	55	0.55	0.8	0.8	1.5	0.0	1.3	0.5	0.0
358 Breadcrumbs, dry, grated	1 cup	88	345	3.45	4.6	3.8	9.4	0.0	4.8	4.5	0.0
Cakes:[14]											
359 Angelfood cake; sector, 2-inch (1/12 of 8-inch-diameter cake)	1 sector	40	110	1.10	1.2	0.1	0.3	0.0	0.0	1.0	0.0
360 Chocolate cake, chocolate icing; sector, 2-inch (1/16 of 10-inch-diameter layer cake)	1 sector	120	445	4.45	2.1	3.0	3.5	1.1[15]	0.8	2.1	0.0
361 Fruitcake, dark (made with enriched flour); piece, 2 by 2 by 1/2 inch	1 piece	30	115	1.15	0.4	0.8	2.4	0.2[15]	1.0	0.7	0.0
362 Gingerbread (made with enriched flour); piece, 2 by 2 by 2 inches	1 piece	55	175	1.75	0.8	1.3	3.8	0.3	1.5	1.0	0.0
Plain cake and cupcakes, without icing:											
363 Piece, 3 by 2 by 1-1/2 inches	1 piece	55	200	2.00	0.8	1.3	0.6	0.5[15]	0.3	0.9	0.0
364 Cupcake, 2-3/4-inch diameter	1 cupcake	40	145	1.45	0.8	0.9	0.6	0.4[15]	0.3	0.5	0.0
Plain cake and cupcakes, with chocolate icing:											
365 Sector, 2-inch (1/16 of 10-inch-layer cake)	1 sector	100	370	3.70	1.7	2.3	1.8	1.0[15]	0.5	1.6	0.0
366 Cupcake, 2-3/4-inch diameter	1 cupcake	50	185	1.85	0.8	1.1	0.9	0.5[15]	0.3	0.7	0.0

[13] Values given also apply when amount of nonfat dry milk in commercial white bread is unknown.
[14] Unenriched cake flour and vegetable cooking fat used unless otherwise specified.

Table A-8. Nutritive Values of the Edible Part of Foods in Shares (Continued)

	Food and Approximate Measure		Weight, Grams	Calories	Shares							
					Calories	Protein	Calcium	Iron	Vitamin A Value	Thiamine	Riboflavin	Ascorbic Acid
	Grain Products (Continued)											
	Cakes (Continued)											
367	Poundcake, old-fashioned (equal weights flour, sugar, fat, eggs); slice 2-3/4 by 3 by 5/8 inch	1 slice	30	140	1.40	0.8	0.2	0.6	0.5[15]	0.3	0.5	0.0
368	Sponge cake; sector 2-inch (1/12 of 8-inch-diameter cake)	1 sector	40	120	1.20	1.2	0.4	1.5	1.0	0.5	1.0	0.0
	Cookies:											
369	Plain and assorted, 3-inch diameter	1 cookie	25	120	1.20	0.4	0.3	0.6	0.1	0.3	0.2	0.0
370	Fig bars, small	1 fig bar	16	55	0.55	0.4	0.4	0.6	0.1	0.3	0.2	0.0
371	Corn, rice and wheat flakes, mixed, added nutrients	1 ounce	28	110	1.10	0.8	0.4	1.5	0.0	2.8	0.0	0.0
	Corn flakes, added nutrients:											
372	Plain	1 ounce	28	110	1.10	0.8	0.2	1.2	0.0	3.0	0.3	0.0
373	Sugar-covered	1 ounce	28	110	1.10	0.4	0.1	0.9	0.0	3.0	0.2	0.0
	Corn grits, degermed, cooked:											
374	Enriched	1 cup	242	120	1.20	1.2	0.1	2.1[16]	0.9[17]	2.5[16]	1.2[16]	0.0
375	Unenriched	1 cup	242	120	1.20	1.2	0.1	0.6	0.9[17]	1.3	0.3	0.0
	Cornmeal, white or yellow, dry:											
376	Whole ground, unbolted	1 cup	118	420	4.20	4.6	0.9	8.2	3.5[18]	11.3	2.2	0.0
377	Degermed, enriched	1 cup	145	525	5.25	4.6	0.3	12.4[16]	3.7[18]	16.0[16]	6.6[16]	0.0
378	Corn muffins, made with enriched degermed cornmeal and enriched flour; muffin, 2-3/4-inch diameter	1 muffin	48	150	1.50	1.2	1.8	2.4	0.5[19]	2.3	1.9	0.0
379	Corn, puffed, presweetened, added nutrients	1 ounce	28	110	1.10	0.4	0.1	1.5	0.0	3.0	0.9	0.0
380	Corn, shredded, added nutrients	1 ounce	28	110	1.10	0.8	0.0	2.1	0.0	3.0	0.9	0.0
	Crackers:											
381	Graham, plain	4 small or 2 medium	14	55	0.55	0.4	0.2	0.6	0.0	0.3	0.5	0.0
382	Saltines, 2 inches square	2 crackers	8	35	0.35	0.4	0.1	0.3	0.0	0.3	0.0	0.0
	Soda:											
383	Cracker, 2-1/2 inches square	2 crackers	11	50	0.50	0.4	0.1	0.6	0.0	0.0	0.0	0.0
384	Oyster crackers	10 crackers	10	45	0.45	0.4	0.1	0.6	0.0	0.0	0.0	0.0
385	Cracker meal	1 tablespoon	10	45	0.45	0.4	0.1	0.3	0.0	0.0	0.0	0.0
386	Doughnuts, cake type	1 doughnut	32	125	1.25	0.4	0.5	1.2[20]	0.2	1.3[20]	0.9[20]	0.0
387	Farina, regular, enriched, cooked	1 cup	238	100	1.00	1.2	0.4	2.1[16]	0.0	2.8[16]	1.2[16]	0.0
	Macaroni, cooked:											
	Enriched:											
388	Cooked, firm stage (8 to 10 minutes; undergoes additional cooking in a food mixture)	1 cup	130	190	1.90	2.5	0.5	4.1[16]	0.0	5.8[16]	2.4[16]	0.0

15 Vitamin A values, if butter or fortified margarine is used, are as follows: Item 360, 2.8; Item 361, 0.6; Item 363, 1.7; Item 364, 1.3; Item 365, 2.6; Item 366, 1.3; Item 367, 1.7.

16 Based on the minimum levels of enrichment specified in standards of identity under the Federal Food, Drug and Cosmetic Act.

17 Yellow; white, trace only.

18 Vitamin A values based on yellow varieties; white, trace only.

19 Based on recipe using white cornmeal; yellow cornmeal, 0.8 share.

20 Made with enriched flour; with unenriched flour: iron, 0.6, thiamine, 0.3; riboflavin, 0.5.

Table A-8. Nutritive Values of the Edible Part of Foods in Shares (Continued)

	Food and Approximate Measure		Weight, Grams	Calories	Shares							
					Calories	Protein	Calcium	Iron	Vitamin A Value	Thiamine	Riboflavin	Ascorbic Acid
	Grain Products (Continued)											
	Macaroni, cooked (Continued)											
	Enriched (Continued)											
389	Cooked until tender	1 cup	140	155	1.55	2.1	0.4	3.8[16]	0.0	4.8[16]	1.9[16]	0.0
	Unenriched:											
390	Cooked, firm stage (8 to 10 minutes; undergoes additional cooking in a food mixture)	1 cup	130	190	1.90	2.5	0.5	1.8	0.0	0.5	0.3	0.0
391	Cooked until tender	1 cup	140	155	1.55	2.1	0.4	1.8	0.0	0.5	0.3	0.0
392	Macaroni (enriched) and cheese, baked	1 cup	220	470	4.70	7.5	14.2	5.9	5.5	5.5	7.6	0.0
393	Muffins, with enriched white flour; muffin, 2-3/4-inch diameter	1 muffin	48	140	1.40	1.7	1.8	2.4	0.3	2.0	1.9	0.0
	Noodles (egg noodles), cooked:											
394	Enriched	1 cup	160	200	2.00	2.9	0.6	4.1[16]	0.6	5.8[16]	2.4[16]	0.0
395	Unenriched	1 cup	160	200	2.00	2.9	0.6	2.9	0.6	1.0	0.5	0.0
396	Oats (with or without corn) puffed, added nutrients	1 ounce	28	115	1.15	1.2	1.8	3.8	0.0	7.0	0.9	0.0
397	Oatmeal or rolled oats, regular or quick-cooking, cooked	1 cup	236	130	1.30	2.1	0.8	4.1	0.0	4.8	0.9	0.0
	Pancakes (griddlecakes), 4-inch diameter:											
398	Wheat, enriched flour (home recipe)	1 cake	27	60	0.60	0.8	1.0	1.2	0.2	1.3	1.0	0.0
399	Buckwheat (buckwheat pancake mix, made with egg and milk)	1 cake	27	55	0.55	0.8	2.1	1.2	0.3	0.8	0.7	0.0
	Piecrust, plain, baked:											
	Enriched flour:											
400	Lower crust, 9-inch shell	1 crust	135	675	6.75	3.3	0.7	6.8	0.0	6.8	3.3	0.0
401	Double crust, 9-inch pie	1 double crust	270	1350	13.50	6.6	1.4	13.5	0.0	13.8	6.7	0.0
	Unenriched flour:											
402	Lower crust, 9-inch shell	1 crust	135	675	6.75	3.3	0.7	2.1	0.0	1.0	0.7	0.0
403	Double crust, 9-inch pie	1 double crust	270	1350	13.50	6.6	1.4	4.1	0.0	2.0	1.2	0.0
	Pies (piecrust made with unenriched flour); sector, 4-inch, 1/7 of 9-inch-diameter pie:											
404	Apple	1 sector	135	345	3.45	1.2	0.4	1.2	0.2	0.8	0.3	0.4
405	Cherry	1 sector	135	355	3.55	1.7	0.7	1.2	3.4	0.8	0.5	0.4
406	Custard	1 sector	130	280	2.80	3.3	4.5	2.4	1.7	1.8	3.6	0.0
407	Lemon meringue	1 sector	120	305	3.05	1.7	0.6	1.8	1.2	1.0	1.7	1.7
408	Mince	1 sector	135	365	3.65	1.2	1.4	4.1	0.0	2.3	0.9	0.4
409	Pumpkin	1 sector	130	275	2.75	2.1	2.4	1.8	18.7	1.0	2.2	0.0
410	Pizza (cheese); 5-1/2-inch sector; 1/8 of 14-inch-diameter pie	1 sector	75	185	1.85	2.9	3.8	2.1	1.7	1.0	2.1	1.7

16 Based on the minimum levels of enrichment specified in standards of identity under the Federal Food, Drug and Cosmetic Act.

Table A–8. Nutritive Values of the Edible Part of Foods in Shares (Continued)

	Food and Approximate Measure		Weight, Grams	Calories	Shares							
					Calories	Protein	Calcium	Iron	Vitamin A Value	Thiamine	Riboflavin	Ascorbic Acid
	Grain Products (Continued)											
411	Popcorn, popped, with added oil and salt	1 cup	14	65	0.65	0.4	0.0	0.9	0.0	0.0	0.2	0.0
412	Pretzels, small stick	5 sticks	5	20	0.20	0.0	0.0	0.0	0.0	0.0	0.0	0.0
	Rice, white (fully milled or polished); enriched, cooked:											
413	Common commercial varieties, all types	1 cup	168	185	1.85	1.2	0.6	4.4[16]	0.0	4.8[16]	0.2[21]	0.0
414	Long grain, parboiled	1 cup	176	185	1.85	1.7	1.2	4.1[16]	0.0	4.8[16]	0.3[21]	0.0
415	Rice, puffed, added nutrients (without salt)	1 cup	14	55	0.55	0.4	0.1	0.9	0.0	1.5	0.2	0.0
416	Rice flakes, added nutrients	1 cup	30	115	1.15	0.8	0.3	1.5	0.0	2.5	0.3	0.0
	Rolls:											
	Plain, pan; 12 per 16 ounces:											
417	Enriched	1 roll	38	115	1.15	1.2	1.0	2.1	0.0	2.8	1.2	0.0
418	Unenriched	1 roll	38	115	1.15	1.2	1.0	0.9	0.0	0.5	0.5	0.0
419	Hard, round; 12 per 22 ounces	1 roll	52	160	1.60	2.1	0.9	1.2	0.0	0.8	0.9	0.0
420	Sweet, pan; 12 per 18 ounces	1 roll	43	135	1.35	1.7	1.3	0.9	0.2	0.8	1.0	0.0
421	Rye wafers, whole-grain, 1-7/8 by 3-1/2 inches	2 wafers	13	45	0.45	0.8	0.3	1.5	0.0	1.0	0.5	0.0
	Spaghetti:											
	Cooked, tender stage (14 to 20 minutes):											
422	Enriched	1 cup	140	155	1.55	2.1	0.4	3.8[16]	0.0	4.8[16]	1.9[16]	0.0
423	Unenriched	1 cup	140	155	1.55	2.1	0.4	1.8	0.0	0.5	0.3	0.0
424	Spaghetti with meat balls in tomato sauce (home recipe)	1 cup	250	335	3.35	7.9	4.5	11.2	9.3	6.5	5.2	9.1
425	Spaghetti in tomato sauce with cheese (home recipe)	1 cup	250	260	2.60	3.7	2.9	6.5	6.3	6.0	3.1	5.8
426	Waffles, with enriched flour, 1/2 by 4-1/2 by 5-1/2 inches	1 waffle	75	210	2.10	2.9	3.0	3.8	1.5	3.3	3.3	0.0
	Wheat, puffed:											
427	With added nutrients (without salt)	1 ounce	28	105	1.05	1.7	0.3	3.5	0.0	3.8	1.2	0.0
428	With added nutrients, with sugar and honey	1 ounce	28	105	1.05	0.8	0.3	2.6	0.0	3.5	0.9	0.0
429	Wheat, rolled; cooked	1 cup	236	175	1.75	2.1	0.7	5.0	0.0	4.3	1.0	0.0
430	Wheat, shredded, plain (long, round, or bite-size)	1 ounce	28	100	1.00	1.2	0.4	2.9	0.0	1.5	0.5	0.0
431	Wheat and malted barley flakes, with added nutrients	1 ounce	28	110	1.10	0.8	0.5	2.1	0.0	3.3	0.5	0.0
432	Wheat flakes, with added nutrients	1 ounce	28	100	1.00	1.2	0.4	3.5	0.0	4.5	0.7	0.0

16 Based on the minimum levels of enrichment specified in standards of identity under the Federal Food, Drug and Cosmetic Act.
21 Riboflavin is based on unenriched rice; when standards are promulgated, the value will be 2.1 shares.

Table A-8. Nutritive Values of the Edible Part of Foods in Shares (Continued)

#	Food and Approximate Measure	Measure	Weight, Grams	Calories	Shares Calories	Protein	Calcium	Iron	Vitamin A Value	Thiamine	Riboflavin	Ascorbic Acid
	Grain Products (Continued)											
	Wheat flours:											
433	Whole-wheat, from hard wheats, stirred	1 cup	120	400	4.00	6.6	1.8	11.8	0.0	16.5	2.4	0.0
	All-purpose or family flour:											
434	Enriched, sifted	1 cup	110	400	4.00	5.0	0.6	9.4[16]	0.0	12.0[16]	5.0[16]	0.0
435	Unenriched, sifted	1 cup	110	400	4.00	5.0	0.6	2.6	0.0	1.8	0.9[16]	0.0
436	Self-rising, enriched	1 cup	110	385	3.85	4.1	10.4	9.4[16]	0.0	12.3[16]	5.0[16]	0.0
437	Cake or pastry flour, sifted	1 cup	100	365	3.65	3.3	0.6	1.5	0.0	0.8	0.5	0.0
438	Wheat germ, crude, commercially milled	1 cup	68	245	2.45	7.5	1.8	18.8	0.0	34.0	7.9	0.0
	Fats, Oils											
	Butter, 4 sticks per pound											
439	Sticks, 2	1 cup	227	1625	16.25	0.4	1.6	0.0	43.6[22]	0.0	0.0	0.0
440	Stick, 1/8	1 tablespoon	14	100	1.00	0.0	0.1	0.0	2.7[22]	0.0	0.0	0.0
441	Pat or square (64 per pound)	1 pat	7	50	0.50	0.0	0.0	0.0	1.3[22]	0.0	0.0	0.0
	Fats, cooking:											
442	Lard	1 cup	220	1985	19.85	0.0	0.0	0.0	0.0	0.0	0.0	0.0
443	Lard	1 tablespoon	14	125	1.25	0.0	0.0	0.0	0.0	0.0	0.0	0.0
444	Vegetable fats	1 cup	200	1770	17.70	0.0	0.0	0.0	0.0	0.0	0.0	0.0
445	Vegetable fats	1 tablespoon	13	110	1.10	0.0	0.0	0.0	0.0	0.0	0.0	0.0
	Margarine, 4 sticks per pound:											
446	Sticks, 2	1 cup	227	1635	16.35	0.4	1.6	0.0	43.6[23]	0.0	0.0	0.0
447	Stick, 1/8	1 tablespoon	14	100	1.00	0.0	0.1	0.0	2.7[23]	0.0	0.0	0.0
448	Pat or square (64 per pound)	1 pat	7	50	0.50	0.0	0.0	0.0	1.3[23]	0.0	0.0	0.0
	Oils, salad or cooking:											
449	Corn	1 tablespoon	14	125	1.25	0.0	0.0	0.0	0.0	0.0	0.0	0.0
450	Cottonseed	1 tablespoon	14	125	1.25	0.0	0.0	0.0	0.0	0.0	0.0	0.0
451	Olive	1 tablespoon	14	125	1.25	0.0	0.0	0.0	0.0	0.0	0.0	0.0
452	Soybean	1 tablespoon	14	125	1.25	0.0	0.0	0.0	0.0	0.0	0.0	0.0
	Salad dressings:											
453	Blue cheese	1 tablespoon	16	80	0.80	0.4	0.5	0.0	0.2	0.0	0.3	0.0
454	Commercial, mayonnaise type	1 tablespoon	15	65	0.65	0.0	0.1	0.0	0.2	0.0	0.0	0.0
455	French	1 tablespoon	15	60	0.60	0.0	0.1	0.3	0.0	0.0	0.0	0.0
456	Home cooked, boiled	1 tablespoon	17	30	0.30	0.4	0.5	0.3	0.5	0.3	0.5	0.0
457	Mayonnaise	1 tablespoon	15	110	1.10	0.0	0.1	0.3	0.2	0.0	0.2	0.0
458	Thousand island	1 tablespoon	15	75	0.75	0.0	0.1	0.3	0.3	0.0	0.0	0.0

16 Based on the minimum levels of enrichment specified in standards of identity under the Federal Food, Drug and Cosmetic Act.
23 Based on the average vitamin A content of fortified margarine. Federal specifications of 15,000 I U per pound equals 87.2 shares.
22 Year-round average.

Table A-8. Nutritive Values of the Edible Part of Foods in Shares (Continued)

	Food and Approximate Measure		Weight, Grams	Calories	Shares							
					Calories	Protein	Calcium	Iron	Vitamin A Value	Thiamine	Riboflavin	Ascorbic Acid
	Sugars, Sweets											
	Candy:											
459	Caramels	1 ounce	28	115	1.15	0.4	1.5	1.2	0.0	0.3	0.9	0.0
460	Chocolate, milk, plain	1 ounce	28	150	1.50	0.8	2.3	0.9	0.5	0.5	1.6	0.0
461	Fudge, plain	1 ounce	28	115	1.15	0.4	0.8	0.9	0.0	0.3	0.5	0.0
462	Hard candy	1 ounce	28	110	1.10	0.0	0.2	1.5	0.0	0.0	0.0	0.0
463	Marshmallows	1 ounce	28	90	0.90	0.4	0.2	1.5	0.0	0.0	0.2	0.0
464	Chocolate sirup, thin type	1 tablespoon	20	50	0.50	0.0	0.1	0.9	0.0	0.0	0.2	0.0
465	Honey, strained or extracted	1 tablespoon	21	65	0.65	0.0	0.0	0.3	0.0	0.0	0.2	0.0
466	Jams and preserves	1 tablespoon	20	55	0.55	0.0	0.1	0.6	0.0	0.0	0.2	0.0
467	Jellies	1 tablespoon	20	55	0.55	0.0	0.1	0.9	0.0	0.0	0.2	0.4
	Molasses, cane:											
468	Light (first extraction)	1 tablespoon	20	50	0.50	0.0	1.2	2.6	0.0	0.3	0.2	0.0
469	Blackstrap (third extraction)	1 tablespoon	20	45	0.45	0.0	4.9	9.4	0.0	0.5	0.7	0.0
470	Sirup, table blends (chiefly corn, light and dark)	1 tablespoon	20	60	0.60	0.0	0.3	2.4	0.0	0.0	0.0	0.0
	Sugars (cane or beet):											
471	Granulated	1 cup	200	770	7.70	0.0	0.0	0.6	0.0	0.0	0.0	0.0
472		1 tablespoon	12	45	0.45	0.0	0.0	0.0	0.0	0.0	0.0	0.0
473	Lump, 1-1/8 by 3/4 by 3/8	1 lump	6	25	0.25	0.0	0.0	0.0	0.0	0.0	0.0	0.0
474	Powdered, stirred before measuring	1 cup	128	495	4.95	0.0	0.0	0.3	0.0	0.0	0.0	0.0
475		1 tablespoon	8	30	0.30	0.0	0.0	0.0	0.0	0.0	0.0	0.0
476	Brown, firm-packed	1 cup	220	820	8.20	0.0	6.7	22.1	0.0	0.5	1.2	0.0
477		1 tablespoon	14	50	0.50	0.0	0.4	1.5	0.0	0.0	0.0	0.0
	Miscellaneous Items											
478	Beer (average 3.6 percent alcohol by weight)	1 cup	240	100	1.00	0.4	0.4	0.0	0.0	0.3	1.2	0.0
	Beverages, carbonated:											
479	Cola type	1 cup	240	95	0.95	0.0	0.0	0.0	0.0	0.0	0.0	0.0
480	Ginger ale	1 cup	230	70	0.70	0.0	0.0	0.0	0.0	0.0	0.0	0.0
481	Bouillon cube, 5/8 inch	1 cube	4	5	0.05	0.4	0.0	0.0	0.0	0.0	0.0	0.0
	Chili powder. See Vegetables, peppers, Item 180.											
482	Chili sauce (mainly tomatoes)	1 tablespoon	17	20	0.20	0.0	0.1	0.3	1.4	0.5	0.2	1.2
	Chocolate:											
483	Bitter or baking	1 ounce	28	145	1.45	1.2	0.8	5.6	0.1	0.3	1.2	0.0
484	Sweet	1 ounce	28	150	1.50	0.4	1.0	1.2	0.0	0.3	0.7	0.0
	Cider. See Fruits, apple juice, Item 217.											

Table A-8. Nutritive Values of the Edible Part of Foods in Shares (Continued)

| | Food and Approximate Measure | | Weight, Grams | Calories | Shares | | | | | | | |
					Calories	Protein	Calcium	Iron	Vitamin A Value	Thiamine	Riboflavin	Ascorbic Acid
	Miscellaneous Items (Continued)											
	Gelatin, dry:											
485	Plain	1 tablespoon	10	35	0.35	3.7	0.0	0.0	0.0	0.0	0.0	0.0
486	Dessert powder, 3-ounce package	1/2 cup	85	315	3.15	3.3	0.0	0.0	0.0	0.0	0.0	0.0
	Gelatin dessert, ready-to-eat:											
487	Plain	1 cup	239	140	1.40	1.7	0.0	0.0	0.0	0.0	0.0	0.0
488	With fruit	1 cup	241	160	1.60	1.2	0.0	0.0	0.0	0.0	0.0	0.0
	Olives, pickled:											
489	Green	4 medium or 3 extra large or 2 giant	16	15	0.15	0.0	0.3	0.6	0.2	0.0	0.0	0.0
490	Ripe: Mission	3 small or 2 large	10	15	0.15	0.0	0.3	0.3	0.1	0.0	0.0	0.0
	Pickles, cucumber:											
491	Dill, large, 4 by 1-3/4 inches	1 pickle	135	15	0.15	0.4	1.3	4.1	0.8	0.0	0.5	3.3
492	Sweet, 2-3/4 by 3/4 inches	1 pickle	20	30	0.30	0.0	0.1	0.6	0.1	0.0	0.0	0.4
	Popcorn. See Grain products Item 411											
493	Sherbet, orange	1 cup	193	260	2.60	0.8	1.1	0.0	0.6	0.5	1.0	1.7
	Soups, canned; ready-to-serve (prepared with equal volume of water):											
494	Bean with pork	1 cup	250	170	1.70	3.3	2.2	6.5	3.8	3.5	1.2	0.8
495	Beef noodle	1 cup	250	70	0.70	1.7	0.3	2.9	0.3	1.3	1.0	0.0
496	Beef bouillon, broth, consomme	1 cup	240	30	0.30	2.1	0.0	1.5	0.0	0.5	0.3	0.0
497	Chicken noodle	1 cup	250	65	0.65	1.7	0.4	1.5	0.3	0.5	0.3	0.0
498	Clam chowder	1 cup	255	85	0.85	0.8	1.3	2.9	5.3	0.8	0.5	0.0
499	Cream soup (mushroom)	1 cup	240	135	1.35	0.8	1.5	1.5	0.4	0.5	2.1	0.0
500	Minestrone	1 cup	245	105	1.05	2.1	1.3	2.9	13.7	1.8	0.9	0.0
501	Pea, green	1 cup	245	130	1.30	2.5	1.6	2.9	2.0	1.3	0.9	2.9
502	Tomato	1 cup	245	90	0.90	0.8	0.5	2.1	5.8	1.5	0.9	5.0
503	Vegetable with beef broth	1 cup	250	80	0.80	1.2	0.7	2.4	18.9	1.3	0.3	0.0
504	Starch (cornstarch)	1 cup	128	465	4.65	0.0	0.0	0.0	0.0	0.0	0.0	0.0
505		1 tablespoon	8	30	0.30	0.0	0.0	0.0	0.0	0.0	0.0	0.0
506	Tapioca, quick-cooking granulated, dry stirred before measuring	1 cup	152	535	5.35	0.4	0.5	1.8	0.0	0.0	0.0	0.0
507		1 tablespoon	10	35	0.35	0.0	0.0	0.0	0.0	0.0	0.0	0.0
508	Vinegar	1 tablespoon	15	2	0.02	0.0	0.0	0.3	0.0	0.0	0.0	0.0
509	White sauce, medium	1 cup	265	430	4.30	4.1	10.9	1.5	7.1	3.0	7.6	0.0

Table A-8. Nutritive Values of the Edible Part of Foods in Shares (Continued)

| | Food and Approximate Measure | Weight, Grams | Calories | Shares | | | | | | | |
				Calories	Protein	Calcium	Iron	Vitamin A Value	Thiamine	Riboflavin	Ascorbic Acid
	Miscellaneous Items (Continued)										
	Yeast:										
	Baker's:										
510	Compressed 1 ounce	28	25	0.25	1.2	0.1	4.1	0.0	5.0	8.1	0.0
511	Dry active 1 ounce	28	80	0.80	4.1	0.4	13.5	0.0	16.5	26.4	0.0
512	Brewer's, dry, debittered 1 tablespoon	8	25	0.25	1.2	0.6	4.1	0.0	31.3	5.9	0.0
	Yoghurt. See Milk, cream, cheese; related products, Item 39										

TABLE A-9. COMPARATIVE DIETARY STANDARDS FOR ADULTS IN SELECTED COUNTRIES AND FAO WITH EXPLANATIONS AS TO THEIR MEANING

The purpose for establishing a national dietary standard is not the same in all countries. Therefore, some variation in nutrient allowances from country to country is to be expected. At the same time, it must be recognized that the "reference" individual will vary from country to country. Furthermore, even in instances when there are presumed similar objectives among countries as to the purpose and usefulness of proposed standards, it can be seen that there is by no means uniform agreement as to the nutrient allowances considered desirable as national guides. Standards are also subject to revision as newer knowledge becomes available. Particular attention should be paid to the footnotes, which explain, in brief form, the basis for nutrient allowances in the various countries and those of FAO. The original publications should be consulted for detailed explanations. The Board is indebted to Dr. L. A. Maynard for the preparation of this table.

Country	Sex	Age, years	Weight, kg	Activity	Calories	Protein, gm	Calcium, gm	Iron, mg	Vitamin A Activity, IU	Thiamine, mg	Riboflavin, mg	Niacin Equiv.[3] mg	Ascorbic Acid, mg
U.S.A.[1]	M	18-35	70	Footnote[2]	2,900	70	0.8	10	5,000	1.2	1.7	19	70
	F	18-35	58	Footnote[2]	2,100	58	0.8	15	5,000	0.8	1.3	14	70
FAO[1]	M	25	65	Footnote[2]	3,200	43[3]	0.4-0.5[4]						
	F	25	55	Footnote[2]	2,300	36[3]	0.4-0.5[4]						
Australia[1]	M	25	65	Footnote[2]	2,700	65	0.7	10	2,500[3]	1.1	1.6	18[4]	30
	F	25	55	Footnote[2]	2,300	55	0.6	12	2,000[3]	0.9	1.4	15[4]	30
Canada[1]	M	25	72	Footnote[2]	2,850	50[3]	0.5	6	3,700[4]	0.9	1.4	9	30
	F	25	57	Footnote[2]	2,400	39[4]	0.5	10	3,700[4]	0.7	1.2	7	30
Central America and Panama[1]	M	25	55	Moderate work	2,700	55	0.7	10	4,333[2]	1.4	1.4	14	50
	F	25	50	Moderate work	2,000	50	0.7	10	4,333	1.0	1.2	10	45
India[1]	M	25.4	55	Moderate work[2]	2,800	55[3]							
	F	21.5	45	Moderate work[2]	2,300	45[3]							
Japan[1]	M	Footnote[2]	56	Moderate work[3]	3,000	70[4]	0.6	10	2,000[5]	1.5	1.5	15	65
	F	Footnote[2]	48.5	Moderate work[3]	2,400	60[4]	0.6	10	2,000[5]	1.2	1.2	12	60
Netherlands[1]	M	20-29	70	Light work	3,000	70[2]	1.0	10	5,500[3]	1.2	1.8	12	50
	F	20-29	60	Light work	2,400	60[2]	1.0	12	5,500[3]	1.0	1.5	10	50
Norway[1]	M	25	70	None given	3,400	70	0.8	12	2,500[2]	1.7	1.8	17	30
	F	25	60	None given	2,500	60	0.8	12	2,500[2]	1.3	1.5	13	30
The Philippines[1]	M	None Specified	53	Moderate work	2,600	55	0.7	6	4,000[2]	1.6	1.4[3]	16	75
	F		45	Moderate work	2,300	45	0.7	10	4,000[2]	1.4	1.1[3]	14	70
South Africa[1]	M	None Specified	73	Moderate work	3,000	65	0.7	9	4,000[2]	1.0	1.6	15	40
	F		60	Moderate work	2,300	55	0.6	12	4,000[2]	0.8	1.4	12	40
United Kingdom[1]	M	20 up	65	Medium work[2]	3,000	87[3]	0.8	12	5,000[4]	1.2	1.8	12	20
	F	20 up	56	Medium work[2]	2,500	73[3]	0.8	12	5,000[4]	1.0	1.5	10	20
U.S.S.R.	M & F			Moderate work					5,000[2]	2.0[3]	2.5	15	70[3]

527

U.S.A.:

[1] Source: <u>Recommended Dietary Allowances</u>, Revised 1963. NAS-NRC Publ. 1146.
Washington (1964).

[2] Allowances are intended for persons normally active in a temperate climate.

[3] Niacin equivalents include dietary sources of the preformed vitamin and the precursor,
tryptophan. 60 mg tryptophan represents 1 mg niacin.

FAO:

[1] Source: Calorie Requirements, FAO. Nutritional Studies, No. 15, Rome (1957).
            Protein Requirements, FAO. Nutritional Studies, No. 16, Rome (1957).
            Calcium Requirements, FAO. Nutrition Meetings Report Series No. 30,
            Rome (1962).
            Mean annual temperature, 10°C.

[2] The activity for the reference man is described as "on each working day he is employed 8 hours in an occupation which is not sedentary, but does not involve more than
occasional periods of hard physical labor. When not at work, he is sedentary for about
4 hours daily and may walk for up to 1-1/2 hours. He spends about 1-1/2 hours on active
recreations and household work." The activity of the reference woman is described as
"she may be engaged either in general household duties or in light industry. Her daily
activities include walking for about 1 hour and 1 hour of active recreation, such as gardening, playing with children, or non-strenuous sport."

[3] The protein value is defined as a safe practical allowance and is based on an average
minimum requirement for a reference protein: Increased by 50% to allow for individual
variability, and by a further percentage in accordance with the estimated protein score of
the protein of the diet. The values given in the table are for a diet similar to that of the
USA, using a coefficient of 1.25 to allow for differences in protein quality, thus arriving
at an allowance of 0.66 gm per kilogram body weight.

[4] The value is considered a safe practical allowance. A range is given to emphasize
that present knowledge does not permit any greater accuracy as to a safe allowance.

Australia:

[1] Dietary allowance for Australia, 1961 revision, <u>Med.Journal Australia</u>, Dec. 30, 1961.
The allowances are designed to be used as a basis for planning food supplies for persons
or groups.

[2] The activities specified are similar to those of the reference man and woman (Calorie
Requirements, FAO Nutritional Studies No. 15, Rome). Mean annual external temperature,
18°C.

[3] Three International Units of carotene equivalent to 1 IU of vitamin A activity.

[4] Performed niacin plus (gm of protein x 0.16).

Canada:

[1] "Recommended daily intakes of nutrients adequate for the maintenance of health among
the majority of Canadians." Issued 1963.

[2] Five categories of activity are listed and described.   The values for calories and
nutrients here given apply to "most household chores," "office work," "laboratory work,"
"shop and mill work," "mechanical trades or crafts," various sports.

[3] Based on normal mixed Canadian diets.

[4] Based on mixed Canadian diet supplying both vitamin A and carotene. As preformed
vitamin A the suggested intake would be two thirds of amounts indicated.

Central America and Panama:

[1] Institute of Nutrition of Central America and Panama (INCAP), <u>Boletin de la Oficina
Sanitaria Panamericana</u>, Supplemento No. 2, Noviembre, 1955, page 225. The figures for
nutrients are designed to meet the needs of all individuals. Average annual temperature,
20°C., activity not defined.

[2] This figure is given in the INCAP table as 1.3 mg of vitamin A and assumes that
two thirds of the activity is supplied from vegetable sources. International units shown
were derived by converting as follows: 1 IU = 0.0003 mg vitamin A alcohol.

Table A-9. Comparative Dietary Standards for Adults in Selected Countries and FAO
with Explanations as to Their Meaning (Continued)

India:

[1] Patwardhan, V.N., Dietary Allowances for India. Calories and Protein. Indian Council of Medical Research, Special Report Series No. 35, New Delhi, 1960. The data are 1958 revisions of earlier figures.

[2] The activities corresponding to the calorie recommendations are detailed in the above publication. "Moderate" refers to activity in a "light industrial occupation."

[3] "An allowance of 1 gm. of protein per kilogram body weight of vegetable proteins in properly balanced diets."

Japan: ·

[1] Nutrition in Japan, 1962, Ministry of Health and Welfare, Tokyo, 1962. Data adopted by the Council on Nutrition in 1960. The allowances are believed to be sufficient to establish and maintain a good nutritional state in typical individuals.

[2] Age not specified.

[3] Five categories of activity are specified for men and four for women, with corresponding intakes for calories and B-vitamins.

[4] Higher intakes are specified for heavy and very hard work.

[5] Requirement for both sexes specified as 2000 IU of preformed vitamin A or 6000 IU of carotene.

Netherlands:

[1] Recommended quantities of nutrients, Committee on Nutritional Standards of the Nutrition Council Voeding 22, 210-214, 1961. The figures for nutrients are set to cover individuals having high requirements. The figures for calories are average requirements.

[2] Assumes one third is from animal sources. Figures are increased for heavy and very heavy work.

[3] Assumes 1500 IU as preformed vitamin A and 4000 IU of activity as carotene.

Norway:

[1] Evaluation of nutrition requirements, State Nutrition Council, 1958. Figures are "somewhat higher than average requirements."

[2] Vitamin A as present in animal foods.

The Philippines:

[1] Recommended daily allowances for specific nutrients, Food and Nutrition Research Center, 1960, "Objectives toward which to aim in planning practical diets."

[2] Assumes two thirds contributed by carotene.

[3] Grams protein x .025.

South Africa:

[1] Recommended minimum daily dietary standards, National Research Council, S.A. Med. J., 30: 108, 1956.

[2] Assumes two thirds contributed by carotene.

United Kingdom:

[1] Report of the Committee on Nutrition, British Medical Association, 1950. The levels of nutrients recommended are believed to be sufficient to establish and maintain a good nutritional state in representative individuals or groups concerned.

[2] Values are given for 6 levels of activity for males and 5 for females. Medium work is described as 8 hours at 100 calories per hour and traveling (130 calories per hour).

[3] The protein allowance is increased with calories on the basis that the protein in the diet should provide not less than 11 per cent of the energy for adults not engaged in hard work.

[4] A mixed diet containing one-third vitamin A and two-thirds carotene.

U.S.S.R.:

[1] New daily vitamin supply standards in man, 1961, Yarusova, N.S., Vop. Pitan., 20: 3, 1961.

[2] IU is equivalent to 0.3 micrograms of natural vitamin.

[3] To be increased up to 50 per cent in far north.

TABLE A-10. APPROXIMATE CALORIE VALUE OF ALCOHOLIC BEVERAGES*

Kind	Quantity	Description	Calories**	Carbo-hydrate, Gm	Alcohol, Gm
Beer ***					
Brandy, gin, rum, and whiskey (Scotch)	45 cc (1-1/2 oz)	1 jigger	109	0	15.8
Cocktails (dry)	75 cc (2-1/2 oz)	1 cocktail glass	155	1.2	21.7
Cordials	20 cc (2/3 oz)	1 cordial glass	67	6.0	6.2
Old-fashioned	180 cc (6 oz)	1 glass	194	12.4	21.1
Tom Collins	300 cc (10 oz)	1 tall glass	203	10.6	23.7
Vermouth					
French	90 cc (3 oz)	1 wine glass	97	0.9	13.5
Italian	90 cc (3 oz)	1 wine glass	154	10.8	16.2
Wines					
Dry	90 cc (3 oz)	1 wine glass	80	3.6	9.4
Sweet	90 cc (3 oz)	1 wine glass	143	12.6	13.6

* Calorie values from these beverages should be counted in estimating the total calories in a diet.

** Calories from alcohol have been calculated on the factor proposed by Atwater and Benedict who found that 98 per cent of the heat of combustion of alcohol was utilized by the human body. The calories per gram of alcohol would thus amount to 98 per cent of 7.07 calories per gram or 6.93 calories per gram.

*** See Item 478 in Table A-4.

Source: C.M. Taylor, Food Values in Shares and Weights, 2nd ed. New York; Macmillan, 1959, p. 104.

TABLE A-11. MINIMUM DAILY REQUIREMENTS OF SPECIFIC NUTRIENTS

U.S. Food and Drug Administration

	Infants	Children 1-5 Years Inclusive	Children 6 Years and Over	Adults	Pregnancy or Lactation
Vitamin A, USP units	1,500	3,000	3,000	4,000	
Vitamin B₁, mg	0.25	0.50	0.75	1.00	
Vitamin B₂, mg	0.60	0.90	0.90	1.20	
Niacin, mg	--	5	7.5	10	
Vitamin C, mg	10	20	20	30	
Vitamin D, USP units	400	400	400	400	
Calcium, gm	--	0.75	0.75	0.75	1.50
Phosphorus, gm	--	0.75	0.75	0.75	1.50
Iron, mg	--	7.5	10	10	15
Iodine, mg	--	0.1	0.1	0.1	0.1

The Minimum Daily Requirements are the amounts of various nutrients that have been established by the Food and Drug Administration as standards for labeling purposes of foods and pharmaceutical preparations for special dietary uses. These are the amounts regarded as necessary in the diet for the prevention of deficiency diseases and generally are less than the Recommended Dietary Allowances. The Minimum Daily Requirements are set forth in the Federal Register, Vol. 6, No.227 (Nov. 22, 1941), beginning on p. 5921, and amended as stated in the Federal Register (June 1, 1957), Vol. 22, No. 106, p. 3841.

Note.–The Recommended Daily Dietary Allowances should not be confused with Minimum Daily Requirements. The Recommended Dietary Allowances are amounts of nutrients recommended by the Food and Nutrition Board of National Research Council, and are considered adequate for maintenance of good nutrition in healthy persons in the United States. The allowances are revised from time to time in accordance with newer knowledge of nutritional needs.

Height	Weights for Men			Weights for Women		
	Low	Median	High	Low	Median	High
Inches	Pounds	Pounds	Pounds	Pounds	Pounds	Pounds
60	---	---	---	100	109	118
61	---	---	---	104	112	121
62	---	---	---	107	115	125
63	(118)	(129)	(141)	110	118	128
64	(122)	(133)	(145)	113	122	132
65	126	137	149	116	125	135
66	130	142	155	120	129	139
67	134	147	161	123	132	142
68	139	151	166	126	136	146
69	143	155	170	130	140	151
70	147	159	174	133	144	156
71	150	163	178	(137)	(148)	(161)
72	154	167	183	(141)	(152)	166)
73	158	171	188	---	---	---
74	162	175	192	---	---	---
75	165	178	195	---	---	---

*Weights were based on those of college men 25 to 29 years old and college women 20 to 24 years old. Measurements were made without shoes and other clothing. The range from "low" to "high" at a given height included the middle 50 per cent of the cases. Half the weights were below the median and half above. Body build will determine where within the ranges given normal weight should be. Weight at any age probably should not vary from these values by more than 5 lb for the shorter adults and 10 lb for the taller ones. Values in parentheses were extrapolated.

From Hathaway and Foard, Home Economics Research Report No. 10. Washington, D.C.: United States Department of Agriculture (1960).

TABLE A-13. DESIRABLE WEIGHTS*

Weight in Pounds According to Frame (in Indoor Clothing)

For Men of Ages 25 and Over

Height (with Shoes on) 1-in. Heels Feet	Inches	Small Frame	Medium Frame	Large Frame
5	2	112-120	118-129	126-141
5	3	115-123	121-133	129-144
5	4	118-126	124-136	132-148
5	5	121-129	127-139	135-152
5	6	124-133	130-143	138-156
5	7	128-137	134-147	142-161
5	8	132-141	138-152	147-166
5	9	136-145	142-156	151-170
5	10	140-150	146-160	155-174
5	11	144-154	150-165	159-179
6	0	148-158	154-170	164-184
6	1	152-162	158-175	168-189
6	2	156-167	162-180	173-194
6	3	160-171	167-185	178-199
6	4	164-175	172-190	182-204

For Women of Ages 25 and Over

Height (with Shoes on) 2-in Heels Feet	Inches	Small Frame	Medium Frame	Large Frame
4	10	92- 98	96-107	104-119
4	11	94-101	98-110	106-122
5	0	96-104	101-113	109-125
5	1	99-107	104-116	112-128
5	2	102-110	107-119	115-131
5	3	105-113	110-122	118-134
5	4	108-116	113-126	121-138
5	5	111-119	116-130	125-142
5	6	114-123	120-135	129-146
5	7	118-127	124-139	133-150
5	8	122-131	128-143	137-154
5	9	126-135	132-147	141-158
5	10	130-140	136-151	145-163
5	11	134-144	140-155	149-168
6	0	138-148	144-159	153-173

For girls between 18 and 25, subtract 1 pound for each year under 25.

*Courtesy of the Metropolitan Life Insurance Company (1960).

TABLE A-14. WEIGHT–HEIGHT–AGE TABLE FOR BOYS AND GIRLS OF SCHOOL AGE [1]

Boys

Age, years	Average Weight, lb	Range[2] in Weight, lb	Average Height, in.	Range[2] in Height, in.
4	38.2	33.7- 42.7	40.9	39.0-42.8
5	43.2	37.7- 48.7	43.9	41.9-45.9
6	47.6	41.3- 53.9	46.1	44.0-48.2
7	52.5	45.4- 59.6	48.2	46.0-50.4
8	58.2	49.5- 66.9	50.4	48.1-52.7
9	64.4	54.6- 74.2	52.4	50.0-54.8
10	70.7	59.2- 82.2	54.3	51.8-56.8
11	77.6	64.5- 90.7	56.2	53.6-58.8
12	85.6	69.8-101.4	58.2	55.3-61.1
13	95.6	77.4-113.8	60.5	57.3-63.7
14	107.9	87.8-128.0	63.0	59.6-66.4
15	121.7	101.1-142.3	65.6	62.5-68.7
16	131.9	113.0-150.8	67.3	64.5-70.1
17	138.3	119.5-157.1	68.2	65.6-70.8

Girls

Age, years	Average Weight, lb	Range[2] in Weight, lb	Average Height, in.	Range[2] in Height, in.
4	37.3	32.5- 42.1	40.9	39.0-42.8
5	42.0	36.1- 47.9	43.6	41.6-45.6
6	46.4	39.6- 53.2	45.8	43.7-47.9
7	51.2	43.7- 58.7	47.9	45.7-50.1
8	56.9	47.5- 66.3	50.0	47.7-52.3
9	63.0	51.9- 74.1	52.0	49.6-54.4
10	70.3	57.1- 83.5	54.2	51.6-56.8
11	79.0	63.5- 94.5	56.5	53.7-59.3
12	89.7	71.9-107.5	59.0	56.1-61.9
13	100.3	82.3-118.3	60.6	58.0-63.2
14	108.5	91.3-125.7	62.3	59.9-64.7
15	115.0	98.8-131.2	63.2	60.9-65.5
16	117.6	101.7-133.5	63.5	61.3-65.7
17	119.0	103.5-134.5	63.6	61.4-65.8

[1] From "Basic Body Measurements of School Age Children," Washington, D.C.: Office of Education, U.S. Department of Health, Education, and Welfare, 1953. This table is a compilation of heights and weights of 296,498 children (152,191 boys and 144,307 girls) from 17 states and the District of Columbia. No data reported before 1930 were included. The measurements were made on subjects wearing light indoor clothing with shoes removed.

[2] The ranges given include the cases which fell within the middle two thirds of those in the sample.

PURPOSE OF RECORD: To supply interesting and helpful information regarding the

growth of _____   _____
(name)   (date of birth)

HOW TO USE THE RECORD(associated with Figs. A-1 to A-6):

Registering Height and Weight Status

    Example: Assume this is the record of Don Jones. Don weighs 43 pounds, is 44 inches in height, and has just had his 5th birthday. Select appropriate figure.

Height

    a) Find age 5 along the top of the chart(Fig. A-3).
    b) Locate 44 inches along the upper left-hand margin.
    c) Plot a point under the 5 and opposite 44.
    d) Just above this dot on the HEIGHT graph write "44.0."

Weight

    a) Find age 5 along the bottom of the chart.
    b) Locate 43 pounds along the lower left-hand margin.
    c) Plot a point above the 5 and opposite the 43.
    d) Just below this dot on the WEIGHT graph write "43.0."

Registering Height and Weight Progress.

    Example: Assume Don is now six months older - at age 5-1/4 years his weight was 44-1/2 pounds, now at 5-1/2 years he weighs 46 pounds and has a height of 45-1/4 inches. Further, assume that points representing Don's height at 5-1/2 and his weight at 5-1/4 and 5-1/2 have been plotted at the appropriate places on Fig. A-3. Having records at more than one age, it is now possible to draw curves of progress. Don's progress over the age period 5 to 5-1/2 years may be shown by drawing lines connecting (a) the two points on the height graph and (b) the three points on the weight graph.

HOW TO INTERPRET THE RECORD:

Interpreting Status.

    1. The measurement figures written above or below each plotted point provide a ready description of each boy's actual height and weight at all of the ages measurements have been taken.

    2. The zones in which a boy's height and weight points for a given age are located indicate his standing, in relation to other boys of the same age. The sample values given at 5 years show Don to fall in the "average zone" for both height and weight.

    3. Whenever a boy's height and weight points do not fall in like zones (e.g., tall and heavy, short and light), the dissimilarity may indicate stockiness or slenderness of build and/or it may furnish an important lead regarding state of health. To illustrate, suppose at the time of first measurement the height point of (Pat Thomas) is found to lie in the "average zone" and his weight in the "light zone." Pat should be referred to a physician for examination. It may be he is a healthy child of slender build. On the other hand, he may have some infection, need an improved diet, or require changes in his daily living habits.

Interpreting Progress

    The difference between a boy's heights (or weights) at two different ages shows the amount of change that has taken place during the interval. For example, Don Jones, between 5 and 5-1/2 years of age gained 1-1/4 inches in height and 3 pounds in weight.

    * Prepared by the Joint Committee on Health Problems in Education of the NEA and AMA, using data prepared by Howard V. Meredith, State University of Iowa. Additional copies may be secured through the order department of the American Medical Association, 535 N. Dearborn St., Chicago 10, Illinois, or of the National Education Association, 1201 Sixteenth St., N.W., Washington, D.C. The Physical Growth Record for Boys and that for Girls are reproduced by courtesy of the Joint Committee.

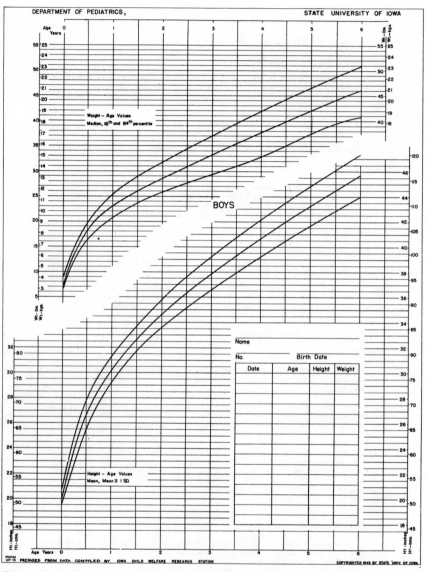

FIGURE A–1. GROWTH CURVES FOR BOYS FROM BIRTH TO SIX YEARS. (*Courtesy of the State University of Iowa.*)

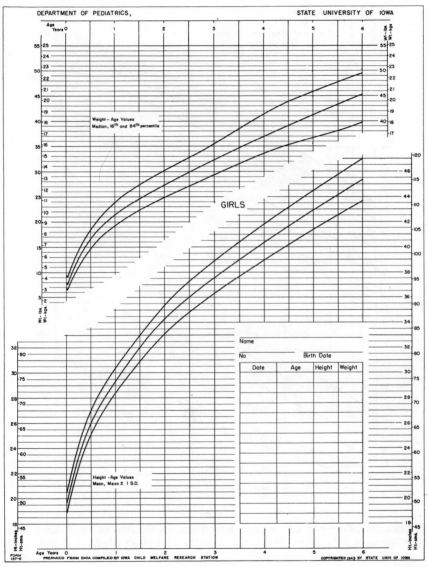

FIGURE A–2. GROWTH CURVES FOR GIRLS FROM BIRTH TO SIX YEARS. (*Courtesy of the State University of Iowa.*)

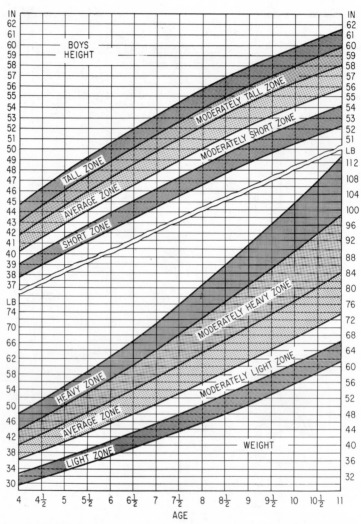

FIGURE A–3. GROWTH CURVES FOR BOYS FOUR TO ELEVEN YEARS. (*Courtesy of the National Education Association and the American Medical Association.*)

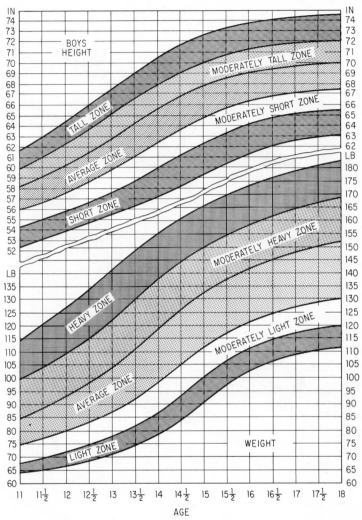

FIGURE A–4. GROWTH CURVES FOR BOYS ELEVEN TO EIGHTEEN YEARS. (*Courtesy of the National Education Association and the American Medical Association.*)

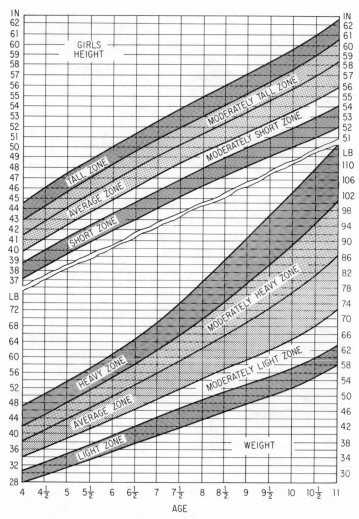

FIGURE A–5. GROWTH CURVES FOR GIRLS FOUR TO ELEVEN YEARS. (*Courtesy of the National Education Association and the American Medical Association.*)

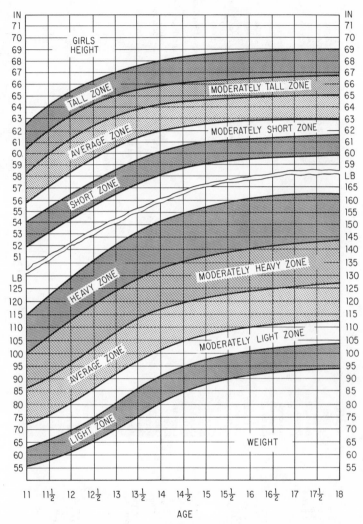

FIGURE A–6. GROWTH CURVES FOR GIRLS ELEVEN TO EIGHTEEN YEARS. (*Courtesy of the National Education Association and the American Medical Association.*)

TABLE A-15. FOOD BUYING GUIDE*

Meat, Poultry, Fish

Fresh or frozen:		Amount to buy per serving
Meat		
Much bone or gristle		1/2 to 1 pound
Medium amounts of bone		1/3 to 1/2 pound
Little bone		1/4 to 1/3 pound
No bone		1/5 to 1/4 pound
Poultry (ready-to-cook):		
Chicken:		
Broiling		1/4 to 1/2 bird
Frying, roasting, stewing		About 1/2 pound
Duck		About 1 pound
Goose		About 2/3 pound
Turkey		About 1/2 pound
Fish and shellfish:		
Whole or round		1 pound
Dressed, large		1/2 pound
Steaks, fillets		1/3 pound
Oysters, shucked (8-12 oysters)		1/3 pint
Shrimp (green)		1/4 pound
Shrimp, cooked, peeled, cleaned		1/8 pound

Canned:	Size of Serving	Servings per unit
Pork loaf, 12-ounce can	2 slices (3-1/2 in. x 1-3/4 in. x 3/8 in.)	4 per can
Corned beef, 12-ounce can	3 ounces	4 per can
Chicken, turkey, boned, 6-ounce can	3 ounces	2 per can
Salmon, 16-ounce can	3 ounces	4 per can
Tunafish, in oil, solid or chunk packed, 7-ounce can	3 ounces	2 per can
Dried:		
Chipped beef	3/4 cup creamed	10 per lb

Vegetables and Fruits[1]

Fresh:	Size of serving	Servings per pound[1]
Asparagus:		
Cut	1/2 cup	4
Spears	4-5 stalks	4
Beans, lima	1/2 cup	2[2]
Beans, snap	1/2 cup	5-6
Beets, diced	1/2 cup	4[3]
Broccoli	2 stalks	3-4
Brussels sprouts	1/2 cup	4-5
Cabbage:		
Raw, shredded	1/2 cup	7-8
Cooked	1/2 cup	4-5
Carrots:		
Raw, shredded	1/2 cup	6-7[3]
Cooked	1/2 cup	4[3]
Cauliflower	1/2 cup	4
Celery, cooked	1/2 cup	5
Chard	1/2 cup	3-1/2
Collards	1/2 cup	4
Eggplant	1/2 cup	5
Kale	1/2 cup	3-1/2
Onions, cooked	1/2 cup	4
Parsnips	1/2 cup	4[3]
Peas	1/2 cup	2[2]
Potatoes	1/2 cup	3-4
Spinach	1/2 cup	2-3
Squash	1/2 cup	2-3
Sweetpotatoes	1/2 cup	3
Tomatoes, sliced or diced	1/2 cup	5
Turnips	1/2 cup	4[3]
Apricots	2 medium	5
Berries, raw	1/2 cup	4-5
Cherries, pitted, cooked	1/2 cup	3
Plums	2 medium	4
Rhubarb, cooked	1/2 cup	3

For apples, bananas, oranges, and pears, count on about 3 (medium size) to a pound; peaches, 4 to a pound.

Dry:	Size of serving	Servings per pound
Beans	1/2 cup	11
Peas, lentils	1/2 cup	10-11

Vegetables and Fruits[1] (Continued)

Canned:	Size of serving	Servings per can
8-ounce can	1/2 cup	2
No. 2 can	1/2 cup	4-5
No. 2-1/2 can	1/2 cup	6-7
No. 3 cylinder (46 oz.)	1/2 cup	11-12
No. 303 can	1/2 cup	3-5

Frozen:	Size of serving	Servings per package (9 to 16 oz.)
Broccoli:		
Spears	2 stalks	3-5
Chopped	1/2 cup	3-5
Cauliflower	1/2 cup	4-5
Corn, whole kernel	1/2 cup	3-5
Peas	1/2 cup	3-5
Others	1/2 cup	3-6

Cereals and Cereal Products

	Size of serving	Servings per pound
Bread, sliced, 1-pound loaf	1 slice	16
Crackers, graham, 1 pound (about 66 crackers)	2 crackers	33
Crackers, saltines, 1 pound (about 140 2"x2" crackers)	4 crackers	35
Flaked corn cereals	1 cup	18-24
Other flaked cereals	3/4 cup	21
Puffed cereals	1 cup	32-38
Cornmeal	1/2 cup	22
Wheat cereals:		
Coarse	1/2 cup	20-27
Fine	1/2 cup	16
Oatmeal	1/2 cup	16
Hominy grits	1/2 cup	20
Macaroni and noodles	1/2 cup	17
Rice	1/2 cup	16
Spaghetti	1/2 cup	18

* Family Food Plans and Food Costs, Home Economics Research Report, No. 20, pages 16-17, Washington, D.C.: U.S. Department of Agriculture (1962).

[1] As purchased. [2] In pod. [3] Without tops.

TABLE A-16. ECONOMY FAMILY FOOD PLAN – Revised 1964*

(Designed for temporary use when funds are limited)

Weekly Quantities of Food [2] for Each Member of Family

Sex-Age Group [1]	Milk, Cheese, Ice Cream [3] (Qt)	Meat, Poultry, Fish [4] (Lb)	(Oz)	Eggs (No)	Dry Beans, Peas, Nuts (Lb)	(Oz)	Flour, Cereals, Baked Goods [5] (Lb)	(Oz)	Citrus Fruit, Tomatoes (Lb)	(Oz)	Dark-Green and Deep-Yellow Vegetables (Lb)	(Oz)	Potatoes (Lb)	(Oz)	Other Vegetables and Fruits (Lb)	(Oz)	Fats, Oils (Lb)	(Oz)	Sugars, Sweets (Lb)	(Oz)
Children:																				
7 months to 1 year	4	1	0	4	0	0	1	0	1	0	0	4	0	12	1	0	0	2	0	2
1 to 3 years	4	1	4	4	0	1	1	12	1	0	0	4	1	0	2	0	0	4	0	4
3 to 6 years	3-1/2	1	8	4	0	4	2	4	1	4	0	4	1	8	2	8	0	6	0	6
6 to 9 years	3-1/2	1	12	5	0	6	3	0	1	8	0	8	2	8	3	0	0	10	0	10
Girls:																				
9 to 12 years	5	1	12	5	0	10	2	12	1	12	0	12	2	8	3	4	0	8	0	10
12 to 15 years	6	2	0	6	0	10	3	0	1	12	1	0	3	0	3	8	0	10	0	10
15 to 20 years	6	2	0	6	0	8	2	12	1	12	0	4	2	8	3	4	0	8	0	10
Boys:																				
9 to 12 years	5	2	0	6	0	8	3	4	1	8	0	12	2	12	3	4	0	10	0	10
12 to 15 years	6	2	0	6	0	10	4	4	1	12	0	12	3	8	3	8	0	14	0	12
15 to 20 years	6	2	8	5	0	10	5	0	1	12	0	12	4	12	3	8	1	0	0	14
Women:																				
20 to 35 years	3	1	12	6	0	10	2	12	1	8	1	8	2	12	3	0	0	8	0	12
35 to 55 years	3	1	12	6	0	10	2	8	1	8	1	8	2	8	2	12	0	6	0	8
55 to 75 years	3	1	8	4	0	6	2	0	1	12	1	0	2	0	2	12	0	6	0	6
75 years and over	3	1	4	7	0	10	1	12	2	0	2	0	2	8	4	4	0	6	0	6
Pregnant [6]	5-1/2	2	0	7	0	10	3	12	3	0	2	0	2	8	4	8	0	6	0	6
Lactating [6]	8	2	0	6	0	10	4	0	3	0	1	8	3	12	4	8	0	12	0	12
Men:																				
20 to 35 years	3	2	0	5	0	8	4	8	1	8	0	12	4	4	3	8	0	14	1	2
35 to 55 years	3	1	12	5	0	8	4	4	1	8	0	12	3	8	3	4	0	12	0	14
55 to 75 years	3	1	8	5	0	6	3	4	1	8	0	12	2	12	3	0	0	12	0	10
75 years and over	3	1	0	5	0	0	3	0	1	8	0	12	2	8	2	12	0	10	0	6

*Source: Family Economics Review, Washington, D.C.: USDA-ARS 62-5, October 1964, p. 19.
[1] Age groups include the persons of the first age listed up to but not including those of the second age listed.
[2] Food as purchased or brought into the kitchen from garden or farm.
[3] Fluid whole milk, or its calcium equivalent in cheese, evaporated milk, dry milk, or ice cream.
[4] Bacon and salt pork should not exceed 1/3 lb for each 5 lb of meat group.
[5] Weight in terms of flour and cereal. Count 1-1/2 lb bread as 1 lb flour.
[6] Three additional quarts of milk are suggested for pregnant and lactating teenagers.

TABLE A-17. LOW-COST FAMILY FOOD PLAN – Revised 1964*

Weekly Quantities of Food[2] for Each Member of Family

Sex-Age Group[1]	Milk, Cheese, Ice Cream[3] (Qt)	Meat, Poultry, Fish[4] Lb	Oz	Eggs No	Dry Beans, Peas, Nuts Lb	Oz	Flour, Cereals, Baked Goods[5] Lb	Oz	Citrus Fruit, Tomatoes Lb	Oz	Dark-Green and Deep-Yellow Vegetables Lb	Oz	Potatoes Lb	Oz	Other Vegetables and Fruits Lb	Oz	Fats, Oils Lb	Oz	Sugars, Sweets Lb	Oz
Children:																				
7 months to 1 year	4	1	4	5	0	0	1	0	1	8	0	4	0	8	1	0	0	1	0	2
1 to 3 years	4	1	12	5	0	1	1	8	1	8	0	4	0	12	2	4	0	4	0	4
3 to 6 years	4	2	0	5	0	2	2	0	1	12	0	4	1	4	3	4	0	6	0	6
6 to 9 years	4	2	4	6	0	4	2	12	2	0	0	8	2	4	4	4	0	8	0	10
Girls:																				
9 to 12 years	5-1/2	2	8	7	0	6	2	8	2	4	0	12	2	4	5	0	0	8	0	10
12 to 15 years	7	2	8	7	0	6	2	12	2	4	1	12	2	8	5	0	0	8	0	12
15 to 20 years	7	2	12	7	0	6	2	8	2	4	1	4	2	4	4	12	0	6	0	10
Boys:																				
9 to 12 years	5-1/2	2	8	6	0	6	3	0	2	0	0	12	2	8	5	0	0	8	0	12
12 to 15 years	7	2	8	6	0	6	4	4	2	0	0	12	3	4	5	4	0	12	0	12
15 to 20 years	7	3	8	6	0	6	4	12	2	0	0	12	4	4	5	8	0	14	0	14
Women:																				
20 to 35 years	3-1/2	3	4	7	0	6	2	8	1	12	1	8	2	0	5	0	0	6	0	10
35 to 55 years	3-1/2	3	4	7	0	6	2	4	1	12	1	8	1	8	4	8	0	4	0	10
55 to 75 years	3-1/2	2	8	5	0	4	2	0	2	0	1	0	1	4	3	12	0	4	0	6
75 years and over	3-1/2	2	4	5	0	4	1	8	2	0	1	0	1	4	3	8	0	4	0	6
Pregnant[6]	5-1/2	3	12	7	0	6	2	12	3	4	2	0	1	8	5	8	0	6	0	6
Lactating[6]	8	3	12	7	0	6	3	12	3	4	1	8	3	4	5	8	0	10	0	10
Men:																				
20 to 35 years	3-1/2	3	8	6	0	6	4	4	1	12	0	12	3	4	5	8	0	12	1	0
35 to 55 years	3-1/2	3	4	6	0	6	3	12	1	12	0	12	3	0	5	0	0	10	0	12
55 to 75 years	3-1/2	3	0	6	0	4	2	12	1	12	0	12	2	4	4	8	0	10	0	12
75 years and over	3-1/2	2	12	6	0	4	2	8	1	8	0	12	2	0	4	4	0	8	0	8

*Source: Family Economics Review, Washington, D.C.: USDA-ARS 62-5, October 1964, p. 15.

1 Age groups include the persons of the first age listed up to but not including those of the second age listed.
2 Food as purchased or brought into the kitchen from garden or farm.
3 Fluid whole milk, or its calcium equivalent in cheese, evaporated milk, dry milk, or ice cream.
4 Bacon and salt pork should not exceed 1/3 lb for each 5 lb of meat group.
5 Weight in terms of flour and cereal. Count 1-1/2 lb bread as 1 lb flour.
6 Three additional quarts of milk are suggested for pregnant and lactating teenagers.

TABLE A-18. MODERATE-COST FAMILY FOOD PLAN – Revised 1964*

Weekly Quantities of Food [2] for Each Member of Family

Sex-Age Group[1]	Milk, Cheese, Ice Cream[3] Qt	Meat, Poultry, Fish[4] Lb	Meat, Poultry, Fish[4] Oz	Eggs No	Dry Beans, Peas, Nuts Lb	Dry Beans, Peas, Nuts Oz	Flour, Cereals, Baked Goods[5] Lb	Flour, Cereals, Baked Goods[5] Oz	Citrus Fruit, Tomatoes Lb	Citrus Fruit, Tomatoes Oz	Dark-Green and Deep-Yellow Vegetables Lb	Dark-Green and Deep-Yellow Vegetables Oz	Potatoes Lb	Potatoes Oz	Other Vegetables and Fruits Lb	Other Vegetables and Fruits Oz	Fats, Oils Lb	Fats, Oils Oz	Sugars, Sweets Lb	Sugars, Sweets Oz
Children:																				
7 months to 1 year	5	1	8	6	0	0	0	14	1	8	0	4	0	8	1	8	0	1	0	2
1 to 3 years	5	2	4	6	0	1	1	4	1	8	0	4	0	12	2	12	0	4	0	4
3 to 6 years	5	2	12	6	0	1	1	12	2	0	0	4	1	0	4	0	0	6	0	8
6 to 9 years	5	3	4	7	0	2	2	8	2	4	0	8	1	12	4	12	0	10	0	14
Girls:																				
9 to 12 years	5-1/2	4	4	7	0	4	2	8	2	8	0	12	2	0	5	8	0	8	0	12
12 to 15 years	7	4	8	7	0	4	2	8	2	8	1	0	2	4	5	12	0	12	0	14
15 to 20 years	7	4	8	7	0	4	2	4	2	8	1	4	2	0	5	8	0	8	0	12
Boys:																				
9 to 12 years	5-1/2	4	4	7	0	4	2	12	2	4	0	12	2	4	5	8	0	10	0	14
12 to 15 years	7	4	12	7	0	4	4	0	2	4	0	12	3	0	6	0	0	14	1	0
15 to 20 years	7	5	4	7	0	6	4	8	2	8	0	12	4	0	6	8	1	2	1	2
Women:																				
20 to 35 years	3-1/2	4	12	8	0	4	2	4	2	4	1	8	1	8	5	12	0	8	0	14
35 to 55 years	3-1/2	4	12	8	0	4	2	4	2	4	1	8	1	4	5	0	0	6	0	8
55 to 75 years	3-1/2	4	4	6	0	2	1	8	2	4	0	12	1	0	4	4	0	6	0	8
75 years and over	3-1/2	3	8	8	0	4	2	4	3	4	2	12	1	8	3	12	0	6	0	8
Pregnant[6]	5-1/2	5	8	8	0	4	2	12	3	4	2	0	1	8	6	12	0	6	0	8
Lactating[6]	8	5	8	8	0	4	3	12	3	8	1	8	2	12	6	4	0	12	0	12
Men:																				
20 to 35 years	3-1/2	5	0	7	0	4	4	0	2	4	0	12	3	0	6	8	1	0	1	4
35 to 55 years	3-1/2	4	12	7	0	4	3	8	2	4	0	12	2	8	5	12	0	14	1	0
55 to 75 years	3-1/2	4	8	7	0	2	2	8	2	4	0	12	2	4	5	8	0	12	0	14
75 years and over	3-1/2	4	8	7	0	2	2	4	2	4	0	12	2	0	5	4	0	8	0	12

* Source: Family Economics Review, Washington, D.C.: USDA-ARS 62-5, October 1964, p. 16.

1 Age groups include the persons of the first age listed up to but not including those of the second age listed.
2 Food as purchased or brought into the kitchen from garden or farm.
3 Fluid whole milk, or its calcium equivalent in cheese, evaporated milk, dry milk, or ice cream.
4 Bacon and salt pork should not exceed 1/3 lb for each 5 lb of meat group.
5 Weight in terms of flour and cereal. Count 1-1/2 lb bread as 1 lb flour.
6 Three additional quarts of milk are suggested for pregnant and lactating teenagers.

TABLE A-19. SUGGESTIONS FOR CUTTING FOOD COSTS *

Although food is usually the largest single expense in a family budget, you can generally reduce the amount you spend for food by—

• Checking weekly specials in foodstore advertisements.

• Preparing a grocery list before you shop.

• Comparing costs and buying food in the form—fresh, frozen, or canned—or the weight or package—that gives the most servings for the money. To make an intelligent choice among brands of the same product, test different ones to see which one gives the greatest quality and number of servings for the money.

• Shopping carefully for low-cost foods within each food group.

• Using grades in making your food purchases. Government grades will enable you to be sure of the quality of the food you buy, and you are then better able to compare prices asked.

• Taking advantage of seasonal abundances. Radio, television, and newspapers call attention to foods in plentiful supply, as listed each month by the USDA. These foods will be at their peak of quality, and sometimes will be offered at lower prices.

• Limiting perishable food purchases to amounts that can be used while they are in top quality.

• Preventing food waste by proper storage and by cooking methods that conserve nutrients.

• Increasing skills in cookery.

• Considering family likes and dislikes when food shopping. Thrifty food buys pay off only if your family eats and enjoys the food.

Here are suggestions that may help you get more food value for your dollars:

• When buying meat, consider the amount of lean meat in the cut, not the cost per pound. Some cuts contain bone, gristle, and fat waste. For example, ground beef and beef short ribs may cost the same per pound but ground beef will give twice as many servings or more per pound as short ribs. Bacon, which is largely fat, is one of the most expensive foods you can buy in terms of protein value.

• Chicken and turkey have a large proportion of bone to lean, but are often bargains compared with other meats. Fish is high in nutrients; often low in cost.

• Eggs are usually a less expensive source of nutrients than most meats. Dry beans and peanut butter are inexpensive alternates for meat.

• Beef, lamb, and pork liver give unusually high nutritive returns for money spent.

• Study bread labels before you buy. Choose bread for weight and food value, not by the size of loaf. Look for bread that is whole-grain or enriched, and that contains milk.

• Buy packaged cereals or any other packaged food by weight, not by the size of the package. To compare prices, first look for the weights listed on the labels and note the prices. Then figure the costs for an ounce or a pound.

• Ready-to-serve cereals in multipacks of small boxes may cost two or three times more per ounce than the same cereal in a larger box. Sugar-coated, ready-to-serve cereals cost more, per ounce, than many common, unsweetened ones, and furnish more calories, but less other food value.

• Cereals you cook yourself (particularly the kinds that take longer to cook) are nearly always less expensive than the ready-prepared ones.

• Baked goods made at home usually cost less than ready-baked ones.

• Nonfat dry milk and evaporated milk cost considerably less per quart when reconstituted than whole fluid milk, and supply comparable amounts of calcium and protein. Reconstituted nonfat dry milk is an excellent beverage for most persons and generally can be substituted for whole fluid milk in cooking. For baking and preparing many other foods, nonfat dry milk does not need to be reconstituted before using. A glass of whole fluid milk usually costs three times as much as a glass of reconstituted nonfat dry milk.

• Choose the type of pack or grade in a canned product that is appropriate to your cooking method. It is thrifty to buy canned tomatoes of low market grade for stews and sauces. A can of solid white meat tuna costs more than the same size can of grated light meat tuna. You may prefer the solid pack for a salad and the grated pack for casseroles and sandwich fillings.

• Consider your time and the quality of the finished product in deciding between convenience foods (those with more than usual services added) and unserviced ones. Compare prices to see if it pays to prepare a product yourself from basic ingredients. Sometimes it does not. How much you enjoy cooking and how much time you can spend will influence your choice.

* Family Food Budgeting: Home and Garden Bulletin No. 94, pages 12-13. Washington, D.C.: U.S. Department of Agriculture (1964).

TABLE A-20. YIELD OF COOKED MEAT PER POUND OF RAW MEAT*

Meat as Purchased	Meat After Cooking (Less Drippings)	
	Parts Weighed	Approximate Weight of Cooked Parts per Pound of Raw Meat Purchased
Chops or steaks for broiling or frying:		Ounces
With bone and relatively large amount of fat, such as pork or lamb chops; beef rib, sirloin, or porterhouse steaks	Lean, bone, fat	10-12
	Lean and fat	7-10
	Lean only	5-7
Without bone and with very little fat, such as round of beef, veal steaks	Lean and fat	12-13
	Lean only	9-12
Ground meat for broiling or frying, such as hamburger, lamb, or pork patties	Patties	9-13
Roasts for oven cooking (no liquid added):		
With bone and relatively large amount of fat, such as beef rib, loin, chuck; lamb shoulder, leg; pork, fresh or cured	Lean, bone, fat	10-12
	Lean and fat	8-10
	Lean only	6-9
Without bone	Lean and fat	10-12
	Lean only	7-10
Cuts for pot-roasting, simmering, braising, stewing:		
With bone and relatively large amount of fat, such as beef chuck, pork shoulder	Lean, bone, fat	10-11
	Lean and fat	8-9
	Lean only	6-8
Without bone and with relatively small amount of, such as trimmed beef, veal	Lean with adhering fat	9-11

* Nutritive Value of Foods. Home and Garden Bulletin No. 72, p. 35. Washington, D.C.: U.S. Department of Agriculture (1964).

TABLE A-21. EXPECTATION OF LIFE AND MORTALITY RATE AT SINGLE YEARS OF AGE

By Race and Sex, United States, 1963

Age, Years	Expectation of Life in Years					Mortality Rate per 1,000				
	Total Persons	White		Nonwhite		Total Persons	White		Nonwhite	
		Male	Female	Male	Female		Male	Female	Male	Female
0	69.9	67.5	74.4	60.9	66.5	25.2	25.1	19.0	46.0	36.9
1	70.7	68.2	74.8	62.9	68.0	1.6	1.5	1.2	3.2	2.9
2	69.8	67.3	73.9	62.1	67.2	1.0	.9	.7	1.9	1.6
3	68.9	66.4	73.0	61.2	66.3	.8	.7	.6	1.4	1.1
4	67.9	65.4	72.0	60.3	65.4	.6	.6	.5	1.0	.9
5	67.0	64.4	71.0	59.3	64.5	.6	.7	.4	1.1	.7
6	66.0	63.5	70.1	58.4	63.5	.5	.6	.4	.8	.6
7	65.0	62.5	69.1	57.4	62.5	.4	.5	.3	.6	.6
8	64.1	61.6	68.1	56.5	61.6	.4	.4	.3	.5	.5
9	63.1	60.6	67.1	55.5	60.6	.3	.3	.3	.5	.5
10	62.1	59.6	66.2	54.5	59.6	.3	.3	.3	.5	.4
11	61.1	58.6	65.2	53.5	58.7	.3	.4	.3	.6	.4
12	60.1	57.6	64.2	52.6	57.7	.4	.4	.3	.7	.4
13	59.2	56.7	63.2	51.6	56.7	.5	.6	.3	.8	.5
14	58.2	55.7	62.2	50.7	55.7	.6	.7	.4	.9	.5
15	57.2	54.7	61.3	49.7	54.8	.7	.9	.4	1.1	.6
16	56.3	53.8	60.3	48.8	53.8	.8	1.1	.5	1.3	.7
17	55.3	52.8	59.3	47.8	52.8	.9	1.3	.5	1.6	.8
18	54.4	51.9	58.3	46.9	51.9	1.0	1.4	.6	1.8	.9
19	53.4	51.0	57.4	46.0	50.9	1.1	1.5	.6	2.1	1.0
20	52.5	50.1	56.4	45.1	50.0	1.2	1.6	.6	2.4	1.1
21	51.5	49.1	55.4	44.2	49.0	1.2	1.7	.6	2.7	1.2
22	50.6	48.2	54.5	43.3	48.1	1.3	1.7	.6	3.0	1.3
23	49.7	47.3	53.5	42.4	47.2	1.3	1.7	.6	3.1	1.4
24	48.7	46.4	52.5	41.6	46.2	1.3	1.7	.7	3.2	1.6
25	47.8	45.5	51.6	40.7	45.3	1.3	1.6	.7	3.3	1.7
26	46.8	44.5	50.6	39.8	44.4	1.3	1.5	.7	3.4	1.9
27	45.9	43.6	49.6	39.0	43.5	1.3	1.5	.7	3.5	2.1
28	45.0	42.7	48.7	38.1	42.5	1.3	1.5	.7	3.7	2.2
29	44.0	41.7	47.7	37.2	41.6	1.4	1.6	.8	3.8	2.4
30	43.1	40.8	46.7	36.4	40.7	1.5	1.6	.8	4.0	2.6
31	42.1	39.9	45.8	35.5	39.8	1.5	1.7	.9	4.2	2.8
32	41.2	38.9	44.8	34.7	38.9	1.6	1.7	1.0	4.4	3.0
33	40.3	38.0	43.9	33.8	38.1	1.7	1.9	1.1	4.7	3.2
34	39.3	37.1	42.9	33.0	37.2	1.9	2.0	1.2	5.1	3.5
35	38.4	36.1	42.0	32.2	36.3	2.0	2.2	1.3	5.4	3.8
36	37.5	35.2	41.0	31.3	35.5	2.2	2.4	1.4	5.8	4.1
37	36.6	34.3	40.1	30.5	34.6	2.4	2.6	1.5	6.3	4.4
38	35.7	33.4	39.1	29.7	33.7	2.6	2.8	1.7	6.7	4.8
39	34.8	32.5	38.2	28.9	32.9	2.8	3.0	1.8	7.2	5.2
40	33.9	31.6	37.3	28.1	32.1	3.0	3.3	1.9	7.8	5.7
41	33.0	30.7	36.3	27.3	31.3	3.3	3.6	2.1	8.4	6.2
42	32.1	29.8	35.4	26.5	30.5	3.6	4.0	2.3	9.0	6.6
43	31.2	28.9	34.5	25.8	29.6	4.0	4.5	2.5	9.5	6.9
44	30.3	28.0	33.6	25.0	28.9	4.4	5.0	2.8	10.1	7.2
45	29.4	27.2	32.7	24.3	28.1	4.8	5.6	3.1	10.6	7.5
46	28.6	26.3	31.8	23.5	27.3	5.3	6.2	3.4	11.3	7.8
47	27.7	25.5	30.9	22.8	26.5	5.8	6.9	3.7	12.1	8.4
48	26.9	24.7	30.0	22.1	25.7	6.4	7.7	4.0	13.3	9.2
49	26.0	23.8	29.1	21.4	24.9	7.0	8.5	4.3	14.7	10.3
50	25.2	23.0	28.2	20.7	24.2	7.7	9.4	4.7	16.3	11.5
51	24.4	22.3	27.4	20.0	23.5	8.4	10.3	5.1	17.9	12.7
52	23.6	21.5	26.5	19.4	22.8	9.2	11.4	5.5	19.3	13.8
53	22.8	20.7	25.6	18.7	22.1	10.0	12.5	5.9	20.6	14.7
54	22.1	20.0	24.8	18.1	21.4	10.9	13.8	6.4	21.6	15.4
55	21.3	19.3	24.0	17.5	20.7	11.8	15.2	7.0	22.7	16.1
56	20.5	18.5	23.1	16.9	20.0	12.8	16.6	7.6	24.0	16.9
57	19.8	17.8	22.3	16.3	19.4	13.9	18.1	8.3	25.5	18.2
58	19.1	17.2	21.5	15.7	18.7	15.1	19.6	9.0	27.4	20.2
59	18.4	16.5	20.7	15.1	18.1	16.3	21.2	9.8	29.7	22.7
60	17.7	15.8	19.9	14.6	17.5	17.6	22.7	10.6	32.1	25.4
61	17.0	15.2	19.1	14.0	17.0	19.0	24.4	11.6	34.5	28.1
62	16.3	14.6	18.3	13.5	16.4	20.6	26.5	12.7	37.6	30.6
63	15.6	14.0	17.5	13.0	15.9	22.5	29.0	14.0	41.5	32.7
64	15.0	13.4	16.8	12.6	15.5	24.7	31.8	15.5	46.1	34.5
65	14.3	12.8	16.0	12.2	15.0	27.1	35.0	17.2	51.5	36.4
66	13.7	12.2	15.3	11.8	14.6	29.5	38.2	18.9	57.0	38.3
67	13.1	11.7	14.6	11.5	14.1	32.0	41.5	20.9	61.5	40.0

Source: National Center for Health Statistics, <u>Vital Statistics of the United States</u>, 1963, Vol. II, Section 5.

Index